PERFORMANCE MODELING OF AUTOMATED MANUFACTURING SYSTEMS

N. VISWANADHAM

Department of Computer Science and Automation
Indian Institute of Science

Y. NARAHARI

Department of Computer Science and Automation
Indian Institute of Science

 PRENTICE HALL, Englewood Cliffs, New Jersey 07632

Library of Congress Cataloging-in-Publication Data

Viswanadam, N.
 Performance modeling of automated manufacturing systems / N. Viswanadham,
 Y. Narahari
   p. cm.
  Includes bibliographical references and index.
  ISBN 0-13-658824-7
  1.Flexible manufacturing systems--Mathematical models. 2. Markov processes.
 3. Queuing theory. 4. Petri nets. I. Narahari, Y. II. Title.
 TS155.6.V57 1992
 670.42'7--dc20   91-41220
            CIP

Acquisitions editor: *Marcia Horton*
Production editor: *Jennifer Wenzel*
Cover design: *Bruce Kenselaar*
Prepress buyer: *Linda Behrens*
Manufacturing buyer: *Dave Dickey*
Supplements editor: *Alice Dworkin*
Editorial assistant: *Diana Penha*

 © 1992 by Prentice-Hall, Inc.
A Simon & Schuster Company
Englewood Cliffs, New Jersey 07632

Printed in the United States of America

10 9 8 7 6 5 4 3 2 1

ISBN 0-13-658824-7

Prentice-Hall International (UK) Limited, *London*
Prentice-Hall of Australia Pty. Limited, *Sydney*
Prentice-Hall Canada Inc., *Toronto*
Prentice-Hall Hispanoamericana, S.A., *Mexico*
Prentice-Hall of India Private Limited, *New Delhi*
Prentice-Hall of Japan, Inc., *Tokyo*
Simon & Schuster of Asia Pte. Ltd., *Singapore*
Editora Prentice-Hall do Brasil, Ltda., *Rio de Janeiro*

To

Subhadra

for her
love and understanding

N.V.

To the memory of my
revered mother

Matrusri Nagavenamma

a unique mother,
whose love sublime,
chastity of thought and action,
indomitable willpower, and
life-long sacrifices
made her divinity personified

Y.N.

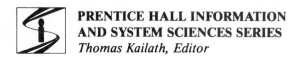

**PRENTICE HALL INFORMATION
AND SYSTEM SCIENCES SERIES**
Thomas Kailath, Editor

CONTENTS

PREFACE

The project of writing this book was initiated on the Vijaya Dasami day, during October 1988. Over the last three years we were able to put together a book that is specifically oriented toward performance issues that arise in automated manufacturing systems. The main goal of this text is to introduce to everyone concerned with automated manufacturing systems (AMSs), i.e., students, researchers, designers, planners, and managers, the analytical modeling tools and their use during the life cycle of an AMS. We have attempted to achieve this through the use of a large collection of pedagogical examples that illustrate the theory and applications. This is the first attempt of its kind, and we hope this book will form the first step toward formulating the so-called *science of manufacturing*, i.e., a set of scientific principles and theories upon which future-generation manufacturing systems are designed and operated.

The outline of the book is as follows. Chapter 1 is a brief introduction. Chapter 2 provides a comprehensive overview of the building blocks of AMSs, with emphasis on hardware, software, and integration aspects. Chapters 3, 4, and 5 are devoted to the three principal analytical modeling paradigms of AMSs, namely Markov chain models, queuing models, and Petri net models, respectively.

This book is designed with an AMS perspective in mind and therefore it should not be treated as a text on stochastic modeling per se. We believe that such a book should first provide a strong insight into the physics of manufacturing systems, and Chapter 2 does just that. We encourage every reader of this book to go through this chapter; we have tried to make it an easy-to-read, systems-level presentation. This material will help the reader to model an AMS "intelligently" and come up with high-fidelity models. As for Chapters 3, 4, and 5, most readers will find the treatment of queuing models and Petri net models as natural and conventional, whereas they may not share the same opinion with regard to Markov chain models. The reader will find that the individual examples in the chapter on Markov models illustrate many facets of AMS behaviour including blocking, deadlock, assembly, reliability, and transient performance. The pace of presentation in Chapter 3 is therefore deliberately leisurely.

The audience for this book comprises two natural groups: engineering students at the senior undergraduate level and first-year students at the graduate level, and professionals (R&D engineers in the industry and factory managers). We have tried to make this a textbook in its true sense, with examples, illustrations, exercise problems, and literature guide. Industrial engineering and business management students form the classical audience for this book. With its systems orientation, the text should also be suitable in electrical and computer engineering schools as a follow-up for a course on robotics. Graduate students in the disciplines of industrial engineering, robotics, and management should find in this book a good mathematical foundation. Factory managers and industry professionals are now aware of the importance of rapid modeling and performance analysis in decision making on the factory floor. We believe this text would be extremely useful for them in understanding the factory floor much better.

We have found it difficult to cover all this material in a one-semester course. While a two-semester course would be ideal, instructors can make a natural choice of topics and design a complete course of about 40 lecture hours. The book assumes adequate familiarity with the fundamental notions of probability theory, elementary calculus, and elementary transform techniques. If the students have prior exposure to a first course on stochastic models, earlier sections of Chapters 3 and 4 could be covered faster and thus an advanced course can be offered based on the material in this book.

Acknowledgments

It is a pleasure to acknowledge many individuals who have helped us make this book a reality. As it happens in most joint ventures, our indebtedness is joint in some cases and individual in others.

For his kind encouragement and the time he spent with us at various stages of the book, we are ever thankful to Professor Thomas Kailath. For the first author (NV), he has been a constant source of inspiration and guidance for over 20 years. We have benefited immensely from the critical comments and suggestions on the manuscript made by Professors P.R. Kumar and David Yao. Our sincere thanks to them. For their enthusiastic and conscientious support in a variety of ways, our warm thanks go to the editorial staff at Prentice Hall, especially, Ms. Elizabeth Kaster, Ms. Jennifer Wenzel, and Ms. Jaime Zampino.

Several people helped us generously in the preparation of the manuscript. We faced several challenging problems, which at times threatened the very feasibility of integrating elements such as text, figures, and tables, from different languages and sources into a coherent whole. Several graduate students have participated in this integration task, including S.M. Sharma, L.M. Khan, R. Ram, and S.R. Chitnis. A special word of thanks goes to S.M. Sharma, who came up with instant, ingenious solutions to all our nightmarish problems in integrating the figures into the text. We would also like to thank Dr. K.D. Minto for answering a myriad of questions on publishing software through E-mail. C.R.M. Sundaram, R. Ram, N. Hemachandra, K. Ravi Kumar, P. Sundarrajan, and P.V. Kamesh enthusiastically went through many portions of the manuscript and gave very useful feedback. K. Ramakrishna, P. Hanumantha Rao, B. Vijayakumar, several master's students, and the many generations of students in our course on computer-aided manufacturing systems also contributed in various ways to this book. In the final stages of preparation of this book, the task of proof-reading was in the efficient hands of N.Hemachandra, K.Ravi Kumar, L.M. Khan, P.Sundarrajan, D. Mohana Sundaram, and C.Srinivas. We warmly appreciate the typing and drafting support we received from V. Vijayakumar and Mary Aziaraiah.

The first author (NV) would like to thank his colleagues and friends across the continents with whom he has collaborated over the years. These include Dr. J.F. Cassidy, Jr., Dr. T.L. Johnson, Dr. J.H. Taylor, Dr. R.S. Baheti, Dr. Austin Spang, Dr. C.H. Nett, Dr. B.L. Deekshatulu, Dr. K.D. Minto, and Dr. V.V.S. Sarma. Several colleagues have helped in this task by providing us with their research papers and through personal discussions. We thank Professors P. Varaiya, P.R. Kumar, S.K. Mitter, S.I. Gershwin, F. Dicesare, A. Desroschers, K.S. Trivedi, Ram Akella, W.M. Wonham, R. Suri, M. Kamath, D. Mitra, M. Vidyasagar, U. Karmarkar, G. Shantikumar, J. A. Buzacott, and K. Stecke.

Both of us are home-grown products of the Indian Institute of Science although with a time gap of 18 years. We feel very indebted to this great institute for the freedom it has let us enjoy in terms of pursuing any intellectual endeavor we sought. We would like to thank the Government of India for generously funding our research in the area of automated manufacturing systems, through the Ministry of Human Resource Development and the Department of Electronics. We also want to thank Professor C.N.R. Rao, director of our institute and a man with vision and immense dynamism, for his encouragement.

Both of us have large families further enlarged by marriage. We appreciate the warmth and understanding displayed by them, and they have kept us going through endless numbers of drafts of various chapters. NV is indebted particularly to his elder brother, S.N. Suryanarayana, and sister-in-law, S.V. Lakshmi, for their care and affection. NV's three children, Sundari, Murthy, and Kiran, grown into adults during the course of writing this book, have displayed understanding, warmth, and love.

The second author (YN) would like to remember all the members of his family: six nephews, five nieces, sister, brother-in-law, five sisters-in-law, five brothers, wife, and above all his revered father, Brahmasri Y. Simhadri Sastry, the light of his life. Their contribution to the success of this project is beyond quantification. YN would also like to remember the encouragement of his dear friends, Kanchi Balaji Rao and K. Surya Subrahmanyam.

Chapter 1
INTRODUCTION

The recent years have seen the emergence of high-performance automated manufacturing systems (AMSs), driven by the quest for increased productivity, flexibility, and competitiveness. These systems are necessarily flexible and thus highly capital-intensive. Modeling and performance evaluation play a vital role in the design and operation of such high-performance AMSs and have received widespread attention of researchers in the last decade. This book presents a unified treatment of analytical modeling techniques for the performance evaluation of AMSs.

1.1 MODELING AUTOMATED MANUFACTURING SYSTEMS

An AMS is often a complex interconnection of various subsystems such as computer-controlled machine centers, assembly stations, inspection machines, and material-handling devices such as automated guided vehicles, robots, and conveyors. An AMS is required to be highly flexible to survive several product life cycles and be fault-tolerant to sustain desired levels of production of various part types in the face of subsystem failures. Resilience to design, demand, and product-mix changes is another desirable

1

attribute of an AMS. These systems are highly capital-intensive, with a mandate to produce high-quality, low-cost products that are competitive in world markets. To guarantee profitable returns on investments on such competitive manufacturing systems, it is essential to have effective design and operation strategies. Mathematical modeling provides a systematic way of decision making in the design and operation of AMSs, and this book is concerned with building and analyzing a class of AMS models that can be described as analytical discrete event models.

AMSs belong to the domain of discrete event dynamical systems (DEDS) in which the evolution of the system in time depends on the complex interactions of the timing of various discrete events, such as the arrival of a raw workpiece, departure of a finished part, failure of a machine, etc. The state of a DEDS changes only at these discrete instants of time, instead of continuously. In the last decade it has been the effort of many active researchers in this area to formulate a single modeling framework or paradigm to describe DEDS faithfully and completely. Several classes of models have emerged in this context. These models can be broadly classified as *qualitative* or *quantitative*. Qualitative models capture logical aspects of system evolution such as controllability, stability, existence of deadlocks in system operation, etc. Finite state automata, Petri nets, extended state machines, and finitely recursive processes fall into this category. Quantitative models, on the other hand, highlight the quantitative system performance in terms of the throughput and the lead time. Quantitative models include discrete event simulation, min-max algebra, Markov chains, stochastic Petri nets, queues, and queuing networks. In this book we are mainly concerned with quantitative modeling of AMSs. We use the more specific term "performance modeling" instead of the general term "quantitative modeling."

1.1.1 Role of Performance Modeling

In the life cycle of an AMS, decision making is involved at various stages of planning, design, and operation. The role of performance modeling is to aid this decision making in an effective way. Typical decisions during the planning and design stages include number and type of machines, number of material-handling devices, number of buffers, size of pallet pool and number of fixtures, best possible layout, tool storage capacity, evaluate candidate AMS configurations, part type selection, machine grouping, batching and balancing decisions, and scheduling policies.

During the operational phase of an AMS, performance modeling can help in making decisions related to finding the best routes in the event of breakdowns, predicting the effect of adding or withdrawing resources and parts, obtaining optimal schedules in the event of machine failures or sudden changes in part mix or demands, and in avoiding unstable situations, such as deadlocks.

Performance modeling can also be used to answer basic design issues such as central storage versus local storage, push production versus pull production, shared resources versus distributed resources, the effect of flexibility, etc. Performance predictions obtained using faithful models can substantially enhance the confidence of potential customers. Also, modeling tools provide the designers and operators of AMSs better insight into the system. This will help in designing better control strategies.

1.1.2 Performance Measures

There are certain generic performance measures using which the performance of an AMS can be described. These are: manufacturing lead time, work-in-process, throughput, machine utilization, capacity, flexibility, performability, and quality. Using performance modeling, one can compute these measures of performance for a given system and use it in decision making. These measures are quite interrelated and each assumes increased importance in a particular context. Some typical questions about AMS that performance evaluation can help answer include:

1. What is the probability that a particular product can be delivered before the deadline?
2. What is the minimum number of working machines required so that the average throughput of finished parts just exceeds the targeted production?
3. How many fixtures/pallets are to be used in order to increase the average machine utilization beyond 80%?
4. Does the given AMS configuration have enough capacity to deliver the required amounts of products in the set deadlines?
5. Which of the candidate layouts offers the best flexibility to part-mix changes?
6. What is the minimum number of resources in the system (machines, transporters, buffers) that would ensure that the probability of producing at least 100 parts in a shift of 8 hours, in the presence of unscheduled downtime, exceeds 95%?

7. What is the effect of machine blocking on throughput and manufacturing lead time? Should we add one more buffer?

8. What are the potential bottleneck resources and congestion points in the system?

9. Are there deadlocks in the system? What is the mean time to deadlock?

10. How do throughput and lead time change when we have one less machine? One more machine? One more transporter? Some more buffers?

11. Is there spare capacity in the system to undertake some low-priority jobs?

1.2 PERFORMANCE MODELING TOOLS

Performance evaluation methods for AMSs fall into two classes: performance measurement and performance modeling. Performance measurement is carried out on existing, operational systems and is generally used for monitoring of key variables, diagnosis of failures, and for possible reconfiguration. Data collection and analysis are routinely done in factories as a part of Management Information Systems reporting.

Performance modeling of AMSs can be either simulation modeling or analytical modeling. Traditionally, discrete event simulation has been widely accepted and employed in factory environments for study of issues in design and operation. Analytical modeling tools such as those based on Markov chains, queuing theory, and stochastic Petri nets are now becoming increasingly popular and have emerged as an alternative to simulation. This book presents a unified treatment of the analytical modeling tools for AMSs.

1.2.1 Simulation Models

Almost every factory floor now uses a general purpose or a custom-built simulator for decision making and analysis. Discrete event simulation modeling offers the scope for building and analyzing detailed models of manufacturing systems. The performance estimates will be very accurate if the number of simulation runs is made large. Consequently, the simulation tool turns out to be computationally expensive.

In a typical AMS simulation, synthetic random inputs are used and the simulation generates corresponding outputs. Several such output samples are collected for statistical analysis. Thus simulation of an AMS will involve the development of a simulation model, coding the model into a simulation program, validating the simulation model, debugging the simulation program, running the simulation for a wide variety of random inputs, and conducting statistical output analysis for obtaining performance measures. The simulation model can be very detailed, taking into account the possible part mixes, machine states, job routing, and flow control and sequencing rules. If the model is detailed, the time required for developing a computer program will be significant and each simulation run will be lengthy. However, simulation is quite popular because of its simplicity and power.

There are now available very attractive, high-level simulation languages such as SIMSCRIPT, GPSS, SLAM, and GASP. All these are available on PCs and Workstations. Recently, object-oriented simulation languages such as SIMULA, SIMMOD, Smalltalk, and C++ have become popular. Simulation languages, exclusively for manufacturing system modeling, such as SIMAN, SIMFACTORY, and CINEMA, have also become popular. Many of these languages are also supported by powerful graphical animation features.

1.2.2 Analytical Models

Analytical models can be solved either in closed form or by using numerical techniques. It is not possible for analytical models to capture every small detail of an AMS. Before building an analytical model, it is essential to decide how much detail to include. Too much detail makes the model solution intractable and too little can make the model unrealistic. Carefully formulated analytical models can, however, provide very adequate information about the system performance. Abstraction of a simple analytical model from a practical system has the added benefit of leading to new insights into the system. Once a tractable analytical model has been formulated, the model and its solution can be fully validated. Typically, such models can be analyzed in very short time and quick feedback about system performance is possible. Often, analytical models can be used to validate detailed simulation models and vice versa.

Research on the development of analytical models for AMS was initiated in the 1970s and this area grew into a very active one in the early 1980s. Much of the work is based on queuing theory. Analytical modeling of computer systems, which was a very active area even in the 1960s, has inspired the development of such models for AMSs. There are now available several software packages for solving analytical models. Some of these, such as CAN-Q, MVAQ, and MANUPLAN, are designed exclusively for manufacturing systems.

This book treats analytical modeling techniques and tools, in the AMS context, in a unified way. The modeling paradigms discussed are: Markov chains, queues and queuing networks, and Petri nets. Markov chains constitute the basis for the other two paradigms. In this sense, queuing models and Petri net models are higher-level models.

1.3 ORGANIZATION OF THE BOOK

This text has four major chapters. Chapter 2 is on the hardware, software, and networking aspects of automated manufacturing systems and is intended to provide a proper setting for discussing modeling issues in the later chapters. Chapters 3, 4, and 5 are devoted to Markov chain models, queuing models, and Petri net models, respectively. In each of these chapters, the presentation is organized as follows:

1. Provide a self-contained exposition of the modeling paradigm.
2. Provide a tutorial introduction to the analysis techniques of the modeling tool through simple but meaningful AMS examples.
3. Discuss algorithmic and computational issues, wherever relevant.
4. Focus on important research contributions in the area of AMS modeling, which are relevant to the theory and application of the tool.
5. Give a number of exercise problems, some having practical relevance and some others with research flavor.
6. Provide a comprehensive list of references to probe further into the topics.

Chapter 2 provides a logical overview of automated manufacturing systems, covering the hardware, software, and integration issues. The emphasis is on the logical operation and control issues and the presentation is systemic. The chapter starts by tracing the evolution of automated manufacturing systems and discusses the product cycle in a manufacturing plant and different types of plant configurations. Generic performance measures of a manufacturing system are then discussed and evaluated for different plant configurations. The modeling techniques and tools described in Chapters 3, 4, and 5 are required to evaluate precisely these performance measures. The building blocks of AMSs – NC (numerically controlled) machines, automated inspection systems, conveyors, industrial robots, and automated guided vehicles – are then discussed. The emphasis is on the management of operations and software control rather than on hardware or mechanical details. Next, plant layouts are discussed, with focus on functional and group technology layouts. The next topic discussed is an important one, flexible manufacturing systems. The issues examined in detail include the architecture and automated operation, flexible assembly systems, deadlocks, and generic performance measures, including flexibility. Finally, computer control systems and integration issues are presented. The main topics covered in this area are control system architecture for AMSs, local area networking in factories, and the manufacturing automation protocol.

Markov chain models constitute the subject of Chapter 3. Most of the analytical models are Markovian in nature. In this sense, Markov chains constitute the basis of most analytical modeling tools. In fact, a Markov chain is a natural modeling paradigm for discrete event dynamical systems because of the notions of discrete states and state transitions. The underlying stochastic process of most high-level models such as queues, queuing networks, and stochastic Petri nets turns out to be a Markov chain. In Chapter 3 we start with some preliminary material on memoryless random variables, stochastic processes, and the Poisson process. We then go on to discuss the theory and steady-state analysis of discrete time and continuous time Markov chains, with the help of generic examples. A case study of the modeling and analysis of a transfer line with limited buffers and unreliable machines is then presented. We next discuss four important special classes of stochastic processes, namely birth and death processes, time reversible Markov chains, Markov chains with absorbing states, and semi-Markov processes. Birth and death processes constitute the basis for early queuing theory work. Time reversible Markov chains have a central role to play in the analysis of product form queuing networks. Markov chains with absorbing states facilitate reliability modeling and also modeling of deadlocks. Semi-Markov processes help in relaxing Markovian assumptions in modeling, in a limited way. The focus in all the above topics is on steady-state analysis. We then turn to transient analysis of Markov models and show its relevance to several modeling situations in manufacturing. We conclude with an overview of computational issues in Markov analysis, where we touch upon the aggregation technique for steady-state analysis and the uniformization technique for transient analysis.

Chapter 4, on queuing models, is in two parts. The first part deals with queues and the second part with queuing networks. The topics covered under queues are Little's law, $M/M/1$ queue, $M/M/m$ queue, batch arrival queuing systems, queues with general distributions, and queues with breakdowns. There is a fair sprinkling of examples of manufacturing systems while discussing the above. Also, there is a case study on analyzing the performance of a flexible machine center, using polling models.

In queuing networks, we start with several illustrative examples and Little's result. We then move on to open queuing networks, where the main result we present is Jackson's theorem, after looking at the analysis of open tandem network, open network with feedback, and the open central server model. The next topic is closed queuing networks where we first discuss two generic examples, those of a closed transfer line and the closed central server network. We then present the Gordon-Newell networks and the analysis of such networks using the well-known convolution and the mean value analysis algorithms. We then go on to study a wider class of networks, popularly called the BCMP networks, having product form structure for their steady-state solution. The next topic covered is on queuing networks with blocking, where we present the examples of closed transfer line with blocking, and the central server model with blocking, and we survey the important results. Approximate analysis techniques are covered next, with an emphasis on the technique of flow-equivalence. The final topic is on the important notion of performability. Here, we formulate the notion of performability for AMSs and present the computation of distribution of performability for typical AMSs.

Petri net models form the subject matter of Chapter 5. We first introduce classical Petri net models and discuss the notions of reachability, boundedness, and liveness. Next, we present an analysis of exponentially timed Petri nets, which are isomorphic to Markov chains. We then discuss the analysis and applications of generalized stochastic Petri nets, the most important class of timed nets. A case study of a Kanban production system is presented next. Later, we discuss deadlock modeling and analysis using Petri net models. Extended classes of Petri nets are treated next. Finally, we conclude with a discussion of integrated models that use both queuing networks and Petri nets to exploit the technique of flow-equivalence in an attractive way.

In the epilogue we briefly dwell on important issues in AMS modeling and design that fall outside the scope of this text.

1.4 BIBLIOGRAPHIC NOTES AND BIBLIOGRAPHY

There is a wealth of literature on computer systems performance modeling in the form of textbooks, survey articles, and research papers. Many of these have influenced the presentation in this book. In particular, we would like to mention the books by Kleinrock [1975], Lavenberg [1983], and Trivedi [1982]. The modeling paradigms for discrete event dynamical systems are well surveyed in the special issue of the *Proceedings of the IEEE* edited by Ho [1989]. The article by Inan and Varaiya [1989] on algebraic models is from this special issue. A finite state automata theoretic framework for modeling AMSs is presented in the paper by Ramadge and Wonham [1987]. Solberg [1977] formulated the first queuing network model of flexible manufacturing systems. Suri [1985] has surveyed the role of evaluative models of AMSs. Discussion about specific evaluative models can be found in the papers by Buzacott and Yao [1986] (queuing models); Cohen, Dubois, Quadrat, and Viot [1985] (min-max algebra); Ho [1987] (perturbation analysis); Law [1986] (simulation); Narahari and Viswanadham [1985] (Petri net models); and Viswanadham and Narahari [1988] (stochastic Petri net models).

BIBLIOGRAPHY

1. **Buzacott, J.A., and D.D. Yao [1986]**. Flexible Manufacturing Systems: A Review of Analytical Models, *Management Science*, Vol. 32, No. 7, July 1986, pp. 890–905.

2. **Cohen, G., D. Dubois, J.P. Quadrat, and M. Viot [1985]**. A Linear System Theoretic View of Discrete Event Processes and Its Use for Performance Evaluation in Manufacturing, *IEEE Transactions on Automatic Control*, Vol. AC-30, No. 3, March 1985, pp. 210–220.

3. **Ho, Y.C. [1987]**. Performance Evaluation and Perturbation Analysis of Discrete Event Dynamic Systems, *IEEE Transactions on Automatic Control*, Vol. AC-32, No. 7, July 1987, pp. 563–572.

4. **Ho, Y.C. [1989] (Ed.)**. Dynamics of Discrete Event Systems, Special Issue of *Proceedings of the IEEE*, Vol. 77, No. 1, January 1989.

5. **Inan, K.M., and P. Varaiya [1989]**. Algebras of Discrete Event Models, *Proceedings of the IEEE*, Vol. 77, No. 1, January 1989, pp. 24–38.

6. **Kleinrock, L. [1975]**. *Queueing Systems, Vol. 1: Theory*, John Wiley, New York.

7. **Lavenberg, S.S. (Ed.) [1983].** *Computer Performance Modeling Handbook*, Academic Press, New York.

8. **Law, A.M. [1986].** Introduction to Simulation: A Powerful Tool for Analyzing Complex Manufacturing Systems, *Industrial Engineering*, Vol. 28, No. 5, May 1986, pp. 46–61.

9. **Narahari, Y., and N. Viswanadham [1985].** A Petri Net Approach to Modeling and Analysis of Flexible Manufacturing Systems, *Annals of Operations Research*, Vol. 3, pp. 449–472.

10. **Ramadge, P.J., and W.M. Wonham [1987].** Modular Feedback Logic for Discrete Event Systems, *SIAM Journal of Control and Optimization*, Vol. 25, No. 5, pp. 1202–1218.

11. **Solberg, J.J. [1977].** A Mathematical Model of Computerized Manufacturing Systems, *Proceedings of Fourth International Conference on Production Research*, Tokyo, Japan, pp. 22–30.

12. **Suri, R. [1985].** An Overview of Evaluative Models for Flexible Manufacturing Systems, *Annals of Operations Research*, Vol. 3, pp. 13–21.

13. **Trivedi, K.S. [1982].** *Probability and Statistics with Reliability, Queuing, and Computer Science Applications*, Prentice-Hall, Englewood Cliffs, New Jersey.

14. **Viswanadham, N., and Y. Narahari [1988].** Stochastic Petri Net Models for Performance Evaluation of Automated Manufacturing Systems, *Information and Decision Technologies*, Vol. 14, pp. 125–142.

Chapter 2
AUTOMATED MANUFACTURING SYSTEMS

This chapter provides a comprehensive, logical overview of automated manufacturing systems. The aim is to create a proper setting for the modeling techniques and tools that will be presented in Chapter 3 (Markov Models), Chapter 4 (Queuing Models), and Chapter 5 (Petri Net Models).

Chapter 2 is organized into eight sections. The first section traces the evolution of manufacturing, covering important developments such as numerically controlled machines, robotics, material handling, and computer control systems, leading to the currently available flexible manufacturing systems. This section also provides a discussion of all design and engineering functions that make up the product cycle in a manufacturing plant. In Section 2, a generic input-output model of manufacturing systems is discussed and different types of plant configurations are presented. Section 3 is devoted to performance measures of manufacturing systems. In this section we identify eight generic performance measures – manufacturing lead time, work-in-process, machine utilization, throughput, capacity, flexibility, performability, and quality. The performance models that will be presented in subsequent chapters are meant to evaluate these performance measures.

In Section 4 we treat in some detail numerically controlled machine centers and automated inspection systems. The emphasis is on the management of operations and control rather than on mechanical or hardware details. In the same spirit, we discuss industrial robots, conveyors, and automated guided vehicles in Section 5, thus covering the material handling equipment. Section 6 is on plant layouts where we mainly distinguish between functional layouts and group technology layouts. The important topic of flexible manufacturing systems forms the subject matter of Section 7. We discuss the architecture and operation of flexible manufacturing systems using a detailed flowchart and logical diagrams. We then present flexible assembly systems and the problem of deadlocks. We also include a discussion on performance measures in the context of flexible manufacturing systems. The last section, Section 8, is on computer control systems. We first present the architecture of a hierarchical control system for automated manufacturing systems. This is followed by a comprehensive discussion of local area networks in manufacturing, including the manufacturing automation protocol. Finally, we bring out the role of database management systems in providing information integration.

2.1 INTRODUCTION

The term *manufacturing* embraces a great many activities, from the production of a pin to the assemblage of combinations of part types to form complex structures such as an aircraft. It can also refer to *flow* or *continuous* processes such as plastics or reaction processes, as in chemical and fertilizer industries. Manufacturing produces real wealth for any country, is a source of employment for the population, and constitutes the backbone for the service sector. In this book we are concerned with manufacturing systems producing *discrete* products rather than flow processes.

2.1.1 History of Manufacturing

Throughout its history, the manufacturing industry has gone through successive periods of great changes. New materials, new techniques, and advanced technology have always been at the root of these changes.

Recent advances in microelectronics and digital computer technologies have resulted in a new, innovative era in manufacturing. Computer-aided automation has created immense potential for producing high-quality goods in small volumes, at low cost.

Further, the market for manufactured products is becoming increasingly international (i.e., companies all over the world are finding heightened competition in what were previously domestic markets). Manufacturing has thus become highly competitive, and companies have had to focus their resources, capabilities, and energies on building a sustainable competitive advantage. Such an advantage may be derived, for example, from lower cost, from higher product performance, from more innovative products, or from superior service. This requires the application of some profoundly new concepts related to production processes, organization of work, and technology.

Several companies with high direct labor content were practicing off-shore manufacturing with a view to take advantage of lower wages. With growth in computer-aided automation, the direct labor content in manufacturing has steadily decreased and several companies have already set the trend away from off-shore manufacturing.

We thus see several changes taking place: in technology, in the variety and number of products, in quality consciousness, and in both political and individual attitudes. Survival, by effectively managing these changes, is the biggest challenge manufacturing industries face today.

Here, we briefly trace some notable landmarks in the history of manufacturing. A scan of this history would provide one with a perspective of where the present industry stands in the evolution of manufacturing.

The Early Stages

Manufacturing involves entrepreneurship, organization of work or logistics, project management, production machines, material handling, marketing, sales, and service. With the growth of civilization, all these facets of manufacturing were practiced and perfected around the world. The unique achievements of our ancestors, such as the Indian, Roman, Greek, and Egyptian temples, cathedrals, and pyramids, would indicate that logistics and project management are not such new ideas after all. Several inventions including the windmill (tenth century), watermill (A.D. 1270), iron furnace (tenth century), spinning wheel, candle- and clock-making (thirteenth century), and the steam engine (eighteenth century), all of which were inspired by human ingenuity and desire for a better standard of living, have contributed to the current state of automated manufacturing. Although industry and trade are as old as humankind, developments in technology have been the prime factors for the recent advances in manufacturing.

Manufacturing science is not easily recognized and is hidden under a variety of more fanciful dressings including marketing, finance, and management. There are a few principles which have a profound effect on the factory system. The *Division of Labor* concepts enunciated by Adam Smith in 1776 as a means for increased productivity had remarkable influence in the creation of the factory system. Eli Whitney pioneered the idea of easily interchangeable parts made to close tolerances to enable on-the-spot repair of muskets (handguns). This idea was taken further by Samuel Colt in the 1830s.

In the early 1800s, a factory generally consisted of a system of productive machines, and the earliest noteworthy example of a factory was one in England for manufacturing pulley blocks. This factory had 44 machines and 10 unskilled operators and is an example of mass production, in which a series of dedicated machines produced a single product.

A significant milestone for integrated manufacture occurred in the year 1913 when Henry Ford developed a flow line on which an engine was progressively assembled in 84 stages. This reduced the labor and increased the rate of production. In view of the excellent results, Ford extended the methodology to the production of the entire vehicle, with a consequent reduction in the price of the motor car, bringing it within the reach of those with moderate salaries and thus greatly expanding the market.

The assembly line of Henry Ford is based on the three principles of *planning*, *scheduling*, and *control*, and also the continuous movement of product through the factory. A scientific approach to Ford's principles was developed by Frederick Taylor, whose theory is known as Scientific Management. Taylor can be considered as the father of time and motion studies.

Developments During the 1950s – 1970s

The transition from the transfer line to the current unmanned, fully automated and flexible manufacturing systems has been achieved through the development of new technologies, such as numerically controlled machine tools, robotics, material handling systems, and computer control systems.

Numerically Controlled Machines

The first numerically controlled (NC) machine center was developed in 1952 at the Massachusetts Institute of Technology for machining complex profiles. Soon its potential benefits in batch production were realized. The development of NC machine centers that could drill, mill, and bore was the next significant event in batch manufacturing. These machine centers were further enhanced in the 1960s by the provision of automatic tool changers, and indexing work tables. The next milestone was in control system development, and this occurred in 1971. Microcomputer-controlled NC machines (also called computer numerical control) were developed for almost the same cost as hard-wired controllers. Computer numerical control (CNC) offered many advantages including storage of many part programs in memory and ability to communicate with other controllers and a central computer. These capabilities led to the development of integrated manufacturing systems.

Robotics

Automation and robotics are two closely related technologies. Robotics, like NC machines, is a form of industrial programmable automation. The history of robotics has roots both in science fiction and in technology development. In the seventeenth and eighteenth centuries, a number of ingenious mechanical devices with the features of robots were devised. The technology for the present generation of robots was developed by Cyril Walter Kenward in 1954 in Britain and by G.C. Devol in the United States. The latter was commercialized by Joseph Engelberger and Devol as *Unimate* in 1962. Since then several robots have been built and used in the industry for various applications including painting, welding, material handling, and assembly.

Material Handling

This is not a new concept but remarkable progress has been made in the field in the recent years, allowing greater automation of manufacturing processes. Developments in floor-mounted and overhead roller conveyors, stacker cranes, and automated guided vehicles (AGVs) have contributed substantially to smooth material flow on the factory floor. Programmable logic controllers of each of these equipment could be interconnected for part flow automation.

Computer controlled material flow is the largest contributor to reduction of waiting time and the work-in-process inventory in comparison with manual loading/unloading and manual material handling systems.

Computer Control Systems

In the 1950s and 1960s, mainframe computers were used for planning, scheduling, and controlling batch production. Several companies integrated the organizational system of the company with the manufacturing system. Use of computers in factories, for accounting, payroll, and maintenance of management information systems has been perfected. The key breakthrough, however, occurred when shop-floor equipment such as machine tools and material handling elements became controlled by the computer. Developments in the local area networks made possible the transfer of information in real time, and this provided further impetus to factory automation.

Flexible Manufacturing Systems

The above developments have naturally culminated in the evolution of automated and flexible manufacturing systems. Automated transfer lines were installed in automobile and other industries for mass production. Such systems, although highly economical, lack flexibility. They would be the choice configurations in steady markets. The small-batch production and custom-made products that account for 75% of total number of workpieces are essentially manufactured in job shops. These shops are inefficient in machine utilizations and have large manufacturing lead times. Flexible manufacturing systems (FMS) have evolved as a solution to efficient mid-volume production of a variety of part types with low setup time, low work-in-process inventory, short manufacturing lead time, high machine utilization, and high quality.

The evolution of FMS started in the early 1960s. One of the first systems that used versatile machine tools and automated material handling was developed by the Sunstrand Corporation in 1965. It had eight NC machine centers and two multispindle drills linked by a computer-controlled roller conveyor system. This system was developed to manufacture 70 different types of aircraft gear box casings from aluminum-magnesium alloy. Although this system did not have the flexibility of current-day

FMSs, it was the first system where automated material flow integration was built into the system.

The first pioneering unmanned flexible machining system was installed at Molins, Deptford, London, to manufacture relatively complex light alloy components for tooling in the tobacco industry. Theodore Williams, director of R&D at Molins, invented this system, named System 24, so called because it was intended to operate for 24 hours a day under computer control, with only the day shift attended by operators. The Molins system was designed to perform a series of operations on a wide variety of parts in random order. It consisted of several NC machines with changeable tool magazines and an automated material handling system. Palletized workpieces and tool magazines were stored in an automatic storage and retrieval system (ASRS). The machine control programs were held on magnetic tapes and were accessed under centralized computer control.

FMSs are at a very early stage of their diffusion. In 1981, there were about 120 FMSs installed worldwide. This number increased to about 230 in 1984. Of these, Japan accounted for about 100, the United States for 60, Germany for 25, and Sweden for 15. However, there has been worldwide attention on flexible automation. Several systems have been installed around the world in the areas of metal products, electronics and computers, electrical machinery, and transportation equipment.

Developments in the 1980s

Other developments also led to further advances in the area of automated manufacturing. These include the drive to conserve natural resources, to improve industrial competitiveness, reduce lead times, and insistence on higher-quality, custom-made products and good after-sales service. Further, the emergence of new materials, new technologies, and new and improved products has made the markets uncertain. In response to such demands, several production planning and control methods emerged concurrently with flexible automation technologies. These include material requirements planning (MRP), manufacturing resources planning (MRP-II), just-in-time (JIT), and optimized production technology (OPT). The emphasis on product quality has given impetus to the development of automatic inspection systems, 100% inspection, in-process gauging, expert system-based failure diagnosis methods, statistical process control, total quality control, and, above all, their integration into the overall computer control system.

These developments have spurred a great change in the manufacturing sector across the globe. The push for intelligent, high-speed, highly flexible manufacturing systems is increasing. The factory of the future using a wide range of new technologies will be paperless and peopleless. Other important developments include simultaneous engineering (i.e., integration of design, manufacturing, and testing into a unified cycle), design for manufacturability, design for testability, electronic prototyping, etc. All this would lead to treating design, manufacturing, and business functions as a single whole, and to the concept of computer integrated manufacturing (CIM).

Technical feasibility apart, it is highly important that these factories are economically efficient. The decade of the 1990s should see the consolidation of these technically feasible systems into economically viable manufacturing systems.

2.1.2 The Product Cycle

The major activities that define the manufacturing enterprise in direct relation to the manufacturing of products include (i) *Marketing*, (ii) *Engineering*, (iii) *Production Management*, and (iv) *Manufacturing*. We briefly dwell on these activities below.

Marketing

The marketing function links the enterprise to its customers and suppliers. It is responsible for the relationship of the enterprise with competition. Information relating to changes in markets and emergence of new markets brought about by technological changes form part of the marketing function.

The objectives of a company are most clearly represented in terms of the products and markets. All companies ultimately seek to differentiate themselves through products. The marketing function, then, would be to look outward to identify clients and their requirements.

Marketing is an important element of an enterprise. It directs the company within the market and in its relationship with customers and competitors. It helps the enterprise to attain its primary objective: to create and serve a customer. The market for manufactured products is becoming increasingly international. In this scenario, companies find themselves having to meet international standards or the local standards of the individual foreign countries.

Traditional marketing strategies look into the past and try to predict the future. This approach might work during periods of stability and when there is little competition. However, in a highly competitive environment, which requires rapid introduction of new and customized products with short lifetimes, a new approach to marketing is needed. Such an approach would involve the development of innovative products, creation of linkages within the factory among the marketing, engineering, and production functions, and responding to customers' needs in functionality, cost, delivery, and service.

Engineering

Here we are concerned with the design of products and development of manufacturing processes to produce these products. Figure 2.1 shows the product cycle from an engineering perspective. These activities are often classified as design engineering and manufacturing engineering.

In the design engineering function, a product is designed by a process of iterative refinement. This starts with a concept, which defines the function of a product. Logical design then establishes product structure and form and a description of the component parts, each of which goes through the design process. Product form defines the geometric properties

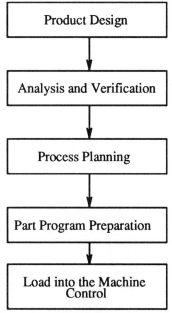

Figure 2.1 Product cycle from the engineering perspective

of parts. Raw materials are identified to suit the physical and chemical properties of the environment. Product design includes design and drafting activities together with the use of modeling, simulation, and electronic prototyping to obtain the optimal design.

The manufacturing engineering function includes facilities planning and process planning. Process planning involves development of route sheets, jigs, fixtures and tools, and part programs for machine tools. The route sheet gives details of the type and number of operations, alternative machines used in conducting these operations, tools used for each operation, and finally the time required for each operation. The route sheet also includes information on the fabrication and assembly operations.

Computer-aided process planning (CAPP) is a key interface between design and manufacturing. There are two approaches to developing CAPP systems: (i) variant approach, and (ii) generative approach. The variant approach involves grouping the parts produced in the plants into families, based on their manufacturing characteristics and establishing a standard process plan for each part family. Process plan preparation for any new part is done through manipulation of the plan for a similar part. The generative approach makes use of the computer to create an individual plan using a set of algorithms to create a viable manufacturing plan.

A combined approach to design and manufacturing engineering has several merits; in particular, re-engineering of products to improve quality and functionality as well as for ease of automated operation. For example, the replacement of electromechanical parts by electronic parts and sheet metal parts by plastic parts has had a profound effect on product design.

Production Management

The role of production management is to plan and control effectively the actual resources of the manufacturing plant so as to meet the production requirements. The resources include materials, tools, fixtures, machines, storage space, material handling equipment, and people. Production management is an area where techniques such as critical-path method (CPM), MRP-II, and JIT are well-established control techniques.

The production management system (PMS) regulates the manufacturing system at the operational level through its decisions of what to buy and make. There are several separate functions identified as constituting the activities in production management. The constituents of PMS and their interconnections are shown in Figure 2.2 and are described below.

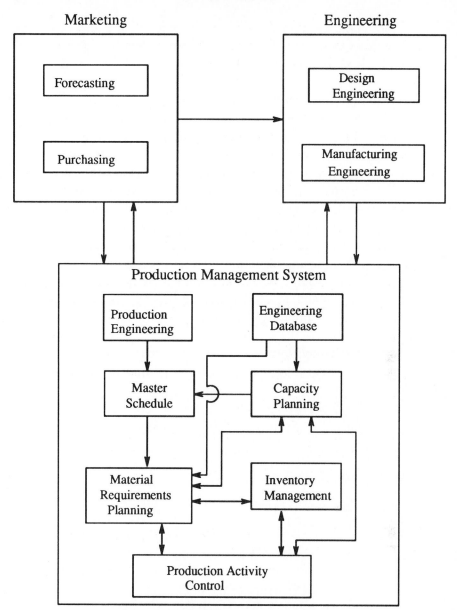

Figure 2.2 Product cycle activity chart

Forecasting

The first step in planning the operation of a production system is to determine an accurate forecast of the demand for the products. This information, combined with the customer orders and inventory, is used as a basis to specify the volume of production for each product type, the work force, and machine scheduling.

Production Planning

Here we are concerned with the determination of production, inventory, and work force levels to meet the demand. This is based on sales forecast and is used to raise or lower production levels for product types and allow launching of new products. This is also called *aggregate planning*. The word *aggregate* means that planning is conducted at a gross level intended to meet the total demand collected over all products, utilizing the total human and equipment resources. This aggregation may take place by consolidating similar items into product groups, different machines into machine centers, different labor skills into labor centers, and different customers into market regions. It is also customary to express aggregate demand in production hours. Aggregate production planning precedes the detailed master production schedule.

Engineering Database

This database contains all the information about the fabrication and assembly: bill of materials, part designs, route sheets, tools, etc. This data is updated to include engineering changes as well. The inputs to this database are provided by the databases of both the design and manufacturing engineering functions.

Master Production Scheduling

The aggregated production plan is disaggregated into a master schedule that specifies how many units of each product are to be delivered and when. In turn, this master schedule must be converted into purchase orders for raw materials, orders for subcontracting, and product schedules for subassemblies and components. These events are timed and coordinated to allow the delivery of the final product on schedule. This schedule must take into account the production capacity in terms of machine time and labor.

Capacity Planning

Capacity planning is concerned with determining the labor and equipment resources needed to meet the production schedule. The master schedule and capacity planning should be compatible. The requirements of the master production schedule should not exceed the capacity. Capacity adjustments can be accomplished on either a short-term or a long-term basis. Short-term capacity planning decisions include: overtime or reducing the workweek, hiring and firing, subcontracting, and inventory stockpiling. Long-term capacity planning includes decisions such as acquisition of new resources and manpower, updating of facilities, and closing down existing facilities and portions of business.

Materials Requirement Planning

MRP converts the master production schedule into a detailed schedule for raw materials and components. More precisely, MRP takes the master schedule data, bill of materials file, and the inventory data and determines when to order raw materials and components for assembled products. It can also reschedule orders in response to variations in production priorities and demand conditions.

Inventory Management

Inventory control is concerned with maintaining certain levels of raw material, semi-finished parts, subassemblies, and finished goods, to act as a buffer between the company and consumers and also between different stages in the manufacturing system. This is considered as insurance against machine failures, uncertain demands, uncertain suppliers, and worker absenteeism. The inventory should be kept low at the same time maintaining satisfactory customer service.

Production Activity Control

Production management systems have two objectives, namely planning and control of manufacturing operations. All the issues discussed above such as master production schedule, MRP, and capacity planning deal with the first objective of planning manufacturing operations. Production activity control or shop-floor control transforms the planning decisions into control commands for the production process. Also, it collects data from the shop floor and passes the data on to higher control levels.

Production activity control has three modules: order release, order scheduling, and order progress. The purpose of the order release module is to provide the necessary documentation that accompanies an order as it is processed through the shop floor. This documentation consists of route sheet, material requisitions, job cards, parts list, etc.

The order scheduling module makes assignments of orders to various machines so that the delivery schedules are met, in-process inventory is minimized, and machine utilization is maximized. Order scheduling involves two steps: (1) machine loading, and (2) job sequencing. Machine loading involves allocating jobs to the machines, and job sequencing determines the order in which the jobs are processed through a work center. Several priority rules could be used for job sequencing. These include shortest processing time, first-come-first-served, least slack, etc. The purpose of the order progress module is to provide data relating to work-in-process and shop order status.

Manufacturing

Manufacturing operations in production are at the heart of the manufacturing enterprise and are directly associated with the making of the products. Products are made by a variety of processes, machines, and skilled labor. The operations include fabrication, assembly, inspection, storage, and transport. The dominant technology is associated with the production process. Flexibility, rapid response to customer requests, product variety, and product quality are the main desirable characteristics of the production system.

Advanced methods based on information technology are becoming increasingly common in factories. Computer-controlled machine tools, laser cutters, and water jets are being used in the fabrication of parts. Electronic assembly equipment such as automatic insertion machines are common in electronic manufacturing. Handling technology includes robots, automated guided vehicles, and devices for machine loading, palletizing, and assembly. Storage technology such as automated carousels and warehousing systems are commonplace in modern factories.

These computer-controlled production processes increase the flexibility of the process and allow manufacture of a broad range of high-quality products.

We have thus defined the major range of activities in a manufacturing enterprise. This serves as an introduction to what follows in the text.

At this stage we would like to discuss briefly some recent developments in competitive manufacturing. These include design for manufacture and simultaneous engineering. Both these developments are concerned with defining product design alternatives to facilitate optimization of the manufacturing system as a whole.

Design for Manufacture (DFM)

Design for manufacture is concerned with understanding how product design interacts with other components of the manufacturing system and in defining product design alternatives, which help facilitate global optimization of the product cycle as a whole. This concept has been used to advantage in design for assembly, which involves minimizing the number of parts to be assembled as well as designing the parts to enable easy assembly.

Many of the DFM principles are deeply rooted in the long history of design and manufacture. Some of these principles include minimizing the total number of parts, developing a modular design, using standard components, designing parts to be multifunctional and having multiuse, designing parts that are easy to fabricate, avoiding separate fasteners, minimizing assembly directions, and handling and maximizing compliance.

DFM is now recognized as the key way to simultaneously minimize cost, assure product quality, and realize the productivity advantages offered by advanced technologies.

Simultaneous Engineering

To appreciate the concept of simultaneous engineering, consider the classical manufacturing model shown in Figure 2.3. In this model, concept decisions, product design, and testing are performed prior to manufacturing system design, process planning, and production. However, one can easily realize that to design a product properly, it is essential that interactions between the product and process enter into consideration at an early stage in the design process. Product concept and manufacturing concept decisions must be made hand in hand in order to obtain an integrated manufacturing system, optimally configured to both product and process requirements. This approach requires the simultaneous engineering model depicted in Figure 2.4.

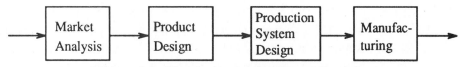

Figure 2.3 Classical model of manufacturing

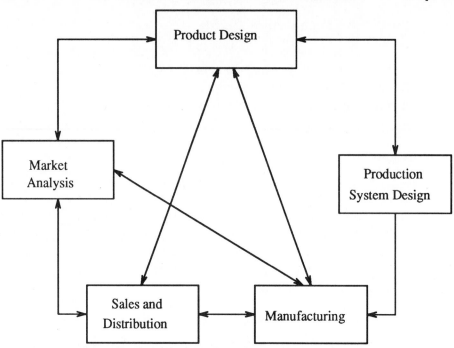

Figure 2.4 Simultaneous engineering model of manufacturing

2.1.3 Manufacturing Automation

Manufacturing has its primary roots in technology. The first Industrial Revolution was largely concerned with mechanization, which is the use of tools and machines to enhance human physical activity. Automation involves the use of computers in the measurement, interpretation, decision making, and corrective action in the control of complex, rapidly changing tasks.

Definition: *Manufacturing automation* is the assemblage of technologies that enable automated manufacture of a variety of quality products.

This assemblage includes versatile machine tools for processing and assembly, automatic material handling systems, and a centralized or distributed computer control system consisting of database management system and other software elements. This kind of automation enables automatic control of workpiece movement and processing and also supports real-time and managerial decision making.

The development of new automation technologies is a continuous and evolutionary process and has its beginnings in the first Industrial Revolution when machines began to take over the repetitive tasks performed by human operators. We can classify automation into four categories:

1. Fixed automation
2. Programmable automation
3. Flexible automation
4. Integrated automation

Fixed Automation

Fixed automation is practiced for high-volume mass production. Here dedicated equipment, optimized to perform a sequence of operations, is used to achieve low cost and high productivity. Generally the equipment is inflexible, and a change in product entails change of equipment. Examples of fixed automation are found in transfer lines and automatic assembly lines. Welding, painting, pick and place robots, and conveyer systems are examples of fixed automation equipment.

Programmable Automation

Programmable automation equipment has the capability to change the sequence of operations to adapt to different product configurations. Generally the equipment has programmable controllers that control the operations and their sequence. By changing the program, the equipment can be programmed to perform a variety of tasks. Examples of programmable automation equipment include NC machines, assembly robots, and automated guided vehicles (AGVs).

Flexible Automation

Flexible automation systems have the capability to maintain competitive production of a variety of part types in low- to mid-volume ranges, in the face of design, demand, and part mix changes, and machine and tool failures. This is achieved by building into the system appropriate redundancies so that it has the capability to adapt to external and internal disturbances. Examples of flexible automation are provided by flexible manufacturing systems. Flexible automation supports scope economies as opposed to scale economies. This point is elaborated in Section 2.1.4.

Integrated Automation

Integrated automation involves logical organization of design, engineering, production, testing, marketing, and distribution functions into a

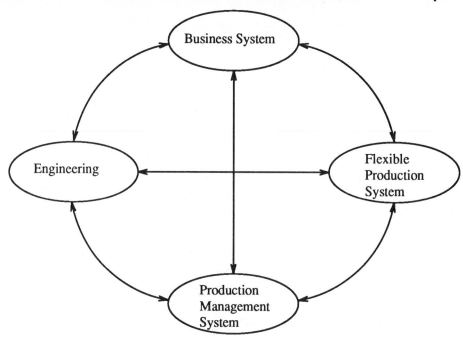

Figure 2.5 CIM and its elements

computer integrated system. This concept thus facilitates integration of all phases of manufacturing from product conception and planning through shipping and delivery, and involves the highest level of integration among the various manufacturing functions of the firm. This concept has led to the development of computer integrated manufacturing (CIM) and involves integration of the various islands of automation into a single coherent system.

Figure 2.5 presents a logical view of CIM. This diagram should be very clear in view of the discussions on product cycle in Section 2.1.2.

2.1.4 Economies of Scale and Scope

Economics literature has supported for several decades the notion that bigger plants producing larger volumes of the same unit are more cost-efficient than smaller plants producing less volumes. High-output volumes are presumed to lead to lower costs. Many industries including chemicals, steel, pulp and paper, petrochemicals, and cement have established larger operating units with the hope of strengthening their competitive position.

A system is said to be exhibiting economies of scale if the size of its physical output, Q, is given by

$$Q = f(kx_i) = k^q f(x_i) \quad \text{for all } x_i$$

where $q > 1$ is a constant, $k > 1$ is the proportion of rise in the inputs, x_i is the input size, and $f(x_i)$ the output size. This implies that doubling all inputs would result in more than doubling the output. Consequently, total cost per unit of output will decline with increase in inputs.

Although successively larger plants have yielded substantial benefits in many cases, it would appear that the widespread faith in economies of scale has not gained much support from theoretical and empirical literature. Most economies of scale are derived from sources other than proportionate expansion of all inputs. Some reasons for the benefits include:

1. **Standardization**: Since the beginning of mass production by Henry Ford, there has been substantial decline in unit production costs in larger plants as compared to the production of a multitude of customized products in small shops. This is a consequence of the increasing division of labor and its heightened productivity from the learning curve effect; the elimination of downtime associated with switching between tasks; the automation of repetitive tasks; closer supervision and quality control of the work performed at each station, and efficient transfer of workpieces among workstations arranged as a linear string.

2. **Sharing of Fixed Costs**: Fixed costs such as research and development, inventory, and equipment are spread over large volumes.

It has been argued by Bela Gold that increases in scale may have made some contributions in some sectors during some periods but that there is no basis, however, for arguing that such contributions have been of major proportion or even that they have been consistently significant.

However, there is no doubt that widespread faith in economies of scale has resulted in large factories with fixed automation equipment. These were working well until the late 1960s. Since the early 1970s, the manufacturing environment has changed, and this change is in evidence in industries such as automotive, consumer goods, electronics, and computers. The characteristics of the changed environment include among others increased product diversity, greatly reduced product life cycles, insistence on quality and after-sales service, and global competition. Manufacturing firms, in this environment, cannot expend huge resources on developing a dedicated production capability since product design will be out of date much before the production facility investments are recovered. One has to replace scale economies by scope economies. In scope economies, the ability of the plant to produce a variety of differentiated versions of similar products will become a crucial variable that determines the cost structure and the competitive positioning of the factory.

Economies of scope exist where the same equipment can produce multiple products more cheaply in combination than separately. More formally, economies of scope exist in a plant producing two products, A and B, at output levels A_i and B_i, respectively, if

$$C(A_1, B_1) < C(A_1, 0) + C(0, B_1)$$

where C(.,.) is the appropriate cost function.

The combination of versatile machine tools, computer-controlled transformation of materials into final products, and rapid information transfer among various pieces of equipment has given several new capabilities to the factories. These include flexibility to manufacture a variety of products with almost negligible changeover times, rapid response to changes in market demand, part mix and equipment breakdowns, faster throughput due to better machine utilization, low in-process inventories, high quality of finished products, and reduced waste. Several of these automated factories are currently in existence.

The above technical capabilities of automated factories support economies of scope (i.e., efficiencies wrought by variety, not volume; smaller factories and short production runs for any given product design rather than large-scale, high-volume factories). The computer-controlled automated factories have multipurpose machine tools. Matching these versatile machines with special purpose programming moves the work of production of small batches toward the smooth flow of chemical process operations. The enhanced flexibility moves the setup costs back into the design process and directly enhances the product line and reduces the inventory. It is more inexpensive to maintain a broader product line and follow the make-to-order philosophy than to follow make-to-stock principles. Since machine tools are programmed and smart, the learning-curve is flat from the first part it manufactures. The economic batch size (i.e., the number of parts in a batch) approaches unity since inventory costs overshadow the changeover costs.

Reducing economic order quantity to unity is of competitive value only if a company's marketing strategy emphasizes customized products and frequent product changes, and if its R&D can provide a constant stream of innovative product improvements and process modifications. As sophisticated information systems integrate the material flow and the information flow, manufacturing inevitably comes to rely more on science than on art. Old thinking about custom markets versus mass markets is obsolete. Big companies will be able to provide custom service and small companies also can serve mass markets. Thus a company's distinctive competence increasingly would come from the manufacturing system.

PROBLEMS

1. Study the four levels of automation discussed in Section 2.1.3 in the context of economies of scale and scope.
2. Give several reasons why scope economies are gaining prominence over scale economies.
3. Investigate what would be the appropriate mathematical models [e.g., linear programming, integer programming, queuing models, simulation, PERT/CPM (project evaluation and review technique/critical path method), etc.] that could be employed in the various steps of the product cycle.
4. It is believed that integration (material flow, information, functional) has a *multiplier* effect on the system performance. Can you substantiate how?
5. Prepare a comprehensive term paper on the history and evolution of manufacturing systems.

2.2 MANUFACTURING SYSTEMS

In this section we discuss some systemic concepts associated with manufacturing. These are applicable to both continuous and discrete manufacturing systems.

Definition: *Manufacturing* is a transformation process by which raw material, labor, energy, and equipment are brought together to produce high-quality goods.

The goods produced naturally should have an economic value greater than that of the inputs used and should be salable in the presence of competition. The transformation process generally involves a sequence of steps called *production operations*. Each production operation is a process of changing the inputs into outputs while adding *value* to the

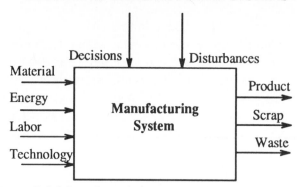

Figure 2.6 Manufacturing system: input-output model

entity. Interspersed between these value-adding operations are the non-value-adding operations, such as transporting, storing, and inspecting. It is necessary to minimize, if not eliminate, the non-value-adding operations.

2.2.1 Input-Output Model

A manufacturing system can be represented by the *input-output model* shown in Figure 2.6. Here the inputs are shown as material, labor, energy, and technology. The raw material is converted into the final quality product. Labor, in the form of blue-collar and white-collar workers, is needed for designing the product, operating the equipment, loading and unloading of the workpieces, and for inspection. The recent trend is to automate most of these functions and elevate the role of the human operator to one of a monitor and supervisor.

Manufacturing technology represents the sophistication and flexibility of the equipment and the extent of material flow integration and information integration built into the system. A manufacturing system can be manual or fully automated; highly dedicated or fully flexible; a collection of isolated machine tools or a fully integrated production system. It is the level of technology that determines whether a given system is a mass production system, job shop, batch production system, or a fully flexible machining system. The technology also determines whether the economies achieved are of the scale type or of the scope type. As we mentioned earlier in Section 2.1.4, the mass production of a narrow range of products leads to economies of scale while low-volume production of a wide variety of products leads to economies of scope.

The manufacturing process produces three outputs: the completed workpiece or the quality product satisfying required engineering specifications; scrap; and waste. Scrap is an inevitable by-product of metal cutting. Waste is of two types. The first type of waste is represented by tools consumed, product rejected during inspection, etc., and the second type of waste is generated by use of system resources for non-value-adding operations. Of course, scrap and waste are undesirable outputs and should both be minimized.

There are two more inputs to a manufacturing system that are important and crucial for its performance. The first one is the set of decisions made at various levels of the hierarchy (long range, medium range, and short range) regarding products manufactured, equipment purchased, plant layout, sequencing and scheduling of parts, loading of parts, etc. These decisions are very important, and the main goal of this book is to present tools for evaluating by analytical means the various decisions. The second kind of inputs are disturbances; these include government action, market fluctuations, competition, equipment failures, and labor problems.

Decisions in the Manufacturing World

Decision making in a manufacturing environment can be very complex because of the alternatives available and the serious and uncertain nature of the outcome of the decisions. There are three levels of decisions in a manufacturing system: strategic, tactical, and operational. The strategic decisions are long term (typically years) and determine the competitiveness and survivability of the firm. These include introduction of new technology, part-mix changes (allocating a new part type for production), system modification and expansion (adding a new machine center or changing the material handling system layout), etc. The second level, or tactical decisions, have a horizon of weeks/days. These include dividing the overall production target into batches, taking into account the availability of raw materials, tools, and due dates. Typical questions include: (i) how many batches, and (ii) how many part types in each batch. The objective is to maximize the utilization of the machines while balancing the workload on the system so that all the machines finish their work for each batch almost simultaneously. The operational level or level-three decisions are concerned with day-to-day control of manufacturing operations. These include: (i) which part type to introduce into the system, (ii) how many workpieces should coexist in the system simultaneously, (iii) which part should be loaded onto the machine next, (iv) how many tools of each type, (v) how to react to tool breakage, and (vi) rescheduling in the case of failures of the machines or the material handling system.

Effective manufacturing management involves addressing simultaneously all three levels of decisions. Failure to do so will reduce management effectiveness, leading to higher costs and reduced competitiveness.

The ultimate purpose of manufacturing is to focus the organization's resources, capabilities, and energies toward building a sustainable advantage over its competitors. Such an advantage may be derived from lower cost, from higher product performance (quality), from more innovative products, or from superior service.

2.2.2 Plant Configurations

Manufacturing is a very broad term and includes many distinctly different types of production operations and products. It can assume many technological and organizational forms. However, it is possible to recognize the following four configurations based on the number of products and volume: continuous flow processes, job shops, batch production, and dedicated production lines.

Continuous Flow Processes

These involve continuous dedicated production of large amounts of bulk product. Here the product types are few and volumes are high. Process manufacturing involves a continuous flow of raw materials through a series of sequential operations. These operations transform the raw materials into a final product. Typical examples of continuous flow processes include chemical plants, oil refineries, plastics, iron and steel, and textile industries.

While complete continuity is rare, a pipeline-type system where each section of the plant processes a certain quantity of materials and passes it on to the next section is frequent. Either section-wise or plant-wise feedback control is used to maximize the overall yield. Product quality, generally in the nature of chemical composition, is maintained by feedback and feedforward control strategies. Availability of intelligent sensors, relatively inexpensive computer technology, and a sophisticated computer control theory of continuous processes have led to fully automated factories that run virtually unmanned.

Job Shops

Low to medium volumes and wide range of products characterize job shops, which are commonplace in mechanical engineering industries. Jobshop manufacturing is commonly used to meet specific customer orders, and there is great variety in the type of work done in the plant. Therefore, the production equipment must be flexible and general purpose to allow for this variety of work, and workers should be highly skilled to perform the range of work assignments. Examples include space vehicles, aircraft, missiles, machine tools, and prototypes of future products.

Job shops are typically very inefficient and have large lead times, large work-in-process inventory, and high costs. The reasons include:

1. An order for a component or subassembly usually involves operations on several different machine tools and there is one-piece at a time part movements. Generally material movement is done by blue-collar workers involving high costs and large delays.

2. The equipment and tooling in a job shop are general purpose and can be set up for almost any part in a family. But the time for setup of a particular job on a general purpose machine tool can take hours or even days.

3. These products have very long development and production times because of the upfront engineering and design times and long lead times for procurement of special components and materials. They also have high cost because of large engineering and design content per order, the higher skilled and higher paid factory work force, and substantially lower learning curve productivity gains.

Batch Production

This category involves the manufacture of medium-size lots of the same item or product. The lots may be produced only once or they may be produced at regular intervals. Lot sizes and the frequency of production of a single item are tied up with the inventory control policies adopted by marketing.

Here again, the manufacturing equipment is general purpose but designed for higher rates of production. Batch production plants include machine shops, casting foundries, plastic moulding factories, and press working shops. Items made in batch-type shops include furniture, textbooks, and household appliances. It has been estimated that as much as 75% of all batch manufacturing is in lot sizes of 50 pieces or less. Hence batch production and job shop production constitute an important portion of the total manufacturing activity.

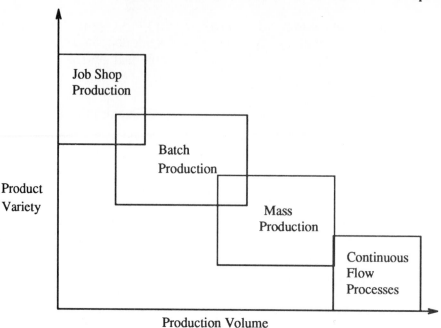

Figure 2.7 Four types of plant configurations

Dedicated High-Volume Production Lines

This is continuous specialized manufacture of identical products. High-volume production lines are characterized by very high production rates and narrow scope. The equipment is dedicated to the manufacture of a single product type such as automobile, light bulbs, appliances, etc. The entire plant is designed and operated for manufacture of a single product type. A very high fixed investment is required for one-of-a-kind specialization of production facilities, such as fixed transfer lines, dedicated conveyors, buffers, etc. Each piece of equipment is optimized in terms of cost and time for the operation it performs and material movement is automated. Additional capacity is created by cloning.

The four types of plant configurations can be distinguished by product variety and production volume. This is shown in Figure 2.7. There is some overlap in the categorization, as the figure indicates.

PROBLEMS

1. Is there a mapping between the four levels of automation discussed in Section 2.1.3 and the different types of plant configurations of Section 2.2.2?

2. Relate the decision levels (strategic, tactical, and operational) in the manu-facturing world to the product cycle diagram (Figure 2.2).

2.3 PERFORMANCE MEASURES

Every manufacturer's mission is to buy raw materials from vendors, trans-form them in a factory into needed products, and deliver these value-added items to customers. This is how they wish to earn profits. Most of them perform this mission poorly and make losses. The prime reason is that they ignore competition and effectiveness. They routinely make low-cost products and stockpile them in the inventory. The products in this inven-tory can become technologically obsolete in a short time. Competitiveness requires that the products have one or more of the following advantages: low cost, high quality, good service, and innovation. Product diversity and delivery time performance are other added virtues. Cost reduction and delivery time performance can be achieved by eliminating all non-value-adding activities, generally termed as waste. Anything other than the minimum amount of equipment, materials, space, information, people, and time essential to add value to the business is a non-value-adding ac-tivity. Examples of waste include: material handling, inspection, storage, inventory, rework, machine breakdowns, shortages, warranty costs, and handling customer complaints.

We shall consider here eight performance measures of any manufac-turing system, which are indicative of its competitive status in the man-ufacturing world. These are:

1. Manufacturing Lead Time
2. Work-in-process
3. Machine Utilization
4. Throughput
5. Capacity
6. Flexibility
7. Performability
8. Quality

We now consider each of these with respect to traditional job shop and batch production. We shall discuss these performance measures again in Section 2.7 in the context of flexible manufacturing systems. The analytical models discussed in this book facilitate a clear understanding of automated manufacturing systems through these performance measures.

2.3.1 Manufacturing Lead Time

We have seen earlier that manufacturing is a transformation process that converts raw materials into quality products and that the process of manufacturing consists of a sequence of machining and assembly operations. In between these operations, non-value-adding operations, as discussed above, are performed. Ideally, we would want to eliminate these wasteful operations or at least minimize the time that a part spends in these operations. The term *lead time* captures the time that a part spends in a manufacturing system. There are two variants of lead time discussed in the literature, namely manufacturing lead time and total lead time. These are defined below.

Definition: The Manufacturing Lead Time (MLT) of a product is the total time required to process the product through the manufacturing plant.

Definition: The Total Lead Time (TLT) of a product is the total time elapsed from the instant at which raw materials are ordered until the instant the finished product is delivered.

Ideally, MLT should be equal to the actual machining and assembly time. This is possible with zero inventories, zero material handling, zero setup time, zero defects, zero breakdowns, and a batch size of one. Certainly these are ideal characteristics to attain manufacturing excellence. In actual practice, however, one would wish to minimize the MLT.

The TLT is a complex quantity since it involves procurement, vendor, manufacturing, engineering, tooling, and customer lead times. Here, we focus on manufacturing lead time and study the following four components that constitute MLT:

1. Setup time
2. Processing time
3. Move time
4. Queue time

While focusing on MLT, we assume that raw materials are currently in stock (i.e., procurement lead time is zero and that we have made these items before; we have on hand the design, the process plan, and the necessary tooling).

In a typical batch processing environment, the MLT is much greater than the actual processing time for the batch. In conventional batch processing, actual processing time and setup time together represent less than 5% of MLT. Queuing and transport times account for the rest of the MLT. We now consider each of the four elements of MLT and discuss methods of reducing each of them.

Setup Time

Definition: Setup time or changeover time is the time required by a machine or a system manufacturing one product type to switch to another product type.

The setup time generally includes times required for fixturing, tool changing, and preparing the workplace. Reducing the setup times has a profound effect on the manufacturing system performance since it increases the flexibility, reduces the work-in-process inventory, and reduces the economic batch size. Low setup times constitute the basis of the just-in-time (JIT) philosophy of manufacturing.

The setup time and thus the setup cost are incurred whenever a new batch is started on the machine. To minimize the setup time and costs, a batch of products is manufactured after a single setup. Large batch sizes on the other hand result in high inventory levels. The economic batch size (EBS) is the batch size for which the total cost, which is the sum of setup and inventory costs, is a minimum. The economic batch size Q is given by

$$Q = \sqrt{\frac{2SD}{I}} \tag{1}$$

where

C = total cost

S = setup cost per batch

D = demand rate for the item

I = inventory carrying cost per item per unit time.

Equation (1) can be easily derived by noting that the total cost C is given by

$$C = \frac{D}{Q}S + \frac{Q}{2}I$$

and then solving $\frac{dC}{dQ} = 0$ for the optimal Q.

From (1), we see that if setup time is reduced by n, then the EBS reduces to $Q/\sqrt{n}$ leading to smaller lot sizes.

If the setup costs are zero, then a batch of size unity becomes economic. Faster changeovers reduce the lead time and result in the JIT approach. Suppose we have, in the route of a part, 10 changeovers each taking 4 hours and we reduce the changeover time to 10 minutes, then we save a lot of time. Smaller lots reduce the inventory on the shop floor, dependence on forecasts, and the cycle time. Also, we do not produce the inventory that would subsequently be lying idle in storage.

Reducing changeover times requires more thought, more modifications, and more practice in making quick changes and more investment. The options may range from buying one large flexible computer-controlled machine with fast changeover times from one product type to another, to installing several small dedicated machines capable of producing only one product and complete avoidance of changeover. Modifying the existing machine tools to create flexibility and fast changeovers is yet another option.

Processing Time

As we discussed earlier, batch processing time is the only time during a product's passage through the production system that real value is being added to it. Other times are non-value-adding and should be minimized. Reduction of changeover time makes possible economic production of small batches and thus a proportionate reduction in the batch processing times.

Move Time

These are the times needed to transport workpieces from one workspot to another. The moving of workpieces could be within the machine shop, within a factory, across factories, or between various subcontracted processes performed by the vendors.

Small batch sizes imply more number of moves between the machine processes for the same production target. The need then would be for a smart material handling system that can make a large number of deliveries of small loads in a short time.

We note that the best material handling is no material handling and optimal move time is zero move time. There are three ways in which transport times could be reduced: (i) creating versatile computer-controlled machine centers with automatic tool changers capable of performing a variety of processing operations, (ii) adapting product layouts or cellular layouts, based on group technology principles, where all machine tools necessary to manufacture a given family of items are located together and in a correct production sequence, and (iii) using more efficient transfer mechanisms such as belt conveyors, fork lifts, chutes, and smart AGVs that can make faster delivery of unit loads.

Queue Times

Queue times or waiting times before the resources such as machine centers, AGVs, etc., are the longest elements that make up the MLT. Queues occur before machine centers and AGVs because there are almost always jobs waiting to be processed by these resources. When a new job arrives at a machine center, it usually has to wait until all the preceding jobs are processed before it can be worked on. The queue length is proportional to the amount of work-in-process. The irony is that operations are performed very efficiently on high-speed machines, taking only a short duration of time, but the work sits in queues for hours, days or even weeks, waiting for its next chance to be processed. If there is no work-in-process inventory and setup times are reduced to zero, then the optimal order size would be unity and the workpiece would flow through the factory with MLT equal to the actual processing time. The three contributory factors for long queues include inadequate capacity, erratic flow, and poor part release policies.

Queue times can be reduced if products are produced as they are needed, work-in-process is kept low, and smaller lots are transported more frequently. The last point implies that the transport lot size need not be equal to the economic batch size.

Example 2.1

Consider a situation where parts arrive at a machine tool in batches of 40. The machine tool takes 10 min to perform the required operation on each workpiece (i.e., 400 min for the entire batch). The entire batch is then transported to the next machine. Assuming that the machine is idle when the batch arrives, the total waiting time for each workpiece with work content of 10 min is 400 min. Suppose the transport lot size is 5 (i.e., once 5 pieces are processed, they would be transported to the next machine), the waiting time is reduced to 50 min. If the transport lot size is made 1, then the waiting time is completely eliminated but the transporter has to make 40 trips instead of one. Separating product lots from transport lots in situations where production lots are large has a profound effect on lead time.

Model to Compute MLT

To write down the flow model of a manufacturing system, we first recognize the four basic operations the workpiece goes through – namely waiting, moving, processing, and inspection. The waiting operation includes waiting for transport, for machining, and storage. Moving time includes all transport time from raw workpiece storage to machine shop and return and time in the machine shop. We assume that every processing is followed by inspection. There could be three outcomes of the inspection operation: (i) workpiece is discarded since it does not conform to specifications, (ii) workpiece requires rework to correct minor errors, and (iii) workpiece is good and can be moved for next operation.

Suppose a batch of Q workpieces is going through a sequence of n operations on n different machines. Figure 2.8 shows the MLT model for this situation. It is clear that only the processing (P) operations are value-adding and others are non-value-adding. Each machine operation involves two waits, one processing, one inspection, and one transport. The W before P includes setup time and queuing time before the machine; W before T denotes the waiting time for transportation and T denotes the transport time.

Figure 2.8 Basic operations in a manufacturing system

Let t_i, s_i, a_i denote, respectively, the processing, setup, and inspection times for the ith operation. Also let q_i denote waiting time in the queue in front of the machine for the ith operation, and m_i the move time for moving the workpiece from ith to $(i+1)$th operation. The symbol m_n denotes the move time required for unloading after the nth operation. In general, all these variables are random. Analysis of the system as a stochastic service system would be done in Chapters 3, 4, and 5 using Markov chains, queuing networks, and stochastic Petri nets, respectively. Here, we restrict our analysis to the deterministic situation (i.e., all variables are known constants). It is easy to derive the following formula for MLT in this situation.

$$MLT = \sum_{i=1}^{n} s_i + Q(t_i + a_i) + m_i + q_i \qquad (2)$$

We can interpret this model for different production situations. For a job shop, $Q = 1$ and the workpiece goes through the cycle (WPIWT) as many number of times as the number of machine operations. If there are n machine operations then we have from (2),

$$MLT = \sum_{i=1}^{n} (s_i + t_i + a_i + m_i + q_i) \qquad (3)$$

For flow-type mass production, the production line is set up in advance, inspection is done as a part of machine operation, the waiting time is determined by the machine with the longest processing time, and move time is the same for all parts and is denoted by m. Thus we have

$$MLT = n \left(m + \max_{1 \leq i \leq n} t_i \right) \qquad (4)$$

In all the above cases, the ratio of MLT to the sum of processing times is a good indicator of the time a part is unnecessarily resident on the factory floor.

Example 2.2

A part undergoes five operations, as shown in Table 2.1, on five different machines. The table gives the setup, queue, and processing times. The average inspection time, moving time, and waiting time before moving add up to 10 h for each operation. We want to find MLT for a batch size of 100.

Table 2.1 Data for part in Example 2.2

Operation No. (i = 1,2,3,4,5)	1	2	3	4	5
Setup time + queue time (h)	4	2	6	3	4
Processing time (min)	4.8	3.6	12	2.4	3

$$MLT = \left(4 + 10 + \frac{480}{60}\right) + \left(2 + \frac{360}{60} + 10\right) + \left(6 + \frac{1200}{60} + 10\right)$$
$$+ \left(3 + \frac{240}{60} + 10\right) + \left(4 + \frac{300}{60} + 10\right)$$
$$= 22 + 18 + 36 + 17 + 19$$
$$= 112 \text{ h}$$

We can easily compute the total batch processing time as 43 h. Ideally, MLT also should have been 43 h. The part is resident on the factory floor for 69 h. without any value being added to it.

Example 2.3

Consider a transfer line with two machines, M_1 and M_2. The processing times on M_1 and M_2 are given by 5.0 min and 3.5 min, respectively. The material transport time from M_1 to M_2 is 0.5 min. The setup time for the transfer line is 150 h. Then the MLT for a batch size of 100 is given by

MLT = 100 (5 + 0.5) = 550 min.

Example 2.4

A job shop specializes in one-of-a-kind orders. A typical part goes through eight operations on eight conventional machines. Each operation on the average takes 20 min of processing time, 15 min of work handling time, and 10 min of tool changing time. Average setup time is 6 h. Moving, inspection, and waiting times add up to 12 h.

A new programmable machine performs all eight operations in a single setup. Programming the machine takes 20 h but is done off-line. Setup time is 10 h. Machining and tool changing times are reduced to 80% and 50% of their conventional values. Work handling time is the same as for one machine. The waiting, inspection, and moving times are the same as in the conventional setup.

We can now compute MLTs in both the cases:

(a) Conventional setup:

$$(MLT)_1 = 8\left(6 + \frac{3}{4} + 12\right) = 150 \text{ h.}$$

Total processing time $= 8 \times \frac{3}{4} = 6$ h.

(b) NC machine:

$$(MLT)_2 = \left(10 + \frac{5 \times 8}{60}\right) + \left(\frac{15}{60}\right) + \left(\frac{16 \times 8}{60}\right) + 12 = 25.05 \text{ h.}$$

Total processing time $= \frac{16 \times 8}{60} = \frac{32}{15}$ h.

We see that the ratio of MLT to actual processing time is more than ten times even in the case of NC machines. Further improvements in MLT should come from reducing setup, moving, and transport times.

2.3.2 Work-in-Process

Work-in-process (WIP) is the amount of semi-finished product currently resident on the factory floor. A semi-finished product is either being processed or is waiting for the next processing operation. In the traditional school of thought, inventories, including WIP, are seen as assets, and inventory built up over a week is considered as value added during the week. Inventories are also seen as the insurance buffer against various uncertainties induced by delayed supplies, machine breakdowns, absenteeism, and uncertain customer orders. Also, WIP builds up owing to the desire to improve the utilization of expensive equipment.

WIP represents an investment by the firm, and many companies incur major WIP costs that are high over long periods of time. The recent trend is to produce the items as required and to consider inventory as evil. Inventory is the evidence of poor design, poor forecasting, poor coordination, and poor operation of the manufacturing system.

A rough measure of the WIP can be obtained by multiplying the rate at which parts flow through the factory with the length of the time parts spend in the factory. We recognize the latter to be the manufacturing lead time. Suppose the manufacturing lead time in a factory is 120 h and its production rate is 20 units/h. Then the WIP is $120 \times 20 = 2400$ units.

As mentioned earlier, WIP should be low. Ideally, it would be nice if there are as many parts waiting as there are being processed. This would ensure that machines will not starve and will keep the WIP low. The number of parts currently being processed is equal to the number of busy machines, which in turn equals the total number of machines multiplied by the utilization factor.

2.3.3 Machine Utilization

High machine utilization is assumed to be good because it amortizes the cost of the machinery faster. Idle time is supposed to be bad since high-priced equipment does not produce anything. The quest for manufacturing efficiency, where efficiency is measured in terms of the utilization of the equipment, encourages shop-floor supervisors and managers to keep work centers busy continuously and to produce items not mandated by current orders but perhaps required to meet future, yet unannounced demand. The more expensive the work center is, the more attention it gets to keep it busy. Ironically, such centers are likely to be high productivity types and would generate huge inventories.

By forcing a machine to run so as to amortize its cost and increase its utilization, one is simply transferring a machine asset into an inventory asset. Is not idle inventory merely idle machinery in a different form? Which one would benefit business more: idle machine asset or idle inventory asset? The answer is, of course, idle machinery. Building up idle inventory may lead to perishable inventory, something customers may not want, resulting in tying up cash in raw materials, creating and managing the inventory, and adding lots of waste. An effective resource utilization is to run the machine to manufacture exactly the right quantity of exactly the right things at exactly the right time.

Example 2.5

In a certain batch production system, a part goes through an average of six operations. Each operation takes 6 min on the average. Average batch size is 25, and 24 such batches are processed during a week. Average setup on each machine for each batch is 5 h and inspection, moving, and waiting after each operation per batch is 10 h. There are 18 production machines in the plant. The plant operates 70 production h a week. Assume that rejection rate is zero. We can now determine various performance measures.

(i) Average production time/unit of product/machine

$$= \frac{\text{Average batch production time}}{\text{Batch size}}$$
$$= \frac{10 + 5 + \frac{25 \times 6}{60}}{25}$$
$$= 0.7 \text{ h}.$$

(ii) Production rate/machine $= 1/0.7$ per h.

(iii) MLT = (Average batch production time) × (Average number of machine operations)

$$= \left(10 + 5 + \frac{25 \times 6}{60} \right) \times 6 = 105 \text{ h}.$$

(iv) Production capacity = Number of units produced/week = (Number of machines) × (Total number of machine hours) × Production rate

$$= 18 \times 70 \times \frac{1}{0.7} = 1800.$$

(v) Actual number of units produced per week

$$= 6 \times 70 \times \frac{1}{0.7} = 600.$$

(vi) Machine utilization

$$= \frac{600}{1800} = 33.33\%$$

(vii) Desired WIP = Number of busy machines = 6 units. The ratio of WIP to the desired WIP is 25, which is very high.

2.3.4 Throughput

For a manufacturing system, the throughput is generally expressed as an hourly or daily production rate (i.e., the number of parts produced per hour or day). The reciprocal of the throughput or production rate is the production time per unit of the product. For transfer lines the throughput approximates the reciprocal of the cycle time (transfer time + longest operation time). In case of job shops, the relationship is not so simple but could be characterized as the number of units leaving the unload station per day or per hour.

2.3.5 Capacity

The term *capacity*, or plant capacity, is used to define the maximum possible output of the transformation process the plant is able to produce over some specified duration. For a continuous plant, the duration is 24 hours a day, 7 days a week, whereas for an automobile plant the capacity is defined over a shift period. Airlines measure their capacity as available seat miles, hospitals as total available beds, steel mills as tons of steel, and oil refineries as barrels of oil. Often, particularly when output is non-homogeneous or the plant produces a variety of products, we can use available machine hours as the measure of capacity.

Capacity is an imprecise term. The best one can do is to plan on averages because of efficiency, absenteeism, idle time, breakdowns, and so on. A little more capacity than what is needed will serve the enterprise well. Investing a little more on the machinery can mean investing in a lot less inventory. One can change capacity rather quickly by changing the staffing levels, hours worked through overtime or short time, and subcontracting.

Capacity can be measured as machine hours available per week or number of good units produced per week and so on; that is,

$$\text{Production capacity per week} = (\text{Number of machines}) \times$$
$$(\text{Number of working hours}) \times (\text{Production rate})$$

2.3.6 Flexibility

Flexibility is an important yet unquantifiable aspect of a manufacturing system. Different manufacturing systems have different kinds of flexibility. Here we bring out some general notions of flexibility and discuss those in the context of plant configurations of Section 2.2.

Definition: A flexible system is one that is able to respond to change, and flexibility is the ability of the system to respond effectively to change.

Changing circumstances include both internal and external changes. Internal changes or disturbances include breakdown of equipment, variability in processing times, worker absenteeism, and quality problems. External changes are typically changes in design, demand, and product-mix. The ability to cope with internal changes requires a degree of redundancy in the system, whereas the ability to cope with external changes requires that the system should be versatile and capable of producing a wide variety of part types with minimal changeover times and costs to switch from one product to another.

The time to process an order and the product variety that can be produced will decide the competitiveness of the manufacturing system. From the definition of flexibility it is clear that *flexibility* is fundamental to achieve *competitiveness*. Also, *flexibility* will provide a strategic advantage to handle risk associated with uncertain markets.

We recognize that a manufacturing system can have varying degrees of flexibility depending on the versatility of the equipment and the way the equipment is managed. In general, high degree of flexibility requires higher levels of automation and more investments. However, such a system will be an adapting organism capable of surviving in uncertain and changing markets.

Let us consider the various types of manufacturing systems and their flexibility. Transfer lines are very effective in producing parts in large volumes at high throughput rates, with the important limitation being that the parts be identical. These highly mechanized lines are very inflexible and will not tolerate variations in part design. In transfer lines, failure of any of the machines would bring down the entire line and thus there is no fault-tolerance. Further in these systems, parts move from one machine to another predefined machine for the next operation. All parts follow the same path. There is no choice in choosing the machine for the next operation. In short, a transfer line does not have any flexibility and cannot tolerate any changes such as design modifications or part-mix changes or machine failures.

Job shops on the other hand are highly flexible and are used for manufacture of one-of-a-kind products. They have versatile machine tools and skilled manpower. The machines have the ability to adapt to product changes. Skilled workers can perform design, drafting, process planning, and machining operations. The job shops have similar machines in several numbers or have versatile machine centers capable of performing a large number of operations in a single setup. These features would make the job shop highly flexible (i.e., it can accommodate design demand and product-mix changes, and can tolerate machine failures). However, in a typical job shop lead times are very high. The design, process planning, setup tool procurement, and changeover times all add up to several weeks or months. Although job shops are highly flexible, they usually suffer from large MLT and high WIP.

2.3.7 Performability

One factor that has major influence on system performance is the unscheduled downtime of the equipment due to failures. Since the manufacturing systems of any configuration are set up with high cost, high productivity and high payback ratio are essential for survival. Traditionally *reliability* and *availability* are measures that capture the percentage of downtime or repair time. The performance in terms of MLT or throughput is captured by using Markov chain models, queuing networks, and stochastic Petri nets. Combined analysis of both performance and reliability is done using the notion of performability. Here we deal with the traditional theories of managing the downtime and defer discussion on performability to Section 4.14.

Reliability

The term *reliability* has a dual meaning in the integrated manufacturing context. In the broad sense, it refers to a wide range of issues relating to design, manufacture, and assembly of the product which are required to work well, and often descriptors such as quality which match the actual product with the specifications and expectations of the user. In a narrow sense, reliability is a measure of "operational success" of the manufacturing system in delivering a quality product, and we consider this later definition here.

Definition: Reliability, $R(t)$, of a manufacturing system is defined as the probability that, under stated operating conditions, it will perform well enough throughout the interval $[0, t]$ to produce quality products.

Let T be the random variable denoting the failure time of the system. Then

$$R(t) = P\{T > t\}$$

Note that

$$R(t) = 1 - F(t)$$

where $F(t)$ is the cumulative distribution function of T. Let $f(t)$ be the density function of T, then the mean time to failure (MTTF) is given by

$$MTTF = \int_0^\infty t f(t) \, dt$$

Let T_R be the random variable representing repair time, then mean time to repair (MTTR) is the expected value of T_R and can be similarly defined.

Availability

Availability is a measure suitable for systems under failure and in repair. A system goes through cycles of failure and repair, and availability answers the question "Is the system available at time t?"

Definition: Instantaneous availability $A(t)$ at time t of a system is the probability that the system is operational at time t.

One can show that limiting availability $A = \lim_{t \to \infty} A(t)$ is given by

$$A = \frac{MTTF}{MTTF + MTTR}$$

Reliability and availability studies are important in transfer lines or in job shops in determining the daily production rates. We have two major constituents in a manufacturing system: the workpiece and the manufacturing system equipment. The equipment can fail because of wear and is maintained either periodically or on failure. The workpiece can also cause faults resulting in line stops. Such examples are jams due to bad parts fed at the workstation, misfeeding and misorientation of parts, tool breakages due to defective parts, etc. Line stoppages due to "workpiece" can occur at any workstation and are usually brief. Equipment faults are generally more serious and take longer to repair. In either case, the production is a function of repair time due to failures and faults, and the development of systematic methods for computing acceptable levels of production in the face of failures is an important subject.

Example 2.6

Consider a five-station transfer line. Let q_i be the probability that a part will join at station i and line stops. Then the frequency of line stops per cycle is equal to $F = \sum_{i=1}^{5} q_i$. If $q_i = 0.02$ for all i, then $F = 0.1$ breakdowns/cycle. Ideal cycle time is given as 1.0 min and average downtime per line stop as 6.0 min. Scrap rate is 5%. Calculate (i) Production rate and (ii) Number of days required to produce 1500 units, when the system works at 70 h/week.

Average production time per work piece = $1.0 + 0.1 \times 6.0 = 1.6$ min

The average production rate = 1/1.6 per min = 37.5/h

Actual production per hour (at 5% scrap rate) = $0.95 \times 37.5 = 35.6$/h

Actual number of weeks required to produce 1500 pieces = $\frac{1500}{35.6 \times 70}$ = 0.6 weeks.

2.3.8 Quality

We have used the expression "quality product" several times in the text. Quality product is the one that fulfills customer expectations by conforming to the specified tolerances. Maintenance of high quality requires conscious efforts in various stages in design and in manufacture.

A customer expects product value to have some relationship to the cost. This implies that the company has an obligation to meet customer demands both in functional and intrinsic values, which are in turn dependent on integrity of the materials and integrity of the manufacturing process. Together they enable the company to supply products free of abnormal, unwanted variations — "products that are made right the first time."

The Japanese have spearheaded the quality control movement that has now caught on throughout the world. They have shown that high quality and low cost can go together, and that quality is an important constituent in attaining competitiveness.

Total quality control (TQC) involves the principle of "quality at source," which means that any errors should be caught and corrected at the source where work is performed. This is in contrast to the widespread industrial practice of inspection by statistical sampling after the lot has already been produced, the defect detection as opposed to defect prevention. The workers and supervisor (not the quality-control inspectors) have the primary responsibility for quality, and any problems with the "process" are corrected immediately since quality control at source provides "*fast feedback on defects*." The effects of total quality control are "fewer rework labor hours" and "less material waste" in addition to higher quality of finished goods. Thus good quality is not expensive but actually increases productivity, because so many costs such as rework, scrap, inspection, customer returns, and warranty costs are all avoided with quality improvement. All these benefits accrue only if production is incharge of quality as well.

The basic principles of total quality control are process control, easy-to-see quality, insistence on compliance, and 100% inspection. We discuss these briefly below.

Process Control

This means correcting the production process by checking the quality while work is being done. Every workstation has an inspection point and every worker is an inspector. Aids such as flowcharts, scatter diagrams, Pareto charts, Fishbone charts, run charts, and statistical control charts can be used to help the operator in his or her task of maintenance of high quality.

Easy-to-See Quality

The plant should be open to inspection by customer teams and quality-testing devices; rooms and environments should be displayed in "understand by a glance" language of charts, displays, and pictures. At most Japanese plants, even defects are displayed in parts per million (PPM) rather than in percentages (%).

Insistence on Compliance

Frequently the inspectors from the quality control department give in to the pressure from manufacturing to pass parts and subassemblies that do not meet the standards. On the other hand, if quality is the first priority, the worker should have the authority to stop the production line to correct quality control problems. This kind of authority puts teeth into quality maintenance policy.

100% Inspection

This means inspection of every item, not just a random sample. This would be possible if the workers in the production department are responsible for quality. Rework when required is performed by the same operator who made the wrong workpiece.

It can be easily seen that "quality products" can only be made by conscious efforts. The practice of "production at any cost" should be discouraged, and manufacture of quality products should be insisted upon. The rate of production may seem to go down due to inspection and checking, but if one compares this with cost of rework and the strategic benefits of competitive edge, quality indeed works out cheaper.

The next generation production systems' managers would need to understand how to use computer-aided technologies to improve the quality and gain competitive advantage. Continual improvement is a must since what was good last year will not make the grade this year.

PROBLEMS

1. Making appropriate assumptions, derive Equation (1) for batch size:

$$Q = \sqrt{\frac{2SD}{I}}$$

2. Let Q_p be the batch size for processing parts and Q_t the batch size for transporting parts across work centers. Examine the implications of the following choices.

   (a) $Q_p = Q_t =$ a small integer

   (b) $Q_p = Q_t =$ a large integer

   (c) $Q_p \ll Q_t$

   (d) $Q_p \gg Q_t$

3. Equation (4) gives the MLT for a typical flow line. Deduce an expression for the average throughput of such a flow line. What is the average machine utilization?

4. Work out an intuitive proof for the result that WIP is equal to MLT times the average rate at which parts flow through a given production system.

5. A homogeneous transfer line with 50 stages is set up for producing a particular product type. Two hundred parts of this type are required. Each part undergoes 50 operations in sequence, each operation taking 5 min. After producing 200 parts of this type, the line is set up for another product type. The line is operated in a synchronous way, in the sense that at the end of each 5-min interval, a part from each stage moves to the next machine on the line, this movement taking 10 s. Assuming that initially the line is set up for this product type, compute the following.

   (a) Time required for producing 200 parts

   (b) MLT and WIP

   (c) Machine utilization

   Now, derive general expressions for the above assuming the number of stages is n, number of parts to be produced is N, operation time on each machine is t, and the move time is u.

6. A synchronous, homogeneous transfer line with k stages has a delay, D, per each stage. Each operation ends with an inspection that decides whether the processing in each stage is okay or not. In the former case (all stages have produced an acceptable part), the finished part from each stage goes to the next stage, the moving operation taking time τ. In the latter case (at least

one stage has produced a "bad" part), the stages that have produced bad parts rework on these parts whereas the remaining stages (that have produced "good" parts) remain idle. Reworking operation is identical to the original operation. Assume that p is the probability that any given stage produces a good part at the end of a first or reworking operation. The processing operations on the stages are mutually independent of one another. Note that parts move to the next machines only if the quality of parts is acceptable in all the stages.

Assume that initially all stages are idle and n raw parts are waiting for processing. Compute

(a) the total average time taken for completing the processing of all n parts.

(b) average utilization of each stage.

(c) average production rate of parts.

(d) average MLT of each part.

2.4 COMPUTER-CONTROLLED MACHINES

Electronics and information technologies have had a significant influence on the control of machine tools and also on the inspection methods. The application of these technologies could be seen in NC (numerically controlled) machine tools and in automated inspection systems. Numerical control uses a program of instructions which is electronically transmitted to the production equipment to regulate its function and operation. We describe here the operation of a computer-controlled machine center, which is the most important subsystem in an automated manufacturing system. Next we consider the problem of inspection using coordinate measuring machines (CMMs), which measure the physical dimensions of the part and have measurement software to interpret these measurements and identify quality problems.

Our presentation here is system oriented and our emphasis is not to present the details of NC programming but to introduce briefly NC machines and CMMs and discuss their role in automated manufacturing.

2.4.1 Numerically Controlled Machines

Computer-controlled machine tools are the building blocks of all advanced manufacturing systems. Computer numerical control is a form of programmable automation in which the machine is controlled by a computer program stored in a microprocessor-based controller. This computer program, called the *part program*, is written for each type of workpiece. By changing the program and the tools, a machine can be made to perform a variety of operations on workpieces of different sizes, shapes, and materials.

Evolution

Numerical control (NC) has since 1954 been a working machine tool controlling technology. It has its genesis in the work of John T. Parsons in the United States. In the late 1940s, Parsons used punch-card equipment to generate the desired surface of an airfoil. In 1948, Parsons demonstrated his concept to the U.S. Air Force, which sponsored a series of projects in the Massachusetts Institute of Technology servomechanisms laboratory, and in 1952 an NC milling machine was demonstrated. Parsons used the numerical definition of workpiece geometry as a mesh of points to act as a control mechanism and direct the machine tool motions that were necessary for metal removal from the raw workpiece. Hence the use of the phrase *numerical control*. Today, NC is a widely accepted and applied technology in the manufacturing world. In most earlier NC machines, the input data in its numerical form was punched on paper or plastic tape and this was interpreted by the machine. Currently, most machine tools have an on-board computer in which the NC programs of several workpieces are stored. These are called computer NC (CNC) machine tools. Input data may still be entered by punched tape, but through the operator interface the part programs can be modified, if necessary. It is possible to store a variety of part programs in the memory of the computer controller. This feature provides *machine flexibility*, which may be defined as the ability of a machine to produce a variety of part types. A CNC machine can produce any part type for which it has a stored part program. Features of CNC can be adopted on other machines; for example, robots.

A later development is the Direct NC (DNC) in which several CNC machines are controlled by a central computer. DNC can manage and maintain a large number of NC programs, downloading them to the individual CNC machines as required. The DNC computer also offers the potential to monitor each CNC machine. Also, DNC is a forerunner for flexible manufacturing systems where a variety of computer-controlled equipment for processing, moving, loading, unloading, and storing, such as CNCs, robots, and AGVs, are controlled by a central computer.

Table 2.2 Routing table for a part type

Operation	#1	#2	#3
Machine	M1(10)/M2(15)	M3(10)	M4(10)/M5(5)

Basic Components of a CNC

An operational CNC system consists of three components:

(i) **Machine Tool**: The machine tool consists of the work table and spindle, as well as the motors and controls necessary to drive them. It also includes the cutting tools, work fixtures, and other auxiliary equipment needed in the machine operation.

(ii) **Controller Unit**: Controller unit is an important part of the CNC system. It accepts the part program and generates output signals that control the functioning of the drives on the machine tool.

(iii) **Part Program**: The part program is the detailed instructions that tell the machine tool what to do.

As we discussed in Section 2.1.2, process planning is the interpretation of the engineering drawing of the workpiece in terms of the processes involved. A route sheet is prepared which lists the sequence of operations, their precedence relationship, alternative machines which perform the operations and machining times, and tools on each machine. Table 2.2 shows a sample routing table. The first entry in the table, for example, means that operation number 1 may be carried out on M_1 (10 min) or on M_2 (15 min). The route sheet is converted into a part program.

There are many NC part programming software packages that are efficient and easy to use. Automatically Programmed Tool (APT), developed at the Massachusetts Institute of Technology, is the first NC programming language. Since then, more than 100 NC part programming languages have been developed. Among these, the widely used languages are APT, ADAPT (Adaptation of APT), EXAPT (EXtended version of APT), UNI-PAT, SPLIT (Sunstrand Processing Language Internally Translated), and PROMPT.

2.4.2 Pallets and Fixtures

Pallets and fixtures are essential components of an automated manufacturing system. Pallets are interfaces between the machines and the workpiece. A fixture is a device that holds the workpiece during machining and assembly operations. A fixtured workpiece on a pallet moves around the system. A pallet may accommodate several fixtured workpieces.

Pallets

A workpiece travels around the machine shop visiting CNC machines, inspection stations, and is transported by some type of material handling system. The fixtured workpiece is carried by the pallet to all the machine centers, and it is thus necessary that all machine centers accept the same form of pallet. A pallet is generally of the same shape as the work table of the machine centers. Thus, a pallet is usually square with chamfered corners, T slots, and tenons for positioning and clamping fixtures. Pallets can be square, rectangular, or circular. They can be made of wood, plastic, or steel.

Fixtures

A fixture is a device that locates and holds a workpiece. The fixture must provide a positive location for the part (i.e., the part orientation and location relative to a prescribed reference frame is known). The characteristics of a fixture are also naturally dependent upon the shape of the workpieces and also the manufacturing process to which it is subjected. Also, there are differences in the requirements for fixtures used in machining and in assembly. Workpieces are subjected to large forces and torques during machining operations, in contrast to relatively small forces and torques during assembly operation.

Fixtures may take many forms. They can range from simple one-part clamps to complex picture frame and pedestal fixtures that allow machining access from several sides, to even larger fixtures accommodating two or more parts that aid in reducing the nonproductive time used for tool changing and part transportation.

There are significant costs associated with fixturing. A fixture is often developed for a specific operation and, consequently, a large number of fixtures will be required in order to manufacture a wide variety of components and products. Design and development of these special-purpose devices require significant investment. Further, these fixtures are to be stored on the shop floor in-between batches and should be retrieved when necessary. The flexibility of the programmable machine tool is enhanced if the fixture is also flexible.

Flexible fixturing involves employing a single fixture type to hold parts or assemblies of different shapes and sizes which may be subjected to varying forces and torques during manufacturing operations. Availability of such devices entails: (i) reduction in fixture design lead time, and (ii) reduction in the total number of fixtures needed in the manufacturing plant. This would lead to significant savings in capital and operational costs. Fixtures are very expensive and account for 10-20% of total system costs.

The complexity and the broad spectrum of parts and varieties of loads that different parts are subjected to prohibit any one class of fixture being universally flexible. Therefore several types of adaptable fixtures need be considered. Various methodologies are being tried out for universal fixturing. One of the emerging technologies with promise is *modular fixture kits*. This is an extension of the classical machinists' approach to developing a variety of fixtures from a combination of elements such as V blocks, clamps, and rectangular blocks, which are traditionally located on a cast iron box plate with either T slots or grid of holes.

Example 2.7

Consider a machine center with a pallet buffer storage of 16 pallets. One hundred different types of workpieces are machined every year. The demand rate for each workpiece type is 100 and they are manufactured in batch sizes of 50 each. Approximately 20 workpiece types are discontinued each year and are replaced by 20 new workpiece types. Average machine time per workpiece is 10 min. Two workpieces are loaded generally onto a pallet so that there is an average pallet cycle of 20 min. Four fixtures are simultaneously present in the system.

A study of the 100 workpiece types has shown that 34% require one fixture setup, 54% require two fixture setups, and 12% require three fixture setups. This gives a total of 178 different fixtures for 100 workpieces. If we need 4 identical fixtures of one type, total number of fixtures in the system is $(178 \times 4) = 712$. For the new parts, $(36 \times 4) = 144$ new fixtures have to be mounted each year.

2.4.3 Machine Centers

Machine tools, until World War II, were designed for single-purpose use, such as drilling, milling, and boring. If a workpiece required several operations, it was taken from one machine to the next. This meant separate setup, operator, and work handling for each machine function. The original NC machine tools were also single-purpose units and thus were saddled with the same disadvantages.

Machine centers are typical of NC machining today. A machine center can execute different operations, such as milling, drilling, boring, facing, threading, and tapping in a single setup on several surfaces of the workpiece. It is characteristic of these machine centers to have structurally integrated automatic pallet changing as well as automatic tool changing from tool magazine. Both these features contribute to an increase in the degree of automation and a decrease in the nonproductive time. They also ensure continuous and simultaneous production of different workpieces. We consider these additional features next.

Components of Machine Centers

(i) **Automatic Tool Changer (ATC):** An automatic tool changer is a device by means of which a cutting tool is automatically selected from a tool magazine and inserted into the machine spindle. The typical number of tool storage locations is 24, 48, 60, and sometimes higher. However, frequent changes in machining tasks brought about by the simultaneous presence of several jobs require frequent replacement of particular job-related tools. Several kinds of tool magazines could be mounted near the machine. These include disk magazine, ring magazine, or chain magazine.

There are a number of other ways to ensure that machines have the tools necessary so that machine flexibility is improved. In some cases, a tool store is maintained very close to the machine, and tools are transferred between the tool magazine and the tool store by means of a gantry robot. The tool store serves a number of machine centers and thus allows swapping of tools between the tool store and the tool magazines. The capability to exchange tools automatically ensures continuous production without disruption in a single setup. It increases the utilization of the machine considerably and provides capability for economical production of smaller lot sizes, resulting in considerable reduction in in-process inventory.

(ii) **Pallet Pools:** Usually, fixtured workpieces wait in a storage area near the machine and are loaded into the machine by means of an automatic pallet changer (APC). This has the advantage that fixturing/defixturing and cleaning of the workpiece can be done independent of the machine cycle. The clamping of parts to the pallets and presetting the tools in the vicinity of the machine minimize the organizationally related idle time, especially when job changeovers are frequent, lot sizes are small, and job repetition frequencies are high.

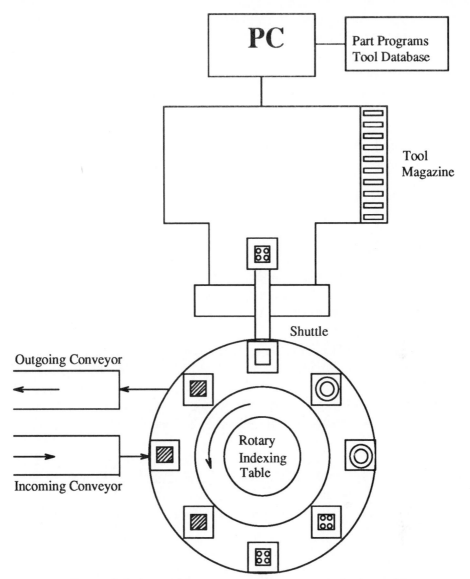

Figure 2.9 A machine center with rotary indexing table

There are several arrangements of a pallet pool. The simplest is the arrangement of a rotary indexing table with four to twelve pallets, according to the machine cycle (see Figure 2.9). The pallets could be loaded either manually or through an input conveyor, or an AGV, at the beginning of the shift, so that the machine can operate unattended for an 8–hour shift. Another arrangement for a pallet pool is shown in

Figure 2.10. Here the palletized workpieces wait in a linear row and are transported to the machine center by a rail-guided vehicle or an AGV. Figure 2.11 shows a cell with two machine centers and a pallet pool.

In the above situation multiple part types arrive at the machine center for machining. The machine center reads the bar code or some other part identification on the workpiece to identify the type of part and accordingly downloads the part programs and loads the tools onto the spindle.

Reduction in fixture costs can also be achieved by scheduling different types of workpieces in succession in place of batch processing. Ability to process simultaneously a number of parts with low setup times substantially reduces the number of fixtures required for unmanned operation. For each job and for each pallet pool setup, only one or two fixtures will be generally needed. However, such a simultaneous operation requires large tool storage capacity.

(iii) Automatic Loading and Unloading: An automatic means to load the pallets onto the machine table is essential. This is done either by a tending robot or an AGV depending on the weight, size, and shape of the workpiece.

(iv) Machine and Tool Monitoring: To avoid quality problems and also to maintain high productivity, both machine monitoring and tool monitoring are essential. Tool monitoring is done by in-process workpiece gauging, imaging, and spindle torque measurements. Tool replacement due to tool wear or tool breakage is done based on recognition of a problem by the diagnostic system. Most machining centers are equipped with probes and hardware/software based expert systems to monitor the machine and tool health. Without the diagnostic system to detect and adjust for wear and to detect and replace broken tools, unmanned operation is not a realistic proposition. Typical methods of sensing tool wear and breakages include:

- changes in workpiece dimensions detected using measurements
- changes in the tool geometry sensed by touch sensors
- increased tool vibration and sound
- surface roughness of the workpiece
- changes in tool load
- changes in cutting temperature.

With automatic monitoring of tool wear and breakage, tools are replaced in time and subsequent damage is avoided. When wear is indicated, replacement of tool occurs at the end of the cut. In the case

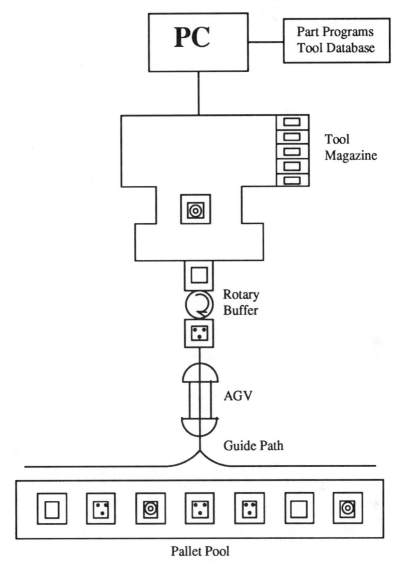

Pallet Pool

Figure 2.10 A machine center with pallet pool and rotary buffer

of tool breakage, the breakage alarm causes the feed and spindle to stop immediately, and the interrupted machining program is not resumed with this workpiece again. This would prevent the new tool being destroyed by fragments of the broken tool in the workpiece and also resuming work on a spoiled workpiece.

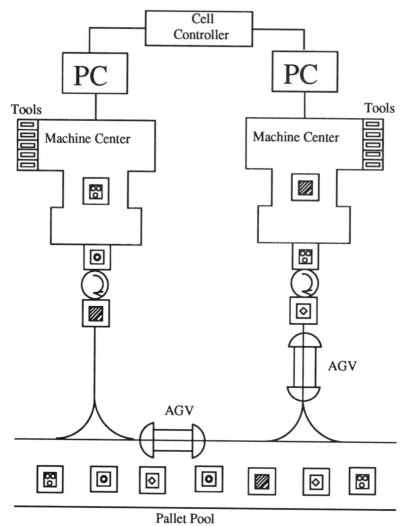

Figure 2.11 A cell with two machine centers and a pallet pool

Machine Center Management

We have seen in the above description that a machine center is a complex object carrying a variety of tools and part programs, with the capability to process a variety of part types. The fixtured workpieces of various types are stored in the pallet pool. The functions of the management control system include: (i) loading, machining, and unloading of the workpiece; (ii) guarding against faulty operation such as wrong loading of workpieces, tool breakages, and other unexpected and undesirable events; (iii) respecting the priorities among part types; and (iv) maximizing the machine utilization and minimizing the necessary equipment such as tools, fixtures, and pallets.

The above management functions depend on scheduling the individual jobs through the machine center. There have been two fundamental kinds of scheduling problems: static and dynamic. The static problem consists of a fixed set of jobs to be scheduled until they are completed. Dynamic scheduling problems are those in which new jobs are continually added over time. The processing times and setup times could either be deterministic or stochastic. To get a feel for the scheduling problem, let us consider the single machine static scheduling problem, i.e., to find the schedule for a fixed set of jobs with deterministic processing times for a single machine center, when all the jobs are available at the start of the scheduling period. If the objective is to minimize the total time to run the entire set of jobs, i.e., the makespan, then it does not matter in which order the jobs are run. In this case the makespan is equal to the sum of all the setup and processing times. However, if the objective is minimize the average time that each job spends at the machine shop, then one should process the job with shortest processing time (SPT) first. Suppose we have three jobs requiring 1, 3, and 5 hours of processing plus setup times. The total time required to run the entire batch under any sequence is 9 hours. If the shortest processing time discipline is followed, then the job with processing time of 1 hour is processed first and its waiting time near the machine center is 1 hour only. The second job waits for 4 hours and the third 9 hours. The average waiting time then is 4.67 hours. If one follows the largest processing time discipline, then the 5–hour job is processed first, then the 3–hour one, and then the 1–hour job. The average waiting time is 7.33 hours.

It is true in a single machine center problem that the SPT always yields minimum average waiting time. SPT also performs well in respect of minimizing the average number of jobs in the system. SPT also performs well even if the criterion is to minimize job lateness. If, however, one wishes to minimize the maximum lateness, the best strategy is to run the jobs in the due date order, from the earliest due date to the latest due date.

Operation of a Machine Center

We consider here an isolated machine center with a pallet pool and a tool store. An AGV transports the workpiece from the pallet pool to the machine center. We present a flowchart (see Figure 2.12) for its operation.

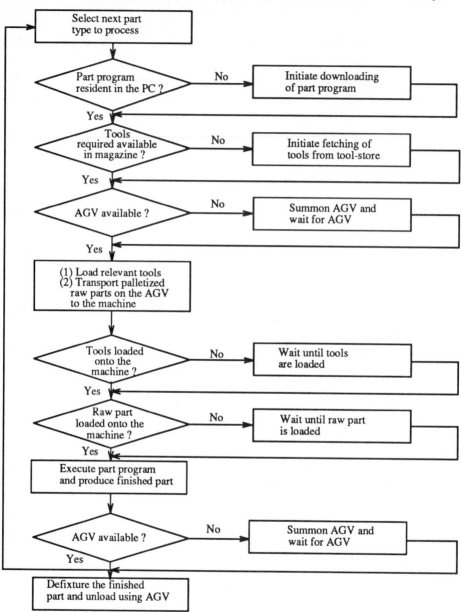

Figure 2.12 Flowchart for the automated operation of a machine

Viewed in another way, the flowchart is the supervisory controller that can manage the machine center. We assume that the supervisory controller database has all the information about part types in the pallet pool, part programs available, tools available in the magazine, and tool store.

Based on the demand and scheduling information, the next part type to be loaded onto the machine is determined. Next the availability of raw workpiece in the pallet pool, part program, and the required tools is checked. An AGV is then summoned for transporting the raw workpiece to the NC machine center. After machining is completed, the finished part is unloaded. The cycle of operations starts again.

If one includes inspection operation in the above cycle then its outcome could be accept, reject, or rework. In the third case, the workpiece joins the queue again for processing. In the first two cases the workpiece is unloaded from the machine.

In summary, the machine center is a very important subsystem in an automated manufacturing system, and its efficient management is vital for the performance of the entire manufacturing system.

2.4.4 Automated Inspection Systems

Inspection seeks to ensure compliance with customer expectations of what a product should be able to do. Product reliability, interchangeability, conformity, compatibility, and acceptability are all examples of customer expectations in addition to satisfying the product specification. A well-designed and properly applied inspection system is vital for competitive manufacturing. Companies cannot survive for long if they allow defective substandard products to reach the marketplace.

One can define inspection as an operation whereby an actual product, in whole or in part, is compared with achievable standards. Automated inspection involves integration of inspection with production in the same cycle. This would save material handling, and defects are identified and rectified more quickly, saving on material and resources. Automated inspection is dependent on a number of different technologies including computers, electronics, optics, ultrasonics, metrology, and photography.

Inspection Methods

Historically, quality control and dimensional inspection activities have been focused on off-line, post-process appraisal (i.e., finding defective material after it has been produced in lots). This strategy is wasteful because it causes time and materials to be invested in products that are not always usable. In essence, inspecting finished products and categorizing them into accept, reject, and rework groups is an expensive and unsound strategy since wasteful production has already occurred. Instead, it should

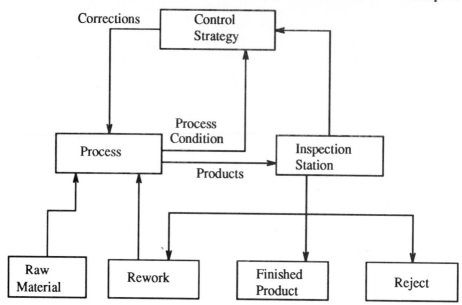

Figure 2.13 Process control system with inspection

be the aim to control the manufacturing process using on-line measurement data (see Figure 2.13).

There are two ways in which on-line inspection can be done: (i) in-cycle or in-process inspection and (ii) post-process inspection. Post-process inspection involves use of separate inspection machines and associated software. We first consider in-process inspection. In this book we discuss only contact inspection methods. Several noncontact methods are also available, based on machine vision, ultrasonics, radiation, electrical field techniques, etc.

In-Process Inspection

Here measuring or gauging is performed as an integral part of the machine tool operation. A machine tool is an XYZ positioning device. If provided with analytical software and probes, it must, like post-process inspection machines, be capable of inspecting the semi-finished workpieces. Probe cycles are incorporated into the CNC machine tool controller to check (i) identity of the part arrived at the machine tool, (ii) proper positioning of the part on the machine tool table, and (iii) the tool wear. In-process inspection is generally not as accurate as post-process inspection using coordinate measuring machines but is adequate and requires lower capital investment. The results of this inspection can be used as feedback data for incorporating part positioning and tool wear corrections. This is done either by taking actual dimensional measurements such as diameter, depth of cut, and so on, or by simply checking whether specified characteristics are met by using a go-no-go gauge.

Post-Process Inspection

Here the measuring or gauging procedure is implemented immediately following each manufacturing operation. It is still on-line because the inspection lot size is one and is done immediately but before the workpiece leaves the workshop. The disadvantage, however, is that if a part is found defective, correction of process could only be done to influence the quality of the next part. The defective part has to go through rework and reinspection procedures.

We now consider post-process contact inspection using coordinate measuring systems.

Coordinate Measuring Systems

The purpose of a coordinate measuring system is not only to check parts but also to evaluate, monitor, and control the performance of machine tools. Generally, it includes (i) coordinate measuring machine (CMM), and (ii) computer hardware and software.

Coordinate Measuring Machines: CMMs are used for post-process inspection wherein the workpiece is removed from the machine tool and is transported to a CMM where measurements are taken and workpiece quality is evaluated for process control purposes. This information could be fed back to the machine center control system for adaptive control.

Computer controlled inspection machines are similar in concept to CNC machine tools. They are versatile machines with accurate positioning sensors, DC motors, and an intelligent computer controller. The CMMs accept the pallet on which the part was manufactured, and the part is loaded the same way parts are loaded onto the NC machines. Thus, inspection using CMMs becomes another operation performed on the part and is integrated into the routing table. CNC inspection machines can be programmed either off-line or by manual teaching. User-friendly, higher-level software packages are available for CMM part programming.

In-process inspection can also be performed manually. In Japanese factories, the worker who is performing the manufacturing operation also performs the inspection procedure.

A CMM consists of a contact probe and a means of positioning the probe in three-dimensional space relative to the workpiece. The location of the probe can be accurately recorded to obtain the data regarding the part geometry. The probe is a significant component of the CMM, and its performance will affect the reliability of the data provided by the CMM. Both optic fiber and electromechanical probes are used to measure classical geometries whereas position-sensitive electromechanical probes are used in compound curved surface geometries.

The probe is fastened firm to the structure of the CMM and moves freely relative to the part located on the work table. There are several CMM configurations available. These include cantilever type, bridge type, column type, and gantry type.

CMM Software: The purpose of a CMM is to provide high-speed reliable data. Decisions regarding the health of the machine tool and the acceptance of the workpiece are done via the software. It is responsible for converting the X, Y, Z point data into three-dimensional features such as planes, spheres, and cylinders and for evaluating relationships between machined part features such as distances, angles, intersections, etc. The software also enables storage of measured features, with a facility to recall the measured features anytime in a new coordinate system if necessary.

The physical advantages of coordinate measuring machines are productivity, flexibility, reduced operation error, and greater accuracy and precision. A recent development is flexible inspection systems (FIS). FIS is an automated inspection cell consisting of one or more CMMs and other inspection equipment linked by a material handling system for automatic movement of workpieces. All the components of FIS are under computer control.

PROBLEMS

1. There are seven jobs waiting to be processed at a machine center. For each job, the processing times and due dates are given in the table below. Assume that the jobs arrived in the sequence ABCDEFG. Compute the average waiting

Job	A	B	C	D	E	F	G
Processing time (hours)	4	13	6	3	11	9	8
Due date (dates from now)	8	37	8	7	39	21	16

time per job, variance of waiting time, and the average number of jobs inside the system, in each case below.

(a) SPT (Shortest Processing Time First) scheduling,

(b) LPT (Longest Processing Time First) scheduling, and

(c) EDD (Earliest Due Date First) scheduling.

2. Assuming two jobs J_1 and J_2 with processing times t_1 and t_2 with $t_1 < t_2$, show that SPT has less average waiting time and less variance in waiting time compared to LPT. Can you generalize this to n jobs?

3. Show in general that SPT leads to the least average waiting time among all *static* scheduling disciplines.

4. In *dynamic* scheduling, the selection is made taking into account any jobs that arrive during the system evolution. Whenever the machine finishes a job, a scheduling decision is made by looking at all jobs existing in the system at that time. In addition to SPT, LPT, and EDD, the following policies can be used in the dynamic scheduling context: (i) FCFS (First-Come-First-Served), (ii) LCFS (Last-Come-First-Served), (iii) LS (Least Slack), and (iv) RO (Random Order). FCFS, LCFS, and RO are self-explanatory. In LS policy, the next job selected is the one with the least slack where slack is defined as the due date minus the service time. The following table gives a list of six jobs, with arrival times, service times, and due dates. For each of the above policies, obtain the sequence in which the jobs are selected, the average waiting time, and the variance of waiting time.

Job	Arrival Time	Service Time	Due Date
J1	5	11	50
J2	7	6	60
J3	13	15	30
J4	30	21	62
J5	31	2	60
J6	32	10	65

5. FCFS, LCFS, and RO are called service time and due date independent disciplines since they do not require the service times or the due dates. Show in general that these three disciplines lead to the same average expected waiting time. Also show that FCFS has the least variance of waiting times.

6. Write a simulation program to evaluate the relative effectiveness of various dynamic scheduling policies under varying workloads. Choose the performance criteria as expected waiting time in system, and variance of waiting time.

7. An NC machine produces parts of three types, A, B, C, in a cyclic sequence, i.e., ABC followed by ABC, and so on. Assume that raw parts are always available. An AGV carries each raw part, one at a time, from the load area to the machine and takes 1 min for this operation. The setup time for each part type is 10 min and the processing times are 20, 30, and 40 min for A, B, and C, respectively. After processing, the AGV is summoned from the load area and the finished part is unloaded into the load/unload area, this operation taking 1 min. Compute the following:

   (a) The cycle time (the time required to produce one part each of types A, B, and C).

   (b) Utilizations of the machine and the AGV.

   (c) MLT for each part type.

8. In the above problem, assume that the setup time is 100 min, batch size is 5, and AGV transport lot size is 2, with raw parts always available. All other parameters remain the same. Now, compute the cycle time where the cycle time is the time for processing one batch of A, followed by one batch of B, followed by one batch of C. What is the MLT for each part type?

9. In a manufacturing facility, each part undergoes two operations, OP1 and OP2, in that sequence. There is an inspection operation at the end of each operation. It is found that p percent of the parts undergoing an operation are of acceptable quality and q percent are rejected without further processing, and $(100 - p - q)$ percent of parts are accepted after some reworking. Compute the total fraction of parts rejected by the system.

2.5 MATERIAL HANDLING SYSTEMS

Material handling is an important aspect in automated manufacturing and is the science and art of moving, packaging, storage, and control of workpieces at various stages of processing.

2.5.1 Introduction

A material handling system (MHS) is defined as a network of moving equipment such as robots, conveyors, and automated guided vehicles. A software-based MHS controller effectively monitors the equipment status and regulates the workpiece movement. It controls the system elements so that the right material is moved at the right time to the right place as required by the route sheet.

In manufacturing organizations, a significant proportion of product cost can be attributed to material handling. This is not surprising when we consider that the MHS spans the spectrum of manufacturing activities from the original receipt of raw materials to the ultimate shipment of the end product. The extent of material handling in a system is a function of the route sheet, layout, and versatility of the machine tools. The principles of effective material handling include:

1. Best material handling is no material handling: Reduction of material handling is possible by the use of computer-controlled machine centers capable of performing multiple operations on the workpiece by automatic change of tools and downloading of appropriate part programs. Also, in certain high-volume transfer lines, transfer of material is done in a pipeline fashion, i.e., the workpiece is transferred directly to the next machine tool as in flow processes, thus cutting down material handling to the minimum possible.

2. Minimal part handling by shortening travel distances: Layout analysis focusing on travel distances, rearrangement of facilities to create easy work flow, equipment-based layout design (circular layout while using a robot handler, linear layout while using an AGV), etc., would help minimize material handling costs and increase their handling effectiveness.

3. Fast response using network of small and smart vehicles: In automated manufacturing environments, there is a trend toward reducing the work-in-process, to cut down waste, to improve quality, and to reduce the manufacturing lead time. This requires an MHS with fast response times to avoid blocking and starving of the workstations. Also, the transfer batch sizes are required to be small to reduce the queue times and also for just-in-time (JIT) delivery. Thus in an automated manufacturing system following JIT principles, the material handling system should be small and smart and should be capable of making frequent deliveries of small lot sizes.

4. Effective scheduling of MHS: The AGVs have to be scheduled using the status information regarding the equipment and the workpieces so that all resources are maximally utilized.

To avoid excessive idle time of the machine tool, flexible manufacturing system (FMS) manufacturers provide rapid exchange of two pallets, one just completed and the other waiting for processing. These buffer techniques allow processing and material handling functions to be performed in parallel. Although utilization of machine tools is thereby improved, there is corresponding increase in work-in-process (WIP).

Despite the push for drastically reduced levels of WIP inventories in FMSs, there would still be need for WIP storage to counter variability in manufacturing processes and prevent blocking and starving of workstations as well as the MHS.

Classification

There are several ways in which material handling equipment can be classified. One method is by the way the equipment works – on the floor or suspended overhead. Another classification is by whether the equipment is operator – controlled or automated. A third way is by the way the equipment travels – over a fixed route or a flexible path.

There are synchronous and asynchronous transport systems. In synchronous systems, all loads moving on the transport network move simultaneously, at the same speed, and with constant space between loads. A carousel or dedicated transfer line are examples of synchronous transport systems. In an asynchronous system, loads can move independent of one another. AGVs form an excellent example of this category.

There are a large number of material handlers used in the industry. Here we confine our discussion to three common types of material handling systems: conveyors, industrial robots, and AGVs.

Flexibilities in MHS

In a flexible manufacturing system, the material movement between the workstations varies with changes in the part mix, implying that the traffic intensity between a given pair of workstations is variable. Also, workpieces encountered may be of varying sizes, shapes, and volumes. This implies that the MHS should have flexibility so as to cope effectively with these variable demands in traffic, routing, and sizes. We define here several possible flexibilities for an MHS.

Traffic Flexibility: This is the ability to accommodate varying load levels between workstations without degradation in response times. Traffic flexibility is achieved as a result of both system size in terms of capacity (number of vehicles) and how the capacity is allocated in operation (scheduling).

Route Flexibility: Route flexibility is the ability to transport a workpiece from a given workstation to any of several other workstations, with the decisions made for that particular workpiece independent of the movement of any other load. For example, a conveyor has no route flexibility since it operates between two fixed locations. An AGV has, however, high degree of route flexibility since a workpiece can be loaded and unloaded at any workstation.

Path Flexibility: Path flexibility is the ability to select the path to be traveled between workstations. Such a flexibility admits the possibility of real-time decision making to avoid congestion in the transport system, thereby improving the response time. For example, a loop conveyor system has no path flexibility whereas an AGV system can take advantage of the guided path network.

Load Flexibility: Load flexibility is the ability to handle loads of varying sizes, shapes, and weights. This kind of flexibility is very valuable when products have relatively short life cycles and future demands are uncertain.

2.5.2 Conveyors

Conveyors constitute a large family of material handling equipment. There are several varieties of conveyors constituting very popular fixed-path material handling equipment. The path is fixed in the sense it can be changed only by making physical adjustments. The advantages of conveyors are many: they operate independently of workers and can be easily interfaced with a wide variety of material handling, process, or storage equipment such as robots, NC machines, etc. They also provide temporary in-process storage. Movement of materials on a conveyor is controlled by programmable controllers (PCs), which can activate switches, drives, and diverters, scan loads, and automatically route workpieces. These PCs are linked to the host computer by a local area network.

Conveyors represent a fairly mature technology, although some varieties such as inverted power and free conveyor are recent innovations.

Conveyor systems can be analyzed using simple mathematical models and certain basic performance measures can be easily derived. Here we consider single direction and continuous loop conveyors interconnecting loading and unloading stations and other machine centers in a machine shop. We use the following notation:

v = conveyor speed

d = spacing between two workpieces

f = feed rate

The following relationship should hold between these three variables:

$$f = \frac{v}{d}$$

Indeed, the time interval between the introduction of raw workpieces onto the conveyor is the direct control variable and f is its reciprocal. As the part flows on the line, the operator has a working envelope and reach-time. Beyond this, the part would flow past the operator and the workstation. Let the reach of the operator be denoted by r. Then the tolerance time is defined by

$$t = \frac{r}{v}$$

Example 2.8

Suppose f = 60 units/h; v = 0.5 m/min; d = 0.5 m; and r = 1 m. Then the operator has 2 min to pick the part before it goes past his reach.

Single Direction Conveyor: Consider a roller conveyor with velocity v and length L connecting a single load station and an unload station, as shown in Figure 2.14. Pallets are introduced by the load station and are unloaded at the unload station. The travel time is given by L/v. Let t_L and t_U denote the load and unload times, respectively. Then obviously

(i) time interval between introduction of two workpieces should be greater than t_L

(ii) for stability, $t_U < t_L$

Continuous Loop Conveyor: Consider a continuous loop conveyor shown in Figure 2.15. Here, the total conveyor can be divided into two sections: delivery loop and return loop. Let L_d be the length of the delivery loop and L_r of the return loop. As earlier, let v be the speed of

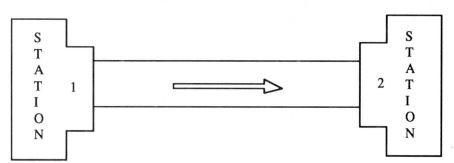

Figure 2.14 Single direction conveyor

the conveyor, then loop travel time is $\frac{L_d + L_r}{v}$. The number of carriers or pallets on the conveyor is equal to $\frac{L_d + L_r}{d}$, where d is the spacing between carriers. Out of these, $\frac{L_d}{d}$ are in the forward loop and carry parts whereas $\frac{L_r}{d}$ are in the return loop and the carriers are not loaded.

Recirculating Conveyors: Earlier models assume that parts loaded at the load station are unloaded at the other end. No accumulation of parts is allowed. However, a closed loop conveyor can be used for in-process storage. Recirculating conveyors exploit this feature.

Example 2.9

Suppose a recirculating conveyor has a total length of 500 ft, a speed of 100 ft/min and a part spacing of 25 ft. Each carrier can hold two parts. Robot load/unload times at either end are 0.2 min. The conveyor takes 5 min to complete the loop and can accommodate 20 carriers, i.e., 40 parts. The flow rate or the feed rate is 4 carriers per minute or 8 parts per minute.

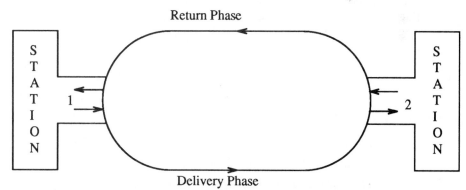

Figure 2.15 Continuous loop conveyor

2.5.3 Industrial Robots

An industrial robot is essentially a device that can move materials, parts, or tools from one point to another under programmed control without human intervention. It can also be easily taught to perform simple tasks such as pick-and-place or spot welding or painting. An industrial robot has many attributes in common with an NC machine tool. The same type of NC technology used in machine tools is used to actuate the robot mechanical arm. The types of servomechanisms used to control the motion along each axis are similar in each case.

History of Robots

The conceptual origins of the modern robot lie in a symbolic stage play written in 1920 by the Czech writer Karel Capek. The theme of the play was a population of human-like machines, manufactured to replace human workers, ultimately turning against human co-workers, killing them all. Capek's play, *Rossum's Universal Robots*, captured the imagination of a wide audience. An early science fiction writer interested in robots was Isaac Asimov.

George C. Devol was awarded the first patent for what could be considered as the first robot. He and Joseph Engelberger formed Unimation Inc., the first company to develop and manufacture robots. In the 1970s several companies manufactured a variety of robots to meet the demands from industry.

Robot Definitions

The definitions of industrial robots vary. The British Robot Association (BRA) defines the robot as a reprogrammable device designed to both manipulate and transport parts, tools, or to do specialized manufacturing, implemented through variable programmed motions for the performance of specific manufacturing tasks. The Japanese Industrial Robot Association (JIRA) specifies industrial robots by the method of input information and the method of teaching, as given below:

1. Manual Manipulators: Manipulators directly operated by human beings.
2. Fixed-Sequence Robot: Robot programmed for a fixed sequence of operations and not reprogrammable.
3. Variable-Sequence Robot: Robot that can be programmed for a given sequence of operations and which can be reprogrammed.

4. Playback Robot: Robots which execute fixed instructions from memory.

5. Numerically Controlled Robot: Robots controlled by digital data as in NC machines.

6. Intelligent Robots: Robots that use sensory perception to evaluate their environment, make real-time decisions, and control their motions accordingly.

By Japanese convention AGVs are counted as robots under category 3 above. Robots are also discussed in terms of generations. First-generation robots are fixed sequence with no sensing or computing power. Second-generation robots are classified as clever robots. They are equipped with a range of sensors and on-board computing power and they can modify their actions in response to small disturbances from the environment. For example, smart sensors can differentiate between large and small components and instruct the robot to transfer large components to one bin and small components into a second bin. Third-generation robots are intelligent robots that can collect information through sensors and have decision-making and problem-solving capabilities.

Industrial Applications of Robots

Industrial robots have a wide range of potential applications in manufacturing systems because they are flexible and programmable themselves. The use of sensors allows the robots to see, hear, touch, and smell the environment. The robot controllers can be generally integrated easily into the manufacturing system environment and are capable of communicating with other programmable controllers. Table 2.3 shows major robot applications in the area of manufacturing.

Basic Robot Elements

There are three basic components of an industrial robot: Manipulator, Controller, and Tooling.

(i) **Manipulator**: The manipulator consists of the base and arm of the robot, including the power supply, which may be electrical, hydraulic, or pneumatic. The manipulator is the device that provides movement in any number of degrees of freedom. The movement of the manipulator can be described in relation to its coordinate system, which may be cylindrical, spherical, anthropomorphic, or Cartesian. Depending on the controller, movement can be point-to-point motion or continuous-path motion.

Table 2.3 Industrial applications of robots

Application area	Examples
Material Handling	Parts handling, palletizing, transporting, heat treating, warehouse service, foundry
Machine Loading	Die-cast machines, automatic presses, NC milling machines, lathes
Spraying	Spray painting
Welding	Spot welding, arc welding, flame cutting
Machining	Drilling, deburring, grinding, forming, sheet metal fabrication
Assembly	Making parts, acquiring parts
Inspection	Position control, tolerance

(ii) Controller: The versatility of a robot arises from its multi-axis mechanical configuration and the robot controller. The ability to reprogram the robot controller gives the flexibility to the robot to perform a wide range of actions. The controller contains various interfaces with both command devices and sensing units. The controller has to define the trajectory of the robot gripper with time and transform this trajectory, which is in Cartesian coordinates, into its base-frame coordinate system and finally into joint movements. Many of these tasks are to be performed in real time. Several easy-to-use robot programming languages such as VAL, MCL, and APT are available.

(iii) Tooling: Tooling is what enables the robot to do a particular job. Tooling is sometimes used synonymously with end effector, although the latter has a more restricted meaning to apply to end-of-arm fixturing to grasp, lift, or turn. Tooling, on the other hand, has a broader context which can apply to power tools for drilling and grinding, as well as for painting and welding guns. Typical end effectors include electromagnets, hooks, vacuum cups, adhesive fingers, and bayonet sockets. There are six basic motions, or degrees of freedom, which provide the robot the capability to move the end effector through the required sequence of motions. The six motions consist of three arm and body motions and three gripper motions. The three arm and body motions consist of vertical traverse, radial traverse, and rotational traverse. The gripper motions are yaw, pitch, and roll.

Different robot configurations generate different characteristic working envelope shapes. The work volume refers to the space within which the robot can operate.

Example 2.10

Suppose a manufacturing cell (see Figure 2.16) consists of an industrial robot, a machine tool, and two conveyors, one incoming to bring raw workpieces into the cell and the other outgoing to deliver the finished parts. The work cycle consists of the following steps: (i) Incoming conveyor delivers raw workpieces into a fixed position. (ii) Robot picks up part from conveyor and loads it onto the machine. (iii) Machine processes the part. (iv) Robot unloads the finished part from machine to the outgoing conveyor.

The control of a cell such as the one described above is accomplished by a work-cell controller that regulates the movement of material through

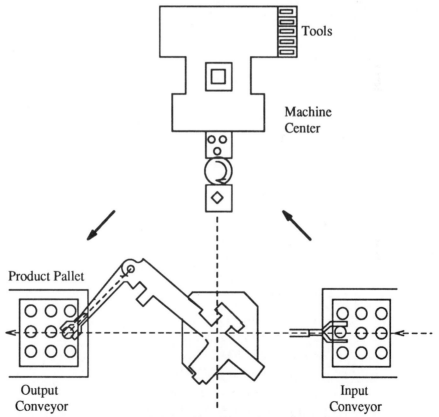

Figure 2.16 A robot cell with a single machine center

the cell. Several safety features such as checking part identity before starting processing, making sure the workpiece is present at a location before instructing a robot to pick it up, and so on, are also included in the controller.

Example 2.11

The details of robot operation times for a conveyor system as in Example 2.10 are given in Table 2.4. Let us compute the cycle time and production rate of this system.

Suppose the machine operation cycle requires 24 s. Assuming an average of 10% system downtime, we are interested in the daily 8-hour shift production level. Arbitrarily selecting the beginning of the machine operation cycle as the beginning of the system cycle, the typical operation sequence is: Unload machine; move to output conveyor; deposit finished part on output conveyor; move to input conveyor; wait for new part to arrive; pick up new part; move to machine; load into machine, and wait for machine to finish.

Thus the cycle time is 36 s. The production then for a 90% efficient 8-hour shift can be computed to be 720 units.

Example 2.12

The analysis of robot loading/unloading of a sequence of several machines is an interesting topic. One can determine cycle time and productivity using this analysis.

Table 2.4 Robot operation times in Figure 2.16

Pick up part from conveyor (including average wait time for part to arrive in pick-up position)	2.6 s
Move robot hand from input conveyor to machine	1.7 s
Load part into machine and take back hand away from machine so the machine can start	1.1 s
Unload part from machine	0.8 s
Move robot hand from machine to output conveyor	1.7 s
Deposit part onto output conveyor	0.3 s
Move from output conveyor to input conveyor	3.8 s

Consider a cell with two machines, B and C. An input conveyor brings the part to the pickup point A, and point D is the pickup point for the outgoing conveyor. Suppose the operation times for a product are: Machine B = 10 min; Machine C = 5 min; Gripper pull-up time = 0.1 min; Gripper release time = 0.1 min. Table 2.5 gives the robot move times.

We first form Table 2.6, which gives the sequence of events and their start and end times in minutes. P1, P2, and P3 represent typical parts.

The above cycle of events repeats. The cycle time (i.e., the time elapsed between successive regeneration points) can be computed easily. If we take the cycle as starting at unload C, then cycle time $(27.0 - 15.8)$ = 11.2 min. If we take the cycle as starting at Drop at D, the cycle time $(27.3 - 16.1) = 11.2$ min. The production rate is simply the reciprocal of the cycle time.

2.5.4 Automated Guided Vehicles

AGVs will certainly play an important role in automating the future manufacturing environments because they are the most flexible means to interconnect all important locations of the factory floor for the horizontal movement of materials. An AGV is a high-tech material handling system consisting of a driverless vehicle following a guide-path under the control of a computer. Unlike other more conventional material handling devices, an AGV can select its own path from among many routes to reach a designated workstation or a warehouse. Some AGV systems can alter dynamically their route based on congestion information and track availability. AGVs form an easily installable, easily maintainable, easily expandable, easily portable, easily interfaceable, highly flexible, and economically viable system of material handling equipment. They have

Table 2.5 Robot operation times in minutes for Example 2.12

From	To			
	A	B	C	D
A	-	0.2	0.4	0.6
B	0.2	-	0.2	0.4
C	0.4	0.2	-	0.2
D	0.6	0.4	0.2	-

Table 2.6 Sequence of events for Example 2.12

Status Before Operation				Operation	Time for Operation
Clock Time in min	Position of Robot	Stations Loaded			
		B	C		
0	A			Pick up at A	0.1
0.1	A			Move to B	0.2
0.3	B			Load B	0.1
0.4	B	P1		Processing at B	10
10.4	B	P1		Unload at B	0.1
10.5	B	P1		Move to C	0.2
10.7	C		P1	Load C	0.1
10.8	C		P1	Processing at C	5
10.8	C		P1	Move to A	0.4
11.2	A		P1	Pick up at A	0.1
11.3	A		P1	Move to B	0.2
11.5	B		P1	Load B	0.1
11.6	B	P2	P1	Processing at B	10
11.6	B	P2	P1	Move to C	0.2
15.8	C	P2	P1	Unload C	0.1
15.9	C	P2		Move to D	0.2
16.1	D	P2		Drop at D	0.1
16.2	D	P2		Move to B	0.4
21.6	B	P2		Unload at B	0.1
21.7	B	P2		Move to C	0.2
21.9	C		P2	Load C	0.1
22.0	C		P2	Processing at C	5
22.0	C		P2	Move to A	0.4
22.4	A		P2	Pick up at A	0.1
22.5	A		P2	Move to B	0.2
22.7	B	P3	P2	Load B	0.1
22.8	B	P3	P2	Processing at B	10
22.8	B	P3	P2	Move to C	0.2
27.0	C	P3		Unload C	0.1
27.1	C	P3		Move to D	0.2
27.3	D	P3		Drop at D	0.1

become very popular, replacing synchronous assembly conveyors, forktrucks, etc. A typical AGV layout is shown in Figure 2.17.

An AGV system is a computer-controlled material handling system comprising several microprocessor-controlled driverless vehicles each of which can automatically perform loading, route selection, and unloading. They interface well with other factory floor equipment both mechanically and electronically. The AGV controllers communicate with other AGV, robot, and workstation controllers as well as the central control computer.

AGV systems are typically powered by 24V or 48V DC industrial batteries. These vary in amp-hour rating according to the installation requirements. Battery charging is usually accomplished by one of two techniques: opportunity-charging or full-cycle charging. The opportunity-charging technique involves the batteries being charged while the vehicle is performing or waiting to perform a task. Stations at which the vehicle is required to stop for any extended period of time become possible charging stations. The full-cycle charging technique requires the AGV to pull itself out of service into a designated charging area.

History of AGVs

The first driverless vehicles capable of following a predetermined path and making simple route selection decisions were developed by A.M. Barrett Jr. in 1954. AGV technology has benefited greatly from developments in the electronics and computer technology during the last 30 years. In the late 1970s, microprocessors became popular controllers onboard AGV vehicles. Usually the central minicomputer software controls the AGV system and individual vehicle control software is resident in the on-board microprocessor. In addition, advanced control capabilities such as real-time communication with all vehicles, continuous location, and status monitoring of all vehicles, etc., are also available. AGVs are certainly at the forefront of material handling technology. They have a tremendous range of automated capabilities. Many systems can go up and down the ramps, open and close automatic doors, use elevators, and perform automatic loading/unloading functions.

Categories of AGVs

AGVs have been applied to the industry in many imaginative ways. Vehicles and systems have been designed to service clean rooms for the manufacture of silicon wafers for integrated circuits, as well as flexible

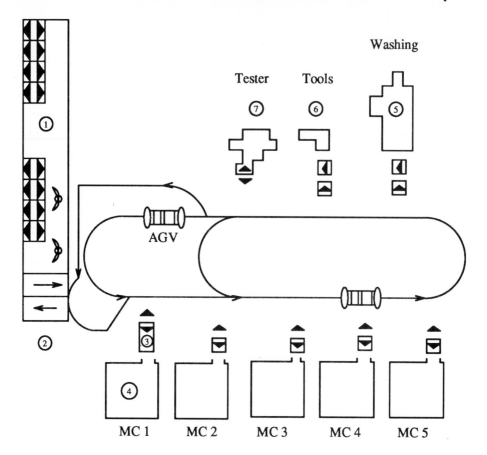

1. Pallet Setup Stations
2. Load-Unload Stations
3. Pallet Buffers
4. Machining Centers

5. Automatic Washing
6. Tool Area
7. Inspection

Figure 2.17 A typical AGV layout

manufacturing cells where grease and metal chips define the environment. Vehicles have been designed to carry 50-pound loads as well as 100,000-pound loads. There is a great deal of variety in vehicle design, but most fall into one of the categories discussed below.

Towing Vehicles: These vehicles consist of an AGV with no load-carrying facilities but with a hitch or tow bar that can pull trailers, carts, pallet jacks, and wheeled racks. These are used where there is a large volume of products to be moved or in retrofit applications where the product has historically been moved by trailers. Towing vehicles have been used in many existing installations and are known to move loads of up to 50,000 pounds.

Unit Load Transporters: These vehicles are designed to carry individual loads on-board the vehicle. Unit load transporters can have an extremely versatile deck design that permits them to be equipped with rollers, belt conveyors, power lifts, or on-board robot arms. These AGVs can either be bidirectional or unidirectional and are used in warehousing as well as on the factory floor. Loads of up to 12,000 pounds are common and loads of up to 60,000 pounds have been carried by unit load transporters.

Assembly Line Vehicles: This vehicle has a fixture on-board that accepts the frame or initial parts of the product that is to be assembled. The vehicle is routed through the various manufacturing stations of the factory where parts and assemblies are added to the product. Opportunity charging is often utilized as is bar code scanning so that the vehicle does not have to get out of sequence for battery exchange and all parts and assemblies are tracked and accounted for.

These AGVs can provide total automatic transfer of materials. Equipped with a shuttle transfer device, they can automatically load products from pickup stations and then carry them to designated drop-off stations. Moreover, unlike other handling systems, AGVs have special features. They can skip assembly sections if equipment in a particular section breaks down, accommodate high-product differentiation, as well as short-product life cycles, handle high production volumes, incorporate work group buffers prior to and after workstations, and minimize index time and idle time.

There are three types of AGV-linked assembly lines: synchronous, asynchronous, or a combination of both. The synchronous line, characterized by the absence of queues between workstations, is balanced by the longest in-station assembly-cycle time in the line. However, this causes it to be inflexible. Hence, synchronous lines usually represent low-product differentiation. An asynchronous assembly line has queues, which act as buffers, before and after workstations and is balanced by the line's average cycle time. There are three workstation/vehicle configurations for an asynchronous assembly system: fixed station build, which delivers a workpiece to a fixed assembly station; mobile work platform, wherein the piece remains on the vehicle throughout the assembly process and is removed only when the entire unit is assembled; and robot build, which consists of a robot on-board or interfacing with an in-station robot.

Robotic Arm Vehicles: These are light load vehicles that have a robotic arm attached to the mainframe of the AGV. This vehicle has the ability to be reprogrammed to perform a variety of tasks. A typical application is the handling of silicon wafers or wafer carriers in dust-free handling rooms. The potential uses for an automatic, reprogrammable arm with legs are almost unlimited.

Flexible Machining System Vehicles: These vehicles transport tools, fixtures, and raw materials to the machining cells and finished goods from the machining cells. They require a high degree of positioning capability, and after docking they are usually pinned to the machining cell. With the application of these vehicles a 24-hour unmanned factory is achievable.

Autonomous AGVs: These are the future generation AGVs that can communicate with other vehicles in the system and with the factory controller. They will have vision capabilities for obstacle avoidance and part recognition. They will have the ability to diagnose their own malfunctions and to order and perhaps replace the assemblies that are defective. They will be able to sense and warn operators of fire, sabotage, and unauthorized intrusion.

Guidance Technologies

AGVs use the same technologies as most machine tools: microprocessors, servo-amps, DC motors with tachs and encoders, stepping motors, programmable logic controllers, hydraulics and relays, and others. What separates AGVs from most of the machines are guidance technologies, wheels and their geometries, and the basic system control functions of AGVs such as routing, traffic management, load transfer, and material handling.

The guidance technologies that are available now or in an advanced stage of development include buried wire, dead reckoning, optical, infrared, inertial positioning reference, triangulation, and ultrasonic and laser imaging. A description of each technology along with its advantages and disadvantages is given below.

1. Buried Wire: Most AGVs in use today are wire guided. This technology uses wire that is either buried in the floor or surface mounted. A radio frequency is induced into the wire, which can be sensed by receivers on-board the vehicle. The major advantage of buried wire is its reliability. It is a tried and proven system. If the vehicles, for some reason, lose the guide-path, then they will come to an immediate halt. Buried wire is also immune to dirt and paper covering the wire path.

The major disadvantage of buried wire is that some factories cannot have their floor cut. Other disadvantages are that it is not easy to add or change paths relative to the nonwire techniques, and if there is a need to keep vehicles running should the system fail, then wire systems are not appropriate.

2. Dead Reckoning: This method is generally used in conjunction with buried wire. It uses optical encoders on the drive wheels or on instrument wheels. These encoders measure wheel rotation. If wheel rotation is the same for both drive wheels, then the vehicle is presumed to be going in a straight line. By controlling relative rotation of both wheels, algorithms can be developed to produce different turning radii. This method is used where many spurs are off the main path or great flexibility in spur position is anticipated. Dead reckoning is generally used only for short distances because wheel slippage can cause positioning errors.

3. Optical: There are a number of optical guidance technologies available. Some use foil tape for a guide-path; others use ultraviolet-sensitive tape or chemicals for the guide-path. These guide-paths are easy to install, economical, and can be changed or expanded with little effort.

Vehicles using optical guidance must have more intelligent on-board control systems. They use preprogrammed maps of the system, optical encoders, and a tape placed perpendicular to the guide-path, which is read by sensors on the vehicle somewhat like reading bar codes, to determine the location of the vehicle in the system. The major disadvantage of optical systems is that the path becomes unreadable when covered by dirt, grease, or debris.

4. Infrared: Infrared guidance systems are still relatively untried in an industrial environment. One of these systems uses an on-board camera that sights off LEDs mounted at the end of aisles. The vehicle is guided by centering the image of the LEDs in the pixel array in the camera. Another system uses infrared technology that places cameras around the periphery of the room or building. Two LEDs are on-board the vehicle, one placed at each end of the vehicle. The cameras track the images of the paired LEDs as the vehicle or vehicles travel about the system.

The major advantage of infrared guidance is reduced installation costs. Infrared is also insensitive to sunlight and fluorescent lamps, which sometimes confuse optical systems. This technology appears to be useful in clean-room applications and in buildings where the floor cannot be cut. The disadvantage of this technology is that guidance requires line-of-sight, so that disruption of guidance occurs when someone or something gets in the way of the camera.

5. Inertial: There are several successful installations using inertial guidance systems. These AGVs have optical encoders to determine vehicle position when compared with an internal preprogrammed map. An on-board gyroscope senses acceleration due to deviation from a straight line. This data is processed and corrective measures are taken to counteract wheel slippage and other error-producing effects and to keep the vehicle on its preprogrammed path. The major advantage of this technology is that it allows clean-room installations and can be reprogrammed easily so as to allow much flexibility in path changes. Disadvantages are the lack of system control and the high cost of the vehicle.

6. Triangulation: This method of guidance uses triangulation to deduce the position of the vehicle relative to three or more reference sources placed about the installation. This method has been applied to AGVs on an experimental basis only. Sources that have been tried are infrared, ultrasonic, microwave, and light. The apparent advantage of these systems is lower installation cost. The critical factor in installing such systems is the ability to develop operative software programs.

7. Ultrasonic and Laser Imaging: Both of these technologies use sensor arrays and sophisticated software to analyze reflected signals to build computer images of their surroundings. These computer images are compared with maps that are preprogrammed into the vehicles and on-board systems. These systems look for reference positioning and obstructions. Programs utilize artificial intelligence techniques to manage the huge amount of data that has to be analyzed. The major advantage of using these technologies comes from the ability to have completely autonomous vehicles. Their use is particularly appealing in hazardous areas. The major disadvantage is the high per-unit cost of application.

AGV Dispatching Rules

Here we consider the dispatching of automated guided vehicles in a manufacturing environment consisting of several machine centers. A typical part visits several of these machine centers, following the routing table, and leaves the system after its machining requirements are met. The parts move between the machine centers, thus generating demand for the

AGVs. The assignment of part-movement tasks to AGVs is the AGV dispatching problem. We present here heuristic rules for the assignment of parts to vehicles and vehicles to parts.

We assume that the AGV is work conserving, i.e., would not be idle when a part is waiting to be moved. When an AGV is released after completing a task, then (i) the AGV remains idle if no part is waiting to be moved, (ii) the AGV starts moving the part if there is only one part waiting to be moved, and (iii) if multiple parts are waiting to be moved, then a set of dispatching rules must be defined to match the vehicle to a part. Similarly, when a set of vehicles is idle and a pickup task is generated by a machine center, criteria must be established for matching an idle vehicle to the task. This is the task-assignment problem for machine-center-initiated tasks. We thus have two types of decisions:

1. **Vehicle Assignment**: This decision involves selection of a vehicle from a set of idle vehicles to pick up a workpiece from a machine center.
2. **Machine Center Assignment**: This decision involves selection of a machine center from a set of machine centers, simultaneously requesting service of a vehicle.

The vehicle dispatching decisions in both of the above situations are to be carefully made since they can affect the material flow, congestion in the network, throughput, and manufacturing lead time. We now present heuristic rules employed in making decisions of both types.

Vehicle Assignment

1. Random Vehicle Rule: Under this rule, the pickup task is assigned randomly to any available vehicle in the shop without regard to the distance between the current vehicle location and the pickup task.

2. Nearest Vehicle Rule: To apply this rule, we first compute the distance of every available vehicle from the demand point. Let d_i be the distance of the ith vehicle from the demand point. It is computed from the guide-path layout and depends on the number of nodes touched and internodal distance. We then have the following rule:

NVR1: The vehicle that is dispatched is vehicle j such that $d_j = min\{d_i\}$ for all idle vehicles i.

Rather than dispatching vehicles based on the shortest distance rule, the dispatching decision could be made based on the shortest travel time, as below.

NVR2: Dispatch the vehicle j for which $\frac{d_j}{s_j} = \min \left\{ \frac{d_i}{s_i} \right\}$ for all idle vehicles i, where s_i is the travel speed of vehicle i.

One may note that shortest distance path may not be the shortest travel time path, because of different travel speeds of the vehicles. Also, congestion among the routes significantly influences the travel time. Thus the shortest travel time rule computed as above may not follow the actual shortest time path.

3. Longest Idle Vehicle Rule: This rule assigns highest priority to the vehicle that has remained idle for the longest period among all idle vehicles. This is equivalent to the dispatching vehicle j such that $t_j = min \{t_i\}$ where $t_i =$ idle time of the ith vehicle. This rule balances the workload among all vehicles.

4. Least Utilized Vehicle: This rule also balances the workload among all the vehicles. Let U_i denote the utilization of the ith vehicle up to the time the vehicle dispatching decision has to be made, then the decision is to dispatch vehicle j, for which $U_j = min \{U_i\}$.

Machine Center Assignment

The performance of a material handling system is judged by the average delivery time, i.e., the time elapsed between the time at which the request for material transfer is initiated until the time it is delivered at the desired destination. Contention arises when requests for a vehicle from machine centers cannot be immediately satisfied. We present below several heuristic rules for ranking the machine center requests for vehicles.

1. **Random:** A list of all machine centers requesting the service of vehicles is obtained and a machine center is randomly selected from this list.

2. **Shortest Distance:** This decision rule dispatches a released vehicle to the machine center that is nearest to the current location of the vehicle. Nearness is measured in terms of the distance or travel time. The idea here is to minimize the idle travel distance. This type of rule discourages service to a machine center located at some distance from the rest of the facilities. Such a machine station, starved of service for a sufficiently long time, will eventually get blocked, i.e., all input and output buffers of the center will be full and no further deliveries would be possible for that center. This may lead to a deadlock situation.

3. **Longest Travel Time:** This decision rule assigns highest priority to the machine center that is farthest away from the vehicle.

4. **Maximum Queue Length:** Here the vehicle chooses the machine center that has the largest number of workpieces waiting in the output buffer. This rule reduces the risk of blocking.

5. **Minimum Unused Buffer Capacity:** Here the vehicle is assigned to the workstation with the minimum number of empty slots in its buffer. Again, any situation leading to the buffers being full is discouraged. This would reduce the risk of blocking and deadlock.

6. **Earliest Arrival to the Shop Floor:** Here jobs are tagged with their time of arrival onto the shop floor. The rule selects the job which has spent the most time in the shop. The idea here is to reduce the manufacturing lead time by giving preference to items that have arrived earlier.

7. **Latest Arrival to the Shop Floor:** Here the job which has spent the least time in the shop is selected for transportation.

8. **Shortest Remaining Processing Time:** Here the job with the shortest remaining processing time on the shop floor is selected for transportation.

We have discussed several decision rules in the context of AGV scheduling. It is difficult to guess which combination of rules would lead to high performance in terms of low WIP, low manufacturing lead time, and other performance measures. Performance evaluation either analytically or via simulation is necessary before selecting any of the dispatching rules.

Analysis of AGV Systems

Here we present simple models useful in computing both the number of AGVs required and cycle times. We will assume that the vehicle operates at a constant speed of v and ignore the acceleration, deceleration, blocking, and other effects that influence the speed. The time elements of a typical AGV schedule include (i) loading at pickup station and unloading at the drop-off station, (ii) travel time to drop-off station, and (iii) idle travel (without load) between deliveries.

Let L_d and L_r be the delivery and return distances and t_h the load/unload handling time. Then the total time per delivery is

$$t_{del} = \frac{L_d}{v} + \frac{L_r}{v} + t_h$$

If there was no traffic congestion, then number of deliveries per hour can be obtained from t_{del}. However, blocking of vehicles, waiting time at intersections, vehicles waiting in line, poor scheduling, and poor layout contribute to degradation in performance. A traffic factor T_f accounts for all these and lies between 0.85 and 1.

$$\text{Number of deliveries per hour per vehicle} = \frac{60T_f}{t_{del}}$$

$$\text{Number of AGVs} = \frac{\text{Number of deliveries required per hour}}{\text{Number of deliveries per hour per vehicle}}$$

Example 2.13

Consider an FMS consisting of two lathes with 30 min average per cycle; two machine centers with average cycle of 1 h; and one machine center with a 3-h cycle. Apart from these workpiece moves, tools are delivered twice a day to the two machine centers and once a day to the others. The total moves in a day are given by

$$2\,(24 \times 2) + 2\,(24 \times 1) + \left(24 \times \frac{1}{3}\right) + (3 \times 2) + (2 \times 1) = 160$$

If each movement takes 8 min, then total movements would take about 21.33 h. Two AGVs are needed in practice, although one would suffice in theory.

PROBLEMS

1. Consider a robot cell with machines B, C, and D. An input conveyor brings the part to the pickup point A and the output conveyor is represented by point E. Each part undergoes an operation on B, followed by C, and followed by D. The operation times on B, C, D are given by 9.1, 9.0, and 5.0 min, respectively. Also, the gripper pull-up time = 0.1 min, and gripper release time = 0.1 min. The robot move times in minutes are given by the table below. Compute the cycle time and the production rate for this system.

From	To				
	A	B	C	D	E
A	-	0.3	0.6	0.9	1.2
B	0.3	-	0.3	0.6	0.9
C	0.6	0.3	-	0.3	0.6
D	0.9	0.6	0.3	-	0.3
E	1.2	0.9	0.6	0.3	-

How will the cycle time and production rate change if there are two robots with robot 1 handling all operations from A to C and robot 2 handling all operations from C to E?

2. Consider a robot cell with one machine M_1, two robots R_1 and R_2, and three conveyors C_1, C_2, and C_3. Incoming parts arrive at the left end of C_1 and through conveyor movement reach the right end of C_1 (30 s). Robot R_1 picks up (5 s) the raw part from C_1, moves to the left end of C_1 (30 s), and deposits the part on C_2 (5 s). Once the part reaches the right end of C_2 (20 s), robot R_2 picks it up (5 s), moves to M_1(20 s) if M_1 is available, and places the part on the machine (5 s). The machine processing takes 5 min. After processing, the part is picked up by R_2 (5 s), which then moves to C_3 (30 s) and deposits the finished part on C_3 (10 s), and robot R_1 picks it up (5 s), unloads it (10 s), and reaches its home point (5 s). Compute the cycle time and production rate under the following assumptions.

   (a) Unprocessed parts are always available at the right end of C_1.

   (b) Each conveyor can only accommodate one part at a time.

   (c) R_1 is involved in two operations: C_1 to C_2 and C_3 to unload. The latter operation gets priority over the former.

   (d) R_2 is involved in two operations: C_2 to M_1 and M_1 to C_3 (increasing order of priorities).

   (e) R_2 will pick up a part from C_2 only if M_1 is free.

3. Write a simulation program to investigate the relative effectiveness of alternative AGV dispatching policies. Make suitable assumptions about the layout.

2.6 PLANT LAYOUT

A manufacturing system consists of several resources including versatile machine tools, robots, AGVs, conveyors, local and central tool stores, load/unload stations, local and central buffers, warehouses, and washing stations. In this section we are concerned with the problem of selecting the most effective arrangement of these physical facilities in a manufacturing system so as to minimize the material handling cost, inventory cost, and manufacturing lead time. This is the *facilities layout* problem. The layout should be expandable and adaptable to changes, easily maintainable, and should promote high employee morale.

Traditionally, the layout problem in a manufacturing system is viewed as a static problem of locating the machines so that the flow of parts between the machines is minimized and this minimal flow is a directed flow with no backtracking. While obtaining such an optimal layout, information is used regarding the current mix of parts, volume of production for each part, and the routing for each part. These parameters are assumed to remain constant over the planning horizon. There are several computer-aided layout techniques such as Computerized Relative Allocation of Facilities Technique (CRAFT) and Computerized Relationship Layout Planning (CORELAP) useful for obtaining standard layouts.

However, in the context of FMSs, dynamic layout problem or layout/re-layout problem is more important. Over time, demands and designs change and consequently the mix of parts, their production volumes, and routing tables also change. This would result in change of product flow among machines. The initial optimal layout may not be optimal any more under the changed circumstances. Since FMS is often justified on the basis of providing a competitive edge in changing markets, its layout should be flexible enough to accommodate changes in designs and demands.

The layout designer of an FMS faces the difficult task of developing a system capable of handling a variety of products with variable demands, alternate and probabilistic routings, at a reasonable operating cost. In particular, during the layout design phase, product mix is highly uncertain and is subject to change because of forecasting errors and demand fluctuations.

In this section we consider group technology and the layouts based on group technology as well as functional layouts, i.e., layouts in which machines are arranged by their function.

2.6.1 Group Technology

Group technology (GT) is a manufacturing principle in which similar parts are identified and grouped together to take advantage of the similarities in the part geometries and operation processes in design and manufacture.

In batch-type manufacturing each part has traditionally been treated as being unique in design, process planning, production control, tooling, and so on. However, by grouping several parts into part families, based on either geometric shapes or operation processes and also forming machine groups or cells that process the designated part families, it is possible to reduce costs and streamline the work flow. Group technology enables batch-manufacturing shops to achieve economies of scale approaching those of mass production, enhanced standardization of parts and processes, and the elimination of both duplication in design and proliferation of different part routings on the shop floor.

The basic concept of group technology has been practiced for many years as part of sound engineering practice or scientific management. A classification and coding system developed by F.W. Taylor for formation of part families was used in manufacturing as early as the beginning of this century. Similarly, in Japan, Germany, and the United States, one can find examples wherein leading industries have exploited the part-family concept in both design and manufacture.

Although the idea that manufactured components can be classified into part families similar to biological families is an age-old one, it was not until 1958 that a Russian engineer, S.P. Mitrofanov, formalized the concept in his book *The Scientific Principles of Group Technology*. Mitrofanov's work was followed closely by E. Brisch of U.K., and H. Opitz of West Germany. Group technology is now finding increasing application in the industry.

Group technology principles and their benefits can be seen by looking at the relationship that exists between finished products and the component parts from which they are made. While assemblies bear little resemblance to one another, the subassemblies exhibit similar features. When the subassemblies are broken down further, the result is a wide range of seemingly diverse parts. Figure 2.18 illustrates the fact that the subassemblies are a collection of items belonging to the same part family.

A part family is a collection of parts that are similar either because of geometric size and shape (design attributes) or because similar processing operations (manufacturing attributes) are required in their manufacture. Parts are considered to be similar with respect to production operations when the same machines and processes are used and when the type, sequence, and tooling requirements are similar.

The part-family concept is central to computer-aided process planning (CAPP) schemes. CAPP involves the automatic generation of a process plan (route sheet) to manufacture a part. The process routing is developed by recognizing the specific attributes of the part in question and relating these attributes to the corresponding manufacturing operations.

2.6.2 Some Typical Layouts

As we mentioned earlier, an FMS consists of a number of machines, pallets, fixtures, workpieces, tools, AGVs, a setup area, tool room, stores,

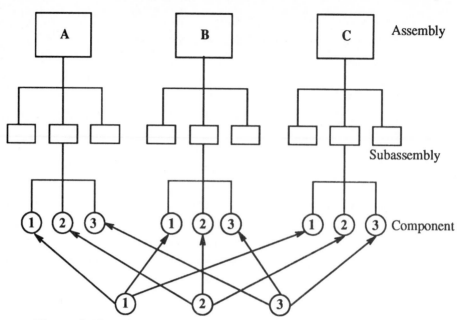

Figure 2.18 Assembly, subassembly, and component relationship

and control room. There are several possible layouts.

1. Functional Layout

This is a layout in which the machines are arranged according to the machine type or function such as turning, milling, boring, and grinding (Figure 2.19). This type of layout is most common because of several reasons: (i) It is easy to manage a group of similar machines than a group of dissimilar machines. (ii) Such layouts are more robust to machine breakdowns, product-mix changes, and rush orders since allocation/reallocation among similar machines is more easily done. Further, routings of functional layouts are standardized. (iii) Functional layouts are also resilient to absenteeism since one operator can cover for the other in view of the similar nature of work content.

There are several disadvantages of functional layout. During the machining of a given part, the workpiece must be moved between sections, with perhaps the same section being visited several times. This results in a significant amount of material handling, a large in-process inventory, usually more setups than necessary, long manufacturing lead times, and high cost.

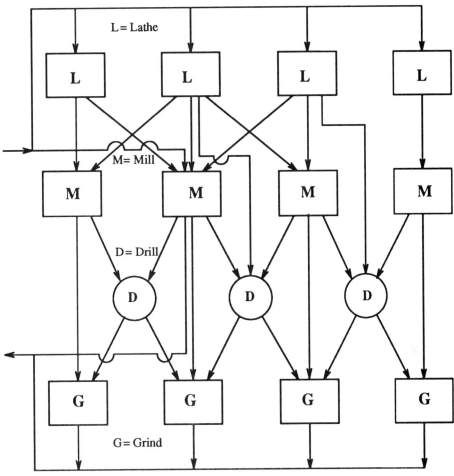

Figure 2.19 Functional layout

2. Cellular Layout

Here each cell consisting of a group of dissimilar machines is dedicated to process a family of parts, as in Figure 2.20. Cellular manufacturing is associated often with group technology, which classifies workpieces based on either geometric similarities or similar processing characteristics. It also tends to obtain mass-production benefits for job shop production.

The primary benefits of cellular manufacturing are reduction in processing time, inventory, and tooling. Overall manufacturing lead time and material handling times are also reduced. Two major benefits are in tooling development and setup time. Since tooling can be created for a family of parts, tooling efforts get distributed over a family of parts.

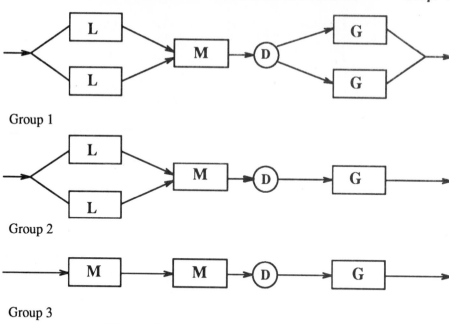

Group 1

Group 2

Group 3

Figure 2.20 Group technology layout

Because the cell is dedicated to a few different families of part types, fixturing and tooling require few changeovers and consequently setup time is reduced. And as each cell caters to a focused part family, it has other benefits such as high machine utilization and low manufacturing lead time. However, managing change in cellular production is more complex, as machine breakdowns cripple the entire cell, and accommodation of changes in product-mix may require a possible re-layout.

Figures 2.19 and 2.20 show functional and cellular layouts for a typical application. From the above discussion, it is clear that there are trade-offs between purely cellular layouts and purely functional layouts. The optimum lies somewhere in between. An analysis based on process planning should serve as a guide to the extent to which cellular manufacturing could be used. Perhaps in any product order, there are few families of parts with enough volume that warrant machine cells for their production, whereas bulk of other products might be manufactured more efficiently in a functional layout.

Layout of Machines in Cell: We consider next the arrangement of machines in a cell. The part transport in these cells is assumed to be through a robot, AGV, or a gantry robot.

In a cell served by a material handling robot, the arrangement of machines is determined by the robot envelope. An AGV serves more effectively if machines are arranged in straight lines. Gantry robots are used for part transport when space is a limiting factor.

Limitations in the linear form can be overcome in a U-shaped layout. This layout allows assignment of a multifunction operator to more than one machine owing to the close proximity of the machines. It provides the flexibility in the number of operators assigned to individual machine centers and also the range of jobs each operator performs. This feature would enable the manufacturing system to adapt to small changes in market demand and consequently in the schedule. Since the machines are nearby, the manufacturing batch size and transport batch size could both be one. The operators can themselves transport the workpieces, or conveyors could be used. Synchronization of operations could be achieved since one unit entering the machine means one unit leaving the machine and entering another.

PROBLEMS

1. The following matrix specifies the usage of machines M_1, M_2, M_3, and M_4 by four different part types p_1, p_2, p_3, and p_4 in a system. The entry corresponding to p_i and M_j $(i, j = 1, 2, 3, 4)$ is equal to 1 if p_i requires M_j for a particular operation and 0 otherwise.

$$\begin{bmatrix} 1 & 0 & 1 & 0 \\ 0 & 1 & 1 & 1 \\ 0 & 1 & 0 & 1 \\ 1 & 0 & 1 & 0 \end{bmatrix}$$

There is one machine of each type in the above system. It is required to obtain a group technology layout with two cells for the above system. Suggest an appropriate cellular layout. Note that shuffling of rows and columns will help. Can you devise general algorithms for obtaining cellular layouts from a matrix specification such as above?

2. A particular system has two machines of type M_1 and two machines of M_2. The system produces three part types with the following routing specifications

$p_1 : M_1 \rightarrow M_2$
$p_2 : M_1 \rightarrow M_1$
$p_3 : M_2 \rightarrow M_2$

The processing times on the machines are 10 min for first operation and 20 min for the second operation. The setup time is 5 min for the first operation of each type and the second operation of part type p_1. The setup times for the second operation of part types p_2 and p_3 are 2 min each. If a part has to travel from one cell to another, the time taken is 10 min. The average waiting time before a machine operation or a material handling operation is 10 min. Neglect the load and unload times. Compute the MLT for each part type, throughput rate for each part type, the average WIP, and the machine utilization for the two layouts given below.

(a) Cellular Layout: two cells, each containing one of M_1 and one of M_2

(b) Functional Layout: two cells, one containing two of M_1 and the other containing two of M_2 .

2.7 FLEXIBLE MANUFACTURING SYSTEMS

In parallel with the developments in computers and automation technology over the past three decades, a new type of production system called the flexible manufacturing system, or FMS, has evolved. By approaching mass-production efficiencies in a more versatile small-batch manufacturing environment, FMS has emerged as a highly competitive manufacturing strategy of the late twentieth century. This technology is especially attractive for medium- and low-volume industries such as automobile, aircraft, steel, and electronics. The philosophy of FMS is ideally suited for unpredictable market environments that demand low-cost solutions for quickly and effectively adapting to changes in product mix, demand, and designs.

We have discussed the evolution of flexible manufacturing systems in the introduction to this chapter. In this section we present the architecture of a typical FMS, and describe the automated operation. We then discuss flexible assembly systems. Next we discuss the issue of deadlocks in FMSs. Finally we examine the performance measures of Section 2.3 in the context of FMSs.

2.7.1 Architecture of FMS

FMS is a manufacturing philosophy. It is a production system based on the economies of scope wherein several part types are simultaneously resident in the system. The subsystems are versatile computer-controlled equipment such as NC machines, AGVs, CMMs, and robots. The setup times are small and the number of buffer spaces provided in the system is minimal. Thus the system follows a flow-type workpiece movement so that the manufacturing lead time almost equals the part processing time. The material flow integration is achieved through a computer-controlled MHS. The automated operation of the system is made possible by the messaging between various controllers via the local area network. An ideal FMS is a production system in which we have zero setup times, zero inventories, zero material handling, zero queue time, and manufacturing lot size of one.

Definition: An FMS can be defined as an integrated computer-controlled configuration of NC machine tools, other auxiliary production equipment, and a material handling system (MHS) designed to simultaneously manufacture low to medium volumes of a wide variety of high-quality products at low cost.

FMS is a highly competitive manufacturing strategy because of its capability to adapt quickly and efficiently to changes in product mix, demands, and designs. Inherent FMS flexibility is based on its system structure, which comprises versatile production machines with minimal changeover times between part types, versatile MHS capable of timely movement of parts and tools, and an on-line computer control of parts, tools, storage, and MHS that exploits the versatility of production and material handling systems to give the desired flexibility.

We now enumerate below the typical elements of an FMS.

1. Versatile NC machines equipped with automatic tool changing and in-process gauging, with capability to carry out a variety of operations.
2. An automated MHS to move parts and tools under the control of a central MHS controller. The MHS may comprise conveyors, carts, industrial robots, AGVs, or a combination of these elements.
3. Load/unload station through which the entry and exit of the parts occur. Entering parts are fixtured and loaded onto pallets, and departing parts are defixtured at these stations.
4. Inspection stations equipped with coordinate measuring machines.
5. Storage in the form of local buffers adjacent to the machines and/or centralized automatic storage and retrieval system (ASRS) for raw and semi-finished workpieces.
6. Tool magazines on the machine tool and a centralized tool store provide tool storage.

7. A hierarchical control system (HCS) that coordinates the working of the machines, tools, and MHS and the movement of workpieces. The HCS generally comprises a local area network interconnecting the programmable controllers (PCs) of the machine tools, MHS controller, and the supervisory computer. An important component of the HCS is a database management system (DBMS) with part programs, scheduling information, tool database (tool type, tool life, remaining life), and workpiece database (route sheet consisting of number and types of operations, machines where these can be performed, time each operation takes, and the tools required). Table 2.7 shows a sample routing table.

Figure 2.21 depicts the architecture of a typical FMS. One can visualize two kinds of integration in such an FMS: *material integration* provided by the MHS and computer control, and the *information integration* provided by the LAN-based computer control system and the DBMS.

In Figure 2.22, we show a typical sequence of operations in an FMS. Initially, incoming raw workpieces are fixtured onto pallets at a load/unload station. These workpieces move to queues at the workstations via the MHS. The sequence of operations on a workpiece is given by the routing table (see, for example, Table 2.7), which also specifies the choice of machines for each operation of each part type. As a result, there are several alternative routes that a workpiece of a given type can traverse while getting processed. In a well-designed system, machines, conveyors, and control elements combine to achieve high productivity, maximum machine utilization, and minimum in-process inventory. Some of the important decisions that the hierarchical controller takes in an FMS are: scheduling and dispatching (which part to introduce into the FMS next and which machine to be assigned to a part; which part to be processed by the machine next), scheduling of the MHS, tool management, system monitoring and diagnostics, and reacting to disruptions such as machine breakdowns, tool breakages, and deadlocks. There are also several off-line decisions such as determining the number of machines, number of AGVs,

Table 2.7 Routing table for an FMS with 5 machines and 3 part types

Part type	op #1	op #2	op #3
Type 1	M1/M2	M3	M4/M5
Type 2	M1/M2/M3	M2/M3	M5
Type 3	M1/M5	M4	M3/M2

machine layout, machine grouping, and batching and balancing that are also important. We will not consider these off-line decisions here.

2.7.2 Automated Workpiece Flow

Here we describe in detail the part flow in an FMS. This description by using the flowchart (Figure 2.22) clearly brings out (i) the manner in which an FMS control system keeps the parts moving, (ii) the decisions to be made, and (iii) real-time, on-line control software requirements. We assume normal operation during this description and will deal with abnormal conditions later in this section.

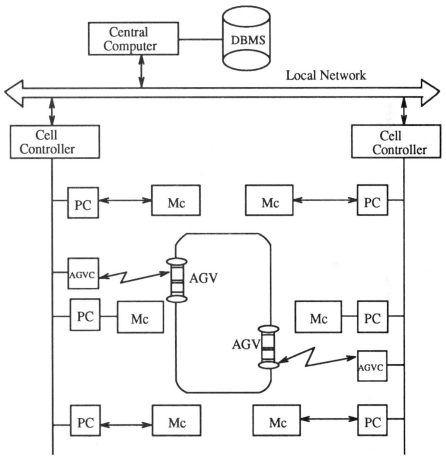

Figure 2.21 Architecture of a typical FMS

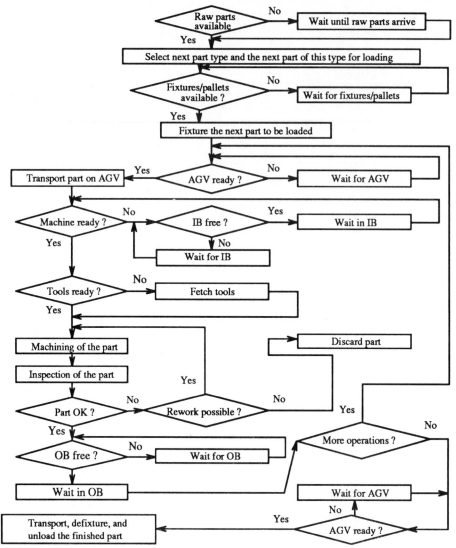

Figure 2.22 Flowchart for the automated operation of FMS

We assume that batching is already done and the decision regarding the part mix is made, the appropriate part programs are resident in the NC machine tools or in the central computer, and the necessary tools are loaded into the tool magazines or available in the central tool store. Thus we have a number of workpieces of different part types waiting at or nearby the load/unload station.

Fixturing

The raw workpieces of a given part type arrive at the load/unload (L/U) station, where fixtures are stored. The bar code on the raw workpiece is read by a laser pen and is communicated to the central computer via the LAN by the L/U station controller. The central computer retrieves the route sheet for this part type from the DBMS. The route sheet contains information about the fixture type, operations to be performed, machines and inspection stations to be visited, tools and time required for each operation, the machine tools capable of performing these operations, and the appropriate part programs. DBMS also has updated information regarding (i) status of all machine tools, (ii) status of all AGVs, robots, and other MHS equipment, (iii) tool locations and tool lives, and (iv) fixture location and availability.

The central computer instructs the L/U station controller to perform the appropriate fixturing operation. Once fixturing is done, a "job done" message is sent to the central computer by the L/U controller.

Entry into the FMS

The question arises as to which part to introduce next into the FMS and when. This is the FMS flow control problem. Most of the classical literature is concerned with generating fixed schedules specifying which operations should be performed on which machine and when. More appropriate in the FMS context might be a real-time scheduling policy, with scheduling decisions based on the actual state of the system such as failed machines, raw material available, pallets and fixtures available, and deviations from the desired production rates.

There are several possible scheduling decisions, each applicable in different situations. Sometimes part types have to be produced in a certain relative ratio, say, for subsequent assembly purposes. A periodic input such as (type 1, type 2, type 2, type 3, type 1, type 3); (type 1, type 2, . . . ,) may be appropriate for some dedicated types of FMSs. Some FMSs may best be operated in the closed-system mode, i.e., when a pallet comes out of the system, a part is chosen that can be fixtured onto the pallet and the pallet with fresh part is sent in again. If more than one part type can use a given pallet type, the part type that is most behind in production is generally chosen. In other situations, a flexible real-time decision concerning which part to input next may be the best.

It is not easy to predict precisely how changing the input sequence will affect the production. Discrete event simulation and analytical modeling are used to evaluate each of these strategies.

Material Handling and Machining

The central computer finds, from the route sheet, all the machines where the first operation can be performed and checks their status: busy or idle, working or failed, number of parts of each type waiting in front of each machine, etc. If the required operation can only be performed on a single machine (i.e., route sheet shows no choice) then the workpiece enters the queue in front of that machine. If a choice is available (i.e., the first operation can be performed on a number of machines), then the central computer selects the machine for processing based on the information regarding availability, speeds, number of workpieces waiting for processing before the machines, etc.

To select the machine for processing, the computer may use any of the following decision rules: (i) Choose the machine which is idle and among idle machines choose the fastest. (ii) If all machines are busy, choose the machine with the least number of parts waiting. This is called the *machine loading* problem. The part waits at the L/U station until the input buffer of the selected machine is free. Once this condition is met the computer sends the transporter to move the fixtured workpiece to the chosen workstation. Once the workpiece is in front of the machine, the central computer actuates the transfer mechanism called the *shuttle* and the workpiece is shifted from the transporter onto the shuttle. The transporter is now free to execute a new move request. The workpiece waits until the part currently being machined is completed and in-process inspection done. There are three possible outcomes of the inspection procedure: (i) the part passes the inspection and is ready for the next operation, (ii) the part requires rework before it can be accepted, and (iii) the part is out of tolerance limits and is to be discarded. For our discussion we assume that the part passes the inspection. Now the two parts and their pallets exchange positions. As the new part and the pallet are moved onto the machine, the proper part program is downloaded to the PLC (programmable logic controllers) from the central computer. Also, when the required tools are fetched after completing the downloading and the "tools ready" signal is received, machining begins. The finished part, now on the shuttle or the output buffer, waits for the transporter sent by the central computer to carry it to the next destination as prescribed in the route sheet. If the destination machine tool is not free then the transporter may unload the semi-processed workpiece in a central storage area for retrieval when the destination station becomes free.

Defixturing

When all the required operations are carried out, the workpiece is transported to the L/U station, now functioning as unload station where the part is removed from the fixture and the fixture is stored until needed.

In the above presentation, we have not elaborated two real-time decisions that have to be made by the central computer; these are: (i) choice of the AGV to perform a transporting task and (ii) assigning priorities among parts waiting to be processed by the same machine tool. The AGV scheduling strategies were covered in Section 2.5. The machine tool may choose the part that has the shortest processing time or the part type that arrived first or the one that has the earliest due date or the one that is most behind schedule.

Essentially four decisions are made by the FMS central computer:

1. When to introduce a part type into the system and which part to introduce.
2. The routes along which the parts are to be sent, i.e., which station to choose for the next operation from among all machines at which this operation can be performed.
3. Which job to be loaded next on a workstation from among those waiting in the local or central buffer area.
4. Which AGV to be scheduled for pickup or which part to be picked up by the AGV (dispatching rules for material handling system).

The central computer should have the intelligence to make the above real-time decisions.

2.7.3 Automated Assembly Systems

One of the most important manufacturing processes is the assembly. This process is required when two or more component parts are to be brought together to produce a finished product.

The early history of assembly process development is closely related to the history of mass production. Thus, the pioneers of mass production are also pioneers of modern assembly processes. Eli Whitney, Oliver Evans, F.W. Taylor, and Henry Ford were all pioneers of mass production as well as assembly processes. It is now generally accepted that the first effective use of all the basic techniques of modern mass assembly was made by Henry Ford in the production of flywheel magnetos for the Model T Ford motor car. Initially, in mass-production systems, material handling and assembly were both handled by operators. Soon mechanical transfer devices were introduced that presented parts to the operator, with consequent improvements in productivity. This is usually referred to as *operator assembly*, and is still the most widely used method for assembling mass-produced parts. As a logical extension, methods of replacing operators by mechanical means for assembly were devised. In *automatic assembly*, simple assembly tasks are performed by automatic workheads and complex tasks are handled by operators. In completely automatic assembly, the entire assembly process is completed without operator assistance.

Modern assembly lines fall into two classes: *dedicated assembly lines* producing large volumes of high-quality products, and *flexible assembly systems* wherein small volumes of a wide variety of assemblies are manufactured. In steady high-volume markets, dedicated high-volume assembly lines are the winners. However, such lines are inflexible. In markets that demand product variety and low to medium volumes, scope economies provide the answer and flexible assembly systems are good candidates for such situations.

The Assembly Task

Broadly speaking, an assembly task is the placement of individual discrete parts into a specific spatial relationship to form an end item. The assembly task basically consists of two activities — the gathering and organizing of parts and the mating and fastening of one to another. The mating and fastening processes could be (i) mechanical fastening, including threaded fastening such as screws, nuts, bolts, etc., riveting, pressure fits, and sewing and stitching; (ii) joining, including welding, brazing, and soldering; and (iii) adhesive bonding, using thermoplastic or thermosetting adhesives to join components together. In an assembly where many parts enter the system to form the finished product, inefficiencies in the system are caused by parts that are out of tolerance, incorrectly supplied or improperly oriented, or incorrectly presented.

Manual Assembly

In manual assembly, one or more operators assemble a product or subassembly. Generally, each assembly process is broken down into individual tasks, and a task graph showing the start and end of each task and their precedence relationship models the assembly process. Each task is performed at a workstation by one or more human operators and all such workstations are arranged in a sequence. The workpiece is transported from one workstation to another either manually by the operator or by using mechanized transporters such as moving conveyor.

Two problems may arise in assembly lines:

1. **Blocking**: An operator after completing the work has to wait for the next operator to finish the task before passing along the semi-finished assembly.
2. **Starving**: The operator is idle, waiting for parts from the preceding operator.

As a result of these two problems, work flow between the workstations may be uneven. Having buffer spaces between the stations often smooths out the production flow. Also, failure at any workstation would stop the entire assembly line. Buffer spaces are often provided between workstations so that short failures do not affect the production rate.

Manual assembly lines are the most common method of producing products in large volumes. Following the *division of labor* concept, each operator is given a specialized task, and as he or she gains experience, the operator would be able to perform this task more quickly and consistently. We have discussed in Section 2.1.4 the learning curve effects in assembly lines and its consequences on economies of scope and scale.

There are several advantages of manual assembly. An operator can perform easily some of the assembly tasks that are difficult to duplicate even on the most sophisticated automatic workhead. An operator can often perform the visual inspection of the part to be assembled; thus parts that are obviously defective can be discarded. In an automatic assembly, the workhead when fed with a faulty part may stop, causing loss of production. Also, a part could be presented in any orientation to the operator. Human operators are dexterous and intelligent machines, able to move to different positions at the workstation, able to adapt to unexpected problems and new situations during the work cycle, capable of manipulating and coordinating multiple objects simultaneously, and able to make use of a wide range of senses in performing the work.

To automate the assembly operations by automating the manual methods of assembly, which depend heavily on the human operator, his skills, and his senses, may not be the best approach. New methods of assembly may need to be devised in such situations.

Automated Assembly

In automatic assembly systems, various assembly operations are performed by separate workheads. The partly completed assemblies are transported automatically from workhead to workheads on work carriers so that the workpiece is presented at the required attitude at each of the workheads, and also the relative motion between the workhead and the assembly is minimized. Part feeding devices, which deliver the components to the assembly workhead, are also important. In the remainder of this section we discuss various types of workheads, transportation mechanisms, and part feeding devices suitable for automatic assembly.

Workheads: Workheads can be dedicated to a particular task or can be programmable. Programmable workheads are flexible and they should be able to perform more than one assembly task. Product style changes can be accommodated in systems comprising programmable workheads since by appropriate change in the programs, different assembly tasks can be performed.

For low production volumes, a single station assembly system with one or two sophisticated robot arms can be employed to build an assembly from a complete set of parts. Such a system is highly flexible and provides perhaps the greatest potential for batch assembly work, where batches of differing products are to be assembled and where a large number of product styles are required.

Assembly robots are available that can be programmed to perform a complicated sequence of manipulations. However, the grippers can handle only a limited number of product types, thus necessitating change in gripper and provision for a gripper store. Availability of programmable universal grippers would be helpful in such situations. Unfortunately, such devices are still in the initial stages of their development.

Transfer Systems: In assembly systems, individual assembly operations are performed at separate workstations, and transfer systems are used to transport workpieces from one station to another. Two standard transfer systems are common, and they are *synchronous* and *asynchronous* systems.

A synchronous production system is an automatic production line consisting of a number of workstations connected in series, and synchronized part transfer occurs between the workstations. A single transfer mechanism controls the entire line so that all the workstations release their parts simultaneously. The cycle time of the line is equal to the processing time of the slowest workstation plus the transfer time. This means that some workstations may be forced to be idle during a portion of the cycle time. All the workstations are idle during transfer of parts. Typical values of cycle times are small, often of the order of minutes.

Workstations in a synchronous line are tightly coupled, and failure of one of the workstations will result in the shutdown of the entire line. The line cannot start until the repair is finished. Synchronous production lines are used in traditional high-demand products with a relatively stable market. These lines carry minimum amount of inventory.

Indexing systems are the most common synchronous production systems. They are of two types, rotary and in-line. With the rotary indexing machine, indexing of the rotary table brings the work carriers under the various workheads in turn, and assembly of the product is completed during one revolution of the table. Thus, at the appropriate station, a completed product may be taken from the machine after each index.

The in-line indexing machine works on a similar principle, but in this case a completed product is removed from the end of the line after each index. With in-line machines, provision must be made for returning the empty work carriers to the beginning of the line.

Asynchronous production lines, or free transfer systems (Figure 2.23), are such that assemblies can accumulate between adjacent stations. Each workhead or operator works independently, and the assembly process is initiated at a workstation by the arrival of a work carrier at the station. With this kind of system, a fault at any station will not necessarily inhibit the operation of other stations since these will continue to function while

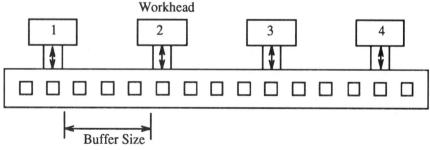

Figure 2.23 Free transfer assembly line

there are work carriers upstream and spaces downstream.

Part-Feeding Techniques: A part must be presented at the assembly station in a manner recognizable by the station. Depending upon the latter's intelligence and versatility, the part may be presented completely randomly or under partial constraint or with a specific orientation. Experience suggests that even with the most dexterous manual assembly, parts which have their position and orientation well defined generally require less effort in subsequent recognition and manipulation. In order to transform a heap of disorganized components into an orderly state ready for assembly, various part-feeding mechanisms have been developed. They perform the basic functions of storage, conveying, orientation, and presentation of parts. Feeding mechanisms can generally be classified as feeders, orienting devices, feed tracks, and escapements. The feeder accepts parts in random orientations, stores them temporarily, and activates them so that they can be subjected to the action of the orienting devices. Parts are then transferred from the feeder to the workhead by means of a feed track, which is designed to maintain the parts in the correct orientation. To enable the part-feeder to supply parts at the precise rate of assembly, they are generally overfed, and escapements are used to *meter out* parts as required.

An alternative way to deliver parts to an assembly machine is to load them into a container or magazine that constrains their orientation. The magazine is then attached to the assembly workhead where parts can be fed by spring action, by gravity, or by assistance of compressed air.

Most conventional part feeders carry out their feeding and orienting functions with fixed mechanical devices that exploit special properties of the part. Their construction depends on the part concerned with little flexibility in handling similar but nonidentical components. Such a limitation is tolerable in dedicated high-volume applications. With programmable automation, such a limitation would be unacceptable since a variety of products in small volumes have to be assembled using the same equipment. The changeover time of the feeders should be as small as possible. While it is possible to use a number of dedicated feeders to serve a variety of parts, it is more economical and often necessary to develop flexible feeders that can serve a variety of products.

Flexible Assembly Systems

A flexible assembly system has the following subsystems:

1. Programmable assembly cells
2. Flexible part-feeding systems
3. System storage
4. Flexible conveying systems
5. Automated inspection stations

In addition to the above general purpose subsystems, it is possible that some product-dependent special stations are integrated into the flexible assembly system. The individual programmable assembly cells, the special stations, and the system storage are linked together by means of AGVs, which can automatically accept palletized assemblies. The storage, which is kept to minimum, acts as a buffer against failures.

The automated operation of the assembly process follows the same description as for FMSs. The assembly process follows a task graph similar to the routing table in the case of an FMS. The workpiece visits the workheads according to the task graph. The transfer system moves the workpiece from station to station.

2.7.4 Deadlocks in Automated Manufacturing Systems

Deadlocks constitute an undesirable phenomenon in AMSs. A deadlock is a situation where each of a set of two or more parts keeps waiting indefinitely for the other parts in the set to release resources. In the context of AMSs, resources refer to machines, buffers, AGVs, robots, fixtures, tools, etc. Deadlocks may arise as the final state of a complex sequence of operations on concurrent parts passing through a system, and are thus generally difficult to predict. Deadlocks lead to degraded performance and ultimately zero throughput. The automated operation of an AMS makes deadlocks an important problem to be tackled. In an improperly designed AMS, the only remedy for deadlock may be manual clearing of machines or AGVs or buffers, and then restart of the system from an initial condition that is known to produce deadlock-free operation under nominal production conditions. The loss of production and the labor cost in resetting the system in this way can be avoided by proper design. Often, deadlocks may result because of simple errors in software specification of the controllers.

We first give an example of a deadlock and next discuss some important issues concerned with deadlock handling such as deadlock prevention and deadlock avoidance.

Example 2.14

Figure 2.24 shows a two-stage manufacturing system comprising two machines, M_1 and M_2, and an AGV. Assume that a given part undergoes manufacturing operations in the following sequence: (i) A fresh part, say p, enters the system when M_1 is free; (ii) after the machining by M_1 is complete, the AGV, if available, picks up p and delivers it to M_2 if M_2 is free, otherwise the part waits for M_2, thus blocking the AGV; (iii) when M_2 finishes processing p, the AGV unloads the part from the system.

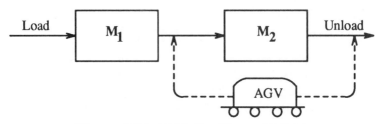

Figure 2.24 AMS for Example 2.14

Now, imagine the following sequence of events, starting with an initial state in which M_1 and M_2 are both free and the AGV is available:

(i) A fresh part, say p_1, enters the system, gets processed by M_1 and is delivered at M_2 by the AGV. M_2 starts processing p_1.

(ii) A second part, say p_2, enters the system, gets processed by M_1, is put on the AGV and transported to M_2, but the part waits on the AGV since M_2 is busy.

(iii) A third part, p_3, enters the system and gets processed by M_1. Meanwhile, M_2 finishes processing p_1.

At this stage, M_1 is blocked because the AGV is not available; the AGV will not become available unless M_2 is free; but M_2 cannot be free until the AGV is available. This is a deadlock, and the entire system comes to a standstill as shown by the event sequence diagram in Figure 2.25.

Deadlocks have been discussed extensively in the computer science literature. In the context of computer operating systems, a deadlock is defined as a situation where a set of two or more processes keeps waiting indefinitely for the other processes in the set to release resources. In the AMS context, processes correspond to the sequence of steps required to manufacture a part or a batch of parts, whereas resources correspond to

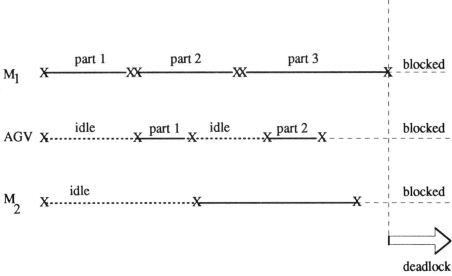

Figure 2.25 Event diagram illustrating the occurrence of deadlock

machines, tools, buffers, AGVs, and fixtures. Four necessary conditions have been identified for the occurrence of deadlocks. These are:

1. Mutual Exclusion — a resource cannot be used by two or more processes simultaneously.

2. No Preemption — when a resource is being used, it is not released unless the process using it finishes with it.

3. Hold and Wait — there must exist a process that is holding at least one resource and is waiting to acquire additional resources that are currently being held by other processes.

4. Circular Wait — there must exist a set of waiting processes $\{p_1, p_2, ..., p_n\}$ such that p_1 is waiting for a resource held by p_2; p_2 is waiting for a resource held by p_3;... p_{n-1} is waiting for a resource held by p_n; and p_n is waiting for a resource held by p_1.

Deadlocks have actually been reported in existing FMSs under certain conditions. Also, it is to be observed that blocking of resources is a prerequisite for the occurrence of deadlocks. We can now see how these necessary conditions are satisfied in the example below.

Example 2.15

The resources in the previous example are the two machines M_1 and M_2 and the AGV. Mutual exclusion is satisfied since each of these can only handle one part at a time. Since the resources cannot be released unless the parts holding it leave it, the no preemption condition is satisfied. The hold and wait condition is satisfied since part p_1 is holding M_2 and waiting for the AGV; part p_2 is holding the AGV and waiting for M_2; and part p_3 is holding M_1 and waiting for the AGV. The circular wait is established in the form of p_2 waiting for p_3 and p_3 waiting for p_2.

Deadlock handling takes four forms: *Deadlock detection, deadlock recovery, deadlock prevention,* and *deadlock avoidance.* Deadlock detection involves finding out that a deadlock has occurred. This will need on-line monitoring of the AMS. Deadlock recovery refers to restart of the system from an initial condition that is known to produce deadlock-free operation. Deadlock recovery can be expensive since it might involve removal of some semi-finished parts from the system or resource preemption. Deadlock detection and recovery go together. Deadlock prevention refers to static resource allocation policies to eliminate completely the possibility of deadlocks. The static allocation is made so as to break one or more of the necessary conditions. It is known that deadlock prevention policies lead to reduction in resource utilization and system throughput. In deadlock avoidance, we let all four necessary conditions be satisfied to enable efficient utilization of resources and avoid a deadlock just before it occurs by breaking one of the necessary conditions. Thus deadlock avoidance involves dynamic resource allocation, using look-ahead.

Deadlock is now recognized as an important issue to be addressed during the design and operation of an AMS. In Section 3.8 we use the modeling framework of Markov chains with absorbing states to investigate quantitative performance issues connected with deadlocks. In Section 5.5, we show deadlock modeling using Petri nets and present a real-time controller for deadlock avoidance.

2.7.5 Performance Measures

We will now turn our attention to some of the performance measures we considered in Section 2.3 in the context of FMSs. For obvious reasons, we first consider flexibility and then several others.

1. Flexibility

In Section 2.3 we defined flexibility as the ability of the system to respond effectively to both internal and external changes. We also discussed flexibility in the context of two plant configurations, transfer lines, and job shops. Here our interest is to examine flexibility in the context of FMSs and discuss its implication on overall operation of the FMS.

In an FMS, flexibility implies that the system has the ability to produce a wide variety of parts and assemblies in required volumes (low to medium) in the face of machine failures. Such a characteristic would provide the system with a competitive advantage in uncertain markets. We define four types of flexibilities: (i) Machine flexibility, (ii) Product flexibility, (iii) Routing flexibility, and (iv) Operation flexibility.

Machine Flexibility: This measures the ease with which a machine can change over from one part type to another. The change over time generally involves setup, tool changing, part-program transfer, and transportation times. The changeover time could be used as a single characteristic to measure machine flexibility. The universe of part types that a machine can produce is another measure of machine flexibility.

Consider the situation when a CNC (computer numerical control) machine center with automatic tool changer and buffer storage has to process a given part-mix. Assume that all the part programs and tools necessary to produce the scheduled parts are available. Further, suppose a pallet-pool stores fixtured parts and adequate number of fixtures are available for each part type. In this situation, the changeover time would be a fraction of the part-processing time and would include transportation time from pallet holding station to machine center, tool changing time, part-program transfer time, and part-positioning and release time.

Machine flexibility defined above is very desirable since it would mean that batch size of 1 would be economical and lead time would be minimal.

In another situation, suppose it is required to introduce a new product. Then the changeover time involves part-program development, cutting-tool preparation, and fixture development. In this instance, changeover time would be orders of magnitude greater than the processing time.

It is clear, however, that changeover time is a function of the machine center capabilities as well as effectiveness of its management. The changeover time in general would be in-between the two extreme cases discussed above.

Product Flexibility: This is a measure of the ability to change over to a new product-mix economically and quickly. The changeover time in this case includes the design, process planning, part-program preparation, tool development, and fixture preparation times. Such a flexibility would certainly heighten the company's potential responsiveness to a competitor's or to market changes. Thus product flexibility is a direct measure of the competitiveness of the firm.

Routing Flexibility: This flexibility measures the ability to manage internal changes such as breakdowns and failures. One can define routing flexibility as the ability to produce the given set of part types in required volumes in the face of failures and breakdowns. The failures could be tool breakages, controller failures, or machine breakdowns. We assume that whatever the nature of failure, repair would be undertaken and eventually normalcy would be restored. During the abnormal period, it is important to maintain production both in terms of part variety and their volumes to meet the due dates and also maintain competitiveness. The FMS should have enough redundancy by way of spare capacity so that specified levels of performance are maintained in the presence of various failures. The redundancy is created by having a number of versatile machine tools capable of performing a variety of operations. As a consequence each part could be manufactured via several routes and each operation could be performed on more than one machine. As machines fail the number of paths available for routing becomes smaller and the total throughput decreases. However, one can strike a compromise between volume and variety and maintain critical levels of production for each part type.

Operation Flexibility: This is the ability to interchange the ordering of several operations for each part type. There is usually some required partial precedence structure for a particular part type. However, for some operations, their respective ordering is arbitrary. Generally process planners do not exploit this flexibility and they fix the ordering of all operations. However, not predetermining the next operation or next machine increases the flexibility to make decisions. Suppose a part type has to undergo both drilling and boring. Either could be done first and the other second. Suppose the drilling machine is busy; then boring could be performed first and vice versa.

We can easily see that operation flexibility is part dependent and it increases the number of alternate routes that a part can flow through on the factory floor. This in turn would increase the steady-state probability that a part could be manufactured in the face of machine failures.

Analysis of Production Task

Consider a production task consisting of several part types $1, 2, ..., T$. Each part type goes through a set of operations, which can be grouped into sequential subsets, $1, 2, ..., I$. That is, all the operations in subset i have to be performed before any operation in subset $(i + 1)$ could be initiated. Let N_i be the number of operations in subset i. Operations n within a subset i $(n = 1, 2, ..., N_i)$ have no sequence constraint and can be performed in any order, i.e., in any permutation of $(1, ..., N_i)$. Each operation can be performed on several alternative workstations. Hence a part-mix analysis on a set of machines can be analyzed at four different levels: (i) Part types, (ii) Sequential subsets of operations, (iii) Unconstrained operations, and (iv) Alternative workstations.

From the above description, it is clear that routing flexibility can be achieved through alternative workstations and the unconstrained operations. Also, there are several routes along which a part can be produced, and choosing the one that minimizes the MLT and maximizes the throughput is an issue.

Example 2.16

Consider an FMS, currently producing two part types p_1 and p_2. Each operation of each part type requires 20 min of processing time on any of the machines M_1, M_2, or M_3. The probability of failure of a machine is $1 - p$. The schedule requires that 12 of each part type be produced in an 8-hour shift. The routing is given by the following table. Find the probability that the required demand on p_1 and p_2 can be met in an 8-hour schedule.

If all the machine centers were identical, i.e., both operations 1 and 2 for part types p_1 and p_2 could be performed on any of the machines M_1, M_2 or M_3, then the required probability is easily obtained. It is simply the probability that either all the three machines or at least two machines are up and working. However, in the present case, to obtain the answer we need to do a little more work. In particular, we have to use the information provided in the routing table to compute the required probability.

Part type	Operation 1	Operation 2
Type 1	M1/M2	M2/M3
Type 2	M1/M2/M3	M1/M3

We first note that if all machines M_1, M_2 and M_3 are working for an 8-hour period then a total of 36 parts could be produced and demands on p_1 or p_2 could be easily met. We claim that the target could be met even if any two machines, i.e., M_1, M_2 or M_2, M_3 or M_3, M_1, are working. To see this we consider three cases. M_1 fails, M_2 fails, and M_3 fails. In all three cases we can find schedules easily so that 12 each of p_1 or p_2 could be produced. Hence we can meet the target, if

(i) All machines are working, or

(ii) At least two of three machines are working.

If p is the probability a machine is working then the probability of the schedule being met is given by

$$p^3 + 3p^2 (1 - p)$$

If $p = 0.9$ then the required probability is given by 0.972.

2. Manufacturing Lead Time

We have defined MLT in Section 2.3 in the general manufacturing system context. We also identified the four constituents of MLT, namely setup time, processing time, move time, and queue time, and we discussed methods generally followed to minimize these times. In an FMS, one could expect the MLT to be as close to part processing time as possible.

An FMS is generally organized with adequate attention paid to material handling, and its components are versatile machine centers interconnected with small and smart vehicles for transport. In addition, tool magazines, tool delivery systems, and pallet pools are provided to cut down waiting time and improve machine utilization. All these facilities in an FMS would reduce changeover time and make batch size of 1 economic. Consequently, setup time and move time are minimized. Queue times are the only significant component of the wasteful portion of MLT. Even this could be minimized by following appropriate flow-control policies and by restricting the number of workpieces simultaneously resident in the system. Further, most items are made as and when required, and the WIP (work-in-process) storage capacity is kept low. All this would help in keeping the queue times to a minimum.

3. Machine Utilization

FMS factories are well planned. Moreover, the machines are versatile and can manufacture a wide variety of part types. Each production order consists of a large number of products in low-medium volumes, so that the total volume in the order would be substantial. Further unnecessary waiting times are kept to a minimum by providing facilities such as tool magazines, automatic tool changers, pallet pools, and so on. Thus one expects significant increase in machine utilization in an FMS.

4. Work-in-Process

As we have seen in the description of FMS, the buffer storage is kept to a minimum and this limits the WIP on the factory floor. Also, MLT is also kept to a minimum by following several waste-reduction methods and flow-control strategies. The combined effect of all this would be to control WIP levels.

5. Capacity

In traditional manufacturing systems, capacity has been thought of as the maximum output attainable under reasonable operating conditions of the plant. However, in an FMS this concept based on output is quite meaningless because of the multiple outputs possible. It is equally meaningless to define capacity in terms of inputs as well. Given the degree of responsiveness of FMSs to consumer demands, the input as well as output composition is likely to change every month or even every week.

One good way of characterizing capacity is through machine capabilities and machine hours. In some sense, this would lead to flexibility concept we were discussing earlier.

PROBLEMS

1. With respect to the flowchart of Figure 2.22, investigate the following issues.

   (a) What are the decision points in the flowchart? Identify suitable modeling tools and algorithms for these decisions.

   (b) Incorporate machine failures, inspection, and assembly operations in the flowchart.

   (c) Identify the blocks in the flowchart that distinguish an FMS from conventional production systems. In particular, how do flexibility and integration influence the different blocks?

   (d) Justify the statement that the flowchart is an abstracted version of a real-time controller for an FMS.

2. Deadlock is an issue extensively researched in the computer science literature, in the context of Operating Systems and Distributed Computing Systems. For example, see the book by Peterson and Silberschatz [1985] and the paper by Coffman, Elphick, and Shoshani [1971]. Identify the commonalities and differences in the phenomenon of deadlocks in computer systems and FMSs. You can study these issues in the context of deadlock prevention, deadlock avoidance, deadlock detection, and deadlock recovery.

3. Repeat the analysis of Example 2.16 for the following routing tables, assuming everything else to be the same.

$$(a) \quad \begin{array}{l} p_1 : \quad M_1/M_2 \rightarrow \quad M_2/M_3 \\ p_2 : \quad M_1/M_2 \rightarrow \quad M_1/M_2 \end{array}$$

$$(b) \quad \begin{array}{l} p_1 : \quad M_1 \rightarrow \quad M_2 \\ p_2 : \quad M_2/M_3 \rightarrow \quad M_3 \end{array}$$

4. Consider the system of Problem 2 in Section 2.6, which involves four machines (2 of type M_1 and 2 of type M_2) and three part types. Neglect all times except processing times and material handling times. Let the processing time for each first operation be 15 min and that for each second operation 25 min. It is required to produce x units of p_1, x units of p_2, and x units of p_3 at the end of the day (8-hour shift period). What is the maximum value of x for (a) cellular layout and (b) functional layout? If p is the probability of a machine not failing in a day and assuming that machines fail independently of one another and are not repaired for the day, what is the probability of meeting the target of x units per day of each part type for (a) cellular layout and (b) functional layout, when $x = 16, x = 12, x = 8$, and $x = 4$?

5. Investigate which of the two systems below has greater routing flexibility.

(a) Routing Table for FMS 1:
$$\begin{array}{l} p_1 : M_2/M_3 \rightarrow M_2/M_3 \\ p_2 : M_1/M_3 \rightarrow M_1/M_3 \\ p_3 : M_1/M_2 \rightarrow M_1/M_2 \end{array}$$
(b) Routing Table for FMS 2:
$$\begin{array}{l} p_1 : M_1/M_2 \rightarrow M_1/M_3 \\ p_2 : M_2/M_3 \rightarrow M_1/M_2 \\ p_3 : M_1/M_3 \rightarrow M_2/M_3 \end{array}$$

2.8 COMPUTER CONTROL SYSTEMS

The computer control system of an AMS manages and controls the total combination of devices, such as NC machines, robots, and AGVs, and makes possible automated operation of the entire production system. The control system is typically an interconnected network of the programmable controllers, cell controllers, and the supervisory computers. Each of these controllers of the individual equipment communicates with other controllers in the system. The software resident in various controllers has the capability to enable automated operation as well as system monitoring and diagnostics.

In this section we are concerned only with computer control systems that enable automated flow of workpieces through the factory by message passing between the various controllers. We discuss in detail the factory communications via the local area networks and the Manufacturing Automation Protocol (MAP). We also consider the Database Management System (DBMS) in the factory automation context. We assume that the material planning and financial control system are handled by the supervisory computer and do not consider these aspects.

2.8.1 Control System Architecture

We have discussed in Sections 2.7.1 and 2.7.2, the architecture and automated operation of an FMS. The flowchart in Figure 2.22 describes the decisions to be made as the workpiece flows through the factory. In a very general sense the flowchart in Figure 2.22 could be interpreted as the controller that drives an FMS and manages the workpiece flow.

Here we consider a structured manufacturing system consisting of a set of cells with each cell comprising a group of machines and material handling devices. Intercell material movement is handled by AGVs or conveyors or some other appropriate material handling equipment. The cell organization may be based on either process layout or group technology layout. For example, a cell may consist of five injection-molding machines each controlled by a programmable controller, or it may consist of two CNC machine centers and an AGV with facilities of tool storage and pallet storage. The generic control system of such a cellular manufacturing system has a hierarchical architecture. There are three levels of real-time control in this hierarchical control system: factory level, cell level, and equipment level.

Factory-Level Control System

At the factory level, the main aim is to produce parts in required volume and variety to meet the customer demands and due date constraints. The control system has to schedule the workload, procure material and tools, and route the workpieces from loading station to the cells, and finally to the unload station. This factory-level control system has to make real-time decisions such as (i) when to introduce another part into the system and which part type to produce; (ii) the disposition of the workpiece when it enters the factory, i.e., cell assignment; and (iii) dispatching and routing of material handling equipment.

As we discussed earlier, the above decisions could be based on fixed assignment strategies or heuristic dynamic strategies. In either case, the factory-level control system should have the information and intelligence to make these decisions in real-time.

Thus the factory-level control system is concerned with the overall coordination and control of the automated manufacturing system comprising several cells. This controller is interfaced to cell controllers and can communicate with equipment controllers via the cell controllers. It also interfaces with the field sensors and load/unload station. It has direct access to the database management system consisting of the part programs, tool databases, routing tables, and equipment status information. This constitutes the highest level in the control hierarchy.

Cell-Level Control Systems

The cell-level control system has limited authority. It is concerned with control of the machines and the routing of the workpiece within the cell. It also should have the intelligence to make decisions regarding (i) which part to enter next into the cell from among those assigned to the cell; (ii) which machine a given part would visit next; (iii) priority among all workpieces waiting in the workstation buffer or cell buffer area: (a) for service by the MHS; (b) for processing by the machine.

The cell controller also has the capability to detect failures in equipment in the cell either by workpiece monitoring or equipment monitoring and to react to these disturbances by re-routing and/or re-scheduling. Also, feedback is provided to the cell controller by the lower-level controllers on any normal and abnormal events that take place. Typical feedback signals include start and end of processes and any error conditions. Error conditions are signaled by intelligent resources such as expert systems and sensors that monitor critical variables. The critical variables could be (i) performance measures such as waiting times, queue lengths, and processing times, which provide indirect means to compute the health of the system, or (ii) directly measured variables such as tool wear, spindle torque, and coil currents, which indicate malfunction of equipment. The first category factors generally indicate deficiencies in planning, scheduling, and control, whereas the second category factors indicate failures of system components. The real-time decisions to be made by the cell controller are essentially material movement decisions and are to be closely coordinated with the workstation and material handling system controllers.

The function of the cell controller is to schedule and control the equipment in the cell to meet the goals set by the factory-level controller. The equipment controller and the cell controller form a communication network with appropriate interfaces and protocols for two-way communication. This enables the cell controller to download part programs to the equipment controllers and also collect the status information from them. The extent of message and data transfer on the network depends on (i) cell controller intelligence in decision making; (ii) the organization of databases whether centralized at the factory level or distributed with each cell having its own database, in which case all the part programs, routing tables for all part types, tool databases, workpiece locations, and status information are all stored at the cell level; and (iii) communication pattern between the cells and the equipment controllers.

The intelligence level of the cell determines the flow of control messages between the controllers, and the database organization determines the amount of transfer of large data files from shop-floor controller to the cell controller and from the cell controller to the equipment controller.

Example 2.17

Suppose we have a cellular manufacturing system with two cells A and B. Consider the following extreme cases:

Case 1: Centralized database organization and strictly hierarchical communication; i.e., no communication among cell controllers.

In this case, the factory-level controller reads the part family of arriving part type either in batches or as single items and allocates it to either Cell A or Cell B. For each part type, the cell controller has to request the routing table, part programs, availability of tools, and information from the factory-level controller. It has to obtain the status of machines, input and output buffers, and local transport availability from the equipment-level controllers. This would result in considerable messaging and transfer of files across the layers. If the factory-level controller is busy or is down, then the cell controller function is affected.

Case 2: Distributed database organization and cell controllers communicate with each other.

In this instance, the responsibility of the factory-level controller ceases once the part family is identified and a cell is assigned. It is informed of the status of various components periodically, and its decisions are requested only for intercell moves. Since all the data, both off-line and on-line, needed for decision making are available at cell level, the messaging and data file transfers are minimized. Intercell communication helps in alerting the cell regarding the arrival of part type. Further, the cell production can proceed even if the factory controller is down for some time. The factory-level controller comes in only when there is significant departure from planned activities.

Equipment Control Systems

The equipment control system is concerned with monitoring and control of the individual equipment such as CNC machines, AGVs, robots, etc. These controllers, called programmable controllers (PCs), are usually microprocessor-based.

The main objective of the equipment-level controller is to translate commands issued or goals set by the cell controller into specific instructions to the actuators (motors, servos, counters, switches, etc.) of the equipment. For example, a command to an AGV controller could be to move a workpiece from position (x_1, y_1), to position (x_2, y_2). The AGV controller analyzes this command and breaks it down to subcommands such as path selection, collision avoidance and periods of acceleration, deceleration, and steady speed. The AGV controller could also be provided with computing power and intelligence to handle higher-level commands or goals. The assignment to the AGV could be "move the workpiece of type 1 from output buffer of Machine A to input buffer of Machine B as soon as Machine B input buffer is free." Machines A and B and the AGV are both in the same cell. Depending on the communication patterns possible among various controllers, we can have several solutions.

1. The PCs communicate only with the cell controller: In this case, we assume that the cell controller updates its own database when input buffer of Machine B is empty and informs this to the AGV controller. This message waits in the AGV controller queue and gets executed when the AGV is free. The AGV controller has to check the identity of the workpiece residing in the output buffer of Machine A before picking up. Route selection and collision avoidance strategies are all decided by the AGV controller itself. Finally, the AGV controller gives a job-done signal to the cell controller.

2. The PCs communicate among themselves as well as with the cell controller: In this case Machine B controller can notify the AGV controller that its input buffer is free, which initiates the material movement action by the AGV. Alternatively, the AGV controller can poll the Machine B controller, and as soon as the input buffer is free the AGV can complete the rest of the tasks.

In the first case, the control and messaging are strictly hierarchical. In the second case the control decisions to the AGV controller still come from the cell controller, but the executions are fully left to the local controller; i.e., the controller can perform all the messaging functions to execute the decision.

Figure 2.26 depicts the hierarchical control system for a cellular manufacturing plant. We note that the controllers at each level receive commands or goals from the controllers at the level above and execute them. In the process, they pass commands to the controllers at the level below. Also, controllers at each level give feedback to those immediately above. A communication network with standardized communication protocols interconnects all the controllers.

Thus we see that the basic components of a computer control system include: (i) programmable controllers, (ii) local area network with appropriate protocols, and (iii) database management system. All these are glued together by the control system software resident in various controllers. We consider these components in detail in rest of the section.

Programmable Controllers

The programmable controller provides the equipment control and is defined as a digital electronic apparatus with a programmable memory for storing instructions to implement specific functions such as logic, sequencing, timing, counting, and arithmetic to control machines and processes.

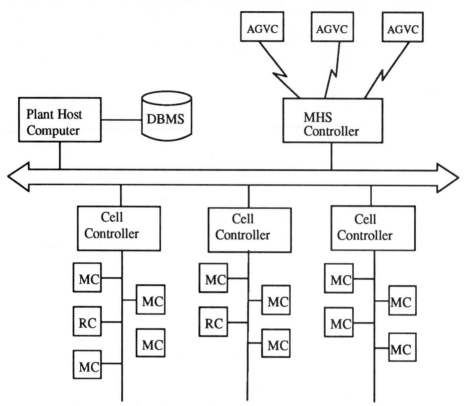

Figure 2.26 Hierarchical control system for an FMS

A programmable controller has primarily two basic units, the central processing unit (CPU) and the input/output (I/O) interface. The CPU has three parts: processor, memory, and power supply. The CPU reads the input data from various sensing devices, executes the stored user program from memory, and sends appropriate output commands to the control devices. This process is repeated on a continuous basis and is called *scanning*. The power supply provides all the voltages necessary for the operation of the controller.

The field devices are connected to the controller through the I/O interface. The purpose of the interface is to condition the input signals received and output signals being sent out. Incoming signals from sensors such as push buttons, limit switches, analog sensors, selector switches, and thumb wheel switches are wired to terminals on the input interface. Devices that would be controlled, such as motor starters, solenoid valves, pilot lights, and position valves, are connected to the terminals of the output interfaces.

There are two basic types of languages commonly encountered in programmable controllers: (a) ladder logic and (b) high-level programming languages. Relay ladder logic forms the basic PC language, while languages similar to Basic, are considered for high-level language implementation.

2.8.2 Factory Communications

In Section 2.8.1 we saw that factory communications enable programmable controllers of factory automation equipment to talk to each other and to the cell and factory-level controllers. This feature is crucial for automated operation of an FMS. A wide range of communication functions among PCs, cell controllers, and supervisory computers is necessary within a factory. These include:

1. Downloading of a program or operational data from the supervisory computer or cell controller to individual programmable controllers.

2. Uploading of production and status information from a PC to the cell controller or the supervisory computer. The production information includes part type currently being worked on, number scheduled, number waiting, due dates, etc. The status information is communicated by each controller and typically is whether the machine is busy, idle or down.

3. Acquisition of production information such as throughput, waiting times, transportation times, machine utilizations, and other performance measures.

4. Maintaining a reliable database by performing multi-sensor integration of the status of equipment, tool wear and usage, fixtures, and raw and semi-finished workpieces.

5. Transfer of real-time data for time-critical operations such as machine tool feedback control, enhanced quality control, monitoring and diagnosis, AGV routing, and part flow control.

Local area networks (LANs) have a major role to play in computer-integrated operations of an automated factory. Factory networks installed are smaller in number than LANs installed for other applications such as banking, E-mail, technical office communications, etc. There are efforts such as the manufacturing automation protocol (MAP) and technical office protocol (TOP) to help facilitate the growth of factory networks.

Currently the programmable devices of various equipment such as robots, conveyors, and machine tools do not talk to each other. The operators are faced with several screens and keyboards in the control room for controlling a miniline. Information from the screen has to be keyed into another. For example, in a typical large establishment, the attendance and work assignment of various employees may be maintained on an IBM machine, work scheduling in every shift done on a DEC machine and a HP machine may be acting as a cell controller. If the cell controller reports a defective machine to the supervisor, then this person has to refer to another machine for rescheduling and a third machine for finding the repair person for the machine. To make each device to talk to the others, they have to be connected via custom-made protocols and point-to-point links. This involves enormous amount of cabling and complex software generation. Such a procedure is both expensive and unreliable.

A number of PC manufacturers also offer custom-made Data Hiways for ease of communications among their own PCs. Thus we have networks such as Allen-Bradley Data Highway, Texas Instruments TIWay, the Gould Modway, the Westinghouse WDPF, and the GE net. It happens that each local network is unique to the supplier and cannot be easily interfaced with one another. Single sourcing has the advantage of compatibility and easy coordination. However, it does not promote competitive environment. The industry becomes captive to the vendor who may try to push his or her own, possibly not the best, solutions at a high price.

To get over these difficulties and to realize fully the potential of computer-aided technologies on the factory floor, there are intense efforts to develop LAN standards. The idea is to use a single broad-band cable for all factory communications traffic. Every device–robot controller, machine tool controller, CMM controller, bar code reader, AGV controller, operator interface–would plug into it and communicate, on demand, with everything else on the cable. Each piece of equipment would have interfaces, which offers plug compatibility with equipment from other vendors. The intent is to develop *open systems*, with publicly standardized architectures so that any vendor can build the computer-control equipment in such a way that it conforms to the standard and hence will communicate with all equipment in the system.

With such an open standard in place, all the computer-controlled equipment in the factory can then communicate with one another, resulting in limitless possibilities. For example, a hierarchical factory-wide manufacturing control system with a database management system would make shop-floor supervision and factory control much easier. Order entry systems could be linked to inventory control and scheduling systems, schedules could be downloaded straight into controllers of equipment, design changes in a particular part could be communicated to all those affected by this change, etc. Thus competitive production is no longer just the application of computers in industry but effective integration of these computer-aided technologies. Communications on the factory floor hold the key for this competitive edge.

Standardization has been a great contributor to success in a variety of areas such as automobiles, traffic control, electricity supply equipment, nuts, bolts, and screws, and also in education systems. Despite a variety of differences, acceptable standards have been achieved across the world in various sectors such as education, communication, manufacturing, etc. One would expect that efforts of standardization on the factory floor in particular and in the computer world in general would be a successful story and standards would soon emerge.

The manufacturing automation protocol initiative of the General Motors Corporation is the most comprehensive proposal to resolve the factory communications issues discussed above. Together with the technical and office protocol covering the associated technical office communications, MAP offers a complete approach to communications in the manufacturing world.

To appreciate the MAP and TOP standards, a background in local area networks is essential. The following section provides an overview of local area communication principles and standards.

2.8.3 Local Area Networks

A computer network is an interconnection of autonomous computers. This means that in a computer network, otherwise independently functioning computers exchange information to achieve a common goal. LANs are a subset of these networks and are distinguished by geographical scope, the data rates, and the application.

LANs are typically confined to a single building or a group of buildings which are close to one another. LANs usually span a distance not greater than 10 km. This feature distinguishes them from wide-area networks. The data rates supported by LANs are between 1 MBps-10 MBps. Optical fiber cables are coming into use for LANs, and these can support bit rates of up to 100 MBps.

In a communication network, data items are transmitted from one point to another by means of electrical signals. An analog signal is a continuously varying electromagnetic wave that may be transmitted over a medium. For example, voice and video are analog signals. A digital sequence is a sequence of voltage pulses that may be transmitted over a wire medium. For instance, binary 1 may represent a constant positive voltage level, and 0 a constant negative voltage level. Digital data can also be converted as analog signals by use of a modem (modulator-demodulator). A codec (coder-decoder) converts a series of binary voltage pulses into analog signals by modulating on a carrier of high frequency.

We define the *bandwidth* of a signal as the range of frequencies contained in the signal. The frequency range of the signal can be shifted from one region of the frequency spectrum to another by modulating the signal on a carrier. A carrier is a sinusoidal signal of much higher frequency than the signal. The process of demodulation involves shifting the frequency content to the basic signal by removing the carrier.

Characteristics of LANs

Four characteristics are important in describing the architecture of any local area network. These allow comparison of one type of network with another. These are:

1. Transmission medium
2. Signaling
3. Network topology
4. Access control methods

1. Transmission Medium: The transmission medium is the physical connection between the nodes on the network. Three media are often used today in local area networks: twisted pair, coaxial cable, and optic fibers.

Twisted Pair: This is a pair of wires twisted together and covered with insulation. This medium is suitable for data communications over limited distances and moderate speeds. It is sensitive to electrical noise, and shielded versions are used to reduce the noise effects. Telephone networks use twisted pairs. These can support up to 24 channels of 4 kHz bandwidth.

Coaxial Cable: A coaxial cable consists of a central conducting copper core surrounded by an insulating material. The insulation is also surrounded by a second conducting layer, which is either a copper wire mesh or solid aluminum sleeve, and finally covered by an outer shield. Coaxial cable is less subject to interference and cross talk than twisted-wire pairs and is able to support data rates of up to 100 MBps. Coaxial cables have been in use for television transmission for many years. This type of cable is also suitable for LAN applications.

There are two types of coaxial cable in common use: 50 ohm and 75 ohm. The 50 ohm cable is used for digital transmission only, whereas the 75 ohm cable is used for both analog and digital transmission. The factory-floor networks use 75 ohm coaxial cable running 5 MB or 10 MB data rates.

Fiber Optic Links: Optical fibers can be used to carry data signals in the form of modulated light beams. An optical fiber consists of an extremely thin cylinder of glass, called the core, surrounded by a concentric layer of glass, known as cladding. Many such fibers are bound into a cable, with all of the fibers surrounded by a protective sheath.

Fiber optics are now becoming widely used in long-haul communications. This method is often considered to be the transmission medium for LANs because of high transmission speeds, large bandwidth, light weight, small size, and immunity from electromagnetic interference. Transmission rates of up to 600 MBps are routinely employed in commercial systems.

2. Signaling Methods: Signaling is the act of propagating the signal through a transmission medium. The three major categories include baseband, broadband, and carrier band.

Baseband: With baseband transmission, data signals are carried over the physical communication medium as discrete pulses that are either electrical or light. This form of transmission provides digital end-to-end signaling, which eliminates the need for a modem. All three media discussed above can carry out baseband transmission. A baseband system is bi-directional; i.e., the signal inserted at any point propagates in both directions.

With baseband transmission, the entire channel capacity is used to transmit a single data channel. Multiple devices attached to a network using baseband transmission share the communication channel by means of time-division multiplexing (TDM). With TDM, devices take turns transmitting; only one device transmits at a time. In LANs, a variety of access control methods are used to determine which station will gain next access to the transmission medium.

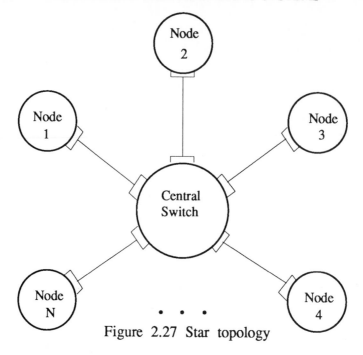

Figure 2.27 Star topology

Broadband: Broadband transmission is widely used in LANs with high bandwidth channels and typically employs analog transmission. The signal is modulated on a carrier and is transmitted on the channel. The frequency spectrum of the medium exceeds that of a single signal and hence it is divided into a number of channels. Each channel can support a different kind of traffic such as data, video text, and voice. This is accomplished by frequency-division multiplexing (FDM) where each signal is modulated onto a different widely separated carrier frequency and transmitted by a separate channel.

Carrier Band: In a carrier band transmission, the entire bandwidth of the medium is used as a single channel. As with broadband, here also analog signaling is used; i.e., the signal is modulated on a carrier and is then transmitted. Carrier-band signaling is also called a single channel broadband.

3. Network Topologies: The topology of a network concerns the way devices are connected by the communication links. The topology determines the data paths that may exist between any pair of stations. Three LAN topologies are very common. They are: star, ring, and bus. These are shown in Figures 2.27, 2.28, and 2.29, respectively.

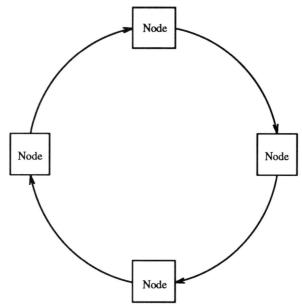

Figure 2.28 Ring topology

Star: In a star configuration, each device (terminal, computer, pro-grammable controller) is connected to a central switch by a point-to-point

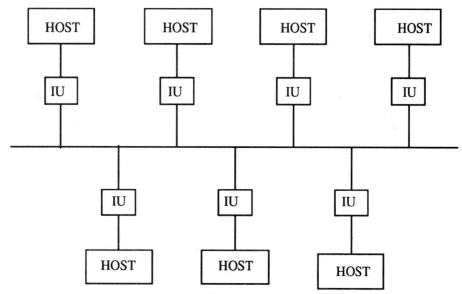

Figure 2.29 Global bus architecture

link. The devices on the network can communicate with one another but only through the common node. The central switch should be up and working for any communication to take place.

Ring: Ring networks use coaxial cable or twisted pair as a transmission medium. The ring network is characterized by a sequence of point-to-point links closing to form a loop. All messages travel on a fixed route and are received by all stations. As with bus topology, the address in the message helps each station to determine whether to accept or reject the message. Each station acts as a repeater and retransmits the message at its original strength.

Bus: In a bus arrangement, all stations are directly connected to a common communication channel. A device first gains access to the channel and transmits in a broadcast mode. This is received by all the devices on the network. Based on the address contained in the message, the station accepts the message or ignores it.

4. Access Control Methods: We have seen earlier that several nodes are connected to a single channel and thus there is contention among nodes to access the channel. Accessing methods determine the node that gains access to the channel to transmit the message. Many access methods have been devised and implemented on LANs. The various accessing methods can be categorized as follows:

Random Control: Carrier Sense Multiple Access with Collision Detection (CSMA/CD), Slotted Ring.

Distributed Control: Token passing: (token ring and token bus), Carrier Sense Multiple Access with Collision Avoidance (CSMA/CA)

Centralized Control: Polling, Time Division Multiple Access (TDMA).

Of these techniques, CSMA/CD, token ring, and token bus are of practical importance. They also form the basis for the IEEE standards for local area networking. CSMA/CD is the protocol used by Ethernet and is also the TOP specification. IEEE 802.3 standard deals with this protocol. Token ring is the basis for IBM's LAN architecture. IEEE 802.5 standard deals with token ring protocol. The MAP network is based on the broadband token bus architecture. Also, IEEE 802.4 standard deals with token bus architecture. We describe these three techniques below.

Token Ring: With ring networks, the most commonly used access method is token passing, which involves the passing of a token from one station to the next. A token is a bit structure that can exist in two states: busy or idle. Typically, a token is a message consisting of 8 bits with all bits equal to 1. Bit stuffing is used to prevent this pattern from occurring in the data.

A station wishing to transmit waits until it detects an idle token pass by and then seizes it. It then transmits the message, marks the token busy, and appends the token to the message. The message, with the attached busy token, circulates around the ring, passing from station to station. Each station copies the message as it comes past. When the message reaches the station that originally sent it, the station changes the token back to free token and removes the message. The free token circulates around the ring until another station wishes to transmit.

Once the station has captured a free token and thus gained access to the use of the ring, there are two types of operation: exhaustive service and nonexhaustive service. In the case of exhaustive service, the station is allowed to transmit all the messages in its buffer. In the case of nonexhaustive service, the station is allowed to transmit only for a specified period.

Token Bus: In a token bus, the stations have a physical bus topology but a logical ring topology. Here, all stations are attached to the transmission medium in a linear sequence. The token is passed into the logical ring sequence, which can be changed under program control. If a system of priorities has to be established, the logical ring can include some nodes more than once. Also, some stations could be receive-only stations; i.e., they listen but cannot transmit.

Token passing systems, both ring and bus, need a controlling station to monitor stations for failure and to generate the token whenever it is lost after a time-out period. This operation is complex and involves heavy overhead.

CSMA/CD: This method has been in use for a number of years and is the most commonly used access method for LANs that employ a bus topology. The CSMA/CD is called a random control technique in the sense that there is no scheduled or predictable time for any station to transmit. Station transmissions occur randomly.

Under CSMA/CD, a station before transmitting first listens to the transmission medium to determine whether another station is currently transmitting. If the transmission medium is quiet, then the station sends the message. The term *carrier sense* indicates that the station listens before it transmits. When a message is transmitted, it travels to all other stations on the network. As the message arrives, each receiving station examines the address of the message. The station processes the message only if it is addressed to it. Because of propagation time delays, it is possible that a collision occurs because two stations can transmit almost simultaneously. The transmission gets garbled and all receiving stations ignore this transmission. Transmitting stations stop transmission as soon as they detect a collision. Each transmitting station attempts retransmission, after waiting for a random amount of time. This time is determined by generating a random number.

The CSMA/CD transmission method is very effective for light traffic environments. Message delivery is very fast. However, under heavy traffic loads, the number of collisions increases and performance in terms of message delay deteriorates because of increased retransmissions.

The CSMA/CD method underlies many of the networks used for office applications. Three prime examples of networks using this protocol are the IEEE 802.3 standard, the technical office protocol (TOP network), and the Ethernet.

2.8.4 Factory Networks

In the factory automation context, the LAN should be reliable, meet stringent specifications on message delivery times, and should be able to operate in hostile environments subject to electromagnetic interference, dust, high temperatures, and voltage fluctuations. One has to choose the medium, topology, and access method so that the reliability and the real-time requirements are met. Media currently used include twisted pair and coaxial cable. Twisted pair is suited for small networks but has problems from electromagnetic interference.

Broadband currently appears to be the technology best suited for the factory environments. Its multichannel capability gives the user a great deal of flexibility. One channel can be used for machine control, another for energy management, a third for video, and so on. A broadband channel is capable of running at data rates of 50 Mbits/s. Coaxial cable is easily installed. Cable television (CATV) components are low cost, easily available, highly reliable, and relatively less susceptible to electromagnetic interference.

Fiber-optic cable is a medium of the future because of light weight, small size, and high bandwidth (up to 600 Mbits/s). It is immune to electromagnetic interference. Currently, however, it is more expensive than coaxial cable.

Access methods represent probably the most controversial area in industrial local networks. One advantage of random access schemes such as CSMA/CD is their ready availability. Ethernet is proven, readily available, and has been installed in thousands of manufacturing sites. Token-passing products are becoming available only recently, after the appearance of the General Motors-sponsored manufacturing automation protocol.

Token-passing access methods have certain characteristics that make them eminently suited to the factory environment.

(i) Token-passing methods ensure that each message can get through in a given time period. Thus the system is more deterministic than CSMA/CD. Real-time traffic can be handled with high reliability. However, with CSMA/CD the access time is random rather than deterministic because of the finite probability of collision and the consequent back-off for retransmission. Thus it is impossible to quote guaranteed minimum response time for messages. This makes CSMA/CD unsuitable for real-time applications.

(ii) Token-passing methods have the same performance characteristics under both light and heavy traffic conditions. However, in CSMA/CD, there is wasted bandwidth because of the time spent in retransmission due to collisions. The CSMA/CD performance is better with light traffic than heavy traffic.

(iii) The token-passing method is prone to two serious error conditions: (a) failure to alter the busy token to idle token by the sending station after the transmission is complete and (b) loss of a token. A token monitor is to be created to handle these two situations.

(iv) In token passing, priorities can be given to critical transmissions, and the access time a station can have each time it seizes a token can be changed. CSMA/CD, on the other hand, is a fair algorithm giving equal opportunity for every one to transmit.

Multinetwork Solution

The solution to the communications problem in a factory cannot be one omnibus data communications network but a hierarchical one. Here we consider a two-level network.

(i) **Level-1 Network**: This network interconnects various lower-level networks and supervisory computers into a plant-wide communication system. This reduces the complexity of the network, increases reliability, makes the network easily expandable, and reduces the cabling requirements. This network should be fairly high speed (10–50 Mbits/s), reliable, and should be able to handle peak loads without performance degradation. Most level-1 networks are custom-built broadband CATV-type coaxial cable networks. Many new products are appearing on the market in response to the General Motors push for a factory network standard.

(ii) **Level-2 Network**: The level-2 networks tie together several programmable controllers possibly into a machine cell. Operations in real-time are very important in this level. Also, these networks have to be low priced because these are more liable to change in a reorganization than level-1 networks.

Generally, any vendor who supplies the shop-floor equipment could supply a proprietary level-2 network. Several vendors including Allen-Bradley, Gould, IBM, DEC, and TI supply these networks. However, interconnecting these level-2 networks may pose problems if the standards are not followed.

2.8.5 Open Systems Interconnection Model

Local area networks, in most of the applications, have to support a wide variety of devices and this can present compatibility problems in terms of both hardware and software. To facilitate this compatibility, efforts are underway to develop a network architecture defining protocols, message formats, and standards to which all equipment must conform. Such an architecture provides coordination between intelligent machines and helps realize the advantages of networking.

There are a number of standards in the LAN community. These are the products of organizations such as the Institute of Electrical and Electronics Engineers (IEEE), the International Standards Organization (ISO), and the American National Standards Institute (ANSI). The second source of LAN standards consists mainly of large corporations whose products are interconnected by company standard protocols. Such examples include International Business Machines (IBM) and Digital Equipment Corporation (DEC), and many others.

The most widely referenced standard for local area networks is the ISO model for Open Systems Interconnection (OSI). Work on OSI standard was initiated by ISO and CCITT (Consultative Committee on International Telegraphy and Telephony). The OSI reference model defines seven layers of protocols, the services provided by each layer, and the functions performed by each layer. This model is not an implementation specification but a reference framework for the development of protocol specifications and standards.

The OSI seven-layered model is shown in Figure 2.30. Thus for a user's application program on one computer to communicate through the network with a program on another computer, the communication can be conceptualized as operating down through these seven layers on one side down and up through the layers on the other side. In the OSI model, each layer is associated with one device function as if it were connected to the corresponding layer on the second device. In actual practice, communication is through the physical link.

Each layer therefore contains rules appropriate to that layer itself and also about its interface with the layers immediately above and below it, if it is an intermediate layer. The advantage of such an approach is that

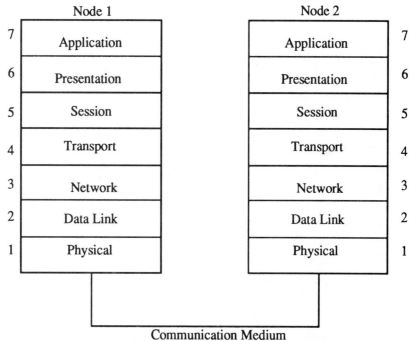

Communication Medium

Figure 2.30 OSI seven-layered architecture

each layer can be considered independently of the other as long as the interfaces remain the same.

Here we provide a formal description of the seven layers of the OSI reference model.

1. Physical Layer: The physical layer provides the direct mechanical and electrical connection between the computer system and the network nodes. Thus it is a means of physical connection to the cable and concerns transmission of raw data over the cable. The functions include the handling of signaling issues and aspects of cable connectors and other components. Examples include broadband cable specification for MAP, specifications for connectors such as the widely used RS232-25 per connector, and collision detection in CSMA/CD.

At the bottom of the physical layer is the modem, the broadband, carrier-band, or other modulation techniques that put signals on the network. The physical layer makes and breaks the connection with the cable medium.

2. Data Link Layer: This layer establishes and maintains a communication path between nodes of the network. It is also concerned with error-free transmission of frames of data. The data link layer establishes connections upon request by the network layer and disconnects them the same way. In the IEEE 802 architecture the data link layer is divided into two sublayers: logical link control (LLC) and media access control (MAC).

LLC sublayer is responsible for medium-independent data link functions. There are two important types of LLC: (i) Connectionless service wherein a frame of data is sent off into the LAN with full address information. No logical connection is established between sending and receiving stations, and each data unit is processed independently. (ii) Connection-oriented service wherein a virtual circuit or connection is established before data are sent and the connection must be maintained while the operation proceeds, and the connection is terminated when the operation ends.

The MAC sublayer is concerned with the method of controlling the sharing of transmission medium among different devices. Examples include token passing or CSMA/CD or polling.

3. Network Layer: The network layer is concerned with routing data from one network node to another. It has the responsibility of ensuring that information is transferred correctly across the network. It involves setting up and maintaining the links necessary; X.25 is a good example of such a protocol.

The network layer should also provide the ability to link all open networks together into a global network. It has the responsibility to route the data between networks and, in the process, to convert connectionless and connection-oriented communications.

4. Transport Layer: One way to split the OSI model is into the bottom four layers, which are concerned with the communications aspects of the data exchange, and the layers five to seven, which are concerned with the applications that will be available to the user.

The transport layer is responsible for providing data transfer between two users at an agreed level of quality. When a connection is established between two users, the transport layer is responsible for selecting a particular class of service to be used, for monitoring transmission to ensure that appropriate service quality is maintained, and for notifying the users if it is not.

One example of a function of transport layer is multiplexing. The transport layer can decide to multiplex transport connections either upwards from a single network connection to several transport connections or downwards, splitting a single transport connection among many network connections.

5. Session Layer: The session layer uses the services provided by the layer below to establish how communication between two users may be initiated, managed, and coordinated and then ended. This layer also determines which of the three modes of interaction the communication may take: simplex, half-duplex, or duplex. Another important service the layer offers is synchronization and checkpointing to keep the two end devices in step with each other.

6. Presentation Layer: Information can be represented in a number of different ways. The presentation layer is responsible for the presentation of information in a way that is meaningful to the network users. This may include character code translation, data conversion, or data compression and expansion.

7. Application Layer: This is the layer that is at the top of the stack. Its primary function is to provide the mechanisms and interfaces that enable an end user to communicate within the network environment. Functions may include logging in, checking the password, requesting file, transferring files, and so on.

2.8.6 Network to Network Interconnections

LANs allow a group of computer-controlled devices or computer users to communicate with one another and to share data. We have seen that multiple networks, i.e., networks of different topology following different access methods and using different transmission media, can exist in a large system such as a factory. For example, a token-bus organization following MAP standard may be used for real-time factory floor control and a CSMA/CD based TOP standard may be used in the design section. It is necessary that data and information be transferred between them. Thus internetworking LANs is an important issue.

There are three interconnection facilities: bridge, router, and gateway. Each of these is suitable in a particular situation, and Table 2.8 summarizes this information.

Bridges: A bridge interconnects physically distinct networks by being a common station that belongs to two or more networks simultaneously. It acts as a store-and-forward switch, receiving messages from elements of one network, checking the address, and forwarding it to a station in another network. A bridge interconnection can be used for networks using different protocols in the physical level and the same protocol at the data link level (see Figure 2.31). For example, a bridge can interconnect carrier-band segments to a broadband backbone and can be used to connect between broadband channels.

Routers: A router is a device that interconnects two physically distinct LANs by implementing a network layer protocol (see Figure 2.32). The networks may differ, however, at the data link and physical layers. Thus, for example, a router could be used on Ethernet with an IBM token ring network. When a router is used to interconnect networks, it functions much like an intermediate node in a wide-area network. Suppose a cell controller of manufacturing cell 1 wants to send a message to the cell

Table 2.8 Network interconnection methods

Interconnection device	Protocols		
	Physical layer	Data link layer	Network layer
Bridge	Different	Same	Same
Router	Different	Different	Same
Gateway	Different	Different	Different

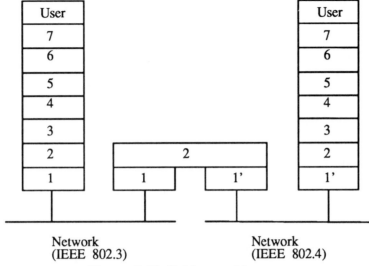

Figure 2.31 Bridge architecture

controller of cell 2, the controllers, being connected to two different networks. With a router, cell controller 1 sends the message to router and router forwards it to the cell controller 2 (see Figure 2.34).

Gateways: The third and most complex method is the gateway. A gateway is used to interconnect networks with different architectures, when the seven layers of the OSI model are different. Since conversion must be provided for protocols at every level, designing a general gateway is extremely complex (see Figure 2.33).

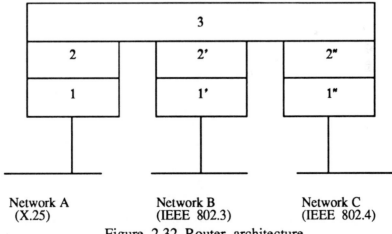

Figure 2.32 Router architecture

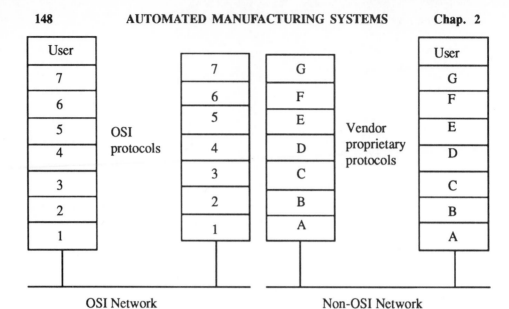

Figure 2.33 Gateway architecture

2.8.7 Manufacturing Automation Protocol

The most significant development in factory communications is the manufacturing automation protocol sponsored by General Motors. Another significant effort is the technical office protocol sponsored by the Boeing Company. MAP is not a proprietary network but an open network combining several standards into a system specification. MAP is aimed at providing a multivendor network for level-1 factory communications. As we saw earlier, level 2 can be a proprietary network but MAP aims at providing multivendor environment even here. Figure 2.34 shows a factory communication architecture using MAP.

The technology of MAP consists of a broadband token bus with coaxial cable as the backbone medium following unacknowledged connectionless service. MAP follows the OSI reference model as the basis for its architecture. As discussed earlier, the OSI model provides guidelines within which specific standards and protocols must fit. A wide range of protocols and features can be selected for any of the seven layers. This means that two different vendors could produce products that follow OSI architecture, yet they could be incompatible because they do not share common protocols and features. In MAP, this choice is limited and protocols and features are rigorously defined to ensure compatibility. In MAP, the seven layers are specified as follows.

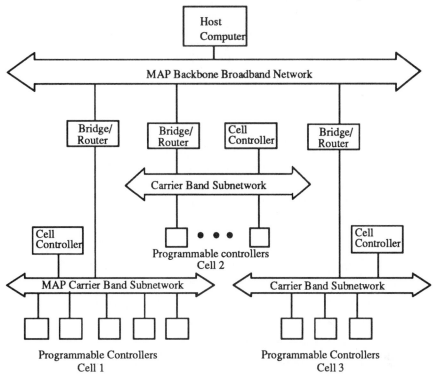

Figure 2.34 Factory communications using MAP

1. Physical Layer: A bus topology using broadband transmission techniques is chosen as MAP standard. IEEE 802.4 broadband standard is followed. This choice allows for the use of components and techniques developed over many years in the CATV. MAP also supports single channel carrier-band transmission using coaxial cable. The modulation technique is phase-coherent frequency modulation at 5 MBps.

2. Data-Link Layer: Token passing is used as the media access method as defined in IEEE 802.4. The logical link layer of the data-link layer follows the IEEE 802.2 standard. MAP specifies connectionless service involving communication using datagrams.

A bridge connects MAP backbone with a carrier-band subnetwork or connects any two MAP networks and operates at the data-link layer.

3. Network Layer: The primary responsibility of this layer is to route messages from one station to another, whether in a single network or across interconnected networks. MAP routing is based on router nodes. The sending station forwards the message to the nearest router, which then forwards it to another route node or to the destination station.

4. Transport Layer: This is an important layer in MAP. The services provided by this layer can be divided into two categories: data transfer and connection management. Connection management services include establishing a connection, terminating a connection, providing status information to the user about the connection, and disconnection. Data transfer services provide normal data transfer and expedited data transfer. Flow control, multiplexing, and error detection and recovery are also activities of this layer.

5. Session Layer: The MAP specifications support full-duplex communication. This layer provides the management of data transfer being carried out by the transport layer. International Standard IS 8327 may be followed here.

6. Presentation Layer: MAP treats this layer as null and bypasses it. It is therefore necessary for all equipment using MAP to employ either binary data or ASCII syntax.

7. Application Layer: The application layer defines the interface through which an end user, either a person or an application program, accesses and uses the network services. This is done through a collection of network utilities and procedure libraries. The MAP specification supports the use of the file transfer, access, and management (FTAM) protocol, the common application service elements (CASE) protocol, the manufacturing message forward standard (MMFS), and the directory services protocol.

MAP on Carrier Band

In carrier band, all the nodes of the network transmit and receive at the same frequency. They follow the token-passing access method. It is used when real-time response is critical. The carrier band MAP is similar to the Instrument Society of America's Proway protocol and the IEEE 802 standards. The need for Mini-MAP or carrier band MAP is felt because of the limitations of the full seven-layer MAP, in many shop-floor control and monitoring situations. The reasons are:

(i) High Cost of Connection: The use of full-blown MAP would be an overkill when connecting a smart sensor, PLC, or even a robot controller to the network. For example, it would never be necessary for plant sensors to pass their information to a corporate planning computer in another plant. To implement full MAP on broadband requires significant processing power and memory and high-cost modems.

(ii) Performance Degradation: If a plant has a large number of devices involving enormous amounts of data, then performance limitations will manifest in low data rates, long connection establishment times, and protocol overheads.

MAP on carrier band eliminates some communication layers to save execution time within a station.

Field Bus

When networking a smart or intelligent plant actuator or sensor to a network, both broadband and carrier band MAP are perceived as complex. Field bus, which coexists with MAP, provides low-cost, high-performance interfacing for sensors or actuators and low-complexity PLC controlled devices. The specifications are still evolving.

2.8.8 Database Management System

In an automated manufactured system environment, material flow integration and information integration have a multiplicative effect on the system performance. The key to integration is provided by the database management system (DBMS), which is a collection of programs and procedures responsible for the collection, storage, retrieval, and dissemination of information of various kinds.

Database technology has primarily been used in manufacturing for business activities such as inventory control, accounting, payrolls, etc. Only recently have databases been used in manufacturing management and their potential in performance enhancement been recognized.

DBMS is also the key element of computer integrated manufacturing (CIM). As shown in Figure 2.35, the DBMS represents the heart of the whole system, supplying each activity with the requested data and providing a common data storage and retrieval structure. Data is really the glue that binds each activity to form an integrated whole.

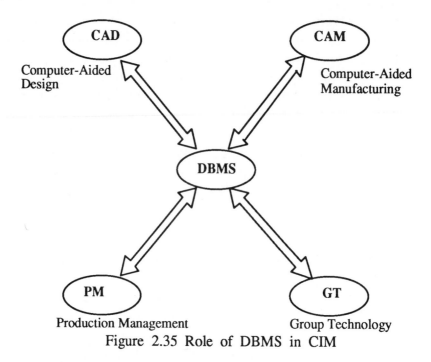

Figure 2.35 Role of DBMS in CIM

A typical CIM database has a hierarchical structure as shown in Figure 2.36. The CIM database is logically and/or physically decomposed into three databases.

1. CAD Database: Contains design data to record geometric models,

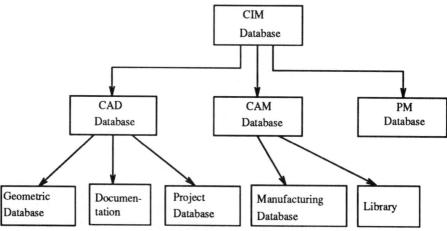

Figure 2.36 Hierarchical structure of CIM database

bills of materials, drawings, and a group technology number for each product series.

2. CAM Database: This contains data about how to manufacture a product or a part. It is composed of a manufacturing database and a library. The former contains the process plans or route sheets, the NC programs, the machine tools, the tools, and the material handling equipment.

3. PM Database: This contains administrative data about the company products, personnel, customers, suppliers, status of inventories, equipment and processes, manufacturing orders, master schedule, workshop loads, etc.

The important role of the DBMS is best illustrated by the discussion in Section 2.7 on the automated part flow in an FMS. We list below the items of data required to be accessed, to ensure smooth flow of workpieces.

1. Route sheets of various part types. Each route sheet contains information about the fixture type, operations to be performed, machines and inspection stations to be visited, tools and time required for each operation, the machine tools capable of performing these operations, etc.

2. Part programs for all part types.

3. Updated information regarding (i) status of all machine tools, (ii) status of all AGVs, robots, and other MHS equipment, (iii) tool locations and tool lives, (iv) fixture locations and availability, and (v) availability of local/central buffers.

4. Sequencing and scheduling information about jobs, i.e., master production schedule.

Database Organization

The two broad database organizations are centralized and distributed. Conceptually, the idea of a central database for all the information governing the activities of an AMS is very appealing. However, in practice, it is unrealistic to have a single monolithic database because of the huge mass of data. The other approach is a distributed scheme, where each department or center maintains control over its own data, but essential data is passed among individual databases requiring that particular data. A distributed approach is also important because of the heterogeneous nature of the manufacturing environment. An effective distributed database requires an information network (LAN, for example) that allows transparent access to data, no matter where it resides. As a result, each user or device is plugged into what appears to be one single logical database even though it is distributed over many physical locations. Though networking is an important factor in an integrated environment, only the DBMS facilitates to provide useful information in the right format to the individual nodes.

Data organization or the manner in which the data is stored in the database is the key to the effectiveness of a DBMS. Over the years, a number of schemes have evolved, and three schemes have emerged as the important ones. These are hierarchical, network, and relational.

In the hierarchical model, data files are arranged in a tree-like structure, which facilitates searches along branch lines. Starting at the root of the tree, each file has one-to-many relationships to its branches; a parent file can have several children but a child file can only have a single parent. A good example of such an organization is a bill of materials (BOM) or an indented parts list, in which each product is composed of assemblies, which are in turn composed of subassemblies and/or component parts. CODASYL is a popular hierarchical database standard. The network model is similar to the hierarchical structure with the extension that any record type or file can be related to any other record type or file. Thus the relationship is many-to-many as opposed to the one-to-many in the hierarchical model. The relational model is currently the most popular because it is relatively easy to design and modify. It is more flexible than the previous two models. This scheme enables many changes to data links (or relations) as the database increases in size and complexity. In other words, it enables data structure changes without changing the subschemes or application programs. ORACLE is a well-known relational DBMS scheme.

Since a factory addresses a multitude of different disciplines, no single model is uniformly suited for all the applications.

In summary, it may be said that DBMS is a very important component of any manufacturing enterprise, and its management can contribute a great deal to the effective operation of the enterprise.

PROBLEMS

1. In the FMS flowchart of Figure 2.22, write down for each block the messages that will be transmitted, assuming a 3-level control system (factory level, cell level, and equipment level) and a centralized database organization.
2. Discuss the similarities and differences in the control system architectures for cellular layouts and functional layouts.

2.9 BIBLIOGRAPHIC NOTES AND BIBLIOGRAPHY

Several books appeared on the market that essentially deal with descriptions of the advanced manufacturing technologies. The books by Ranky [1983,1986], Hartley [1984], Groover and Zimmers [1985], Boothroyd, Poli, and Murch [1982], Redford and Lo [1986], Bonetto [1988], Talavage and Hannam [1988], and Groover [1989] provide descriptions of the NC machine, material handling, robotic, and FMS technologies. Groover [1989] and Talavage and Hannam [1988] introduce modeling tools to the reader. The books on CAD/CAM and CIM of Rembold *et al* [1985], Besant and Lui [1986], and Weatherall [1987] provide adequate descriptions of computer-aided technologies as relevant to manufacturing.

Several books appeared that deal with robotics. Indeed, it is now a very mature area of research. Some books on robotics include those by Nof [1985], Fu *et al* [1987], Koren [1987], and Wolovich [1987].

Several handbooks appeared with experts contributing articles on technologies, techniques, and case studies. Such books include the *Manufacturing High Technology Handbook* by Tijunelis and McKee [1987], FMS handbook by Charles Draper Laboratory [1983], the Prentice-Hall illustrated handbook by Fuchs [1988], the CIM handbook by Teicholz and Orr [1987], and the production handbook by White [1987]. Also, the SME series on automated assembly, edited by Lane and Stranaham [1986], is a good addition to the subject.

History of manufacturing is a very fascinating one. Section 2.1.1 of this text provided an overview. All the books and handbooks deal with this to a small or large extent. The *Handbook of Industrial Engineering* [Salvendy, 1982] has articles dealing with the history of manufacturing. Hatvany [1983] surveys all the FMS factories around the world. The two reports by Ingersoll Engineers [1984,1985] describe technologies as well as survey the advances made in this area worldwide. The description of product cycle and various types of automation is standard material. A more comprehensive discussion on economies of scale and scope is contained in the articles of Gold [1981], Goldhar and Jelinek [1983], and Talaysum *et al* [1986].

A discussion on performance measures can be found in the books by Groover [1989], Mather [1988], Schonberger [1982,1987], Vollmann *et al* [1988], Browne *et al* [1988], and Hayes *et al* [1988]. These books were written with a different focus but have interesting material on how to run automated manufacturing plants. The paper by Kanth and Viswanadham

[1989] examines the issue of reliability of AMSs. In Section 2.4 we concentrated only on management of CNCs and CMMs and their role in AMSs. All the books mentioned above and cited in the bibliography deal with this topic. Our presentation in Sections 2.3 and 2.4 is distinct and is oriented toward management of resources to obtain high performance. Scheduling is an important and vast subject in the area of manufacturing systems. We have only given a brief overview in this text. For recent work on scheduling multi-machine, multi-part type manufacturing systems, see the papers by Perkins and Kumar [1989], Kumar and Seidman [1990], and Lu and Kumar [1991].

Material handling is a vast subject. Section 2.5 presented a discussion on three commonly used handling devices: conveyors, robots, and AGVs. Hammond [1986] and the Prentice-Hall handbook by Fuchs [1988] provide a good survey on AGV technologies. The papers by Blair [1982], Egbelu and Tanchoco [1983,1984], Davis [1986], and Gaskins and Tanchoco [1987] deal with modeling, dispatching rules, and performance evaluation via simulation of AGV systems. The papers by Maxwell *et al* [1981,1982] describe methods of analysis of MHSs. Muth and White [1979] provide an excellent survey on modeling of conveyor systems.

Layout is an important aspect of AMSs. Gallagher and Knight [1986] provide a good introduction to GT methods. The papers by Kusiak [1985] and Kusiak and Heragu [1987a,1987b] survey the state-of-the-art in this area. Sinha and Hollier [1984] and Wemmerlov and Hyer [1987] examine the scheduling and cell formation issues in cellular manufacturing systems. Solberg and Nof [1980] and Nof, Barash, and Solberg [1979] bring out the issue of performance analysis of various layouts and examine the problem of flow control.

Section 2.7 on FMSs describes the architecture, deadlocks, and other performance issues as well as flexible assembly systems. The papers by Viswanadham *et al* [1990] and Vollman *et al* [1988] formed the basis for this section. Flexibility is an important issue. Our sources on this subject include the articles by Browne *et al* [1984], and Chatterjee *et al* [1984]. Deadlock issues are common to both computer systems and AMSs. Our sources include Coffman *et al* [1971], Peterson and Silberschatz [1985], Viswanadham *et al* [1990], and Vollman *et al* [1988].

The section on computer control systems is an important one. Recent advances in this area have been in defining architectures for computer control, factory communication standards, and DBMS. The papers by McClean, Bloom, and Hopp [1982] and Simpson, Hocken, and Albus

[1982] describe a hierarchical architecture for AMS control. The book by O'Grady [1986] is a good introductory text on this subject.

There are several books dealing with MAP/TOP communication standards; for example, the ones by Hollingum [1986], Jones [1988], and Dwyer and Ioannou [1987]. This is an important subject. Good textbooks on local networks include the ones by Fortier [1989], Hammond and O'Reilly [1986], Hutchison [1988], and Stallings [1984]. DBMS issues are discussed in Beeby [1983], Blackburn *et al* [1983], Furlani *et al* [1989], Vernadat [1984], and in the article that appeared in *American Machinist and Automated Manufacturing* [1987].

BIBLIOGRAPHY

1. **American Machinist and Automated Manufacturing** [1987]. Database Management: Gateway to CIM — A Special Report, *American Machinist and Automated Manufacturing*, October 1987, pp. 81–88.

2. **Beeby, W.D.** [1983]. The Heart of Integration: A Sound Database, *IEEE Spectrum*, Vol. 20, No. 5, May 1983, pp. 44–48.

3. **Besant, C.B., and C.W.K. Lui** [1986]. *Computer-Aided Design and Manufacture*, 3rd edition, Ellis Horwood Ltd., Chichester, West Sussex, UK.

4. **Blackburn, C.L., O.O. Storoasli, and R.E. Fultron** [1983]. The Role and Application of Database Management in Integrated Computer-Aided Design, *Journal of Aircraft*, Vol. 20, No. 8, pp. 717–725.

5. **Blair, E.L.,** [1982]. An Experimental Investigation of Material Handling in Flexible Manufacturing Using Computer Simulation, *Proceedings of 1982 Winter Simulation Conference*, pp. 513–520.

6. **Bonetto, R.** [1988]. *Flexible Manufacturing Systems in Practice*, North Oxford Academic Publishers Ltd., London.

7. **Boothroyd, G., C. Poli, and L.E. Murch** [1982]. *Automatic Assembly*, Marcel Dekker.

8. **Browne, J., D. Dubois, K. Rathmill, S. Sethi, and K.E. Stecke** [1984]. Classification of Flexible Manufacturing Systems, *The FMS Magazine*, pp. 114–117.

9. **Browne, J., J. Harhen, and J. Shivnan** [1988]. *Production Management Systems: A CIM Perspective*, Addison-Wesley, Workingham, UK.

10. **Charles Stark Draper Laboratory** [1983]. *Flexible Manufacturing Systems Handbook*, Volumes I-III, Available from US Department of Commerce, NTIS, Springfield, Virginia.

11. **Chatterjee, A., M.A. Cohen, W.L. Maxwell, and L.W. Miller** [1984]. Manufacturing Flexibility: Models and Measurements, *Proceedings of the First ORSA/TIMS Conference on FMS*, pp. 49–64.

12. **Coffman, Jr., E.G., M.J. Elphick, and A. Shoshani** [1971]. System Deadlocks, *ACM Computing Surveys*, Vol. 3, No. 2, June 1971, pp. 67–78.

13. **Davis A. Deborah** [1986]. Modeling AGV Systems, *Proceedings of the 1986 Winter Simulation Conference*, pp. 568–573.

14. **Dwyer, J., and A. Ioannou** [1987]. *MAP and TOP Advanced Manufacturing Communications*, Kogan Page Ltd., London.

15. **Egbelu, P.J., and J.M.A. Tanchoco** [1983]. Designing the Operations of Automated Guided Vehicle System Using AGVSIM, *Proceedings of the Second International Conference on AGV Systems*, pp. 21–29.

16. **Egbelu, P.J., and J.M.A. Tanchoco** [1984]. Characterization of Automated Guided Vehicle Dispatching Rules, *International Journal of Production Research*, Vol. 22, No. 3, pp. 359–374.

17. **Fortier, Paul J.** [1989]. *Handbook of LAN Technology*, Intertext Publications, McGraw-Hill, New York.

18. **Fu, K.S., R.C. Gonzalez, and C.S.G. Lee** [1987]. *Robotics*, McGraw-Hill, Singapore.

19. **Fuchs, J.H. (Ed.)** [1988]. *The Prentice-Hall Illustrated Handbook of Advanced Manufacturing Methods*, Prentice-Hall, Englewood Cliffs, New Jersey.

20. **Furlani, C.M., D. Libes, E.J. Barkmeyer, and M.J. Mitchell** [1989]. Distributed Databases on the Factory Floor, in *Computerization and Networking of Materials Databases*, (Eds.) Glazman, J.S., and J.R. Rumble, Jr., American Society for Testing and Materials, Philadelphia, pp. 126–134.

21. **Gallagher, C.C., and W.A. Knight** [1986]. *Group Technology Production Methods in Manufacture*, Ellis Horwood Ltd., Chichester, UK.

22. **Gaskins, R.J., and J.M.A. Tanchoco** [1987]. Flow Path Design for AGV System, *International Journal of Production Research*, Vol. 25, No. 5, pp. 667–676.

23. **Gold, Bela** [1981]. Changing Perspectives on Size, Scale, and Returns: An Interpretive Survey, *Journal of Economic Literature*, Vol. XIX, pp. 6–33.

24. **Goldhar, J.D., and M. Jelinek** [1983]. Plan for Economies of Scope, *Harvard Business Review*, Nov–Dec 1983, pp. 141–148.

25. **Groover, M.P.** [1989]. *Automation, Production Systems, and Computer-Integrated Manufacturing*, Prentice-Hall of India, New Delhi.

26. **Groover, M.P., and E.W. Zimmers, Jr.** [1985]. *CAD/CAM: Computer-*

Aided Design and Manufacturing, Prentice-Hall of India, New Delhi.

27. **Hammond, G.** [1986]. *AGVs at Work, Automated Guided Vehicle Systems*, IFS (Publications) Ltd., Bedford, UK.

28. **Hammond, J.L., and P.J.P. O'Reilly** [1986]. *Performance Analysis of Local Computer Networks*, Addison-Wesley, Reading, Massachusetts.

29. **Hartley, J.** [1984]. *FMS at Work*, IFS (Publications) Ltd., Bedford, UK.

30. **Hatvany, J. (Ed.)** [1983]. *World Survey on CAM*, Butterworths, Seven Oaks, UK.

31. **Hayes, R.H., S.C. Wheelwright, and K.B. Clark** [1988]. *Dynamic Manufacturing Creating a Learning Organization*, Free Press, New York.

32. **Hollingum, J.** [1986]. *The MAP Report*, IFS (Publications) Ltd., and Springer-Verlag, New York.

33. **Hutchison, D.** [1988]. *Local Area Network Architectures*, Addison-Wesley, Workingham, UK.

34. **Ingersoll Engineers** [1984]. *The FMS Report*, IFS (Publications) Ltd., Bedford, UK.

35. **Ingersoll Engineers** [1985]. *Integrated Manufacture*, IFS (Publications) Ltd., Bedford, UK.

36. **Jones, V.C.** [1988]. *MAP/TOP Networking*, McGraw-Hill, New York.

37. **Kanth, M., and N. Viswanadham,** [1989]. Reliability Analysis of Flexible Manufacturing Systems, *International Journal of Flexible Manufacturing Systems*, Vol. 2, pp. 145–162.

38. **Koren, Y.** [1987]. *Robotics for Engineers*, McGraw-Hill International, Singapore.

39. **Kumar, P.R., and T.I. Seidman** [1990]. Dynamic Instabilities and Stabilization Methods in Distributed Real-Time Scheduling of Manufacturing Systems, *IEEE Transactions on Automatic Control*, Vol. 35, No. 3, March 1990, pp. 289–298.

40. **Kusiak, A.** [1985]. The Part Families Problem in Flexible Manufacturing Systems, *Annals of Operations Research*, Vol. 3, pp. 279–300.

41. **Kusiak, A., and S.S. Heragu** [1987a]. The Facilities Layout Problem, *European Journal of Operations Research*, Vol. 29, pp. 229–251.

42. **Kusiak, A., and S.S. Heragu** [1987b]. Group Technology, *Computers in Industry*, Vol. 9, pp. 83–91.

43. **Lane, J.D., and J.D. Stranaham (Ed.)** [1986]. *Automated Assembly*, Society of Manufacturing Engineers, Dearborn, Michigan.

44. **Levitt, T.** [1983]. The Globalization of Markets, *Harvard Business Review*,

Vol. 61, No. 3, pp. 92–102.

45. **Lu, S.H., and P.R. Kumar** [1991]. Distributed Scheduling Based on Due Dates and Buffer Priorities, *IEEE Transactions on Automatic Control*, To appear in 1991.

46. **Mather, H.** [1988]. *Competitive Manufacturing*, Prentice-Hall, Englewood Cliffs, New Jersey.

47. **Maxwell, W.L., and J.A. Muckstadt** [1982]. Design of Automated Guided Vehicle Systems, *IIE Transactions*, Vol. 14, No. 2, pp. 114–124.

48. **Maxwell, W.L., and R.C. Wilson** [1981]. Dynamic Network Flow Modeling of Fixed Path Material Handling Systems, *IIE Transactions*, Vol. 13, No. 1, pp. 12–21.

49. **McClean, C.R., H.M. Bloom, and T.H. Hopp** [1982]. The Virtual Manufacturing Cell, *Proceedings of IFAC/IFIP Conference on Information and Control Problems in Manufacturing Technology*, Gaithersberg, Madison, October 1982, McGregor and Werner.

50. **Muth, E.J., and J.A. White** [1979]. Conveyor Theory: A Survey, *AIIE Transactions*, Vol. 11, No. 4, pp. 270–277.

51. **Nof, S.Y. (Ed.)** [1985]. *Handbook of Industrial Robotics*, John Wiley, New York.

52. **Nof, S.Y., M.M. Barash, and J.J. Solberg** [1979]. Operational Control of Item Flow in Versatile Manufacturing Systems, *International Journal of Production Research*, Vol. 17, No. 5, pp. 479–489.

53. **O'Grady, P.J.** [1986]. *Controlling Automated Manufacturing Systems*, Kogan Page Ltd., London.

54. **Perkins, J.R., and P.R. Kumar** [1989]. Stable, Distributed, Real-Time Scheduling of Flexible Manufacturing/Assembly/Disassembly Systems, *IEEE Transactions on Automatic Control*, Vol. 34, No. 2, February 1989, pp. 139–148.

55. **Peterson, J.L., and A. Silberschatz** [1985]. *Operating System Concepts*, 2nd edition, Addison-Wesley, Reading, Massachusetts.

56. **Ranky, P.G.** [1983]. *The Design and Operation of Flexible Manufacturing Systems*, IFS (Publications) Ltd., Bedford, UK, and North Holland Publishing Co., Amsterdam, The Netherlands.

57. **Ranky, P.G.** [1986]. *Computer Integrated Manufacturing*, Prentice-Hall, Englewood Cliffs, New Jersey.

58. **Redford, A., and E. Lo** [1986]. *Robots in Assembly*, Open University Press, Milton Keynes, UK.

59. **Rembold, U., C. Blume, and R. Dillmann** [1985]. *Computer-Integrated Manufacturing Technology and Systems*, Marcel Dekker, New York.

60. **Salvendy, G. (Ed.)** [1982]. *Handbook of Industrial Engineering*, John Wiley, New York.

61. **Schonberger, R.J.** [1982]. *Japanese Manufacturing Techniques: Nine Hidden Lessons in Simplicity*, Free Press, London.

62. **Schonberger, R.J.** [1987]. *World Class Manufacturing Casebook Implementing JIT and TQC*, Free Press, London.

63. **Simpson, J.A., R.J. Hocken, and J.S. Albus** [1982]. The Automated Manufacturing Research Facility of the National Bureau of Standards, *Journal of Manufacturing Systems*, Vol. 1, No. 1, pp. 17–31.

64. **Sinha, R.K. and R.H. Hollier** [1984]. A Review of Production Problems in Cellular Manufacture, *International Journal of Production Research*, Vol. 22, No. 5, pp. 773–789.

65. **Solberg, J.J., and S.Y. Nof** [1980]. Analysis of Flow Control in Alternative Manufacturing Configurations, *Journal of Dynamic Systems, Measurement, and Control*, Vol. 102, pp. 479–489.

66. **Stallings, W.** [1984]. *Local Networks*, Macmillan, New York.

67. **Talavage, J., and R.G. Hannam** [1988]. *Flexible Manufacturing Systems in Practice, Applications, Design, and Simulation*, Marcel Dekker, New York.

68. **Talaysum, A., M.Z. Hassan, D. Wisnosky, and J.D. Goldhar** [1986]. Scale vs. Scope: The Long-Run Economies of the CIM/FMS Factory, in *Advances in Production Management Systems 85*, Elsevier Science Publishers, New York, pp. 57–82.

69. **Teicholz, E., and J.N. Orr (Ed.)** [1987]. *Computer-Integrated Manufacturing Handbook*, McGraw-Hill, New York.

70. **Tijunelis, D., and K.E. McKee (Ed.)** [1987]. *Manufacturing High Technology Handbook*, Marcel Dekker, New York.

71. **Vernadat, F.** [1984]. A Conceptual Schema for a CIM Database, *Proceedings of AUTOFACT 6*, Anaheim, California, October 1984, North Holland, Amsterdam, The Netherlands, pp. 11.24–11.41.

72. **Viswanadham, N., Y. Narahari, and T.L. Johnson** [1990]. Deadlock Prevention and Deadlock Avoidance in Flexible Manufacturing Systems Using Petri Net Models, *IEEE Journal of Robotics and Automation*, Vol. 6, No. 6, pp. 713–723.

73. **Vollmann, T.E., W.L. Berry, and D.C. Whybark** [1988]. *Manufacturing Planning and Control Systems*, 2nd edition, Dow Jones-Irwin, Homewood, Illinois.

74. **Weatherall, A.** [1987]. *Computer Integrated Manufacturing from Fundamentals to Implementation*, Butterworth & Co. Ltd., London.

75. **Wemmerlov, U., and N.L. Hyer** [1987]. Research Issues in Cellular Manufacturing, *International Journal of Production Research*, Vol. 25, No. 3, pp. 413–431.

76. **White, J.A. (Ed.)** [1987] *Production Handbook*, 4th edition, John Wiley, New York.

77. **Wolovich, W.A.** [1987]. *Robotics: Basic Analysis and Design*, Holt, Rinehart & Winston, New York.

78. **Yao, D.D.** [1985]. Material and Information Flows in Flexible Manufacturing Systems, *Material Flow*, Vol. 2, pp. 143–149.

Chapter 3
MARKOV CHAIN MODELS

Markov chains constitute the basic stochastic model of discrete event systems and therefore of automated manufacturing systems. This chapter is devoted to a discussion of Markovian modeling of AMSs. Chapter 4 is concerned with queue models and queuing network models, and Chapter 5 with Petri net models. The models discussed in Chapters 4 and 5 only represent a high-level description of a basic underlying Markov chain. Consequently, the theory of Markov chains is the fundamental basis for all the modeling paradigms discussed in this book.

This chapter is organized into 11 sections. The discussion in each section is motivated and exemplified by simple and appropriate situations in automated manufacturing. Sections 3.1 and 3.2 cover preliminary material on geometric and exponential random variables, stochastic processes, and Poisson process. In Sections 3.3 and 3.4, we present the theory and steady-state analysis of discrete time Markov chains and continuous time

Markov chains, respectively. After presenting several illustrative manufacturing examples in these two sections, we present a detailed case study of a transfer line in Section 3.5. The next four sections are devoted to four important special classes of Markov chains. Section 3.6 deals with birth and death processes, which are central to queuing theory, whereas Section 3.7 contains a discussion of time reversible Markov chains, which provide a basis for the theory of product form queuing networks. Section 3.8 treats the interesting problem of deadlocks in the framework of Markov chains with absorbing states. Semi-Markov processes, which facilitate relaxing the Markovian assumptions in a limited way, constitute the subject matter of Section 3.9. Section 3.10 is on transient analysis of Markov chains, and we show that there are several situations in automated manufacturing for which transient analysis is more appropriate than steady-state analysis. Finally, Section 3.11 is on the important topic of computational methods for the steady-state and transient analyses of Markov chains.

3.1 MEMORYLESS RANDOM VARIABLES

Memoryless property, also called the *Markovian* property, is unique to the *geometric* random variable among discrete random variables and to the *exponential* random variable among continuous random variables. These two memoryless random variables form the basis of the theory of Markov processes.

3.1.1 Geometric Random Variable

The geometric random variable describes the number of *independent and identical Bernoulli trials* required to obtain the first success. The range of a geometric random variable X is the set $\{1, 2, 3, ...\}$ and the probability mass function (pmf) is given by

$$P\{X = k\} = (1 - p)^{k-1} p \qquad k = 1, 2, 3, ... \qquad (1)$$

where p is the probability of success of each Bernoulli trial. The mean of X can be shown to be

$$E[X] = \frac{1}{p} \qquad (2)$$

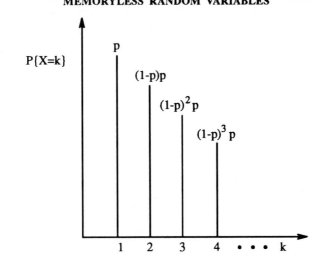

Figure 3.1 PMF of a geometric random variable with parameter p

This implies that we need $1/p$ independent Bernoulli trials, on an average, to obtain the first success. The pmf of a geometric random variable with parameter p is depicted in Figure 3.1.

In manufacturing situations, the geometric random variable can be used to model the number of time units required to process a workpiece, to fix a tool, to move a part from one machine center to another, to set up a machine, and so on. Further, it can model the number of time units for which a machine or a tool remains in working condition before a failure occurs and the number of time units the repair of a failed component would take.

For a given positive integer m, let us first compute $P\{X > m\}$. In what follows, we use the symbols $\vee$ and $\wedge$ for denoting the logical *or* and logical *and* operations, respectively. We have

$$
\begin{aligned}
P\{X > m\} &= 1 - P\{X \leq m\} \\
&= 1 - P\{(X = 1) \vee (X = 2) \vee \ldots \vee (X = m)\} \\
&= 1 - P\{X = 1\} - P\{X = 2\} - \ldots - P\{X = m\} \\
&= 1 - p - (1 - p)p - \ldots - (1 - p)^{m-1}p \\
&= (1 - p)^m
\end{aligned}
\tag{3}
$$

Now let us consider the probability $P\{X = m + n \mid X > m\}$ for $m \geq 1$ and $n \geq 1$. This is equal to

$$\frac{P\{(X = m + n) \wedge (X > m)\}}{P\{X > m\}} = \frac{P\{X = m + n\}}{P\{X > m\}}$$
$$= \frac{(1 - p)^{m+n-1} p}{(1 - p)^m}$$
$$= (1 - p)^{n-1} p$$
$$= P\{X = n\}$$

Thus we have

$$P\{X = m + n \mid X > m\} = P\{X = n\} \qquad m, n \geq 1 \qquad (4)$$

The property described by (4) is called the *memoryless property* of the geometric random variable. Note that the RHS (right hand side) of (4) depends only on n, which means that the random variable does not have memory of m which represents the history in this case.

It can also be verified that

$$P\{X > m + n \mid X > m\} = P\{X > n\} \qquad m, n \geq 1$$
$$P\{X \leq m + n \mid X > m\} = P\{X \leq n\} \qquad m, n \geq 1$$

Example 3.1

The lifetime of a tool carrying out machining operations can be specified by the number of operations it will last before breaking because of wear and tear. Let us assume that the lifetime of a particular tool is a random variable X, geometrically distributed with parameter 0.01. This means that the tool will last an average of 100 machine operations. If it is known that the tool has already lasted 50 operations, then by the memoryless property,

$$P\{X > 50 + n \mid X > 50\} = P\{X > n\} \qquad n \geq 1$$

Also note that if the tool has lasted m operations ($m \geq 1$) already, then the probability of lasting 10 more operations is given by

$$P\{X > 10 + m \mid X > m\} = P\{X > 10\} \qquad m \geq 1$$

What is more interesting is that the geometric random variable is the unique discrete random variable satisfying the memoryless property. To see this, let us start with a discrete random variable X with range $\{1, 2, 3, ...\}$, satisfying the property (4).

For $k = 1, 2, 3, ...$, consider $P\{X = k\}$. Substituting $n = k$ and $m = 1$ in (4), we get

$$
\begin{aligned}
P\{X = k\} &= P\{X = k+1 \mid X > 1\} \\
&= \frac{P\{X = k+1 \ \wedge \ X > 1\}}{P\{X > 1\}} \\
&= \frac{P\{X = k+1\}}{1 - P\{X = 1\}}
\end{aligned}
$$

Thus we have the recursive relation

$$P\{X = k+1\} = (1 - p)\, P\{X = k\}$$

where $p = P\{X = 1\}$. Unfolding the above recursion, we get

$$P\{X = k+1\} = (1 - p)^k p$$

The above is the same as (1), thus implying that X is a geometric random variable with parameter p.

3.1.2 Exponential Random Variable

This is often called the *negative exponential* distribution and is used extensively in modeling because of its *memoryless* property and resulting analytical tractability. This is the unique continuous random variable satisfying the memoryless property. In the manufacturing context, the following are usually modeled by the exponential distribution: time between successive arrivals of raw workpieces, processing time on a machine, machine setup time, material handling time, message transmission time, lifetime of a tool, time to failure of a machine or an AGV or robot or any other component, and time required to repair a failed component.

The cumulative distribution function (CDF) of an exponential random variable X with parameter λ ($\lambda > 0$) is defined by

$$
\begin{aligned}
F_X(x) &= 0 && \text{for } x < 0 \\
&= 1 - e^{-\lambda x} && \text{for } 0 \le x < \infty
\end{aligned}
\tag{5}
$$

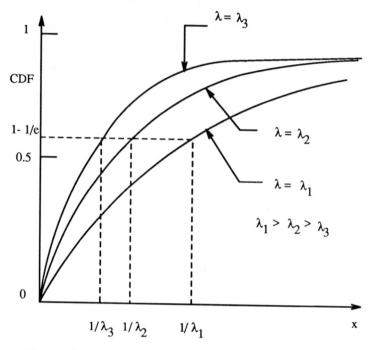

Figure 3.2 CDF of an exponential random variable

Parameter λ is called the rate of X and is the lone parameter of X. We often use the notation $X = EXP(\lambda)$. The mean of X is given by

$$E[X] = \frac{1}{\lambda} \tag{6}$$

The probability density function (pdf) of X can be obtained to be

$$
\begin{aligned}
f_X(x) &= 0 & x \le 0 \\
&= \lambda e^{-\lambda x} & x > 0
\end{aligned} \tag{7}
$$

Also the following relations can be immediately derived.

$$P\{X > x\} = e^{-\lambda x} \qquad\qquad x \ge 0$$

$$\tag{8}$$

$$P\{x \le X \le y\} = e^{-\lambda x} - e^{-\lambda y} \qquad 0 \le x \le y$$

Figure 3.2 shows the CDF of an exponential random variable with parameter λ, for various values of λ.

We now show the memoryless property for any exponential random variable $X = EXP(\lambda)$. Consider, for $x, y \geq 0$,

$$P\{X > x+y \mid X > x\} = \frac{P\{X > x+y \wedge X > x\}}{P\{X > x\}}$$

$$= \frac{P\{X > x+y\}}{P\{X > x\}}$$

$$= \frac{e^{-\lambda(x+y)}}{e^{-\lambda x}} = e^{-\lambda y} \qquad \text{using (8)}$$

$$= P\{X > y\} \tag{9}$$

Thus

$$P\{X > x+y \mid X > x\} = P\{X > y\} \;\; \forall \; x, y \geq 0 \tag{10}$$

Similarly, it can be shown that

$$P\{X \leq x+y \mid X > x\} = P\{X \leq y\} \;\; \forall \; x, y \geq 0 \tag{11}$$

Equations (10) and (11) are equivalent statements of the memoryless property of a continuous random variable.

Example 3.2

Let the time to failure X of a machine be exponentially distributed with rate 0.01 per h. This would mean that the mean time between failures (MTBF) of this machine is 100 h. If it is known that the machine has already operated for 50 h, then the memoryless property implies that

$$P\{X > 50 + x \mid X > 50\} = P\{X > x\} \qquad \forall x \geq 0$$

Also, if it is known that the machine has operated for x h, then we have

$$P\{X > 10 + x \mid X > x\} = P\{X > 10\} \qquad \forall x \geq 0$$

To show that the exponential random variable is the unique continuous random variable having memoryless property, we start with a *nonnegative* random variable, X, satisfying the memoryless property (11) and deduce the differential equation

$$\frac{dF_X(x)}{dx} = [1 - F_X(x)] \frac{dF_X(0)}{dx}$$

Solving the above differential equation, we obtain

$$F_X(x) = 1 - e^{-\lambda x} \qquad \text{if} \quad x > 0$$
$$= 0 \qquad\qquad \text{if} \quad -\infty < x \leq 0$$

where $\lambda = \frac{dF_X(0)}{dx} = f_X(0)$. This is the same as (5) and hence X is exponentially distributed with rate λ.

PROBLEMS

1. Given a geometric random variable G with parameter p, show that $E[G] = 1/p$. If $X = EXP(\lambda)$, show that $E[X] = 1/\lambda$.

2. The number of machine operations a particular tool lasts has been observed to be a geometric random variable with parameter 0.01.

   (a) What is the probability that the tool lasts at least 2 machine operations?

   (b) Given that the tool has already lasted 98 operations, what is the probability that it will break only after 100 operations in all?

3. The time required to repair a machine is an exponentially distributed random variable with mean 30 min.

   (a) What is the probability that a repair time exceeds 30 min?

   (b) Given that a repair duration exceeds 1 h, what is the probability that the repair takes at least $1\frac{1}{2}$ h?

4. If G_1 and G_2 are independent geometric random variables with parameters p_1 and p_2, respectively, show that

$$P\{G_1 < G_2\} = \frac{p_1(1 - p_2)}{p_1 + p_2 - p_1 p_2}$$

If $X_1 = EXP(\lambda_1)$ and $X_2 = EXP(\lambda_2)$, and X_1 and X_2 are independent, show that

$$P\{X_1 < X_2\} = \frac{\lambda_1}{\lambda_1 + \lambda_2}$$

Generalize the above property for three or more memoryless random variables.

5. Given G_1 and G_2 as in problem 4, define $G = min(G_1, G_2)$. Show that G is geometrically distributed with parameter $p_1 + p_2 - p_1 p_2$. Assuming X_1 and X_2 as in problem 4 and defining $X = min(X_1, X_2)$, show that $X = EXP(\lambda_1 + \lambda_2)$. Attempt a generalization of the above result.

6. Complete the proof of the important result that the exponential random variable is the unique memoryless continuous random variable.

7. Attempt an interpretation of the results in problems 4 and 5 in typical manufacturing situations such as assembly operations.

3.2 STOCHASTIC PROCESSES IN MANUFACTURING

In this section we introduce stochastic processes and present several examples in the manufacturing context. We then discuss the Poisson process, which has significant use in modeling.

Definition: A *stochastic process* is a collection of random variables, $\{X(t) : t \in T\}$, where $X(t)$ is a random variable for each $t \in T$.

The set T is called the *index set* of the process and a $t \in T$ is called an *index*, or a *parameter*. The values taken by $X(t)$ are called the *states* of the stochastic process, corresponding to the index t. The set of all values that $X(t)$ may assume is called the *state space*, denoted by S. Often, the index t is interpreted as time, and we shall follow this interpretation in the rest of the book.

Definition: If the index set T is a countable set, then the stochastic process is said to be a *discrete time process*, or a *discrete parameter process*. If T is an interval of the real line, the stochastic process is called a *continuous parameter process*, or a *continuous time process*.

Definition: If the state space S of a stochastic process $\{X(t) : t \in T\}$ is a countable set, we call the process a *chain*.

Depending on the countable or continuous nature of the index set and the state space, we have the following different types of stochastic processes:

1. Discrete time, discrete state space processes,

2. Discrete time, continuous state space processes,

3. Continuous time, discrete state space processes, and

4. Continuous time, continuous state space processes.

3.2.1 Examples of Stochastic Processes

A stochastic process basically models the evolution in time of physical systems. We shall consider some examples below, in the manufacturing context.

Example 3.3

Consider a single machine prone to failures and let us examine its state at discrete points of time $t_0, t_1, t_2, \ldots$. Let the state be designated 0 if the machine is up and 1 if the machine is down (that is, getting repaired). The machine will keep changing its state as time evolves. Let X_i denote the state of the machine at time t_i, $i = 0, 1, 2, \ldots$. Then $\{X_i : i \in \mathbf{N}\}$ is a stochastic process. Note that each X_i is a discrete random variable with range $\{0, 1\}$. Thus the state space is $S = \{0, 1\}$ and the index set is $T = \{t_0, t_1, t_2, \ldots\}$. So, this stochastic process is a discrete time chain.

Example 3.4

In the above example, if the state of the machine is examined at any instant of time, then the index set is the real interval $[0, \infty)$ and the stochastic process $\{X(t) : t \geq 0\}$, where $X(t)$ denotes the state of the machine at time t, is a continuous time chain.

Example 3.5

Let us consider a manufacturing facility in which arrivals of raw parts occur randomly. Starting from time $t = 0$, let $X(t)$ denote the number of parts that have arrived until a current instant of time, $t \, (> 0)$. We know that $X(t)$ is a discrete random variable that can take values in the set $\{0, 1, 2, \ldots\}$. The collection of these discrete random variables, $\{X(t) : t \in [0, \infty)\}$ would constitute a continuous time chain. Such processes are called *counting processes*. The well-known *Poisson process*, which we will study in Section 3.2.2, is an example of such a process.

Example 3.6

Consider a manufacturing facility comprising a single NC machine that can process n different types of parts $(n \geq 0)$. The different types of parts arrive randomly into the system. The machine is failure-free and can continuously process parts. In this case, the machine can be in exactly $(n + 1)$ states $\{0, 1, 2, ..., n\}$, where the state 0 corresponds to machine idle (no part available for processing) and the state i, for $i = 1, 2, ..., n$, corresponds to the machine processing a part of type i. If $X(t)$ is the state of the machine at time t, then $\{X(t) : t \geq 0\}$ is a continuous time chain.

Example 3.7

In a typical automated manufacturing system, we have seen in Chapter 2 that robots and AGVs are used for material handling. Let us say we are looking at the movement of a robot arm along a particular trajectory and measure the distance traversed by the robot arm in a given span of time. Or, let us say we are measuring the distance traveled by an AGV in a given span of time. Assume that the speed of the robot arm or the AGV is random and let $X(t)$ denote the distance covered in time t. Then $\{X(t) : t \geq 0\}$ is a continuous time stochastic process with continuous state space (since distance is in general a real number). If we are measuring the distances traveled at intervals of, say, every second, then we have a discrete time stochastic process with continuous state space.

The dynamical evolution of activities in an automated manufacturing system can be modeled by a stochastic process. In this chapter we will be studying certain important classes of stochastic processes that arise frequently in the manufacturing context. These are: Poisson processes, discrete time Markov chains, continuous time Markov chains, birth and death processes, time reversible processes, and semi-Markov processes.

3.2.2 Poisson Process

The Poisson process is a continuous time stochastic process with discrete state space, with some special properties that make it a very popular and natural choice for modeling arrivals of parts into a manufacturing facility, arrivals of jobs into a computing center, arrivals of telephone calls in a telephone exchange, arrivals of messages to be transmitted on a local network, and so on. Poisson process derives its name from the famous Poisson random variable and has a particularly nice relationship with the memoryless property since the inter-arrival times are independent and identical exponential random variables. We shall motivate the definition of a Poisson process with the following discussion in which we obtain a model for arrival of customers using simple assumptions.

Example 3.8

Consider a manufacturing facility where the raw parts arrive one at a time, at random instants of time. Let $X(t)$ be the number of raw parts that have arrived in the time interval $[0, t]$ where $t > 0$. Clearly, $X(t)$ is a discrete random variable taking values in the set $\{0, 1, 2, ...\}$ and the family of random variables $\{X(t) : t > 0\}$ is a continuous time stochastic process with discrete state space. Now partition the above time interval into n subintervals of equal length equal to t/n. If n is very large, t/n will be infinitesimally small. In each such subinterval, it is reasonable to assume that at most one arrival can occur. That is, either there is no arrival or exactly one arrival, and the probability of two or more arrivals tends to 0 as $n \to \infty$. Further, we assume that

1. Probability of an arrival occurring in a subinterval of length t/n is proportional to the length t/n. Let the constant of proportionality be λ so that probability of exactly one arrival $= \frac{\lambda t}{n}$, and probability of no arrival $= 1 - \frac{\lambda t}{n}$.

2. Arrivals of different raw parts into the system occur in an independent way.

In the above scenario, each subinterval of length t/n can be visualized as a Bernoulli trial with success as an arrival and failure as no arrival. The number of arrivals during the interval $[0, t]$ can be modeled as a binomial random variable with number of trials equal to n and the probability of success equal to $\lambda t/n$. Thus, using the pmf of binomial random variable, we have, for $k = 0, 1, 2, ..., n$,

$$P\{\text{exactly } k \text{ arrivals in the interval } [0, t]\} = P\{X(t) = k\}$$

$$= \binom{n}{k} \left(\frac{\lambda t}{n}\right)^k \left(1 - \frac{\lambda t}{n}\right)^{n-k}$$

$$= \frac{(n)(n-1)...(n-k+1)}{n^k} \frac{(\lambda t)^k}{k!} \left(1 - \frac{\lambda t}{n}\right)^{n-k}$$

In the limit as $n \to \infty$, we have, for $k = 0, 1, 2, ...,$

$$P\{X(t) = k\} = \lim_{n \to \infty} \frac{n}{n} \frac{n-1}{n} \cdots \frac{n-k+1}{n} \frac{(\lambda t)^k}{k!} \left(1 - \frac{\lambda t}{n}\right)^{n-k}$$

$$= \frac{(\lambda t)^k}{k!} \lim_{n \to \infty} \left(1 - \frac{\lambda t}{n}\right)^{n-k}$$

It can be shown, using standard calculus, that

$$\lim_{n \to \infty} \left(1 - \frac{\lambda t}{n}\right)^{n-k} = e^{-\lambda t}$$

Thus we have

Poisson

$$P\{X(t) = k\} = \frac{e^{-\lambda t}(\lambda t)^k}{k!}; \qquad k = 0, 1, 2, \ldots \tag{12}$$

The above expression corresponds to that of the pmf of a Poisson random variable with mean λt. Thus the number of arrivals in the interval $[0, t]$ follows a Poisson random variable. Now let us look at the collection of Poisson random variables $\{X(t) : t \geq 0\}$. This constitutes the Poisson process.

It is interesting to evaluate (12) for $k = 0$. We get

$$P\{X(t) = 0\} = e^{-\lambda t} \quad (t > 0)$$

Note that the above gives the probability of no arrival in the entire interval $[0, t]$. If T denotes the inter-arrival time (that is, time between successive arrivals), the above probability can be interpreted as $P\{T > t\}$. Thus

$$P\{T > t\} = e^{-\lambda t} \quad (t > 0) \quad \text{exponential}$$

It is easy to see that T is exponentially distributed. Thus inter-arrival times of a Poisson process are exponentially distributed whereas the number of arrivals in a time interval $[0, t]$ is a Poisson random variable.

We now define a Poisson process and state without proof several interesting properties satisfied by Poisson processes. We first define a counting process.

Definition: A stochastic process $\{X(t) : t \geq 0\}$ is called a *counting process* or an *arrival process* if $X(t)$ represents the total number of *events* (for example, arrivals of raw parts into a manufacturing system) that have occurred up to time t.

Definition: A counting process $\{X(t) : t \geq 0\}$ is said to possess *independent increments* if the random variables that represent the number of events occurring in disjoint intervals are mutually independent.

Definition: A counting process $\{X(t) : t \geq 0\}$ is said to possess *stationary increments* if the number of arrivals in an interval $(t, t + h]$, given by $X(t + h) - X(t)$, is independent of the epoch t at which the interval is located.

Definition: A counting process $\{X(t) : t \geq 0\}$ is said to be a *Poisson process* if

1. $X(0) = 0$
2. The process has independent increments
3. The process has stationary increments
4. The probability of two or more arrivals in an interval of length h tends to 0 as h tends to 0

Number of Arrivals in an Interval

Starting with the above definition, one can show, for a Poisson process, that the number of arrivals during an interval of length t is a Poisson random variable with mean λt where λ is given by

$$\lambda = \lim_{h \to 0} \frac{1}{h} \left[P\left\{ X(s + h) - X(s) = 1 \right\} \right] \quad \text{for any } s > 0$$

Recall how the above property was deduced in Example 3.8. The parameter λ is called the *rate* of the Poisson process.

Inter-Arrival Times

Let T_n denote the elapsed time between the $(n-1)$st arrival and the nth arrival. Then it can be shown that T_n, $n = 1, 2, 3, ...,$ are independent and identically distributed (i.i.d.) exponential random variables with rate given by λ.

Superposition of Poisson Processes

Let us say parts of different types are arriving into a manufacturing facility as Poisson processes in an independent way. Let $\lambda_1, \lambda_2, ..., \lambda_n$ be the rates of these Poisson processes. Then it can be shown that the superposition of these Poisson processes as shown in Figure 3.3 is also a Poisson process. The rate of this pooled arrival stream can be shown to be equal to the sum of the rates of the individual Poisson streams.

Decomposition of a Poisson Process

Consider that raw parts are arriving into a manufacturing system with n machines, according to a Poisson process with rate λ. An arriving raw part is probabilistically assigned to one of the n machines, as shown in Figure 3.4, according to an independent probability distribution $[p_1, p_2, ..., p_n]$, with $p_1 + p_2 + ... + p_n = 1$. Then we have n input streams to the n machines. We can visualize the original Poisson process to have

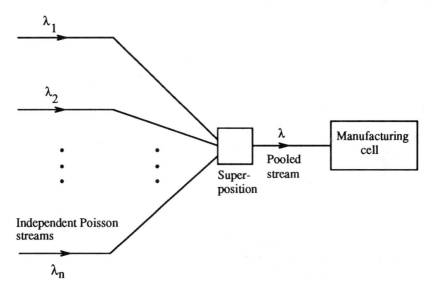

Figure 3.3 Superposition of independent Poisson processes

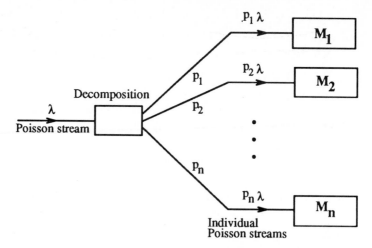

Figure 3.4 Decomposition of a Poisson process

branched out into n streams. It can be shown that these individual streams
are Poisson processes with rates $\lambda p_1, \lambda p_2, ...,$ and λp_n, respectively.

Example 3.9

Let raw parts arrive into a manufacturing facility from two independent
sources in Poisson fashion, with rates 5/ h and 10/ h respectively (Figure
3.5). Then the overall arrival of raw parts will correspond to a Poisson
process with rate 15/ h. Thus the inter-arrival times of raw parts into
the system would be independently and identically distributed exponential

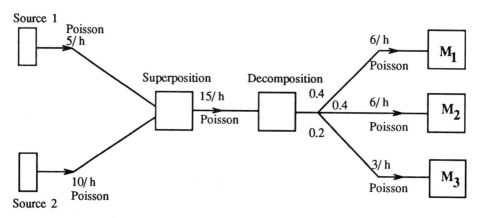

Figure 3.5 Example to illustrate superposition and decomposition

random variables with rate equal to 15/ h or mean $\frac{1}{15}$ h (4 min). If the system comprises three machines M_1, M_2, and M_3 and if 40% of jobs are scheduled onto M_1, 40% onto M_2, and the rest onto M_3, then the inputs for the three machines would be Poisson processes with rates 6/ h, 6/ h, and 3/ h respectively. Therefore, inter-arrival times of raw parts at M_1 and M_2 are exponentially distributed with means 10 min each and the inter-arrival times at M_3 are exponentially distributed with mean 20 min.

PROBLEMS

1. For a Poisson process $\{X(t) : t \geq 0\}$, define S_n as the total time until the nth arrival occurs, where $n \geq 1$. Compute the distribution of S_n.

2. A machine produces parts in such a way that the stream of finished parts is a Poisson process with rate $\lambda = 10$ per h.

   (a) What is the probability that it produces no finished part in 1 h?

   (b) What is the expected time at which the 20th finished part is produced?

   (c) What is the probability that 100 parts are produced in a shift of 8 h, assuming that the machine works nonstop during the shift?

3. Show that the sum of n mutually independent Poisson random variables with parameters $\lambda_1, \lambda_2, ..., \lambda_n$, is a Poisson random variable with parameter $\lambda_1 + \lambda_2 + ... + \lambda_n$.

4. Prove for a Poisson process that inter-arrival times are independently and identically distributed exponential random variables.

3.3 DISCRETE TIME MARKOV CHAIN MODELS

In this section we consider an important special class of discrete time stochastic processes with countable state space. These are *discrete time Markov chains* (DTMCs). Let $T = \{t_0, t_1, t_2, ...\}$ denote the discrete time instants at which a stochastic process $\{X(t) : t \geq 0\}$ is observed and let $X_0, X_1, X_2, ...$ denote the corresponding values of $X(t)$. Note that $X_0, X_1, X_2, ...$ are all random variables. Since the state space S is countable, S can also be written without loss of generality, as

$$S = \{0, 1, 2, ...\} = \mathsf{N}$$

Now for $n \in \mathsf{N}$ and $j \in \mathsf{N}$, if $X_n = j$, we say that the state of the stochastic process at time t_n is j. X_0 is the initial state of the system.

Note that the instants of observations $t_0, t_1, t_2, ...$, need not be equally spaced. That is, in general, $t_{n+1} - t_n$ could be different for different values of n.

3.3.1 Definitions and Notation

We first define a DTMC and introduce a matrix notation for describing the transitions among the states in a DTMC.

Definition: A *discrete time Markov chain* or DTMC is a discrete time stochastic process, $\{X_n : n \in \mathsf{N}\}$, with countable state space S, such that for all $n \in \mathsf{N}$ and for all $i, j, i_0, i_1, ..., i_{n-2} \in S$,

$$P\{X_n = j \mid X_{n-1} = i; \quad X_{n-2} = i_{n-2}; \quad ...; \quad X_1 = i_1; \quad X_0 = i_0\}$$
$$= P\{X_n = j \mid X_{n-1} = i\}$$

$$(13)$$

The above property is called the *Markov property*. Intuitively this property implies that given the *current* state of the system, the *future* is *independent* of the *past*. That is, the dynamic behavior of a DTMC is such that the probability distributions for its future evolution depend only on the present state and not on how the process arrived in that state.

Consider, for $m, n \in \mathsf{N}$ and $i, j \in S$,

$$p_{ij}(m, m+n) = P\{X_{m+n} = j \mid X_m = i\}$$

The above conditional probabilities completely describe the DTMC. These probabilities are also called the *n-step transition probabilities*. If the value of each $p_{ij}(m, m+n)$ is independent of m, such a DTMC is called *a homogeneous* DTMC. Thus we have the following definition.

Definition: A DTMC $\{X_n : n \in \mathsf{N}\}$, with state space S, is said to be *homogeneous* if for all $i, j \in S$ and $m, n \in \mathsf{N}$ the transition probabilities $p_{ij}(m, m+n)$ depend only on n and are independent of m. That is,

$$p_{ij}(m, m+n) = p_{ij}(n) \quad \forall i, j \in S; \quad \forall m, n \in \mathsf{N} \qquad (14)$$

If the above probabilities depend on m also, we say the DTMC is *non-homogeneous*. Physically speaking, in a homogeneous DTMC, the pattern of evolution of the DTMC would be given by the same values of transition probabilities at all instants of time. In the case of a non-homogeneous DTMC, the values of transition probabilities would be different at different instants of time. There are several physical phenomena which are non-homogeneous: for example, tool breakages in manufacturing systems (which depend on the wear and tear of the tools); vehicular traffic at a busy road junction; and traffic of telephone calls at a telephone exchange. However, several stochastic phenomena in the manufacturing context satisfy homogeneity, and in the sequel we shall only discuss homogeneous DTMCs and refer to them simply as DTMCs.

For DTMCs, the probabilities $p_{ij}(n)$ are called n-step transition probabilities. In particular, the probabilities $p_{ij}(1)$, also written as p_{ij}, are called the one-step transition probabilities. Thus we have

$$p_{ij} = P\{X_n = j \mid X_{n-1} = i\}; \qquad n \geq 1 \qquad (15)$$

The one-step transition probabilities are specified in the form of a matrix denoted by P, called the *transition probability matrix* (TPM). Thus,

$$P = [p_{ij}] = \begin{bmatrix} p_{00} & p_{01} & p_{02} & \cdots \\ p_{10} & p_{11} & p_{12} & \cdots \\ p_{20} & p_{21} & p_{22} & \cdots \\ \cdot & \cdot & \cdot & \cdots \\ \cdot & \cdot & \cdot & \cdots \\ \cdot & \cdot & \cdot & \cdots \end{bmatrix}$$

P belongs to a class of matrices called *stochastic matrices* in which the entries satisfy the following two properties:

$$0 \leq p_{ij} \leq 1 \qquad \forall\, i, j = 0, 1, 2...$$
$$\sum_j p_{ij} = 1 \qquad \forall\, i = 0, 1, 2, ... \qquad (16)$$

Often, a DTMC is also described by a *state transition diagram*, which is a labeled directed graph where each node represents a particular state of the DTMC and a directed arc from a node i to another node j (including itself) represents a one-step transition from state i to state j. This directed arc is labeled by p_{ij}. If $p_{ij} = 0$, no directed arc is included from node i to node j.

3.3.2 Sojourn Times in States

We have seen in Section 3.1 that the geometric random variable is the unique memoryless discrete random variable. The Markov property of DTMCs leads to geometric residence times in individual DTMC states.

Definition: Given a state i of a DTMC $\{X_n \in S : n \in \mathbb{N}\}$, the *sojourn time* T_i of the state is a discrete random variable that gives the number of time steps for which the DTMC resides in that state before transiting to a different state.

We shall now show that the sojourn time T_i in a state i is a geometric random variable. First, we note that

$$P\{T_i > n\} = p_{ii}^n$$

Now consider

$$
\begin{aligned}
P\{T_i = n\} &= \sum_{k=n}^{\infty} P\{T_i = k\} - \sum_{k=n+1}^{\infty} P\{T_i = k\} \\
&= P\{T_i > n-1\} - P\{T_i > n\} \\
&= p_{ii}^{n-1} - p_{ii}^n = p_{ii}^{n-1}(1 - p_{ii})
\end{aligned}
$$

The above is precisely the pmf of a geometric random variable with success probability $= 1 - p_{ii}$ [Equation (1)]. Thus in a DTMC, the mean number of time steps the DTMC spends in a state i is equal to the reciprocal of $(1 - p_{ii})$. Intuitively, this result follows from the Markovian property of DTMCs.

3.3.3 Examples of DTMCs in Manufacturing

We now give several examples of DTMCs in the manufacturing context to get a feel for the definitions and concepts introduced.

Example 3.10

Consider a manufacturing facility comprising a single machine that is prone to failures. At any instant of time, the machine is either working properly (state 0) or is undergoing repair following a breakdown (state 1). Consider that the state of the machine is being examined once every hour. Let a be the probability that the machine fails in a given hour and b the probability

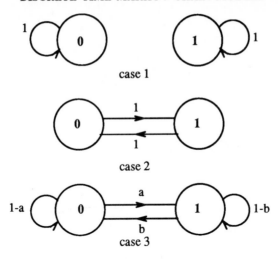

case 1

case 2

case 3

Figure 3.6 DTMC models for a single-machine system

that the failed machine gets repaired in a given hour. More specifically, a is the probability that the machine is in the failed condition by the next observation given that it is working in the current observation. Similarly, b is the probability that the machine gets repaired by the next observation given that it is in the failed state in the current observation. Assume that these probabilities remain the same immaterial of the history of the working of the machine. Also, we assume that these probabilities are the same at any observation epoch. The above system can be formulated as a homogeneous DTMC $\{X_n \in S : n \in \mathbb{N}\}$, where $S = \{0, 1\}$ and the time instants $t_0, t_1, t_2, ...$, correspond to $0, 1$ h, 2 h, ..., respectively. The TPM is given by

$$P = \begin{bmatrix} 1 - a & a \\ b & 1 - b \end{bmatrix} \qquad 0 \le a, b \le 1$$

The state transition diagram is depicted in Figure 3.6. There are three cases here, namely:

   Case 1: $a = b = 0$

   Case 2: $a = b = 1$

   Case 3: neither case 1 nor case 2

   In the first case, the mean sojourn time of each state is infinity, as can be intuitively seen from the state diagram. In the second case, the mean sojourn time of each state is equal to 1 because each corresponds to

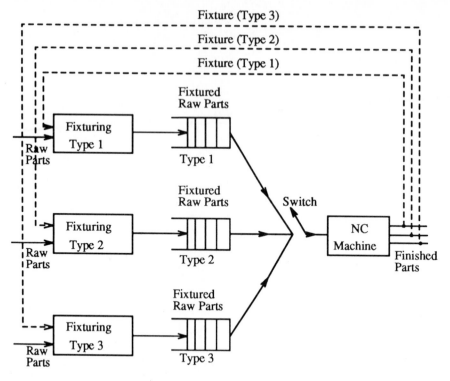

Figure 3.7 An NC machine processing three types of parts

a geometric random variable with success probability 1. In the final case, the mean sojourn time of state 0 is $1/a$ and that of state 1 is $1/b$.

Example 3.11

Consider an NC machine processing parts that may belong to one of three part types (Figure 3.7). Assume that raw parts of each type are always available and wait in separate queues. Let us look at this particular system when the NC machine starts processing a fresh part. We can consider the system evolution as constituting a homogeneous Markov chain, with state space given by $S = \{1, 2, 3\}$ where each state corresponds to the type of part getting processed. The observation epochs $t_0, t_1, t_2, \dots$ are given by the time instants at which the ith part $(i = 1, 2, 3, \dots)$ is taken up for processing.

Suppose that the NC machine processes the parts in a *cyclic way*, i.e., a type 1 part followed by a type 2 part followed by a type 3 part, and the same sequence repeated again and again. The state transition diagram is

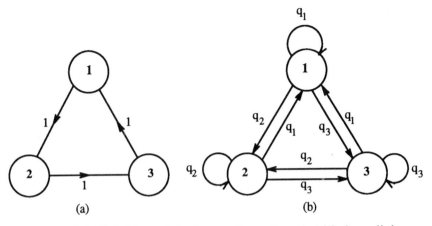

Figure 3.8 DTMC models for cyclic and probabilistic policies

shown in Figure 3.8(a). The TPM of this system is:

$$P = \begin{bmatrix} 0 & 1 & 0 \\ 0 & 0 & 1 \\ 1 & 0 & 0 \end{bmatrix}$$

Now, suppose that the type of the next part to be processed is selected *probabilistically* ; part type i is chosen next with probability q_i $(i = 1, 2, 3)$, where $0 < q_i < 1$, $q_1 + q_2 + q_3 = 1$. In this case, the state transition diagram is shown in Figure 3.8(b) and the TPM is given by

$$P = \begin{bmatrix} q_1 & q_2 & q_3 \\ q_1 & q_2 & q_3 \\ q_1 & q_2 & q_3 \end{bmatrix}$$

Example 3.12

Consider the queuing network model shown in Figure 3.9. This model represents an FMS with a single AGV and m machines $M_1, M_2,...,M_m$. This is the classical model suggested by Solberg [1977] and in fact the first queuing network formulation for FMSs. The closed nature of the model is used to model a fixed number of fixtures or pallets in the system. After transportation by the AGV (which could correspond to unloading operation or transfer across machines), a part leaves the system with probability q_0 (in which case a new part is loaded into the system using the fixture

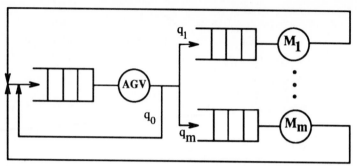

Figure 3.9 Closed central server queuing network model

released by the leaving part) or undergoes one more operation on one of the machines with probabilities $q_1, q_2, ..., q_m$, respectively. After processing by a machine, the part returns to the AGV queue in order to get unloaded or get transported to a different machine. Let there be a single job in this system and let us look at the progress of this job in the system. It is easy to note that the job can be in $(m + 1)$ states: 0 (if getting serviced by AGV), and i (if getting serviced by M_i, $i = 1, 2, ..., m$). The flow of the job can be described by a DTMC model. The TPM of this DTMC model is

$$P = \begin{bmatrix} q_0 & q_1 & q_2 & \cdots & q_m \\ 1 & 0 & 0 & \cdots & 0 \\ 1 & 0 & 0 & \cdots & 0 \\ \cdot & \cdot & \cdot & \cdots & \cdot \\ \cdot & \cdot & \cdot & \cdots & \cdot \\ \cdot & \cdot & \cdot & \cdots & \cdot \\ 1 & 0 & 0 & \cdots & 0 \end{bmatrix}$$

Figure 3.10 shows the state transition diagram of the above DTMC model. We shall consider this example several times in later sections and chapters in various contexts.

Example 3.13

Here we consider a system comprising two machines that are identical in all respects. The machines are prone to failure, but there is no repair facility. The state space in this case is $S = \{0, 1, 2\}$ where $i\,(i = 0, 1, 2)$ is the number of machines that have failed. Let a be the constant probability of failure of a machine in a given time interval, assuming that successive observation points are equally spaced. For instance, it could be that we are watching the system every hour and a is the probability of a machine failing in any given hour. We shall formulate this system as a homogeneous DTMC.

Let us first examine state 0 and compute the transition probabilities p_{00}, p_{01}, p_{02}.

$p_{01} = P\{\text{exactly one machine fails in a given hour}\} = 2a(1 - a)$

$p_{02} = P\{\text{both machines fail in a given hour}\} = a^2$

$p_{00} = P\{\text{none of the machines fail in a given hour}\} = (1 - a)^2$

Note that $p_{00} + p_{01} + p_{02} = 1$. We can compute the other transition probabilities on similar lines. The TPM is given by

$$P = \begin{bmatrix} (1-a)^2 & 2a(1-a) & a^2 \\ 0 & 1-a & a \\ 0 & 0 & 1 \end{bmatrix}$$

The state transition diagram of the DTMC is shown in Figure 3.11. It is to be observed that once the DTMC reaches state 2, it is *absorbed* and has to stay there forever. Such states are called *absorbing states*. We shall study such states in more detail in Section 3.8.

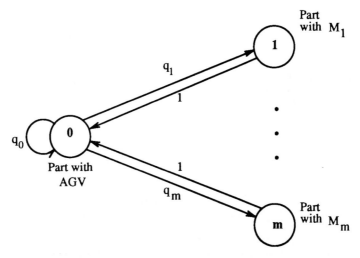

Figure 3.10 DTMC model for the central server network

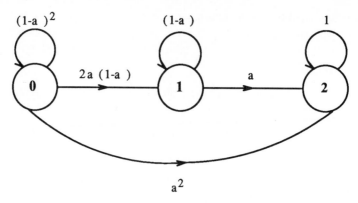

Figure 3.11 DTMC model of a two-machine system with no repair

So far we have seen finite DTMCs, with finite number of elements in the state space. We shall examine some DTMCs with infinite state space in some later sections. However, to give an immediate example, we can consider a Poisson process as a DTMC if we observe the system only when an arrival occurs into the system.

3.3.4 Chapman-Kolmogorov Equation

The evolution of a DTMC $\{X_n \in S : n \in \mathbb{N}\}$ can be described by the *Chapman-Kolmogorov equation* (C-K equation) which are *difference equations* for obtaining multiple-step transition probabilities. To derive these, we first consider, for $m, n \geq 0$ and for $i, j \in S$,

$$p_{ij}(m+n) = P\{X_{m+n} = j \mid X_0 = i\}$$

Let us look at X_m, the state of the DTMC at the mth time step. See Figure 3.12. X_m could be any element of S and hence by the *total probability theorem*, we may write

$$p_{ij}(m+n) = \sum_{k \in S} P\{X_{m+n} = j; \quad X_m = k \mid X_0 = i\}$$

The RHS in the above equation may be written as

$$\sum_{k \in S} P\{X_{m+n} = j \mid X_m = k; \ X_0 = i\} \ P\{X_m = k \mid X_0 = i\}$$

By the Markovian property, the above becomes

$$p_{ij}(m+n) = \sum_{k \in S} P\{X_{m+n} = j \mid X_m = k\} \; P\{X_m = k \mid X_0 = i\}$$

Thus we have for $m, n \geq 0$ and $i, j \in S$,

$$p_{ij}(m+n) = \sum_{k \in S} p_{ik}(m) \; p_{kj}(n) \tag{17}$$

The above equation is one form of the celebrated C-K equation. Using this equation, n-step transition probabilities can be computed in terms of one-step transition probabilities. To see how, consider $P(n)$, the matrix of n-step transition probabilities. That is, $P(n) = [p_{ij}(n)]$. First we observe that $P(0) = I$. Substituting $m = 1$ and $n = n - 1$ in (17) and using the matrix form, we obtain $P(n) = PP(n-1)$.

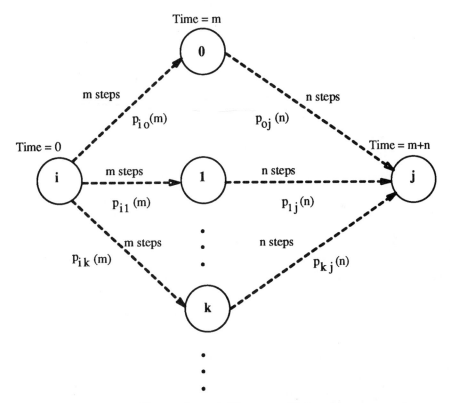

Figure 3.12 An illustration of Chapman-Kolmogorov equations

Solving this recurrence with initial condition $P(0) = I$, we get

$$P(n) = P^n; \qquad n \geq 0 \qquad (18)$$

Thus the matrix of n-step transition probabilities is the nth power of the TPM. It can be verified that $P(n)$ is again a *stochastic matrix* (see Problem 6 at the end of this section). We shall use the above result to investigate the evolution of the DTMC, starting from the initial state.

Evolution of State Probabilities

We assume that the state space is $S = \{0, 1, 2, ...\}$ and we denote

$$p_j(n) = P\{X_n = j\}; \quad n = 0, 1, 2, ...; \quad j = 0, 1, 2, ...$$

It can be seen by the *total probability theorem* that

$$P\{X_n = j\} = \sum_{i \in S} P\{X_n = j \mid X_0 = i\} \ P\{X_0 = i\}$$

Thus we have

$$p_j(n) = \sum_{i \in S} p_i(0) \, p_{ij}(n) \qquad (19)$$

Let $\Pi(n) = [\, p_0(n) \quad p_1(n) \quad p_2(n) \quad ...\,]$. Note that $\Pi(0)$ gives the pmf of the initial random variable X_0 whereas $\Pi(n)$ gives the pmf of the random variable X_n. In matrix notation, (19) becomes

$$\Pi(n) = \Pi(0) P(n) = \Pi(0) P^n \qquad n = 0, 1, 2, ... \qquad (20)$$

Thus, knowing the pmf of the initial random variable X_0 and the TPM, we can compute the pmf of any X_n for any $n \in \mathbb{N}$. We shall illustrate this by way of an example.

Example 3.14

Consider the two-state Markov chain of Example 3.10, with TPM given by

$$P = \begin{bmatrix} 1 - a & a \\ b & 1 - b \end{bmatrix} \qquad 0 \leq a, b \leq 1$$

We shall discuss this system under three cases as done earlier.

Case 1: $a = b = 0$: Here P is the identity matrix.

$$P = \begin{bmatrix} 1 & 0 \\ 0 & 1 \end{bmatrix} = I;$$

$$P(n) = P^n = I$$

Since $P^n = P$, there is no change in the state of the Markov chain. This can be easily seen from the state transition diagram (Figure 3.6). Let the initial state be state 0 so that $\pi(0) = \begin{bmatrix} 1 & 0 \end{bmatrix}$. We have that $\pi(n) = \begin{bmatrix} 1 & 0 \end{bmatrix}$; $\forall\, n = 1, 2, 3, ...$, and thus the system will remain forever in state 0. Similarly, if $\Pi(0) = \begin{bmatrix} 0 & 1 \end{bmatrix}$, the system will remain forever in state 1.

Case 2: $a = b = 1$: Here P is given by

$$P = \begin{bmatrix} 0 & 1 \\ 1 & 0 \end{bmatrix}$$

It is easy to see in this case that

$$P = \begin{bmatrix} 1 & 0 \\ 0 & 1 \end{bmatrix} \quad \text{for } n \text{ even}$$

$$= \begin{bmatrix} 0 & 1 \\ 1 & 0 \end{bmatrix} \quad \text{for } n \text{ odd}$$

The above implies, for example, that if the initial state is 0, then it will be in state 0 after even number of steps and in state 1 after odd number of steps. This can be easily verified as follows. Let $\Pi(0) = \begin{bmatrix} 1 & 0 \end{bmatrix}$. Then

$$\Pi(n) = \begin{bmatrix} 1 & 0 \end{bmatrix} \quad \text{for } n \text{ even}$$

$$= \begin{bmatrix} 0 & 1 \end{bmatrix} \quad \text{for } n \text{ odd}$$

If $\Pi(0) = \begin{bmatrix} 0 & 1 \end{bmatrix}$, the situation simply reverses.

Case 3: Here, $|\, 1 - a - b\,| < 1$. It has been shown by Bhat [1984] that

$$P^n = \begin{bmatrix} \frac{b + ax^n}{a+b} & \frac{a - ax^n}{a+b} \\ \frac{b - bx^n}{a+b} & \frac{a + bx^n}{a+b} \end{bmatrix}$$

where $x = 1 - a - b$. If the initial state is state 0, then $\Pi(0) = [1 \quad 0]$ and we have

$$\Pi(n) = \Pi(0) P^n = \left[\frac{b + ax^n}{a+b} \quad \frac{a - ax^n}{a+b} \right]; \qquad n = 1, 2, ...$$

If the initial state is state 1, then

$$\Pi(n) = \left[\frac{b - bx^n}{a+b} \quad \frac{a + bx^n}{a+b} \right]; \qquad n = 1, 2, ...$$

Let us look at what would happen as $n \to \infty$. Since $\mid x \mid < 1$, $x^n \to 0$ as $n \to \infty$ and so we get for both the cases $\Pi(0) = [1 \quad 0]$ and $\Pi(0) = [0 \quad 1]$ that

$$\lim_{n \to \infty} \Pi(n) = \left[\frac{b}{a+b} \quad \frac{a}{a+b} \right]$$

Firstly, the above is independent of n and secondly, it is independent of the initial pmf $\Pi(0)$. Also, as $n \to \infty$, the matrix P^n becomes

$$\lim_{n \to \infty} P^n = \left[\begin{array}{cc} \frac{b}{a+b} & \frac{a}{a+b} \\ \frac{b}{a+b} & \frac{a}{a+b} \end{array} \right]$$

The physical interpretation here is that as $n \to \infty$, that is, after sufficient time has elapsed, the DTMC settles down to a behavior whereby it visits state 0, $\frac{b}{(a+b)}$ percent of the total number of time steps on an average and visits state 1, $\frac{a}{(a+b)}$ percent of the total number of time steps on an average. In this case, we say that the DTMC has reached *steady-state*. The probabilities $\frac{b}{(a+b)}$ and $\frac{a}{(a+b)}$ are called the *steady-state* or *limiting probabilities* of states 0 and 1, respectively. *Steady-state probabilities* for a DTMC, if they exist, convey useful information about the system.

3.3.5 Steady-State Analysis

Here we discuss the analysis of a useful class of DTMCs, namely those having a steady-state probability distribution. Such DTMCs are often encountered in the manufacturing context. We assume a DTMC $\{X_n \in S : n \in \mathbb{N}\}$ where S is either $\mathbb{N}$ or a finite set $\{0, 1, 2, ..., s\}$.

Limiting Probabilities

Frequently we are interested in studying the *limiting* behavior of the transition probabilities $p_{ij}(n)$ and the state probabilities $p_j(n)$, i.e., when

$n \to \infty$. These limiting probabilities may or may not exist in the general case. Often, the terms *long-run* or *equilibrium* or *steady-state* behavior are used in this context. Suppose the following limiting probabilities exist and are unique.

$$\lim_{n \to \infty} p_j(n) \qquad j = 0, 1, 2, \ldots$$

$$\lim_{n \to \infty} p_{ij}(n) \qquad i, j = 0, 1, 2, \ldots$$

Then it can be shown for any $j = 0, 1, 2, \ldots$, (see Problem 8 in this section) that

$$\lim_{n \to \infty} p_j(n) = \lim_{n \to \infty} p_{ij}(n) \qquad \text{for } i = 0, 1, 2, \ldots$$

We use the notation

$$y_j = \lim_{n \to \infty} p_j(n).$$

If y_j's exist and are unique, then we can see that

$$\lim_{n \to \infty} P^n = \begin{bmatrix} Y \\ Y \\ \cdot \\ \cdot \\ \cdot \\ Y \end{bmatrix}$$

where $Y = [\, y_0 \;\; y_1 \;\; y_2 \;\; \ldots \,]$. Recall how the above results are illustrated by Example 3.14.

For a general DTMC, y_j's may or may not exist. Here we would be interested in studying those DTMCs for which these limiting state probabilities exist. We discuss below the conditions under which y_j's exist and add up to 1, thus forming a valid probability distribution.

Communication Classes and Irreducibility

Definition: Let $i, j \in S$. State j is said to be *accessible* from state i if $p_{ij}(n) > 0$ for some $n \geq 0$. The states i and j are said to *communicate* if each is accessible from the other.

It can be seen that :

1. State i communicates with itself for all $i = 0, 1, ...$

2. If state i communicates with state j, then state j communicates with state i, for all $i, j = 0, 1, 2, ...$

3. If state i communicates with state j and state j with state k, then state i communicates with state k for all $i, j, k = 0, 1, 2, ...$

The above properties imply that the relation of communication is an equivalence relation and hence the state space is partitioned into equivalence classes where each class comprises states that only communicate among themselves.

Definition: In a DTMC, the equivalence classes corresponding to the relation of communication are called the *communication classes*.

Definition: A DTMC is called *irreducible* if there is only a single communication class, that is, all states communicate with one another.

Definition: A communication class A in a DTMC with state space S is said to be *closed* if no state belonging to S but not to A is accessible from any state of A and *open* otherwise.

Example 3.15

Consider the single machine example with state space $\{0, 1\}$ (Figure 3.6). When $a = b = 0$ (case 1), state 0 communicates with itself alone and similarly state 1. Neither is accessible from the other and so they don't communicate. Obviously, the DTMC is not irreducible and there are two closed communication classes $\{0\}$ and $\{1\}$.

When $a = b = 1$ (case 2), then state 0 communicates with state 1 and the chain is irreducible with a single closed communication class $\{0, 1\}$.

In case 3, where $|1 - a - b| < 1$, again state 0 communicates with state 1 and the chain is irreducible.

Example 3.16

Consider the two-machine system, with the state space $\{0, 1, 2\}$ (Figure 3.11). Here state 1 is accessible from state 0 but not vice versa. Hence states

0 and 1 do not communicate. Similarly, though state 2 is accessible from state 1, they do not communicate. The chain is of course not irreducible and we have three classes, $\{0\}, \{1\}$, and $\{2\}$. The classes $\{0\}$ and $\{1\}$ are open while the class $\{2\}$ is closed.

Transience, Recurrence, and Periodicity

Consider a DTMC $\{X_n : n \geq 0\}$. For $i = 0, 1, 2, ...$, define $f_{ii}(k)$ as the probability that the DTMC returns to state i, for the first time, in exactly k steps. Note that $f_{ii}(1) = p_{ii}$. If f_i is the probability of the DTMC ever returning to state i, then

$$f_i = \sum_{k=1}^{\infty} f_{ii}(k)$$

Let v_i be the mean number of steps taken by the DTMC to return to state i, after leaving it. It is easy to see that

$$v_i = \sum_{k=1}^{\infty} k f_{ii}(k)$$

Definition: A given state i of a DTMC is said to be *recurrent* if $f_i = 1$ and *transient* if $f_i < 1$.

Definition: A recurrent state i is said to be *positive recurrent* or *non-null recurrent* if v_i is finite and *null recurrent* if v_i is infinity.

Physically speaking, if state i is recurrent, then the DTMC will certainly return to state i whenever it leaves it. If state i is transient, there is a non-zero probability that the DTMC will not return to state i. A recurrent state is positive recurrent if the mean number of steps required for returning to the state is finite. Recurrent states are further classified as periodic or aperiodic, as in the following definition.

Definition: The *period* of a recurrent state i, denoted by d_i, is the greatest common divisor of the set of positive integers n such that $p_{ii}(n) > 0$. State i is said to be *aperiodic* if $d_i = 1$ and *periodic* with period d_i if $d_i > 1$. Positive recurrent, aperiodic states are called *ergodic* states.

Example 3.17

We consider the single machine example with state space $\{0, 1\}$ (Figure 3.6). In case 1 ($a = b = 0$), we note that

$$f_{00}(1) = 1; \quad f_{00}(k) = 0 \quad \text{for } k = 2, 3, \dots$$
$$f_{11}(1) = 1; \quad f_{11}(k) = 0 \quad \text{for } k = 2, 3, \dots$$

Therefore $f_0 = f_1 = 1$ and both the states are recurrent. Also, $v_0 = v_1 = 1$ and therefore both the states are positive recurrent. Further, both the states can be easily verified to be aperiodic.

In Case 2 ($a = b = 1$), we have

$$f_{00}(1) = 0; \quad f_{00}(2) = 1; \quad f_{00}(k) = 0 \quad \text{for } k = 3, 4, \dots$$
$$f_{11}(1) = 0; \quad f_{11}(2) = 1; \quad f_{11}(k) = 0 \quad \text{for } k = 3, 4, \dots$$

Since $f_0 = f_1 = 1$, both the states are recurrent. Also, $v_0 = v_1 = 2$ and hence both the states are positive recurrent. Since $p_{00}(2k) = 1$ and $p_{00}(2k + 1) = 0$ for $k = 0, 1, 2, \dots$, state 0 is periodic with period 2. Similarly, state 1 is periodic with period 2.

In case 3 ($|1 - a - b| < 1$), we have

$$f_{00}(1) = 1 - a$$
$$f_{00}(2) = ab$$
$$f_{00}(3) = a(1 - b)b$$
$$f_{00}(k + 2) = a(1 - b)^k b \quad \text{for } k = 2, 3, \dots$$

It can be verified that $f_0 = 1$ and hence state 0 is recurrent. Similarly, state 1 is recurrent. Also,

$$v_0 = (1 - a) + 2(ab) + \sum_{k=3}^{\infty} ka(1 - b)^{k-2}b$$

v_0 can be verified to be finite and therefore state 0 is positive recurrent. Similarly, state 1 is positive recurrent. Also, both the states are aperiodic.

Example 3.18

In the two-machine system with failures and no repair (Figure 3.11), we see that

$$f_{00}(1) = (1 - a)^2; \quad f_{00}(k) = 0 \quad \text{for } k = 2, 3, \dots$$

Thus $f_0 = (1 - a)^2 < 1$ if $a \neq 0$. Therefore, state 0 is transient. State 1 is similarly transient, whereas state 2 is positive recurrent and aperiodic.

Results for Classification of States

Here we present several results that are useful in classifying the DTMC states. We do not prove these results here and the reader is urged to prove the results (see Problem 9 in this section).

1. Transience, recurrence, positive recurrence, and periodicity are *class properties*. That is, if state i is transient (recurrent), (positive recurrent), (periodic), and state i communicates with state j, then state j is also transient (recurrent), (positive recurrent), (periodic). This result is called the *class property theorem*.

2. All states in an open communication class are transient. All states in a finite closed communication class are positive recurrent. Null recurrent states can only occur in infinite closed communication classes.

3. In a finite DTMC, (i) not all states are transient, and (ii) all recurrent states are positive recurrent. Therefore, in a finite irreducible DTMC, all states are positive recurrent.

4. A state i is recurrent if and only if $n_i = \infty$, where n_i is the mean number of returns to state i, starting from state i.

To compute the term n_i in the last result, we proceed as follows. Consider a DTMC $\{X_n : n \geq 0\}$ and define the following indicator random variable :

$$I_i(k) = 1 \quad \text{if } X_k = i$$
$$= 0 \quad \text{otherwise.}$$

If N_i denotes the number of visits to state i by the DTMC, then, using the above indicator function,

$$N_i = \sum_{k=1}^{\infty} I_i(k)$$

The mean number of returns to state i can be obtained as

$$n_i = E\left[N_i \mid X_0 = i\right]$$

$$= E\left[\sum_{k=1}^{\infty} I_i\left(k\right) \mid X_0 = i\right]$$

$$= \sum_{k=1}^{\infty} E\left[I_i\left(k\right) \mid X_0 = i\right]$$

$$= \sum_{k=1}^{\infty} p_{ii}\left(k\right)$$

Thus knowing the k-step transition probabilities, one can compute n_i and investigate recurrence.

Example 3.19

In this example we illustrate some of the above results for the single-machine system with state space $\{0, 1\}$ (Figure 3.6). In case 2 ($a = b = 1$), we have already seen in Example 3.17 that both the states are positive recurrent with period 2. This verifies the *class property theorem*. The class $\{0, 1\}$ is a finite closed communication class and hence both the states are positive recurrent. Thus properties 1, 2, and 3 are easily verified. Further, for $i = 0, 1$,

$$p_{ii}\left(k\right) = 1 \quad \text{for } k = 2, 4, 6, \ldots$$
$$= 0 \quad \text{for } k = 1, 3, 5, \ldots$$

Therefore, $n_i = \infty$, which again confirms that both the states are recurrent.

In case 3 ($\mid 1 - a - b \mid < 1$), properties 1, 2, and 3 can again be verified easily. Also, from Example 3.14,

$$p_{00}\left(k\right) = \frac{b + ax^k}{a + b}; \quad p_{11}\left(k\right) = \frac{a + bx^k}{a + b}$$

where $x = 1 - a - b$. It can again be verified that $n_0 = \infty$ and $n_1 = \infty$ and therefore both the states are recurrent.

Existence and Computation of Limiting Probabilities

For an irreducible DTMC, with all positive recurrent states, it can be shown that the following limiting probabilities exist:

$$y_j = \lim_{n \to \infty} p_j(n) \qquad j = 0, 1, 2, \ldots$$

The above probabilities satisfy

$$y_j \geq 0 \qquad j = 0, 1, 2, \ldots$$

$$\sum_{j=0}^{\infty} y_j = 1$$

Also, these limiting probabilities are unique and independent of the initial probability distribution. We know that

$$p_j(n) = \sum_{i=0}^{\infty} p_i(n-1) p_{ij} \qquad n = 1, 2, 3, \ldots; \quad j = 0, 1, 2, \ldots$$

Taking the limit on both sides as $n \to \infty$, we obtain

$$\lim_{n \to \infty} p_j(n) = \lim_{n \to \infty} \sum_{i=0}^{\infty} p_i(n-1) p_{ij}$$

Assuming the existence of unique limits above, we obtain

$$y_j = \sum_{i=0}^{\infty} y_i p_{ij} \qquad j = 0, 1, 2, \ldots$$

In matrix notation, we have

$$Y = YP \qquad \text{where } Y = [\, y_0 \ \ y_1 \ \ y_2 \ \ldots] \tag{21}$$

Y is called the vector of *limiting* or *steady-state* probabilities. Thus the unique limiting probabilities of an irreducible DTMC with positive recurrent states may be obtained as the solution of the following:

$$Y = YP$$

$$\sum_{j=0}^{\infty} y_j = 1 \tag{22}$$

$$y_j \geq 0 \qquad j = 0, 1, 2, \ldots$$

Since $Y = YP$, we have, multiplying on both sides by P, $YP = YP^2$. Repeating this, we get

$$Y = YP^n \qquad \text{for } n = 1, 2, 3, \dots$$

Comparing the above equation with (20), we can conclude that, if we choose Y as the initial probability distribution, the probability distribution for subsequent time steps would remain invariant. For this reason, Y is also called a *stationary* probability vector.

It can be further shown that in an irreducible DTMC, all states are positive recurrent if and only if there is a unique stationary probability vector Y satisfying (22).

Aperiodic Case: If the DTMC is irreducible and positive recurrent with aperiodic states, then y_j is to be interpreted as the visit ratio for state j, i.e., the long-run fraction of the total number of time steps for which the DTMC resides in state j. In fact

$$y_j = \frac{1}{v_j} = \lim_{n \to \infty} p_{jj}(n)$$

Note that v_j is the mean recurrence time of state j, i.e., the mean number of steps between successive visits to state j.

Periodic Case: If the DTMC is irreducible and positive recurrent with periodic states having period d, then again y_j has the same interpretation as above. However, $\lim_{n \to \infty} p_{jj}(n)$ does not exist, whereas the following limit does exist:

$$\lim_{n \to \infty} p_{jj}(nd) = \frac{d}{v_j} = y_j$$

We now briefly summarize the results for other classes of DTMCs.

Non-Irreducible Case: For a DTMC with two or more positive recurrent communication classes, each class will have its own unique stationary probability vector. Also, the overall limiting probability vector, i.e., the vector of limiting probabilities of all the states in the DTMC, will be stationary. However, there will be an infinite number of overall limiting probability vectors.

Transient Case: For any transient state j, the limiting probability $y_j = 0$. That is, in the steady-state, the DTMC visits transient states with zero probability.

Null Recurrent Case: Recall that null recurrent states can only occur in infinite closed communication classes. For each null recurrent state, the limiting probability $y_j = 0$.

We now illustrate the steady-state analysis of DTMCs for several examples, considered above.

Example 3.20

Let us look at the single-machine example with state space $S = \{0, 1\}$ (Figure 3.6). First, let us consider case 3, i.e., $|1 - a - b| < 1$. Here $Y = (y_0, y_1)$. We have seen that the DTMC is irreducible, positive recurrent, and aperiodic. So we can obtain the unique stationary probabilities as the solution of:

$$[y_0 \ \ y_1] = [y_0 \ \ y_1] \begin{bmatrix} 1 - a & a \\ b & 1 - b \end{bmatrix}$$

$$y_0 + y_1 = 1$$

It is easy to see that

$$y_0 = \frac{b}{a + b} \quad \text{and} \quad y_1 = \frac{a}{a + b}$$

as we have already observed earlier in Example 3.14. If $a = \frac{1}{5}$ and $b = \frac{3}{5}$, then we have $y_0 = \frac{3}{4}$ and $y_1 = \frac{1}{4}$. The interpretation is that on an average, the DTMC visits state 0 for 75% of the total number of time steps and state 1 for 25% of the total number of time steps.

We now look at case 2 ($a = b = 1$). Here again the DTMC is irreducible with positive recurrent states, but periodic with period 2. In this case also, we have a unique stationary probability vector given by $y_0 = \frac{1}{2}$ and $y_1 = \frac{1}{2}$. So, on an average, 50% of the visits are to state 0 and the other 50% of the visits are to state 1.

In case 1, we have $a = b = 0$ and there are two communication classes $\{0\}$ and $\{1\}$. The equation $Y = YP$ together with $y_0 + y_1 = 1$ gives an infinite number of solutions,

$$Y = [y_0 \quad 1 - y_0] \qquad \text{where } 0 \leq y_0 \leq 1$$

Each class has a stationary probability vector of its own, in this case, $y_0 = 1$ and $y_1 = 1$. But there is an infinite number of overall stationary probability vectors. This will generically happen in the case of non-irreducible DTMCs. Each closed communication class will have its own limiting probability vector.

Example 3.21

Consider the example of an NC machine processing three different part types (Figure 3.7). The state space is $\{1, 2, 3\}$. In the case of cyclic processing, the DTMC is irreducible, positive recurrent, and periodic with period 3. The unique stationary probabilities can be easily shown to be given by $y_1 = y_2 = y_3 = \frac{1}{3}$. In the case of probabilistic selection, assuming $0 < q_1, q_2, q_3 < 1$, the DTMC is irreducible, positive recurrent, and aperiodic, and the unique limiting probabilities are given by $y_1 = q_1$; $y_2 = q_2$; $y_3 = q_3$. Here y_1, y_2, and y_3 give the relative number of times type 1, type 2, and type 3 parts are processed by the NC machine. It is interesting to note the equivalence in the results for the cyclic sequence and the probabilistic selection with $q_1 = q_2 = q_3 = \frac{1}{3}$. However, the underlying Markov chains are different.

Example 3.22

Consider the closed central server network of Figure 3.9. If $0 < q_i < 1$ for $i = 0, 1, ..., m$, then this DTMC is irreducible, positive recurrent, and aperiodic, and the unique stationary probabilities may be obtained as the solution of the normalizing equation and the following equations:

$$y_0 = y_0 q_0 + \sum_{i=1}^{m} y_i$$

$$y_j = y_0 q_j \qquad j = 1, 2, ..., m$$

It can be easily seen after normalizing that

$$y_0 = \frac{1}{2 - q_0} \quad \text{and} \quad y_j = \frac{q_j}{2 - q_0} \quad j = 1, 2, ..., m$$

Example 3.23

In the DTMC of the two-machine system with failures and no repair (Figure 3.11), we have two transient states 0 and 1, one aperiodic positive recurrent state 2, and three communication classes $\{0\}, \{1\}$, and $\{2\}$. Here we have $y_0 = 0$; $y_1 = 0$; $y_2 = 1$; this can be seen intuitively. State 2 is also called an absorbing state. Here, whatever the initial probability distribution, the chain ends up in state 2 and stays there permanently. In the automated manufacturing context, such states correspond to deadlocks or unrecoverable states. We will discuss such DTMCs in detail in Section 3.8.

PROBLEMS

1. Compute the mean sojourn times of the states in the DTMCs discussed in Examples 3.10, 3.11, 3.12, and 3.13.

2. Obtain the n-step transition probability matrices for Examples 3.11, 3.12, and 3.13.

3. Extend Example 3.10 to the case where the machine can be in three states, namely, 0 (busy); 1 (under repair); and 2 (idle). Assume that the system is observed only when it changes state and that

$$P = \begin{bmatrix} 0 & \frac{1}{2} & \frac{1}{2} \\ 1 & 0 & 0 \\ 1 & 0 & 0 \end{bmatrix}$$

Draw the state transition diagram, compute the mean sojourn times, and the matrix of n-step transition probabilities.

4. Given the TPM P of a single machine system (Example 3.10)

$$P = \begin{bmatrix} 1 - a & a \\ b & 1 - b \end{bmatrix} \quad \begin{matrix} 0 \le a, b \le 1 \\ |1 - a - b| < 1 \end{matrix}$$

show that

$$P(n) = \begin{bmatrix} \frac{b + ax^n}{a+b} & \frac{a - ax^n}{a+b} \\ \frac{b - bx^n}{a+b} & \frac{a + bx^n}{a+b} \end{bmatrix} \quad \text{where } x = 1 - a - b.$$

5. Let $X_0, X_1, ...,$ be a sequence of i.i.d. (independent and identically distributed) Bernoulli random variables with parameter p, i.e., for each $k = 0, 1, 2, ...,$

$$P\{X_k = 0\} = 1 - p; \quad P\{X_k = 1\} = p$$

(a) Show that the stochastic process $\{Y_n : n \geq 0\}$ defined by

$$Y_n = \sum_{k=0}^{n} X_k$$

is a DTMC. Classify this DTMC and write down the TPM.

(b) If $X_0, X_1, ...,$ are independent but not identical random variables with parameters $p_0, p_1, ...,$ what about the process $\{Y_n : n \geq 0\}$? Is it still a Markov chain?

(c) Investigate the case when $X_0, X_1, ...,$ are neither independent nor identical.

6. Given that P is a stochastic matrix, show, for $n = 2, 3, ...,$ that P^n is also a stochastic matrix.

7. Any transition probability matrix P is a *stochastic* matrix; that is, $p_{ij} \geq 0$ for all i and j, and $\sum_j p_{ij} = 1$ for all i. If, in addition, the column sums are also unity, that is, $\sum_i p_{ij} = 1$, for all j, then matrix P is called *doubly stochastic*. If a Markov chain with a doubly stochastic P is irreducible, aperiodic, and finite with n states, show that the steady-state probabilities are given by $y_j = \frac{1}{n}$ for all j.

8. Assuming standard notation, and existence and uniqueness of limiting probabilities, show that

$$\lim_{n \to \infty} p_j(n) = \lim_{n \to \infty} p_{ij}(n) \quad \text{for } i, j = 0, 1, ...$$

9. Attempt a proof of the four results for classification of states, presented in Topic 3.3.5 (Steady-State Analysis).

10. Assume that a machine is in one of three states: 0 (busy), 1 (idle), and 2 (undergoing repair). Observing its state at 8 *A.M.* everyday, it is believed that the system approximately behaves like a homogeneous Markov chain with the following TPM:

$$P = \begin{bmatrix} 0.6 & 0.2 & 0.2 \\ 0.1 & 0.8 & 0.1 \\ 0.6 & 0 & 0.4 \end{bmatrix}$$

Prove that the chain is irreducible, and determine the steady-state probabilities.

11. Consider a system with two machines M_1 and M_2, both of which are failure prone. Parts get processed at M_1 first. After processing at M_1, they move to M_2 if M_2 is free. Otherwise, they wait on M_1, thus blocking M_1. After processing at M_2, the finished part leaves the system. The processing times on M_1 and M_2 are geometrically distributed with parameters p_1 and p_2, respectively. The mean time between failures is geometric with parameters f_1 and f_2, respectively; the repair times are geometric with r_1 and r_2 as parameters. When a machine fails, it is repaired and will resume the processing of the partially finished part. Identifying a suitable state space for this system, develop a DTMC model and investigate its properties.

12. In a particular manufacturing system, there are two machines M_1 and M_2. M_1 is a high-precision NC machine that produces finished parts at a very fast rate, and M_2 is a slow, low-precision machine. M_2 is employed only when M_1 is down, and it is assumed that M_2 doesn't fail. Assume that the processing time of parts on M_1, the processing time on M_2, the time to failure of M_1, and the repair time of M_1 are independent geometric random variables with parameters p_1, p_2, f, and r, respectively. Identify a suitable state space for the DTMC model of the above system and compute the TPM. Investigate the steady-state behavior of the DTMC.

13. It is a common practice to have standby redundant units in manufacturing systems so as to attain a high degree of reliability. Suppose two machines are available, one in use and one on a standby basis. The probability that a machine that is in use fails during a unit time period is p. It takes 3 units of time to repair a failed machine. Define a process with state space $S = \{(20), (10), (11), (12), (01), (02)\}$ where in a typical state $(i, j), i$ is the number of machines in working condition and j is the expended repair time in unit time periods. Show that this process is a DTMC. Write down the TPM, classify the states, and compute the steady-state probability distribution. What are the performance measures that one can compute for the above system, using the steady-state probabilities?

14. A machine component is replaced, as a rule, once in 5 weeks. However, it has been found to wear out in less than 5 weeks in some cases. It is found that 10% of the components were replaced at the end of the first week; 15% of the week-old components were replaced at the end of the second week; 35% of the 2-week-old components were replaced at the end of the third week; and 40% of the 3-week-old components were replaced at the end of the fourth week. Set up the transition probability matrix of a DTMC formulation of the above situation. Obtain the age distribution of a component after the

system has been in operation for a long time. A component is i weeks old, $i = 0, 1, 2, 3, 4$. What is the expected length of time until its replacement? Can you recommend any replacement policy based on these results?

15. A manufacturing system has three machines. On any day, each working machine breaks down with probability p, independent of other machines. At the end of each day, the machines that are down are sent to a repairer who can work on only one machine at a time. When there are one or more machines to repair at the beginning of a day, the repairer fixes and returns exactly one at the end of that day. Let X_n be the number of working machines at the end of day n (beginning of day $n + 1$), after breakdowns and repairs that day are included.

    (a) What fraction of days begin with j working machines, $j = 0, 1, 2, 3$? What is the average number of working machines at the beginning of a typical day?

    (b) If a working machine at the beginning of a day brings in a revenue of r and each machine repair cost is C, what is the net reward (revenue – cost) per day?

16. Design and implement a software package for computing the steady-state probability distribution of a positive-recurrent, irreducible DTMC, given its TPM. Verify the results of the several problems above, using your package.

3.4 CONTINUOUS TIME MARKOV CHAIN MODELS

In this section we consider an important special class of continuous time stochastic processes with countable state space. These are *continuous time Markov chains* (CTMCs). In the performance modeling of AMSs, CTMCs are very relevant, since the evolution of activities in an AMS follows a continuous trajectory and traverses through a countable set of states.

3.4.1 Definitions and Notation

We start with the definition of a CTMC and introduce some notation.

Definition: A discrete state space, continuous time process $\{X(t) : t \geq 0\}$ with state space S is called a continuous time Markov chain, if the following *Markov* or *memoryless* property is satisfied: for all

$s \geq 0, u \geq 0, t \geq s,$ and $i, j, x(u) \in S,$

$$P\{X(t) = j \mid X(s) = i; \quad X(u) = x(u) \quad \text{for} \quad 0 \leq u < s\}$$
$$= P\{X(t) = j \mid X(s) = i\} \quad (23)$$

Definition: Given a CTMC $\{X(t) : t \geq 0\}$ with state space S, the probabilities

$$p_{ij}(s, t) = P\{X(t) = j \mid X(s) = i\}$$

are called the *transition probabilities* corresponding to states $i, j \in S$ and $s \geq 0, t \geq s.$

Remark: By definition, for $s \geq 0,$ $p_{ij}(s, s)$ takes the value 1 for $i = j$ and 0 otherwise.

Definition: A CTMC $\{X(t) : t \geq 0\}$ is said to be *homogeneous* or is said to have *stationary transition probabilities* if $p_{ij}(s, t),$ for each $s \geq 0$ and $t \geq s$ does not depend on s and depends only on $t - s.$

Remark: In the case of a homogeneous CTMC, we can write

$$p_{ij}(s, t) = p_{ij}(t - s)$$
$$= P\{X(u + t - s) = j \mid X(u) = i\} \qquad \forall u \geq 0$$

3.4.2 Sojourn Times in States

The sojourn times in the individual states of a CTMC are exponentially distributed, as shown below.

Definition: Given a state i of a CTMC $\{X(t) : t \geq 0\}$, the sojourn time T_i of state i is a continuous random variable that represents the span of time the CTMC spends in that state on each visit to the state.

Consider a CTMC $\{X(t) : t \geq 0\}$ and let i be any state of the CTMC. Assume that T_i is the sojourn time of state i. By the Markovian property in a CTMC, we know that the way in which the past trajectory of the process influences the future evolution is completely specified by giving the current state of the process. In particular, we need not specify how long the process has been in its current state. This means that the remaining time in state i must have a distribution that depends only upon i and not upon how long the process has been in state i. Formally,

$$P\{T_i > s + x \mid T_i > s\} = h(x) \quad \forall s \geq 0, \quad x \geq 0 \qquad (24)$$

where $h(x)$ is a function only of the additional time and is independent of the expended time s. Now, we have

$$P\{T_i > s + x \mid T_i > s\} = \frac{P\{T_i > s + x \land T_i > s\}}{P\{T_i > s\}}$$

$$= \frac{P\{T_i > s + x\}}{P\{T_i > s\}}$$

Using (24) in the above, we get

$$P\{T_i > s + x\} = P\{T_i > s\} \, h(x) \qquad (25)$$

Setting $s = 0$ and observing that $P\{T_i > 0\} = 1$, we obtain

$$P\{T_i > x\} = h(x)$$

Thus (25) becomes

$$P\{T_i > s + x\} = P\{T_i > s\} P\{T_i > x\}; \quad s, x \geq 0$$

The above can be seen to be equivalent to (10), which constitutes the memoryless property of continuous random variables. It has been shown in Section 3.1.2 that the exponential random variable is the unique memoryless continuous random variable. Thus the sojourn time of every state in a CTMC is exponentially distributed.

Definition: For any given state i, let $T_i = EXP(a_i)$. If $a_i = 0$, the state is said to be an *absorbing state*; if $a_i = \infty$, the state is said to be *instantaneous*; and if $0 < a_i < \infty$, the state is said to be *stable*.

Most of the CTMCs discussed in this section have only stable states. We discuss absorbing states in Section 3.8.

3.4.3 Examples of CTMCs in Manufacturing

Now we consider several manufacturing situations which can be formulated as CTMC models. These examples will be discussed throughout Section 3.4.

Example 3.24

A manufacturing system comprising a single NC machine that works on an inexhaustible supply of raw workpieces can be modeled as a CTMC under the following assumptions. The machine works on parts, one at a time, and takes an exponentially distributed amount of time to process each part. The processing times of all parts are independent and identically distributed. Each time the machine finishes processing a part, it is set up for the next part, the setup operation taking an exponentially distributed time. The machine is also prone to failures with time between failures exponentially distributed. The failed machine is immediately repaired, the repair time being exponentially distributed. If all the random variables involved are mutually independent, then we have a model with state space $\{0, 1, 2\}$ where the states have the following interpretation.

0 : Machine being set up for the next part.

1 : Machine processing a part.

2 : Machine failed, being repaired.

If $X(t)$, for $t \geq 0$, represents the state of the system at time t, then $\{X(t) : t \geq 0\}$ is a CTMC. Let the rates of the random variables be given by s = setup rate; p = processing rate; f = failure rate; r = repair rate. If s, p, f, and r are independent of the time parameter t, then the above model becomes a homogeneous CTMC. The sojourn times T_0, T_1, and T_2 in the three states are exponentially distributed because the model is a CTMC. It can be verified that $T_0 = EXP(s)$ since only setup operation is in progress in state 0 and that $T_2 = EXP(r)$ since only repair operation is in progress in state 2. In state 1, there are two possibilities, viz., processing finishes without occurrence of failure and the machine fails before finishing processing. In either case, the CTMC will go out of state 1. If random variables X_1 and X_2 represent the processing time and time to failure, respectively, then it can be noted that $T_1 = min(X_1, X_2)$. Since $X_1 = EXP(p)$ and $X_2 = EXP(f)$, T_1 will be $EXP(p + f)$ (see problem 5 in Section 3.1).

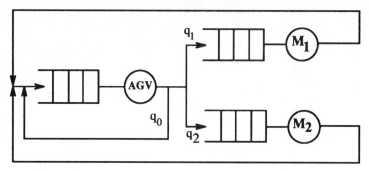

Figure 3.13 Central server network with one AGV and two machines

In the above system, two policies can be followed in the event of the machine failure and subsequent repair. One policy is to resume the processing of the unfinished part and the other policy is to discard the unfinished part and take up a fresh part for processing. We shall call these two policies *resume policy* and *discard policy*, respectively. Note that the discard policy entails a fresh setup operation after each repair. Intuitively, it is easy to see that the resume policy will lead to better throughput. The CTMC models for the resume policy and the discard policy will be different though the state spaces are the same, and by analyzing the two CTMC models, it will be possible to say how much better the throughput will be in the case of the resume policy.

Example 3.25

In Example 3.12, we looked at the central server queuing network model of an FMS with a single AGV and m machines M_1, M_2, ..., M_m. Consider the case $m = 2$, i.e., there are only two machines. The system is depicted in Figure 3.13. Assume that the processing times on the AGV and the machines are mutually independent exponential random variables with rates μ_0, μ_1, and μ_2 respectively. If the number of fixtures in the system is fixed at n, then there are exactly n parts in circulation inside the network at any instant of time. For example, if $n = 1$, there is exactly one part inside the system and the part can be getting serviced by the AGV, or M_1, or M_2. This leads to three states:

0 : Part being transported by AGV

1 : Part getting processed by M_1

2 : Part getting processed by M_2

If $X(t)$, for $t \geq 0$, represents the state of the system at time t, then the process $\{X(t) : t \geq 0\}$ can be considered as a CTMC. The sojourn times T_0, T_1, and T_2 can be seen to be given by $T_0 = EXP(\mu_0)$; $T_1 = EXP(\mu_1)$; $T_2 = EXP(\mu_2)$. If $n = 2$, then there are exactly two parts in circulation in the system and the state space will comprise the following six states:

$1 : (011) :$ One part with M_1 and the other with M_2

$2 : (101) :$ One part with AGV and the other with M_2

$3 : (110) :$ One part with AGV and the other with M_1

$4 : (200) :$ Both parts with AGV

$5 : (002) :$ Both parts with M_2

$6 : (020) :$ Both parts with M_1

In states $4, 5$, and 6, both the parts are with a single resource. This means that one of the parts is getting processed and the other waiting in the queue. To represent each state, we have used the notation (k_0, k_1, k_2), where k_0 is the number of parts with AGV, and k_i, $i = 1, 2$, is the number of parts with machine M_i. Note that we have $k_0 + k_1 + k_2 = 2 = n$. In this case, we have six states with sojourn times given by

$T_1 = EXP(\mu_1 + \mu_2)$; $T_2 = EXP(\mu_0 + \mu_2)$; $T_3 = EXP(\mu_0 + \mu_1)$
$T_4 = EXP(\mu_0)$; $T_5 = EXP(\mu_2)$; and $T_6 = EXP(\mu_1)$.

For a general value of n, the state space of the resulting CTMC model will be the set

$$\{(k_0, k_1, k_2) : \quad k_0 + k_1 + k_2 = n; \quad k_0 \geq 0, k_1 \geq 0, k_2 \geq 0\}$$

The reader is urged to verify that the total number of states in the above set is $\frac{(n+1)(n+2)}{2}$. By analyzing the above CTMC model, we can compute important performance measures such as manufacturing lead time, average work-in-process, and machine utilizations. The model can also be used in making decisions such as: how many fixtures, how many buffers, how many AGVs, and optimum routing probabilities (q_0, q_1, q_2).

Example 3.26

Assembly stations constitute an important component of AMSs. In Figure 3.14, a simple manufacturing system is shown with three machines M_1, M_2, and M_3, of which M_3 is an assembly workstation. In this system, raw

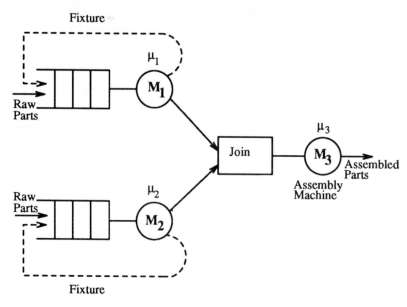

Figure 3.14 An assembly cell

parts of type 1 are fixtured and processed by M_1, and raw parts of type 2 are fixtured and processed by M_2. When M_3 is idle, the parts processed by M_1 and M_2 are defixtured and the two parts are assembled by M_3 into a finished product, which is then unloaded. The released fixtures can be used for fixturing fresh raw parts. The box labeled Join indicates the assembly operation. We make the following assumptions: (1) The processing times on M_1, M_2, and M_3 are mutually independent exponential random variables with rates μ_1, μ_2, and μ_3, respectively. (2) Raw parts of type 1 and type 2 are always available. (3) There is exactly one fixture for type 1 parts and one fixture for type 2 parts. (4) Fixturing and defixturing times are negligible. (5) There is an infinite sink that consumes the finished products as soon as unloaded and unloading time is negligible. (6) There is no buffer in front of M_3, as a consequence of which M_1 and M_2, after finishing processing, may get blocked and have to wait until M_3 is free.

The system can be formulated as a CTMC model with the following states. Note that each state is described by a 3-tuple (x_1, x_2, x_3) where x_i is the individual condition of machine M_i. The component x_i is designated I if M_i is idle, P if M_i is processing a workpiece, and B if M_i is blocked, waiting for the next machine.

(PPI) : M_1 and M_2 busy, M_3 idle

(BPI) : M_1 blocked, M_2 busy, M_3 idle

(PBI) : M_1 busy, M_2 blocked, M_3 idle

(PPP) : All three machines busy

(BPP) : M_1 blocked, M_2 and M_3 busy

(PBP) : M_2 blocked, M_1 and M_3 busy

(BBP) : M_1 and M_2 blocked, M_3 busy

When the number of fixtures in the above system is increased and, in addition, a buffer introduced in front of M_3, another CTMC model can be visualized. CTMC analysis for this system can lead to computation of performance measures such as machine utilizations, throughput, average work-in-process, and manufacturing lead time.

Example 3.27

Consider a system with two machines M_1 and M_2, where M_1 is a fast machine and M_2 is a slow machine. Raw parts are always available and have to undergo one operation each, which may be carried out on M_1 or M_2. Figure 3.15 shows the flow of parts in the system. Each machine after finishing processing a part will immediately start working on the next raw part. We assume that fixturing, defixturing, loading, unloading, and machine setups are all instantaneous. Each machine can randomly fail, and after a possible repair, it will resume processing. We assume that the

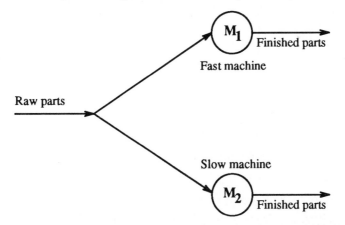

Figure 3.15 A system comprising two heterogeneous machines

processing times of parts on M_1 and M_2 are exponential random variables with rates, μ_1 and μ_2, respectively $(\mu_1 > \mu_2)$. The times to failure of M_1 and M_2 are identical exponential random variables with rate f and the repair times are identical exponential random variables with rate r. All the random variables are mutually independent. The system can be modeled as a CTMC with four states shown below:

0 : (00) : M_1 and M_2 both working

1 : (01) : M_1 working; M_2 failed

2 : (10) : M_1 failed; M_2 working

3 : (11) : Both machines failed.

The average throughput rate of the system will be $(\mu_1 + \mu_2)$ in state 0; μ_1 in state 1; μ_2 in state 2; and zero in state 3. To compute the average throughput of the system, we need to analyze the above CTMC model.

Let n be the number of identical repair facilities in the above system. We can examine three cases: $n = 0$, $n = 1$, and $n = 2$. If $n = 0$, the sojourn times of the four states are: $T_0 = EXP(2f)$; $T_1 = EXP(f)$; $T_2 = EXP(f)$; and $T_3 = \infty$. Observe that once state 3 is reached, the system is permanently crippled since there is no repair. Such a state is called an absorbing state. We will study Markov chains with absorbing states in Section 3.8. If $n = 1$, the sojourn times will be: $T_0 = EXP(2f)$; $T_1 = EXP(f + r)$; $T_2 = EXP(f + r)$; and $T_3 = EXP(r)$. If $n = 2$, the sojourn times T_0, T_1, and T_2 are the same as for $n = 1$. T_3 will be $EXP(2r)$ since there are two identical repair facilities.

Two important performance indices for such systems are (steady-state) *reliability* and *performability*. Reliability of a system is the probability that the system is not down, e.g., in this case, the probability that the system is not in state 3. Performability is a measure of the performance of the system in the face of failures. For example, we have seen that the system here can exhibit four throughput levels at any point of time: $(\mu_1 + \mu_2)$ (state 0), μ_1 (state 1); μ_2 (state 2), and zero (state 3). If $N(t)$ is the number of parts produced by time t $(t \geq 0)$, then $N(t)$ is a performability measure for the above system. For $n = 0, 1, 2$, one can compute $N(t)$ to find out the effect of repair. This will be pursued in Section 3.4.5.

3.4.4 Equations for CTMC Evolution

We now enunciate the Chapman-Kolmogorov equations and the Kolmogorov differential equations which form the basis for CTMC analysis. We first derive the equations for a non-homogeneous CTMC and then present the special case of homogeneous CTMCs.

Chapman-Kolmogorov Equation

Consider a (non-homogeneous) CTMC $\{X(t) : t \geq 0\}$ with state space $\{0, 1, 2, ...\}$. We use the indices $i, j,$ and k to denote typical states and the indices $s, u,$ and t to denote the time parameter. For $0 \leq s \leq t$, consider the transition probabilities $p_{ij}(s,t) = P\{X(t) = j \mid X(s) = i\}$. The transition probabilities can be expressed in matrix form as

$$H(s,t) = [\, p_{ij}(s,t)\,]$$

Now, similar to the Chapman-Kolmogorov equation for a DTMC, we can derive that

$$p_{ij}(s,t) = \sum_k p_{ik}(s,u)\, p_{kj}(u,t) \; ; \quad 0 \leq s \leq u \leq t \qquad (26)$$

In matrix form, (26) can be written as

$$H(s,t) = H(s,u)\, H(u,t) \; ; \quad 0 \leq s \leq u \leq t \qquad (27)$$

These are the *Chapman-Kolmogorov equations* for a CTMC.

Kolmogorov Differential Equations

Let h be an infinitesimal increment in time. Replacing u by t and t by $t + h$ in (27), we get

$$H(s, t + h) = H(s,t)\, H(t, t + h)$$

Now subtracting $H(s,t)$ from either side, we get

$$H(s, t + h) - H(s,t) = H(s,t)\,[H(t, t + h) - I]$$

Dividing either side by h and taking the limit as $h \to 0$, we obtain

$$\lim_{h \to 0} \frac{H(s, t+h) - H(s,t)}{h} = H(s,t) \left(\lim_{h \to 0} \frac{H(t, t+h) - I}{h} \right)$$

This leads to the partial differential equation

$$\frac{\partial H(s,t)}{\partial t} = H(s,t) Q(t) \qquad (28)$$

with initial conditions $H(s,s) = I$, where the matrix $Q(t)$ is given by

$$Q(t) = \lim_{h \to 0} \left(\frac{H(t, t+h) - I}{h} \right) \qquad (29)$$

(28) gives the so-called *forward* Kolmogorov equation. The matrix $Q(t)$ is called the *infinitesimal generator* of the CTMC and is also called the *transition rate matrix*. Before commenting on the elements of $Q(t)$, we shall derive the *backward* equation. For this, we again start with (27).

In the earlier case, we had replaced t by $t + h$ (increment to t which is "forward" compared to s). Now we substitute $u = s + h$ (that is, we are incrementing s, which is "backward" compared to t). We obtain from (27),

$$H(s,t) = H(s, s+h) H(s+h, t)$$

Let us subtract $H(s+h, t)$ from either side, divide by h, and take the limit as $h \to 0$. We then obtain

$$\lim_{h \to 0} \frac{H(s,t) - H(s+h, t)}{h} = \lim_{h \to 0} \left(\frac{H(s, s+h) - I}{h} \right) H(s+h, t)$$

Rearranging terms, this may be written as

$$\frac{\partial H(s,t)}{\partial s} = -Q(s) H(s,t); \qquad 0 \le s \le t \qquad (30)$$

with initial conditions $H(s,s) = I$. Equation (30) is called the *Backward Kolmogorov* equation.

Interpretation of Q(t)

The elements of $Q(t)$ are given by

$$q_{ii}(t) = \lim_{h \to 0} \frac{p_{ii}(t, t+h) - 1}{h} \qquad (31)$$

$$q_{ij}(t) = \lim_{h \to 0} \frac{p_{ij}(t,\ t+h)}{h} \qquad i \neq j \qquad (32)$$

From (31) and (32), we have

$$1 - p_{ii}(t, t+h) = -h q_{ii}(t) + o(h)$$
$$p_{ij}(t, t+h) = h q_{ij}(t) + o(h)$$

where $o(h)$ denotes any function that goes to zero faster than h itself.

Thus we may say that $-q_{ii}(t)$ is the rate at which the process departs from state i, if it is in that state at time t. Similarly, given that the CTMC is in state i at time t, $q_{ij}(t)$ is the rate at which the CTMC moves from state i to state $j\ (j \neq i)$ in the time interval $(t, t+h)$. Now since

$$\sum_j p_{ij}(s,t) = 1 \qquad \forall\, i \quad \text{and} \quad \forall\, s \leq t,$$

the equations (31) and (32) for $q_{ii}(t)$ and $q_{ij}(t)$ imply that

$$\sum_j q_{ij}(t) = 0 \qquad \forall\, i \qquad (33)$$

Thus the sum of the elements of any row of the matrix $Q(t)$ is zero.

Evolution of State Probabilities

It can be shown that the equations (28) and (30) have the same solution given by

$$H(s,t) = \exp\left[\int_s^t Q(u)\, du\right] \qquad (34)$$

where the expression $\exp(At)$, for a square matrix A, is defined as the following matrix power series:

$$\exp(At) = I + At + A^2 \frac{t^2}{2!} + A^3 \frac{t^3}{3!} + \dots$$

Now let us consider the individual state probabilities. We use the notation

$$p_j(t) = P\{X(t) = j\} \quad \text{and}$$
$$\Pi(t) = [\, p_0(t) \quad p_1(t) \quad p_2(t) \ \dots]$$

By the total probability theorem, we have for any j,

$$p_j(t) = \sum_i P\{X(0) = i\} \ P\{X(t) = j \mid X(0) = i\}$$

$$= \sum_i p_i(0) \ p_{ij}(0, t)$$

In matrix notation, the above becomes

$$\Pi(t) = \Pi(0) H(0, t)$$

Using (34), we get

$$\Pi(t) = \Pi(0) \ \exp\left(\int_0^t Q(u) \, du\right) \tag{35}$$

The above equation gives a method of computing the state probabilities $\Pi(t)$ at time t, knowing $\Pi(0)$, the state probabilities at time 0, and the transition probability matrix $H(0, t)$. Note that the above equation holds in general for any non-homogeneous CTMC.

3.4.5 Analysis of Homogeneous CTMCs

This section assumes importance since the models considered in this chapter correspond to homogeneous CTMCs. We deduce the analytical equations for homogeneous CTMCs and describe how steady-state analysis is carried out. Consider a homogeneous CTMC $\{X(t) : t \geq 0\}$ with state space $\{0, 1, 2, ...\}$. Recall that in a homogeneous CTMC, the transition probabilities $p_{ij}(x, x + t)$ do not depend on x and depend only on t. We can therefore adopt the following notation:

$$p_{ij}(t) = p_{ij}(x, x + t) \quad \forall x$$
$$q_{ij} = q_{ij}(x) \quad \forall x$$
$$Q = Q(x) = [q_{ij}] \quad \forall x$$
$$H(t) = H(x, x + t) = [\, p_{ij}(t) \,] \quad \forall x$$

In matrix form, the Chapman-Kolmogorov equation (27) becomes

$$H(x + t) = H(x) \ H(t) \tag{36}$$

The forward and backward equations can be derived starting from (28) and (30) and will be given respectively by

$$\frac{dH(t)}{dt} = H(t)Q; \quad H(0) = I \tag{37}$$

$$\frac{dH(t)}{dt} = QH(t); \quad H(0) = I \tag{38}$$

The forward equations (37) expressed in terms of the individual elements yield

$$\frac{dp_{ij}(t)}{dt} = q_{jj}p_{ij}(t) + \sum_{k \neq j} q_{kj}p_{ik}(t) \tag{39}$$

The backward equations (38) expressed in terms of the individual elements yield

$$\frac{dp_{ij}(t)}{dt} = q_{ii}p_{ij}(t) + \sum_{k \neq i} q_{ik}p_{kj}(t) \tag{40}$$

The solution for $H(t)$ can be derived from (34) to be given by

$$H(t) = \exp(Qt) \tag{41}$$

Note that using the above solution, we can compute $p_{ij}(t)$. That is, we can compute the probabilities of reaching designated states in time t. Thus the above equation summarizes the evolution in time of a homogeneous CTMC.

Consider now the state probabilities

$$p_j(t) = P\{X(t) = j\} \qquad j = 0, 1, 2...$$

Recall the notation

$$\Pi(t) = [\, p_0(t) \quad p_1(t) \quad p_2(t)...] \quad \text{for} \quad t \geq 0$$

To obtain $\Pi(t)$ from the initial state probabilities $\Pi(0)$ and the infinitesimal generator Q, we use (35) which now becomes

$$\Pi(t) = \Pi(0)\exp(Qt) \tag{42}$$

The matrix differential corresponding to the above solution can be verified to be

$$\frac{d\Pi(t)}{dt} = \Pi(t)Q \tag{43}$$

It is to be noted that (43) describes the evolution over time of the individual state probabilities. The individual terms of (43) are

$$\frac{dp_j(t)}{dt} = q_{jj}p_j(t) + \sum_{k \neq j} q_{kj}p_k(t) \tag{44}$$

Note that (39) and (40) give the differential equations that govern the evolution over time of the transition probabilities of a homogeneous CTMC whereas (44) gives the differential equations governing the evolution of individual state probabilities. The solution to (39) and (40) is given by (41) whereas the solution to (44) is given by (42). In Section 3.10, we will examine in detail the solution of these differential equations in order to carry out *transient analysis*. For the present, we shall look at the limiting behavior of a homogeneous CTMC, i.e., in the limit $t \to \infty$.

Steady-State Analysis

In the DTMC context, we have examined the meaning of properties such as communication between states, irreducibility, periodicity, recurrence, and positive recurrence. These terms have identical meaning in the CTMC context, and their definitions can be obtained by simply replacing the discrete time parameter n by the continuous time parameter t. It can be shown that for an irreducible and positive recurrent homogeneous CTMC, the limiting probabilities $\pi_j = \lim_{t \to \infty} p_j(t)$ always exist. Further, it can be shown that these probabilities $\pi_1, \pi_2, ...$, satisfy the following properties.

1. The limiting probabilities constitute a probability distribution, i.e., $\sum_j \pi_j = 1$. The probability π_j, $j = 0, 1, 2, ...$, is to be interpreted as the long-run proprtion of residence time in state j.

2. These probabilities are unique, i.e., independent of the initial state.

3. The limiting probabilities are stationary in the sense that if the initial state is chosen as

$$\Pi(0) = \Pi = [\pi_0 \ \ \pi_1 \ \ \pi_2 \ ...],$$

then the probabilities $\Pi(t)$ at any time $t \geq 0$ will be the same as $\Pi(0)$.

The probabilities $\Pi = [\pi_0 \ \pi_1 \ \pi_2 \ ...]$ are said to constitute the *steady-state probability distribution* of the CTMC and the CTMC is referred to as an *ergodic* CTMC. The vector Π can be obtained from (43) by setting

$$\frac{d\Pi(t)}{dt} = 0$$

as these probabilities are constant. Thus Π, the steady-state probability vector, can be obtained as the solution of

$$\Pi Q = 0$$
$$\sum_j \pi_j = 1 \tag{45}$$
$$\pi_j \geq 0 \quad j = 0, 1, 2, ...$$

Equation (45) is the key to computing the steady-state probabilities of an ergodic CTMC. An individual term of $\Pi Q = 0$ will be given by

$$q_{jj}\pi_j + \sum_{k \neq j} q_{kj}\pi_k = 0; \quad j = 0, 1, 2, ... \tag{46}$$

From (33), we have,

$$\sum_j q_{ij} = 0 \qquad i = 0, 1, 2, ...$$

Hence, we can write (46) as:

$$\pi_j \left(\sum_{k \neq j} q_{jk} \right) = \sum_{k \neq j} q_{kj}\pi_k \tag{47}$$

Figure 3.16 is a pictorial representation of (47). The LHS (left hand side) of (47) represents the net outflow from state j while the RHS represents the net inflow into state j. For this reason, the above equation is called the *rate balance equation* for state j. Thus the solution of an ergodic Markov chain involves writing down all the rate balance equations and solving them together with the normalizing equation $\sum_j \pi_j = 1$.

We shall now discuss the steady-state analysis for the examples presented in Section 3.4.3.

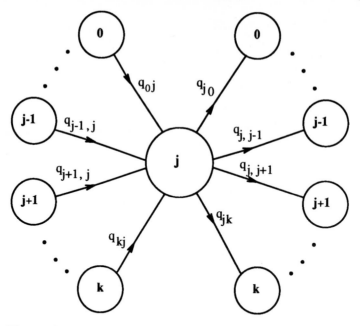

Figure 3.16 Steady-state rate balance for a typical state

Example 3.28

Consider the single-machine system of Example 3.24 where the CTMC model has 3 states: 0 (setup), 1 (processing), and 2 (undergoing repair). First, let us assume resume policy. Figure 3.17 shows a *state transition diagram*, which captures the transitions among these three states using directed arcs. Each arc is labeled with the corresponding transition rate. The transition rate matrix or the infinitesimal generator Q of this CTMC model is given by

$$Q = \begin{bmatrix} -s & s & 0 \\ p & -(p+f) & f \\ 0 & r & -r \end{bmatrix}$$

In state 0, the machine is being set up. After the setup operation, the machine starts processing and so transits to state 1 with rate s. As to why the rate is s can be deduced from the definition of transition rates given in equations (31) and (32). In state 1, there are two possibilities: (i) machine finishes processing and transits back to state 0, and (ii) machine fails before

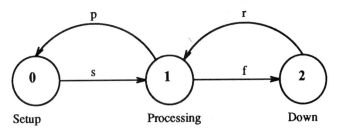

Figure 3.17 CTMC model under resume policy

finishing processing. Since the processing time and the time to failure are independent exponential random variables, the transition rate is p in the former case and f in the latter case. In state 2, the machine gets repaired and the next state is always state 1 and it is reached with rate r. The entries q_{00}, q_{11}, and q_{22} of the Q matrix are computed using the relations

$$q_{00} = -(q_{01} + q_{02})$$
$$q_{11} = -(q_{10} + q_{12})$$
$$q_{22} = -(q_{20} + q_{21})$$

which are a consequence of (33) (i.e., the sum of the entries in any row of Q is zero).

It is easy to verify that the CTMC is ergodic, since it is irreducible and finite with positive recurrent states. Therefore, a steady-state probability vector $\Pi = (\pi_0, \pi_1, \pi_2)$ exists satisfying (45). That is, we have,

$$\pi_0 s = \pi_1 p$$
$$\pi_1 (p + f) = \pi_0 s + \pi_2 r$$
$$\pi_2 r = \pi_1 f$$
$$\pi_0 + \pi_1 + \pi_2 = 1$$

The first three equations above are also precisely the rate balance equations (47) which can be obtained from the state transition diagram (Figure 3.17) by observation. These equations, together with the normalizing equation $\pi_0 + \pi_1 + \pi_2 = 1$, yield the following values.

$$\pi_0 = \frac{pr}{pr + rs + fs}; \quad \pi_1 = \frac{rs}{pr + rs + fs}; \quad \pi_2 = \frac{fs}{pr + rs + fs}$$

Let us evaluate these probabilities for the following typical parameter values:

s = setup rate = 20 per hour

p = processing rate = 4 per hour

f = failure rate = 0.05 per hour

r = repair rate = 1 per hour

We obtain $\pi_0 = 0.16$; $\pi_1 = 0.80$; and $\pi_2 = 0.04$. The interpretation is that, on an average, the machine gets set up for an operation 16% of the total time, processes parts for 80% of the total time, and is down for 4% of the total time. Thus the efficiency of the system is 80%.

The average throughput rate or the average production rate R of the system is the number of parts produced per hour, and in this case it is given by

$$R = \pi_1 p = \frac{rsp}{pr + rs + fs} = \frac{1}{\frac{1}{s} + \left(1 + \frac{f}{r}\right)\frac{1}{p}}$$

In the above equation, note that $1/s$ is the average setup time and $1/p$ is the average processing time. Assuming $p = 4$ per hour, $f = 0.05$ per hour, and $r = 1$ per hour, we get

$$R = \frac{1}{\frac{1}{s} + \frac{21}{80}}$$

Thus to improve the throughput of a given system, one has to decrease the setup times. This is a well-known thumb rule in automated manufacturing. Also, in the above relation for R, the second term in the denominator, i.e., $\left(1 + \frac{f}{r}\right)\frac{1}{p}$ is usually referred to as the *mean completion time* since it represents the mean total time spent on a workpiece by the machine. The reciprocal of $\left(1 + \frac{f}{r}\right)$ is called the *steady-state availability* of the system. Steady-state availability is the probability that the system is functioning in a productive way. Note that the mean completion time is the ratio of mean processing time to the steady-state availability.

Let us now examine the same system under the *discard policy* (i.e., after repair of the machine, the partially processed part is discarded and the machine is set up for a fresh raw part). Figure 3.18 shows the state transition diagram in this case. Observe that the arc from state 2 to state 1 in Figure 3.17 is now replaced by an arc from state 2 to state 0. The Q

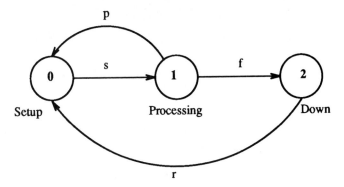

Figure 3.18 CTMC model under discard policy

matrix is now given by

$$Q' = \begin{bmatrix} -s & s & 0 \\ p & -(p+f) & f \\ r & 0 & -r \end{bmatrix}$$

The present CTMC model is also ergodic and the steady-state probabilities π'_0, π'_1, and π'_2 can be computed by solving the rate balance equations. It can be verified that

$$\pi'_0 = \frac{rp + rf}{rp + rf + rs + fs}; \quad \pi'_1 = \frac{rs}{rp + rf + rs + fs};$$
$$\pi'_2 = \frac{fs}{rp + rf + rs + fs}$$

Comparing these with those of π_0, π_1, and π_2 obtained earlier, we can infer that $\pi'_0 > \pi_0$; $\pi'_1 < \pi_1$; and $\pi'_2 < \pi_2$. Assuming the same typical values as in the resume policy, we get $\pi'_0 = 16.17$; $\pi'_1 = 79.84$; and $\pi'_2 = 0.039$. Thus it is clear that the *resume policy* leads to better throughput than the *discard policy*, which is quite intuitive. In this case, the actual expression for R turns out to be

$$R = \frac{1}{\frac{1}{s} + \left(1 + \frac{1}{s} + \frac{f}{r}\right)\frac{1}{p}}$$

Example 3.29

Here we will examine the single-machine system with resume policy, processing *batches* of parts. In this case, we assume that after each setup operation, the machine processes exactly n parts, then is set up again for the next batch of n parts. Each setup operation has a duration of $EXP(s)$ and the processing time on an individual part is $EXP(p)$. Further, the machine may fail during the processing, and after repair, it resumes processing. The time to failure is $EXP(f)$ and the repair time is $EXP(r)$. As usual, all the random variables involved are mutually independent and also the machine does not fail during setup. The state space of the CTMC model in this case is given by

$$S = \{0, 1, 2, ..., n, n+1, n+2, ..., 2n\}$$

where the interpretation of the states is:

0: machine being set up for the next batch of parts

i $(1 \leq i \leq n)$: machine processing ith part of a batch

$n+i$ $(1 \leq i \leq n)$: machine getting repaired, after failing while processing ith part of a batch.

The state transition diagram of the CTMC is shown in Figure 3.19. It can be verified that the CTMC is irreducible and positive recurrent. If $\pi_0, \pi_1, ..., \pi_{2n}$ are the steady-state probabilities, we have the rate balance equations given by

$$\pi_0 s = \pi_n p$$
$$\pi_1 (p + f) = \pi_0 s + \pi_{n+1} r$$
$$\pi_i (p + f) = \pi_{i-1} p + \pi_{n+i} r \qquad i = 2, 3, ..., n$$
$$\pi_{n+i} r = \pi_i f \qquad i = 1, 2, ..., n$$

From the above equations, it can be derived that

$$\pi_1 = \pi_2 = ... = \pi_n = \frac{s}{p} \pi_0$$

$$\pi_{n+1} = \pi_{n+2} = ... = \pi_{2n} = \frac{fs}{rp} \pi_0$$

Using the normalization condition, we get

$$\pi_0 = \frac{pr}{pr + nsr + nsf}$$

The average steady-state throughput rate R in this system is given by

$$R = \left(\sum_{i=1}^{n} \pi_i \right) p = \frac{nsrp}{pr + nsr + nsf} = \frac{1}{\frac{1}{ns} + \left(1 + \frac{f}{r}\right)\frac{1}{p}}$$

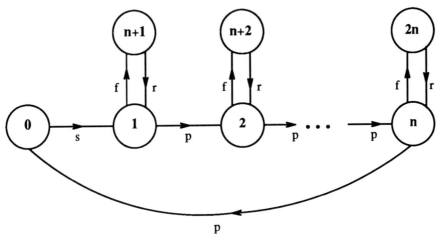

Figure 3.19 CTMC model under resume policy for batch processing

The above expression is very similar to what we obtained for resume policy in Example 3.28. The expression $\left(1 + \frac{f}{r}\right)\frac{1}{p}$ can be interpreted as the *mean completion time* or the average time spent by the machine on each individual part, whereas the reciprocal of $\left(1 + \frac{f}{r}\right)$ corresponds to the *steady-state availability* of the system.

Example 3.30

Let us investigate the steady-state performance of the closed central server network model of Example 3.25, when the number of fixtures is $n = 2$. We have seen that the CTMC model has six states given by

$$S = \{(k_0, k_1, k_2) : \ k_0 \geq 0, \ k_1 \geq 0, \ k_2 \geq 0, \ k_0 + k_1 + k_2 = 2\}$$

where $k_0, k_1,$ and k_2 are the numbers of jobs with the AGV, M_1, and M_2, respectively. Figure 3.20 shows the state transition diagram for the CTMC model. This CTMC is irreducible and positive recurrent. Let the steady-state probability of state (k_0, k_1, k_2) be denoted by $\pi(k_0, k_1, k_2)$. One can solve the rate balance equations and obtain expressions for these probabilities. Using these, the following steady-state performance measures can be computed.

Utilizations:

AGV utilization $= \pi(101) + \pi(110) + \pi(200)$

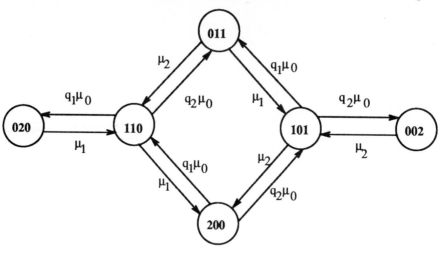

Figure 3.20 CTMC model for the central server network with two jobs

M_1 utilization = $\pi(011) + \pi(110) + \pi(020)$

M_2 utilization = $\pi(011) + \pi(101) + \pi(002)$

Mean number of parts in individual nodes:

In AGV subsystem (AGV Queue + getting serviced by AGV) = $\pi(101) + \pi(110) + 2\pi(200)$

In M_1 subsystem = $\pi(110) + \pi(011) + 2\pi(020)$

In M_2 subsystem = $\pi(011) + \pi(101) + 2\pi(002)$

Throughput rate:

When the AGV utilization is multiplied by μ_0, the rate at which AGV transports parts, we obtain the average number of parts undergoing an AGV operation in unit time. Of these, q_0 percent of the parts, on an average, correspond to finished parts since the arc in Figure 3.13 labeled q_0 corresponds to unloading operation. Therefore the throughput of finished parts is given by

$$R = q_0\mu_0 \left[\pi(101) + \pi(110) + \pi(200) \right]$$

In the above example, we have demonstrated the computation of important performance measures using steady-state probabilities.

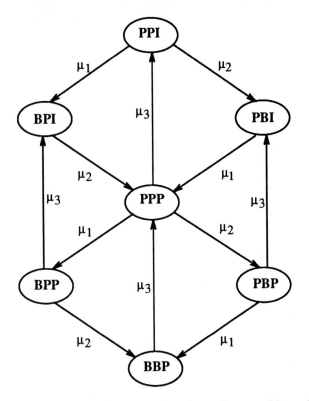

Figure 3.21 CTMC representation of assembly cell

Example 3.31

We have seen in Example 3.26 that the assembly cell of Figure 3.14 has 7 states in its CTMC model where each state is a triple (x_1, x_2, x_3) with x_i, $i = 1, 2, 3$, representing the individual state of machine M_i. The individual states of a machine could be P (processing), B (blocked), and I (idle). The state transition diagram of the above CTMC model is shown in Figure 3.21. By inspection of this CTMC model, we can infer its irreducibility and positive recurrence. The rate balance equations can be written down by looking at Figure 3.20 and the steady-state probabilities $\pi(x_1, x_2, x_3)$ can be computed. The following can be evaluated.

Machine utilizations:

Utilization of $M_1 = \pi(PPI) + \pi(PBI) + \pi(PPP) + \pi(PBP)$

Utilization of $M_2 = \pi(PPI) + \pi(BPI) + \pi(PPP) + \pi(BPP)$

Utilization of $M_3 = \pi(PPP) + \pi(BPP) + \pi(PBP) + \pi(BBP)$
Throughput rate:

The throughput rate R can be obtained as,

$$R = \mu_3 [\pi(PPP) + \pi(BPP) + \pi(PBP) + \pi(BBP)]$$

Example 3.32

In Example 3.27 we considered a system with two machines, M_1 and M_2, which was formulated as a CTMC model with four states given by

   0: M_1 and M_2 both working
   1: M_1 working and M_2 failed
   2: M_1 failed and M_2 working
   3: Both machines failed.

If there is no repair facility, we have observed that the model will be a Markov chain with an absorbing state, namely state 3. Figure 3.22 shows the state transition diagram of the CTMC model. In this case, the CTMC is not irreducible since the states $0, 1$, and 2 are transient states.

We shall now evaluate the performance of this system with one repair facility and two repair facilities. Figure 3.23 is the CTMC model with one repair facility. It is assumed that in state 3, where both the machines are down, the repair facility will spend its time equally between M_1 and M_2. Consequently, the arc from state 3 to state 1 and the arc from state 3 to state 2 are each labeled by $r/2$. This CTMC model is irreducible and

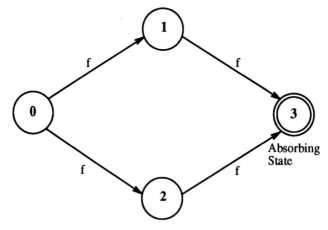

Figure 3.22 CTMC model with no repair station

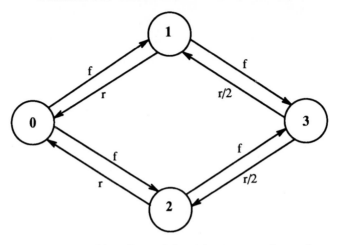

Figure 3.23 CTMC model with one repair station

positive recurrent and it can be verified that the steady-state probabilities π_0, π_1, π_2, and π_3 are given by

$$\pi_0 = \frac{r^2}{r^2 + 2fr + 2f^2}$$

$$\pi_1 = \pi_2 = \frac{fr}{r^2 + 2fr + 2f^2}$$

$$\pi_3 = \frac{2f^2}{r^2 + 2fr + 2f^2}$$

When there are two identical repair facilities, the CTMC model will be similar to that in Figure 3.23, except for the labels on the directed arcs from state 3 to state 2 and from state 3 to state 1. The steady-state probabilities in this case are given by

$$\pi_0' = \frac{r^2}{r^2 + 2fr + f^2}$$

$$\pi_1' = \pi_2' = \frac{fr}{r^2 + 2fr + f^2}$$

$$\pi_3' = \frac{f^2}{r^2 + 2fr + f^2}$$

We can immediately conclude that

$$\pi_0' > \pi_0; \quad \pi_1' > \pi_1; \quad \pi_2' > \pi_2; \quad \text{and} \quad \pi_3' < \pi_3$$

The steady-state *availability* of the system is the steady-state probability that the system is not down (i.e., at least one machine is in working condition). If A and A' are the steady-state availabilities with one repair facility and two repair facilities, respectively, we have

$$A = 1 - \pi_3 = \frac{r^2 + 2fr}{r^2 + 2fr + 2f^2}$$

$$A' = 1 - \pi_3' = \frac{r^2 + 2fr}{r^2 + 2fr + f^2}$$

Clearly, $A < A'$, which goes according to intuition. If $f = 0.1$ per hour (i.e., a machine fails on an average once in 10 hours) and $r = 1$ per hour (i.e., average repair time is 1 hour), we have $A = 0.9836$ and $A' = 0.9917$.

Recall that M_1 is a fast machine with a production rate of μ_1, and M_2 is a slow machine with a production rate of μ_2 parts per hour. The average steady-state throughput rate in the system will then be equal to the weighted average of the throughput rates in the four states. If R and R' are the average throughput rate values with one repair facility and two repair facilities, respectively, then we have

$$R = \pi_0 (\mu_1 + \mu_2) + \pi_1 \mu_1 + \pi_2 \mu_2$$

$$R' = \pi_0' (\mu_1 + \mu_2) + \pi_1' \mu_1 + \pi_2' \mu_2$$

Note again that $R' > R$. Thus the system with two repair facilities has greater availability and also performs better.

Now, consider another system, similar to the above, i.e., with two machines, say M_3 and M_4. If the production rate of M_3 is μ_1 parts per hour (i.e., same as M_1) and that of M_4 is μ_3 parts per hour, where $\mu_3 > \mu_2$, then it is interesting to note the following points:

(1) The second system has the same availability as the original system.

(2) The second system performs better than the original system in terms of throughput. This is because $\mu_3 > \mu_2$.

3.4.6 Embedded Markov Chain in CTMCs

Let us examine the evolution of a CTMC $\{X(t) : t \geq 0\}$ only at those time instants when a state change occurs. This leads to the stochastic process $\{X_n : n \geq 0\}$ where X_0 is the initial state, X_1 is the state reached on the first transition, X_2 is the state reached on the second transition, and so on. Note that $n = k$ corresponds to the instant of time at which the CTMC changes state for the kth time, $k = 0, 1, 2, \dots$. The process

$\{X_n : n \geq 0\}$ is a discrete time stochastic process and it can be shown to be a DTMC. This leads to the following definition.

Definition: Given a CTMC $\{X(t) : t \geq 0\}$, the discrete time process $\{X_n : n = 0, 1, 2, ...\}$ where X_n denotes the state reached by the CTMC after n state transitions is a discrete time Markov chain called the *embedded Markov chain* (EMC) of the CTMC.

We shall now derive the one-step transition probabilities of the EMC of a CTMC $\{X(t) : t \geq 0\}$. Let the state space be $\{0, 1, 2, ...\}$, with typical states indicated by indices i, j, and k. Let $Q = [q_{ij}]$ be the infinitesimal generator of the CTMC and $P = [p_{ij}]$ the TPM of the EMC. Consider state i of the CTMC. Now, p_{ij} is the probability that the system, currently in state i, next transits to state j. If T_{ij}, $i \neq j$, is the random variable representing the time to reach state j from state i, then T_{ij} is exponentially distributed with rate q_{ij}. Now, for $i \neq j$,

$$p_{ij} = \frac{q_{ij}}{\sum_{k \neq i} q_{ik}}$$

since the T_{ik}'s are mutually independent exponential random variables with rates q_{ik}. As we are observing the system only at instants of change of state, $p_{ii} = 0$; $i = 0, 1, ...$

Thus the transition probabilities of the EMC are given by

$$\begin{aligned} p_{ij} &= 0 & &\text{if } i = j \\ &= \frac{q_{ij}}{\sum_{k \neq i} q_{ik}} & &\text{if } i \neq j \end{aligned} \tag{48}$$

It can be shown that a CTMC $\{X(t) : t \geq 0\}$ and its EMC $\{X_n : n \geq 0\}$ have the same communication classes. In particular, the CTMC is irreducible and positive recurrent if the EMC is irreducible and positive recurrent. Recall that such an EMC will have a unique steady-state probability vector $Y = [y_0 \ y_1 \ y_2 \ ...]$, given by

$$YP = Y$$

$$\sum_j y_j = 1$$

$$y_j \geq 0 \quad \forall j$$

Now, what is the relation between Π and Y, where $\Pi = [\pi_0 \ \pi_1 \ \pi_2 \ ...]$ is the steady-state probability vector of the CTMC ? It can be shown that

$$\pi_i = \frac{y_i m_i}{\sum_j y_j m_j} \qquad i = 0, 1, 2, ... \tag{49}$$

where m_j is the mean sojourn time of the CTMC state j. It is not difficult to see that

$$m_j = \frac{1}{\sum_{k \neq j} q_{jk}} \tag{50}$$

since the sojourn time in each state of a CTMC is exponentially distributed.

Now, for $j = 0, 1, 2, ...$, the probability y_j is to be interpreted as the *visit ratio* of j or the *relative number of visits* to state j in the long run and π_j is to be interpreted as the long-run proportion of time the CTMC resides in state j.

The above discussion will be used at several places subsequently. We shall now illustrate the computation of steady-state probabilities of a CTMC using the EMC approach.

Example 3.33

We have seen that the CTMC model of the single-machine system of Example 3.28 has three states $0, 1$, and 2, with steady-state probabilities

$$\pi_0 = \frac{pr}{pr + rs + fs}; \quad \pi_1 = \frac{rs}{pr + rs + fs}; \quad \pi_2 = \frac{fs}{pr + rs + fs}$$

Recall that the resume policy is used in Example 3.28 (Figure 3.17). Let us see how we can derive the above expressions for π_0, π_1, and π_2 using the EMC approach. Let P be the TPM of the EMC. First note that $p_{00} = p_{11} = p_{22} = 0$. Now, $p_{01} = 1$ since from state 0, we can transit to only state 1, so when a change of state occurs, the next state is certainly state 1. Also it is easy to see that $p_{02} = 0$ since a direct transition from state 0 to state 2 cannot occur (see Figure 3.17). Verify that $p_{00} + p_{01} + p_{02} = 1$. If the current state is state 1, the next state is 0 or 1 with probabilities

$$p_{10} = P \ \{\text{processing finishes before failure}\} \ = \frac{p}{p+f}$$

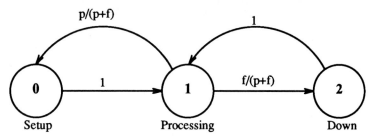

Figure 3.24 EMC of the CTMC model of Figure 3.17

$p_{12} = P\ \{\text{failure occurs before finishing of processing}\} = \frac{f}{p+f}$

If the current state is 2, then the next state has to be state 1, and so $p_{21} = 1$, which in turn implies that $p_{20} = 0$. Thus,

$$P = \begin{bmatrix} 0 & 1 & 0 \\ \frac{p}{f+p} & 0 & \frac{f}{f+p} \\ 0 & 1 & 0 \end{bmatrix}$$

The state transition diagram of the EMC is depicted in Figure 3.24. Observe that the EMC is also irreducible, with positive recurrent states. Therefore, a steady-state probability vector $Y = (y_0, y_1, y_2)$ exists, which can be verified to be given by

$$y_0 = \frac{a}{2}; \quad y_1 = \frac{1}{2}; \quad y_2 = \frac{1-a}{2} \qquad \text{where } a = \frac{p}{f+p}$$

The next step is to compute the mean sojourn times m_j in the individual states. It can be verified easily, using (50), that

$$m_0 = \frac{1}{s}; \quad m_1 = \frac{1}{p+f}; \quad m_2 = \frac{1}{r}$$

Finally, we compute π_0, π_1, and π_2, the steady-state probabilities for the CTMC, using (49). We obtain

$$\pi_0 = \frac{y_0 m_0}{y_0 m_0 + y_1 m_1 + y_2 m_2} = \frac{pr}{pr + rs + fs}$$

$$\pi_1 = \frac{y_1 m_1}{y_0 m_0 + y_1 m_1 + y_2 m_2} = \frac{rs}{pr + rs + fs}$$

$$\pi_2 = \frac{y_2 m_2}{y_0 m_0 + y_1 m_1 + y_2 m_2} = \frac{fs}{pr + rs + fs}$$

Indeed, these are the same as derived earlier. The reader is urged to note carefully the difference in the interpretation of the π_j's and the y_j's.

PROBLEMS

1. In the single machine system of Example 3.24, assume that when the machine fails, it is determined whether the semi-finished part can be reworked (probability q) or is to be discarded (probability $1 - q$). That is, with probability q, we resume the processing on the part whereas with probability $1 - q$, we discard the part. Develop and solve the CTMC in this case. Repeat for the batch processing system of Example 3.29.

2. For the closed central server network with one AGV and m machines M_1, M_2,..., M_m (see Figure 3.9), and n jobs in the system, compute

   (a) the number of states in the state space of the CTMC model, and

   (b) the mean sojourn time in a typical state $(k_0, k_1, ..., k_m)$.

3. In a system comprising two identical machines, incoming raw parts undergo an operation and leave the system. Assume that fixtured raw parts are always available. Each machine, after finishing the processing on a part, is set up for the next part. Also, the machines can fail while processing, in which case they are repaired. Machines do not fail when being set up. For the above system,

   (a) Write down the state space of a CTMC model.

   (b) Assume that there is one repair facility. Also, let s be the setup rate, f the failure rate, p the processing rate, and r the repair rate. Compute the mean sojourn time in each state in the case of (i) resume policy, and (ii) discard policy.

   (c) Develop the CTMC models in (b).

4. Consider the assembly cell of Example 3.26 (Figure 3.14). Develop the state space and compute the mean sojourn times, assuming that:

   (a) There are two fixtures each for parts entering M_1 and M_2. Raw parts are always available.

(b) There are two input buffers, buffer 1 and buffer 2, for machine M_3. Buffer 1 can accommodate one part from M_1, and buffer 2 can accommodate one part from M_2.

5. Starting from the definition of transition rates in equations (31) and (32), derive the elements of the infinitesimal generator in Example 3.28.

6. Derive the Kolmogorov differential equations for a homogeneous CTMC starting from those for a non-homogeneous CTMC.

7. Consider a single-machine system. The machine is prone to failures with failure rate λ. Once failed, the repair proceeds in two phases. In phase 1, the cause of failure is determined in exponential time with rate μ_1. Immediately after, in phase 2, the machine is repaired, repair time being exponentially distributed with rate μ_2. Formulate this system as a 3-state CTMC, prove that the CTMC is ergodic, and compute the steady-state probabilities. Steady-state availability of this system is the steady-state probability that the system is working. What is the steady-state availability in this case?

8. The service in a single-machine system proceeds in two phases as shown in Figure 3.P.1. A fixtured raw part first undergoes an operation on the machine (processing rate μ_1) and then undergoes a quality-control inspection (inspection rate μ_2). After inspection, the probability of acceptance is p. An accepted part is defixtured (defixturing rate μ_3) and delivered to the customer. A rejected part will be processed again by the machine, after which it will again be inspected. If there is only one fixture in the system, formulate a CTMC model making suitable assumptions. Compute the average throughput rate and the average time spent by a part in the system.

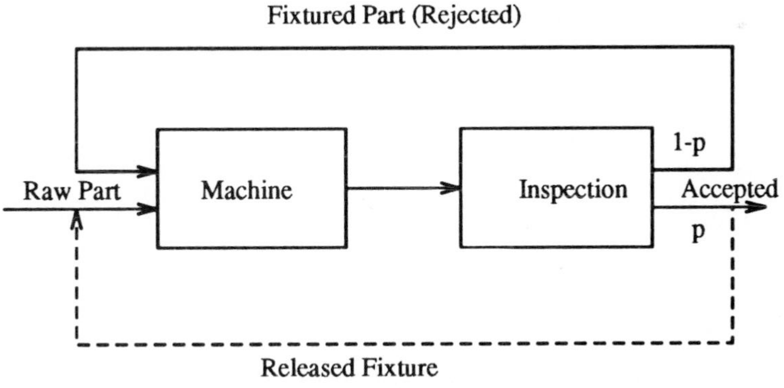

Fixtured Part (Rejected)

Figure 3.P.1

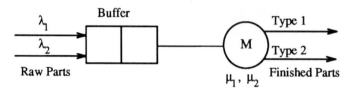

Figure 3.P.2

9. In the system shown in Figure 3.P.2, parts of two types arrive into a finite
queue of size 2 according to Poisson processes with rates λ_1 and λ_2, respectively. Arrivals are lost if the queue is full. When the machine completes the
service of a part, it will start processing a part from the queue, if available.
When the queue contains a part of type 1 and a part of type 2, the following
scheduling rules can be used to select the next part to process.

(a) Select the part type that arrived earlier into the queue (FCFS).
(b) Select part type 1 (Priority rule)
(c) Select part type i with probability q_i with $q_1 + q_2 = 1$ (Probabilistic
selection).
(d) Select part type 1 if the last part the machine finished processing is of
type 2, and vice versa.

Construct a CTMC model in each of the above cases assuming processing
rate μ_i for part type i. Evaluate and compare the values of throughput rates
in each case. Attempt to compute the average time a part of type i would
spend in the system.

10. Write a software package to compute the steady-state probabilities of an
irreducible, positive recurrent CTMC. Use the package to verify the results
for the above problems.

11. Making relevant assumptions, derive the result in equation (49), to compute
the steady-state probabilities of a CTMC in terms of those of the embedded
Markov chain.

12. Using the embedded Markov chain approach, obtain the steady-state probabilities for the following examples discussed in this section.

(a) Example 3.28 (Discard policy)
(b) Example 3.30 (Closed central server network)

3.5 AN EXAMPLE: MARKOV MODEL OF A TRANSFER LINE

In the previous section we presented steady-state performance analysis for CTMC models of several illustrative manufacturing situations. We now consider a more detailed example. The system studied is a traditional flow shop or a transfer line. Much of what appears in this section is taken from the paper by Gershwin and Berman [1981]. The system comprises two machines M_1 and M_2 with an intermediate storage in-between, as shown in Figure 3.25. The workpieces enter the first machine, and an operation takes place. The pieces are then moved to the buffer and they later proceed to the second machine. When processing is complete there, workpieces leave the system. The performance of such a system is generally affected by the variations in the behavior of the stages, whether due to failures or processing time fluctuations. The effect of these variations is reduced by the intermediate storage, which temporarily holds in-process inventory. When one stage is under repair or taking an unusually long time to process a part, the buffer enables the work to continue elsewhere.

We now present a CTMC model of the above system by making some appropriate assumptions. We show how the model can be used in the design of the system, by facilitating the estimation of production rate and average in-process inventory, in the presence of machine failures, blocking and starving of machines, and processing time fluctuations.

We list below the various assumptions that need to be made in order to obtain a tractable CTMC model for the above system.

1. A machine M_i $(i = 1, 2)$ can be in two possible states: operational $(\alpha_i = 1)$ or under repair $(\alpha_i = 0)$. When machine M_i fails, a transition occurs from $\alpha_i = 1$ to $\alpha_i = 0$. Similarly, when a repair takes place, α_i changes from 0 to 1 . Service, failure, and repair times are exponential

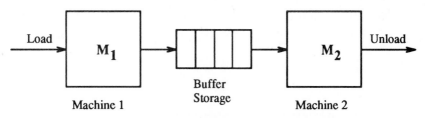

Figure 3.25 A two-machine transfer line

random variables with parameters $p_i, f_i,$ and r_i $(i = 1, 2)$, respectively. All these random variables are mutually independent.

2. If a machine is operational, it cannot process parts if none are available to it or if there is no room in which to put the processed parts. In the former case, the machine is said to be *starved*, and in the latter it is *blocked*. It is assumed that M_1 is never starved and M_2 is never blocked. Also, blocked or starved machines, because they are not operating, are not vulnerable to failure.

3. The buffer is finite, with capacity N $(N \geq 1)$.

A CTMC model can now be constructed for the given system. If $n, 0 \leq n \leq N + 1$ represents the number of parts in the buffer plus the number of parts in M_2, then the state of the system can be described by the triple (n, α_1, α_2). Note that there are seven parameters to the model: $p_1, p_2, f_1, f_2, r_1, r_2,$ and N. The number of states in the state space will be $4(N + 2)$. For example, if $N = 1$, there are 12 states, namely (000), (001), (010), (011), (100), (101), (110), (111), (200), (201), (210), and (211). Of these, the states (000), (010), (200), and (201) are *transient* states because blocked machines and starved machines don't fail. The other states are *recurrent*, and the state transitions among these recurrent states are shown in Figure 3.26. It can be verified that the recurrent states alone will constitute an irreducible, positive recurrent chain.

3.5.1 Rate Balance Equations

In the general case where N is the capacity of the buffer, the state space is given by

$$S = \{(n, \alpha_1, \alpha_2) : \quad 0 \leq n \leq N + 1; \quad \alpha_1 = 0, 1; \quad \alpha_2 = 0, 1\}$$

Let $\pi(n, \alpha_1, \alpha_2)$ be the limiting probabilities of the states. Let us define two indicator functions $I_1(.)$ and $I_2(.)$ to keep track of the starving and blocking of machines. That is, for $i = 1, 2$, we define

$$I_i(n) = 1 \text{ if } M_i \text{ is neither blocked nor starved}$$
$$= 0 \text{ otherwise}$$

where n has the usual interpretation of the number of jobs in the buffer plus the number of jobs in the machine M_2. We have,

$I_1(N+1) = 0$ since M_1 is blocked,

$I_1(n) = 1$ for $0 \le n \le N$ since M_1 is neither blocked nor starved,

$I_2(0) = 0$ since M_2 is starved, and

$I_2(n) = 1$ for $1 \le n \le N+1$ since M_2 is neither blocked nor starved.

Also, for ease of notation, we define $I_i(-1) = I_i(N+2) = 0$; for $i = 1, 2$.

Figure 3.27 shows the transitions into and out of a typical state (n, α_1, α_2). The rate balance equations can be written down as follows,

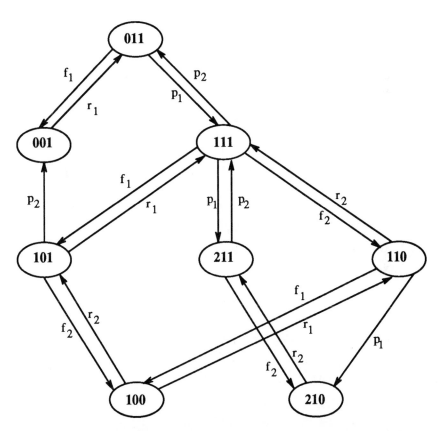

Figure 3.26 CTMC model of the transfer line of Figure 3.25

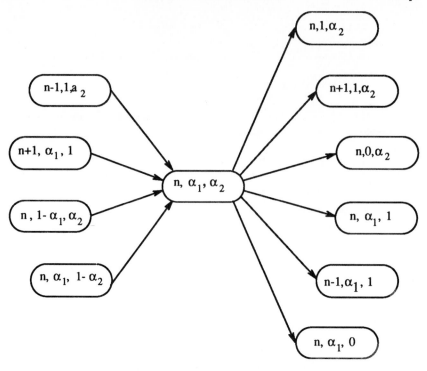

Figure 3.27 In-flow and out-flow for a typical state

for $0 \leq n \leq N+1$; $\alpha_1 = 0, 1$; and $\alpha_2 = 0, 1$.

$$
\pi(n, \alpha_1, \alpha_2) \sum_{i=1}^{2} [r_i(1 - \alpha_i) + (p_i + f_i)\alpha_i I_i(n)]
$$
$$
= \pi(n - 1, 1, \alpha_2) p_1 \alpha_1 I_1(n - 1) + \pi(n + 1, \alpha_1, 1) p_2 \alpha_2 I_2(n + 1)
$$
$$
+ \pi(n, 1 - \alpha_1, \alpha_2)[r_1 \alpha_1 + f_1(1 - \alpha_1) I_1(n)]
$$
$$
+ \pi(n, \alpha_1, 1 - \alpha_2)[r_2 \alpha_2 + f_2(1 - \alpha_2) I_2(n)]
$$

Note that the left side of this equation represents the rate of leaving state (n, α_1, α_2) and the right side is the rate of entering it.

3.5.2 Steady-State Analysis

To get explicit expressions for the steady-state probabilities $\pi(n, \alpha_1, \alpha_2)$, the states are classified into *internal states* in which $1 \leq n \leq N$ and *boundary states*, which are the rest of the states. For any general N, there are eight boundary states, $(0,0,0), (0,1,0), (N+1,0,0), (N+1,0,1),$ $(0,0,1), (0,1,1), (N+1,1,0),$ and $(N+1,1,1)$. Of these the first four states are transient states because of the starving of M_2 or blocking of M_1. Therefore, we have

$$\pi(0,0,0) = \pi(0,1,0) = \pi(N+1,0,0) = \pi(N+1,0,1) = 0$$

To obtain the steady-state probabilities of the other boundary states and all the internal states, Gershwin and Berman [1981] have given an efficient algorithm. This algorithm is based on the observation that the probabilities of the internal states have the form

$$\pi(n,\alpha_1,\alpha_2) = c\, X^n Y_1^{\alpha_1} Y_2^{\alpha_2} \quad 1 \le n \le N$$

where $c, X, Y_1,$ and Y_2 are computed by using the above expression in the rate balance equations.

The state description will be more complicated for a transfer line with three or more stages. In such a case, the state of each machine as also that of each buffer needs to be specified. For an arbitrary transfer line with finite buffers and unreliable machines, the steady-state analysis has to be carried out by efficient numerical methods.

3.5.3 Performance Evaluation

Using the steady-state probabilities, the following performance measures can be computed.

1. **Efficiency of M_i:** This is defined as the probability that machine M_i is operating on a workpiece or as the fraction of time in which the ith machine produces parts. This can be expressed as:

$$E_1 = \sum_{n=0}^{N} \sum_{\alpha_2=0}^{1} \pi(n,1,\alpha_2)$$

$$E_2 = \sum_{n=1}^{N+1} \sum_{\alpha_1=0}^{1} \pi(n,\alpha_1,1)$$

2. **Expected in-process inventory**: This is the average number of parts residing in the buffer and machine M_2, and is given by

$$\sum_{n=0}^{N+1} \sum_{\alpha_1=0}^{1} \sum_{\alpha_2=0}^{1} n\pi\,(n, \alpha_1, \alpha_2)$$

3. **Production rate**: This is the rate at which finished parts emerge from the system and is given by $\mu_2 E_2$.

The performance measures defined above can be computed for various values of the parameters $p_1, p_2, f_1, f_2, r_1, r_2$, and N. It has been found by extensive numerical experiments that:

1. As any machine becomes more productive, due to increase in p_i or increase in r_i or decrease in f_i, the system production rate increases until a limit and then saturates.

2. The average in-process inventory increases when the first machine becomes more productive, and it decreases when the second machine becomes more productive.

3. As N increases, the production rate increases to a limit and then reaches a saturation value. This limit is the production rate in isolation of the least productive machine.

The above modeling experiments show that the model behaves in a manner consistent with intuition and can be used for fixing transfer line layouts. Specifically, given cost data (capital cost for machines and buffers; cost rate for in-process inventory; cost for delaying demand), profit rate, and demand data, it should be possible to evaluate each possible configuration and then to search for the best.

PROBLEMS

1. For the two-stage transfer line discussed in this section, let the state description (n, α_1, α_2) be altered in the following way. Let n indicate the number of parts in the buffer only, so that $0 \le n \le N$ where N is the capacity of the buffer. Define α_1 and α_2 appropriately. Identify the boundary states and transient states for a general N. Write down the general rate balance equations. For $N = 1$, identify all the recurrent states in the CTMC model and obtain a state transition diagram for these recurrent states.

2. An important assumption that has been made while developing the CTMC model of the two-stage transfer line is that M_1 will start processing only if the buffer is not full. If we let M_1 start processing as soon as it is free, how will the CTMC model change? What can you say about the new values of efficiencies, throughput rate, and expected in-process inventory?

3. Consider a 3-stage transfer line instead of a 2-stage one. We now have three machines interspersed by two buffers of capacities, say N_1 and N_2, respectively (Figure 3.P.3). Assume that the operational rules of this system are the same as for the 2-stage transfer line.

   (a) How many states will the CTMC model have?

   (b) What will be the boundary states and transient states?

   (c) Attempt to write down the rate balance equations for the CTMC model.

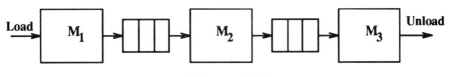

Figure 3.P.3

4. Consider a 2-stage, closed transfer line. In this system a constant number of jobs, say N, will circulate inside the network. This models a flow line in which a limited number of fixtures are available. Incoming raw parts are fixtured and undergo operations at M_1 and M_2. Finished parts are defixtured and unloaded. The released fixture is immediately used for fixturing a raw part. Fixturing times, loading times, defixturing times, and unloading times are negligible compared to processing times. Let N_1 and N_2 be the capacities of buffer 1 and buffer 2, respectively. When a machine finishes processing and finds the next buffer full, it will get blocked until a part leaves that buffer. The state of the system can be specified as a pair (k_1, k_2) where k_i is the number of parts in buffer i and machine M_i $(i = 1, 2)$.

   (a) For $N = 3$, $N_1 = N_2 = 1$, develop a CTMC model of the above system.

   (b) Develop a CTMC model for $N = 3$, $N_1 = N_2 = 2$. Will this be different from the model for $N_1 = N_2 = \infty$?

   (c) Compute the number of states for a general N, assuming $N_1 = N_2 = \infty$.

   (d) If $N_1 < \infty$ and $N_2 < \infty$, then observe that N has to be chosen less than or equal to $N_1 + N_2 + 1$. In such a case, attempt to compute the total number of states in the resulting model.

(e) What is the throughput rate of the above model? How is it related to the total time spent by a fixtured part inside the system?

5. Use a software package for CTMC analysis (see Problem 10 in Section 3.4) to analyze the CTMC models of transfer lines discussed in this section (Section 3.5) and described in the Problems 1–4 above.

3.6 BIRTH AND DEATH PROCESSES IN MANUFACTURING

Birth and death processes (BD processes) constitute a highly structured class of CTMCs. BD processes have played a significant role in the development of queuing theory, as will be seen in Chapter 4. There are several situations in automated manufacturing systems that can be modeled and analyzed using BD processes. In this section we discuss the steady-state analysis of BD processes and present several examples in the manufacturing context.

Definition: A homogeneous CTMC $\{X(t): t \geq 0\}$ with state space $\{0, 1, 2, ...\}$ is called a *birth and death process* if there exist constants $\lambda_i \, (i = 0, 1, ...)$ and $\mu_i \, (i = 1, 2, ...)$ such that the transition rates are given by

$$q_{i,i+1} = \lambda_i \qquad i = 0, 1, 2, ...$$
$$q_{i,i-1} = \mu_i \qquad i = 1, 2, ...$$
$$q_{ij} = 0 \qquad \text{for} \quad |i - j| > 1$$

In state $i \; (i \geq 0)$, λ_i is called the *birth rate* and $\mu_i \; (i \geq 1)$ the *death rate*.

A BD process can have infinite number of states. The state transition diagram of an infinite BD process is shown in Figure 3.28 and that of a finite BD process is shown in Figure 3.29. The birth rate and the death rate in each state i are assumed to depend only on i and are independent of time. Note from the figures that each state (except the

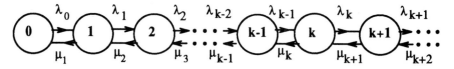

Figure 3.28 An infinite birth and death process

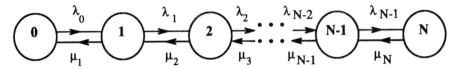

Figure 3.29 A finite birth and death process

boundary states) has exactly two neighbors and transitions are only allowed between neighboring states. Also in a given state, births and deaths occur independently of each other.

In this section we describe the steady-state analysis of irreducible and positive recurrent BD processes. We then study the steady-state behavior of some well-known finite BD processes. Note that an irreducible, finite BD process will be positive recurrent.

3.6.1 Steady-State Analysis of BD Processes

We first note that a BD process is irreducible provided each $\lambda_i > 0$ and each $\mu_i > 0$. To investigate the steady-state behavior of a BD process, let us assume for the moment that steady-state probabilities exist and are unique. If $\pi_k\,(k \geq 0)$ denotes the steady-state probability of state k, then the rate balance equations for a BD process can be written down as (see Figure 3.28):

$$\lambda_0 \pi_0 = \mu_1 \pi_1$$
$$(\lambda_k + \mu_k)\,\pi_k = \lambda_{k-1}\pi_{k-1} + \mu_{k+1}\pi_{k+1} \qquad k \geq 1 \tag{51}$$

The recursion in equation (51) can be unfolded as

$$\begin{aligned}
\lambda_k \pi_k - \mu_{k+1}\pi_{k+1} &= \lambda_{k-1}\pi_{k-1} - \mu_k \pi_k \\
&= \lambda_{k-2}\pi_{k-2} - \mu_{k-1}\pi_{k-1} \\
&= \lambda_0 \pi_0 - \mu_1 \pi_1 \\
&= 0
\end{aligned}$$

Thus we have

$$\begin{aligned}
\pi_k &= \frac{\lambda_{k-1}}{\mu_k}\,\pi_{k-1} \qquad \text{for} \quad k \geq 1 \\
&= \frac{\lambda_0 \lambda_1 ... \lambda_{k-1}}{\mu_1 \mu_2 ... \mu_k}\,\pi_0
\end{aligned}$$

Using the fact that $\sum_j \pi_j = 1$, we get

$$\pi_0 = \frac{1}{1 + \sum_{k \geq 1} \prod_{i=0}^{k-1} \left(\frac{\lambda_i}{\mu_{i+1}}\right)} \tag{52}$$

$$\pi_k = \pi_0 \prod_{i=0}^{k-1} \left(\frac{\lambda_i}{\mu_{i+1}}\right) \qquad k \geq 1 \tag{53}$$

The above limiting probabilities are non-zero, provided that the following series converges:

$$\sum_{k \geq 1} \prod_{i=0}^{k-1} \left(\frac{\lambda_i}{\mu_{i+1}}\right)$$

It can be shown that a BD process is positive recurrent and hence the steady-state probabilities exist if and only if the following two conditions are satisfied:

$$\sum_j \left(\lambda_j \frac{\lambda_0 \ldots \lambda_{j-1}}{\mu_1 \ldots \mu_j}\right)^{-1} = \infty \tag{54}$$

$$\sum_j \frac{\lambda_0 \ldots \lambda_{j-1}}{\mu_1 \ldots \mu_j} < \infty \tag{55}$$

It is easy to see that a finite BD process always satisfies (54) and (55) and therefore is positive recurrent.

3.6.2 Typical BD Processes in Manufacturing

Several queuing situations such as the $M/M/1$ queue and the $M/M/m$ queue correspond to infinite BD processes. These will be treated in detail in Chapter 4. We now discuss several other examples of BD processes.

Example 3.34

A BD process with the death rates $\mu_k = 0$ for all $k \geq 1$, as shown in Figure 3.30, is called a *pure birth process*. It can be shown that the Poisson process

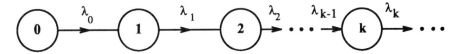

Figure 3.30 A pure birth process

is a pure birth process. Another special case is the *pure death process* in which case all birth rates $\lambda_k = 0$ for $k \geq 0$ (Figure 3.31). A pure death process will start in some state $N > 0$ at time $t = 0$ and gradually goes to state 0, which will be an *absorbing state*. A pool of failure-prone machines with no possibility of repair on breakdown provides an example of a pure death process. An important point to be noted is that steady-state analysis will not throw much light on the behavior of a pure birth process or a pure death process. *Transient analysis* is important for such systems.

Example 3.35

In Examples 3.28 and 3.29 we looked at a single-machine system that leads to a three-state CTMC model. The model in Figure 3.17 corresponds to the *resume policy* while the one in Figure 3.18 represents the *discard policy*. Note that the first CTMC model is a finite BD process whereas the second one is not a BD process.

Example 3.36

Consider a manufacturing facility comprising M identical machines and a single repair facility. Suppose that the amount of time each machine runs before breakdown is exponentially distributed with rate λ while the repair of a failed machine is exponentially distributed with rate μ. The failure times and the repair times are mutually independent.When a machine fails and finds the repair facility busy, it waits in a queue. The resulting system is well known as the *machine repairman model* and is depicted in Figure 3.32. This model, like the central server model, has been extensively used

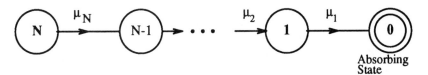

Figure 3.31 A pure death process

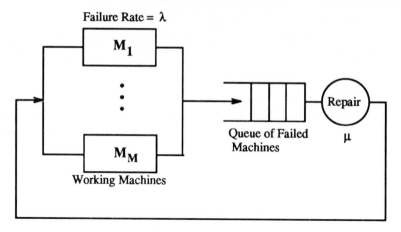

Figure 3.32 Machine repairman model

in the computer systems arena to model a multi-terminal, multi-programmed computer system. We shall formulate this as a BD process and answer the following questions: (1) What is the average number of failed machines? (2) What proportion of time is each machine in use? (3) What is the probability that at least k $(0 < k \le M)$ machines are in working condition?

Let the state of the system be k $(k = 0, 1, 2, ..., M)$ where k is the number of failed machines. The system is a finite BD process with $M + 1$ states with parameters given by

$$\mu_k = \mu \qquad\qquad k = 1, 2, ..., M$$
$$\lambda_k = (M - k)\lambda \qquad k = 0, 1, 2...., M - 1$$
$$= 0 \qquad\qquad\quad k = M$$

The state transition diagram is shown in Figure 3.33. It can be deduced that the steady-state probabilities $\pi_0, \pi_1, ..., \pi_M$ are given by

$$\pi_k = \frac{\frac{M!}{(M-k)!}\left(\frac{\lambda}{\mu}\right)^k}{1 + \sum\limits_{k=1}^{M}\left(\frac{\lambda}{\mu}\right)^k \frac{M!}{(M-k)!}} \qquad k = 0, 1, 2, ..., M$$

The average number of machines not in use $= \sum\limits_{k=0}^{M} k\pi_k$. Therefore the average number of machines in use $= M - \sum\limits_{k=0}^{M} k\pi_k$.

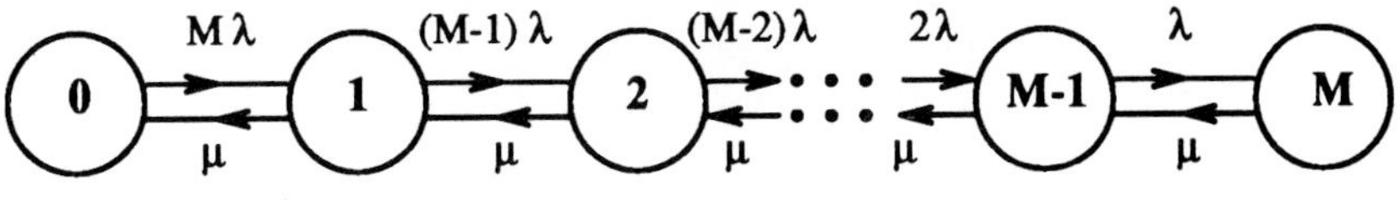

Figure 3.33 CTMC representation for the machine repairman model

The proportion of time each machine is in use can be obtained by dividing the average number of machines in use by the total number of machines. Therefore, we have

$$\text{machine utilization} = \frac{M - \sum\limits_{k=0}^{M} k\pi_k}{M}.$$

The probability that at least k machines are in use is given by the probability that less than k machines are failed and therefore it is given by

$$1 - \sum_{i=k+1}^{M} \pi_i$$

If $M = 1$, then we have only two states, 0 and 1. The steady-state probabilities in this case are given by

$$\pi_0 = \frac{\frac{1}{\lambda}}{\frac{1}{\lambda} + \frac{1}{\mu}}; \quad \pi_1 = \frac{\frac{1}{\mu}}{\frac{1}{\lambda} + \frac{1}{\mu}}$$

π_0 gives the steady-state probability that the system is in working condition and is the *steady-state availability*. $\frac{1}{\lambda}$ is the mean time to failure and is abbreviated as MTTF. $\frac{1}{\mu}$ is the mean time to repair and is abbreviated as MTTR. Note that a system with low *reliability* will have a small MTTF, but if MTTR is also low (that is, fast repairs), the system may possess a high *availability*.

Example 3.37

Here we shall give another interpretation to the *machine repairman* model in the manufacturing context. Consider an AMS in which a limited number M of fixtures ($M \geq 1$) is available but there are enough numbers of machines ($\geq M$). The machines are identical. Each fixtured part undergoes exactly one operation on any one of the machines, and a finished part is unloaded by an AGV. At the unloading station, the finished part is defixtured and a fresh raw part (raw parts are assumed to be always available) is fixtured and brought by the AGV to be loaded onto one of the machines. Since the number of machines is greater than the number of fixtures, a fixtured raw part can be directly loaded onto an available machine. If a finished part finds the AGV busy, it will wait in a queue. The machine operation time for each part is assumed to be exponentially distributed with rate λ. The sum of the AGV transportation time from the pool of machines to the load/unload station and back, the defixturing time, and the fixturing time, is assumed to be exponentially distributed with rate μ.

It is easy to map the above system onto the machine repairman model depicted in Figure 3.32. The above model captures the contention for the AGV and since there is no contention for machines, the model predicts the system performance in an optimistic way. The utilization U of the AGV is given by $U = 1 - \pi_0$ since π_0 is the probability that the AGV is idle. The throughput rate R of the system is given by $R = U\mu$. Average number N of parts waiting for and getting serviced by AGV is given by $N = \sum_{k=1}^{M} k\pi_k$. A measure of interest for this system would be L, the average *manufacturing lead time*, which is the average time a fixtured part spends in the system. A fixtured raw part first spends an average time of $\frac{1}{\lambda}$ getting serviced by a machine and would spend in the AGV subsystem an average time of $\frac{k+1}{\mu}$ if k customers are in the AGV subsystem when this part entered the AGV queue. When this part is about to enter the AGV queue, there cannot be more than $M - 1$ parts in the AGV subsystem. Therefore, the probability p_k of such a part finding k customers in the AGV subsystem is

$$p_k = \frac{\pi_k}{1 - \pi_M} \qquad k = 0, 1, 2, ..., M - 1$$

It can now be seen that L is given by

$$L = \frac{1}{\lambda} + \sum_{k=0}^{M-1} \left(p_k \frac{(k+1)}{\mu} \right)$$

$$= \frac{1}{\lambda} + \frac{1}{\mu(1 - \pi_M)} \sum_{k=0}^{M-1} \pi_k(k+1)$$

It is interesting to compute the variation of L with M, i.e., when the number of parts inside the system is increased from 1 to the number of machines.

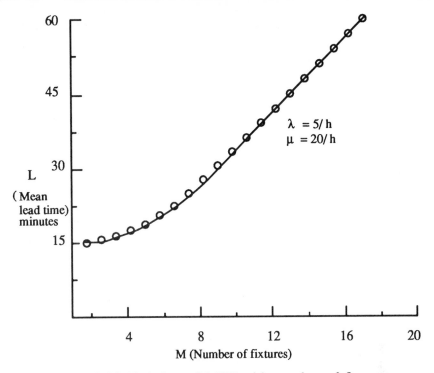

Figure 3.34 Variation of MLT with number of fixtures

L has a minimum value of $\frac{1}{\lambda} + \frac{1}{\mu}$. As M is increased, there is increased contention for AGV, and AGV utilization increases toward unity. In the limit $M \to \infty$, L will be a linear function of M. Once the AGV is fully utilized, releasing more jobs into the system will only increase L dramatically. Figure 3.34 shows a typical graph of L versus M.

PROBLEMS

1. A job shop comprises three identical machines and a certain number n of identical repair facilities. λ and μ are, respectively, the failure rate and repair rate for each machine, where it is assumed that the time to failure and the time to repair are both exponentially distributed. What is the utilization of each machine in the following cases: (1) $n = 1$, (2) $n = 2$, (3) $n = 3$? What will happen if $n = 0$?

2. A system consists of M identical machines and a single repair facility. As usual, λ and μ are the failure rate and repair rate, respectively. The last step in the repair process is a quality control inspection, and with probability p, the

repair is considered inadequate, in which case the machine will go back into the queue for repair. Determine the steady-state distribution of the number of components at the repair facility.

3. Formulate the cyclic transfer line with two machines and two buffers of Problem 4 in Section 3.5 as a BD process for a general $N (\geq 1)$ and $N_1 = N_2 = \infty$. Obtain the steady-state probability distribution and compute (i) throughput rate and (ii) manufacturing lead time. If both the buffers are finite, will the CTMC model still remain a BD process?

3.7 TIME REVERSIBLE MARKOV CHAINS IN MANUFACTURING

In this section we study a class of Markov chains having a special structure exhibited by several useful classes of open and closed queuing networks. We first discuss time reversible DTMCs and later discuss time reversible CTMCs. The significance of time reversibility arises because this property is equivalent to satisfying the so-called *detailed balance equations*, given in equation (56) for DTMCs and in equation (62) for CTMCs. The detailed balance equations are different from the rate balance equations for CTMCs, and are in fact stronger than the rate balance equations. That is, ergodic CTMCs satisfy the rate balance equations but not necessarily the detailed balance equations. Queuing networks whose underlying Markov processes are time reversible are said to satisfy the *local balance* property. Using the property of time reversibility, we can establish several important results in queuing theory, such as:

1. The departure process of queuing systems such as the $M/M/1$ queue and the $M/M/m$ queue, in steady-state, is a Poisson process with the same rate as that of the arrival process.

2. Queuing networks such as the tandem network and the Gordon-Newell network are product form (i.e., the steady-state joint probabilities can be expressed as the product of marginal probabilities, up to a normalization constant). This leads to simplified analysis of such networks.

In this section we shall illustrate the concept of time reversibility through manufacturing examples.

Definition: Given a discrete time process $\{X_n : -\infty < n < \infty\}$ and an arbitrary positive integer m, the *reversed process* of the given process is defined as the discrete time process $\{X_{m-i} : i = 0, 1, 2, ...\}$. Given a continuous time process $\{X(t) : -\infty < t < \infty\}$ and an arbitrary positive real number τ, the *reversed process* is defined as the continuous time process $\{X(\tau - t) : 0 \le t < \infty\}$.

Note that the reversed process of a stochastic process corresponds to the sequence of random variables, going backwards in time.

3.7.1 Time Reversible DTMCs

Consider an ergodic DTMC $\{X_n : -\infty < n < \infty\}$ with transition probabilities p_{ij} and stationary probabilities y_i. Assuming that the DTMC is in steady-state, that is, it has been in operation for a sufficiently long time, it can be shown that the reversed process is also a DTMC with transition probabilities given by

$$r_{ij} = P\{X_m = j \mid X_{m+1} = i\}$$
$$= \frac{P\{X_{m+1} = i \mid X_m = j\}\ P\{X_m = j\}}{P\{X_{m+1} = i\}}$$
$$= \frac{p_{ji} y_j}{y_i}$$

With the above notation, we now have the following definition.

Definition: A stationary, ergodic DTMC is said to be *time reversible* if the transition probabilities of the DTMC are the same as the transition probabilities of the reversed process.

That is, if p_{ij} and r_{ij} are the transition probabilities of the DTMC and the reversed process, respectively, then $r_{ij} = p_{ij}$ for all i, j. Alternatively,

$$y_i p_{ij} = y_j p_{ji} \qquad \text{for all } i, j \tag{56}$$

where y_i's are the stationary probabilities of the DTMC.

The condition in (56) can be stated that, for all states i and j, the rate $y_i p_{ij}$ at which the DTMC goes from i to j is equal to the rate $y_j p_{ji}$ at which it goes from j to i. Figure 3.35 gives a pictorial representation of (56). Note that a transition from i to j going backward in time is

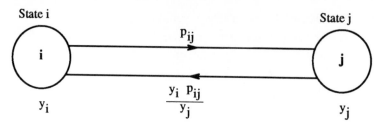

Figure 3.35 Condition for time reversibility

equivalent to a transition from j to i going forward in time. The balance equations of (56) are called the *detailed balance equations.*

To verify if a given DTMC with transition probabilities p_{ij} is time reversible, we can proceed as follows. Let us say, we find non-negative numbers x_i satisfying

$$\sum_i x_i = 1 \quad \text{and} \quad x_i p_{ij} = x_j p_{ji} \quad \text{for all} \ i, j \qquad (57)$$

Then we find, for all i, j, that

$$\sum_i x_i p_{ij} = \sum_i x_j p_{ji} = x_j \sum_i p_{ji} = x_j$$

Since the limiting probabilities y_i of the given DTMC are the unique solution of the above, it follows that $x_i = y_i$ for all i. Therefore (57) is the same as (56), which is the condition for time reversibility. Equation (57) could be used as the basis for verifying whether or not a given DTMC is time reversible.

Example 3.38

Consider a DTMC with state space $\{0, 1, 2, ..., M\}$ and transition probabilities

$$p_{01} = \alpha_0 = 1 - p_{00}$$

$$p_{MM} = \alpha_M = 1 - p_{M,M-1}$$

$$p_{i,i+1} = \alpha_i = 1 - p_{i,i-1}, \qquad i = 1, 2, ..., M - 1$$

The state transition diagram is shown in Figure 3.36. Such a DTMC is called a *random walk*. To see the significance of a random walk in the manufacturing context, consider a single-machine system with a buffer of capacity $(M - 1)(M \geq 1)$. The number of jobs inside this system can take on the values $0, 1, 2, ..., M$. As soon as the buffer is full, assume that fresh arrivals are inhibited or lost. Arrivals of raw parts constitute a Poisson process with rate λ and each part has an exponential service time with rate μ. The system is observed at discrete epochs corresponding to each arrival and each departure. Then the DTMC $\{X_n : n = 0, 1, 2, ...\}$ where X_n is the number of parts in the system at the nth discrete epoch can be verified to be a random walk with

$$\alpha_0 = 1; \quad \alpha_M = 0; \quad \text{and} \quad \alpha_i = \frac{\lambda}{\mu + \lambda} \quad \text{for } i = 1, 2, ..., M - 1$$

We can give the following intuitive argument to show that a random walk is time reversible. For any i, between two transitions from i to $i+1$, there must be one transition from $i + 1$ to i and vice versa, since the only way to re-enter i from a higher state is via state $i + 1$. Therefore, the number of transitions from i to $i + 1$ must at all times be within 1 of the number from $i + 1$ to i. This means that the rate of transition from i to $i + 1$ equals the rate from $i + 1$ to i.

We now show by verifying (56) that the given DTMC is time reversible. To simplify our discussion, let us assume $M = 2$ and $\alpha_0 = \alpha_1 = \alpha_2 = \alpha, \alpha \neq 0$. It is easy to verify that this is an ergodic DTMC with transition probabilities given by

$$P = \begin{bmatrix} 1 - \alpha & \alpha & 0 \\ 1 - \alpha & 0 & \alpha \\ 0 & 1 - \alpha & \alpha \end{bmatrix}$$

The unique stationary probabilities $Y = (y_0, y_1, y_2)$ can be obtained by solving $YP = Y$ and $y_0 + y_1 + y_2 = 1$, and can be shown to be

$$y_0 = \frac{(1 - \alpha)^2}{1 + \alpha^2 - \alpha}; \quad y_1 = \frac{\alpha(1 - \alpha)}{1 + \alpha^2 - \alpha}; \quad y_2 = \frac{\alpha^2}{1 + \alpha^2 - \alpha}$$

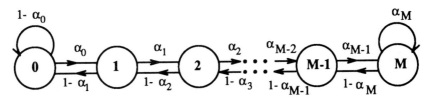

Figure 3.36 A random walk

It can be easily seen that $y_0 p_{01} = y_1 p_{10}$; $y_0 p_{02} = y_2 p_{20}$; $y_1 p_{12} = y_2 p_{21}$; and therefore the given DTMC is time reversible. It can also be verified that y_0, y_1, and y_2 are the unique solution of the equations

$$x_0 + x_1 + x_2 = 1 \quad \text{and} \quad x_i p_{ij} = x_j p_{ji} \quad \text{for } i = 0, 1, 2$$

In fact, to investigate time reversibility, this latter method is preferred since it does not require verification of ergodicity of the DTMC and computation of the stationary probabilities.

3.7.2 Time Reversible CTMCs

Consider a CTMC that is ergodic, with transition rates q_{ij}. Then it can be shown that the reversed process is also a CTMC. We have earlier seen in Section 3.4.6 that the sequence of states visited by a CTMC constitutes a DTMC called the embedded Markov chain (EMC). Also, we have seen that if the CTMC is ergodic, then its EMC is also ergodic. If p_{ij} are the transition probabilities of the EMC, then recall that the limiting probabilities y_i of the EMC are given as the solution of

$$y_i = \sum_j y_j p_{ji} \quad \forall i \quad \text{and} \quad \sum_i y_i = 1$$

Also recall that the stationary probabilities π_i of the CTMC are given as

$$\pi_i = \frac{y_i m_i}{\sum_j y_j m_j} \tag{58}$$

where m_i is the mean sojourn time of state i. Time reversibility in the case of a CTMC can be formulated in terms of the time reversibility of the EMC, leading to the following definition.

Definition: An ergodic CTMC is said to be *time reversible* if its embedded Markov chain is time reversible. That is, if the transition probabilities p_{ij} of the EMC satisfy

$$y_i p_{ij} = y_j p_{ji} \quad \text{for all } i, j \tag{59}$$

where y_i are the stationary probabilities of the EMC.

Using (58) and (59), we get the condition for the time reversibility of CTMCs as

$$\pi_i m_j p_{ij} = \pi_j m_i p_{ji} \qquad \text{for all } i, j \tag{60}$$

Note that m_i is the mean sojourn time of state i and so $(1/m_i)$ will be the rate at which the CTMC leaves state i. Consequently, (p_{ij}/m_i) is the rate at which the CTMC goes from state i to state j. In other words,

$$\frac{p_{ij}}{m_i} = q_{ij} \qquad \text{for all } i, j \tag{61}$$

Using (60) in (61), we obtain the condition for the time reversibility of CTMCs as

$$\pi_i q_{ij} = \pi_j q_{ji} \qquad \text{for all } i, j \tag{62}$$

In physical terms, (62) is the same as (56). As in the case of DTMCs, the balance equations (62) are called the *detailed* or *local balance equations*. Note that all ergodic CTMCs satisfy the rate balance equations of a CTMC but only time reversible CTMCs satisfy the detailed balance equations. Also, the rate balance equations can be obtained by summing up appropriate sets of local balance equations. In effect, each rate balance equation becomes separable into a set of individual local balance equations.

Given a CTMC with transition rates q_{ij}, if we can find non-negative x_i's such that

$$\sum_i x_i = 1 \quad \text{and} \quad x_i q_{ij} = x_j q_{ji} \qquad \text{for all } i \neq j \tag{63}$$

then it can be shown that the CTMC is time reversible and x_i's represent the limiting probabilities. The above gives a way of checking for the time reversibility of an ergodic CTMC.

Example 3.39

Consider an ergodic birth and death process, which we discussed in Section 3.6. See Figure 3.28 for the state transition diagram of a BD process. Given a state i, we observe that between successive transitions from i to $i + 1$, the process must return to state i and this can only occur through $i + 1$ and

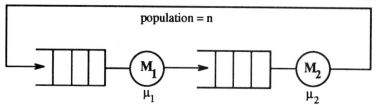

Figure 3.37 A closed transfer line with two machines

vice versa. Therefore, in any length of time t, the number of transitions from i to $i+1$ must equal to within 1 the number from $i+1$ to i. Thus, as the number of such transitions goes to infinity as $t \to \infty$, it follows that the rate of transitions from i to $i+1$ equals the rate from $i+1$ to i.

The above intuitive argument shows that an ergodic BD process is time reversible. This result has considerable significance in queuing theory, since several common queuing structures are described by BD processes.

An important result in queuing theory that can be proved using the time reversibility of BD processes is that departure process of the $M/M/1$ and $M/M/m$ queues has identical characteristics as the arrival process.

Example 3.40

Figure 3.37 shows a closed transfer line with two machines. The service times on M_1 and M_2 are independent exponential random variables with rates μ_1 and μ_2, respectively. Assume that there are n fixtures or pallets, so that the number of jobs circulating in the network is constant and equal to n. If k_1 and k_2 represent the job populations in the two nodes, the pair (k_1, k_2) would represent a typical state of the system. Since $k_1 + k_2 = n$, we have $n+1$ states. For $n = 3$, the CTMC model is depicted in Figure 3.38.

We notice that the CTMC model here is a finite BD process and therefore is time reversible. The local balance equations can be written

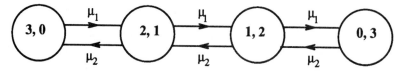

Figure 3.38 CTMC model for a population of 3

down easily as shown below:

$$\pi(3,0)\,\mu_1 = \pi(2,1)\,\mu_2$$
$$\pi(2,1)\,\mu_1 = \pi(1,2)\,\mu_2$$
$$\pi(1,2)\,\mu_1 = \pi(0,3)\,\mu_2$$

In the above, $\pi(k_1, k_2)$ is the stationary probability of the state (k_1, k_2). Verify how, by combining the above equations in different ways, one can obtain the rate balance equations for the individual states. For example, the rate balance equation for state $(2,1)$ is

$$\pi(2,1)\,(\mu_1 + \mu_2) = \pi(3,0)\,\mu_1 + \pi(1,2)\,\mu_2$$

The above equation is obtained as the sum of the first two local balance equations. The important point to note here is that the rate balance equations become separable into local balance equations, by virtue of time reversibility. The local balance equations above also lead to the following equations:

$$\pi(2,1) = \frac{\mu_1}{\mu_2}\,\pi(3,0)$$

$$\pi(1,2) = \left(\frac{\mu_1}{\mu_2}\right)^2 \pi(3,0)$$

$$\pi(0,3) = \left(\frac{\mu_1}{\mu_2}\right)^3 \pi(3,0)$$

Since we have $\pi(3,0) + \pi(2,1) + \pi(1,2) + \pi(0,3) = 1$, we easily obtain

$$\pi(3,0) = \frac{\mu_1^3 \mu_2^3}{\mu_2^3 + \mu_1 \mu_2^2 + \mu_1^2 \mu_2 + \mu_1^3}\left(\frac{1}{\mu_1}\right)^3$$

$$\pi(2,1) = \frac{\mu_1^3 \mu_2^3}{\mu_2^3 + \mu_1 \mu_2^2 + \mu_1^2 \mu_2 + \mu_1^3}\left(\frac{1}{\mu_1}\right)^2\left(\frac{1}{\mu_2}\right)$$

$$\pi(1,2) = \frac{\mu_1^3 \mu_2^3}{\mu_2^3 + \mu_1 \mu_2^2 + \mu_1^2 \mu_2 + \mu_1^3}\left(\frac{1}{\mu_1}\right)\left(\frac{1}{\mu_2}\right)^2$$

$$\pi(0,3) = \frac{\mu_1^3 \mu_2^3}{\mu_2^3 + \mu_1 \mu_2^2 + \mu_1^2 \mu_2 + \mu_1^3}\left(\frac{1}{\mu_2}\right)^3$$

A general way of expressing the above probabilities would be

$$\pi(k_1, k_2) = \frac{1}{C}\rho_1^{k_1} \rho_2^{k_2}$$

where C is a normalization constant, $\rho_1 = \frac{1}{\mu_1}$ and $\rho_2 = \frac{1}{\mu_2}$. ρ_1 is a parameter of node 1 and ρ_2 is a parameter of node 2. Thus the solution for the queuing network above is expressible in a *separable form* or *product form*. The above general expression will hold for $n > 3$ also.

Product-form networks constitute a very useful class of queuing networks because efficient computational algorithms can and have been developed for their analysis. The point to note is that the local balance property or time reversibility is crucial for a product-form solution to exist.

Example 3.41

Consider the central server FMS model of Examples 3.12 and 3.30 (Figure 3.9), with number of fixtures $= 1$. There are three states, namely

    0: part with AGV

    1: part with M_1

    2: part with M_2

The resulting CTMC is ergodic and the transition rate matrix is given by

$$Q = \begin{bmatrix} -(q_1\mu_0 + q_2\mu_0) & q_1\mu_0 & q_2\mu_0 \\ \mu_1 & -\mu_1 & 0 \\ \mu_2 & 0 & -\mu_2 \end{bmatrix}$$

The steady-state probabilities can be seen to be

$$\pi_0 = \frac{\mu_1\mu_2}{\mu_1\mu_2 + q_1\mu_0\mu_2 + q_2\mu_0\mu_1}$$
$$\pi_1 = \frac{q_1\mu_0\mu_2}{\mu_1\mu_2 + q_1\mu_0\mu_2 + q_2\mu_0\mu_1}$$
$$\pi_2 = \frac{q_2\mu_0\mu_1}{\mu_1\mu_2 + q_1\mu_0\mu_2 + q_2\mu_0\mu_1}$$

It is now easy to verify (62) and therefore the above CTMC is time reversible. In fact, for any value of number of fixtures and for any number of machines, the resulting CTMC model can be shown to be reversible. Even if the buffers are finite, leading to blocking, the CTMC model will still be reversible, as shown by Yao and Buzacott [1987]. Here again, the existence of a product-form solution can be proved, starting from the local balance equations.

PROBLEMS

1. Given an ergodic DTMC with transition probabilities p_{ij} and stationary probabilities y_i, show that the reversed process is also a DTMC, with transition probabilities r_{ij} given by

$$r_{ij} = \frac{y_j p_{ji}}{y_i} \qquad \text{for all } i, j$$

2. Show that the reversed process of an ergodic CTMC is also an ergodic CTMC.

3. Consider the random walk of Example 3.38, having $M + 1$ states. Verify its time reversibility by computing the solution of the equations

$$x_i p_{ij} = x_j p_{ji} \quad \text{for all } i, j$$
$$\sum_i x_i = 1$$

4. Show for an ergodic CTMC that the detailed balance equations (62) imply the rate balance equations for the individual states.

5. Show that an ergodic birth and death process is time reversible, by using the steady-state probabilities computed in Section 3.6 and verifying the property $\pi_i q_{ij} = \pi_j q_{ji}$ for all i, j.

6. Derive a product-form solution for the closed transfer line system of Example 3.40, for any arbitrary population n.

7. Consider a system comprising two machines M_1 and M_2 and a repair facility to service them. Assume that the time to failure of machine M_i is exponentially distributed with rate λ_i and that the repair time is exponentially distributed with rate μ_i $(i = 1, 2)$. The repair facility divides its efforts equally if both machines are down. Formulate the above system as a 4-state CTMC and prove its time reversibility.

3.8 ABSORBING STATES AND MODELING OF DEADLOCKS

We have seen in Examples 3.13 and 3.32 that an absorbing state of a Markov chain is one in which the chain would stay forever, once having entered it. Such Markov chains lead to some interesting AMS models and can capture deadlocks in manufacturing systems.

3.8.1 Examples of Absorbing States

We now present several examples of models having absorbing states.

Example 3.42

Consider an AMS in which a typical part undergoes two operations. The first operation is on machine M_1 and the second operation on machine M_2. At the end of each operation, an inspection machine determines whether or not the operation carried out meets the requirement of quality. If the quality is acceptable, the part is okayed for further processing or unloading. Otherwise, it is decided whether some rework can be done on the part in order to make it acceptable for further processing. If even rework cannot salvage the part, the part is scrapped. A typical part in the above system can be in any of the five states given below:

    0: Raw part ready for first operation

    1: Part getting processed by M_1

    2: Part getting processed by M_2

    3: Finished part

    4: Scrapped part

Assume that p is the probability that a part will be scrapped after an operation or rework, and q the probability that a rework is carried out after an operation or a rework. The parameters p and q can be determined from the statistical data available from the system. Under suitable assumptions, the above system can be formulated as a DTMC with two absorbing states, namely 3 and 4. Figure 3.39 shows the above DTMC. States 3 and 4 are shown by double circles to indicate that they are absorbing states. Using this DTMC, we can compute the overall fraction of parts that get scrapped as also the fraction of parts that satisfy the quality specifications.

Example 3.43

The central server model shown in Figure 3.40 is similar to the one discussed in Example 3.12, except that the arc labeled q_0 corresponds to an infinite sink of finished parts. Recall that this network models an FMS with an AGV and m machines M_1, M_2,...,M_m. Depending on where a job is getting processed, the job can be in $(m + 1)$ states, namely 0 (AGV), and i (M_i, $i = 1, 2, ..., m$). There is also an additional state called $(m + 1)$,

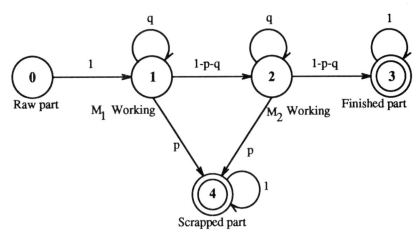

Figure 3.39 DTMC model for Example 3.42

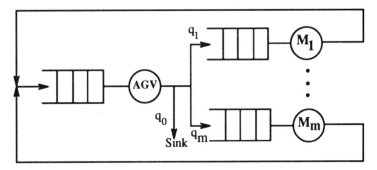

Figure 3.40 Central server model with an absorbing state

which corresponds to a finished part. This state can be visualized as an absorbing state since a finished part does not undergo any more operations. The resulting DTMC model is shown in Figure 3.41. Using this DTMC with absorbing states, we can compute the mean number of visits made by a part to the AGV or to any machine.

Example 3.44

Here we examine an AMS with deadlocks and show that deadlocks can be captured by absorbing states.

In the simple AMS depicted in Figure 3.42, there is a single machine that produces parts, with processing time exponentially distributed with rate μ. Raw parts arrive onto an input conveyor according to a Poisson process

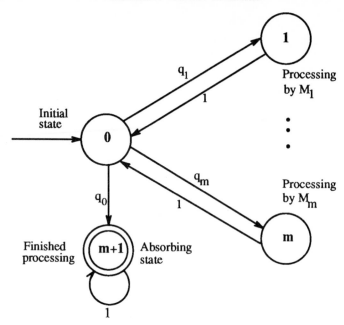

Figure 3.41 DTMC model for Example 3.43

with rate λ. A robot picks up a raw part from the input conveyor and loads it onto the machine if the machine is free or to its buffer if the machine is busy. The robot picks up the finished part and puts it on the output conveyor. There is a buffer in front of the machine where raw parts can wait if the machine is busy. Arrival of raw parts into the system is inhibited whenever the machine is busy, the buffer is full, and the robot is holding a raw part. Hence, if the buffer capacity $= n$, the maximum number of jobs inside the system $= n + 2$. Robot transfer times are negligible compared to inter-arrival times and processing times.

First consider the case where there is no buffer. Here the states of the system are $0, 1, 2$, and 3, with the following interpretation:

0: No raw parts, machine idle

1: Machine processing a part, no raw parts waiting

2: Machine processing a part, robot holding a raw part

3: Machine waiting for the robot to transfer the finished part and the robot waiting for the machine to release the finished part.

The CTMC model of the above system is shown in Figure 3.43(a). State 1 transits to state 2 as soon as a fresh raw part arrives. The robot

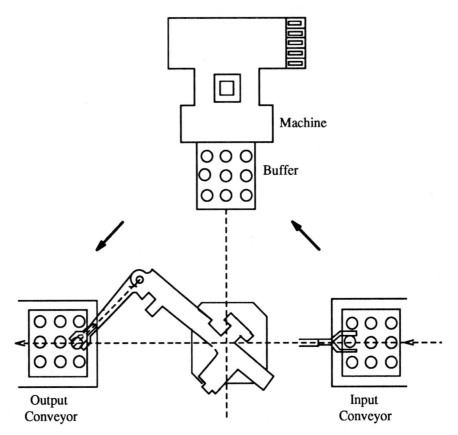

Figure 3.42 A robot cell to illustrate deadlock

picks up the part and waits to put it on the machine, currently busy. After the machine is through with the processing, it waits for the robot to unload the finished part, but is unable to load the finished part onto the robot since the latter is holding another part. If the robot controller and the machine controller are not programmed to react to such events, then each will wait for the other indefinitely. Such a state is a *deadlock*, which stops all production in the system. In this case, it is easy to see how such a deadlock can be prevented (for example, don't load a raw part onto the robot when the machine is busy), but in a real-life AMS environment with a large number of machines and concurrent interactions, deadlocks are certainly possible and therefore need careful study. In the example being discussed, we have a CTMC with three transient states $\{0, 1, 2\}$ and one absorbing state, namely state 3.

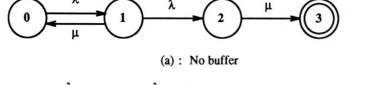

(a) : No buffer

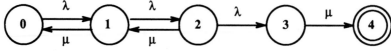

(b) : Buffer capacity = 1

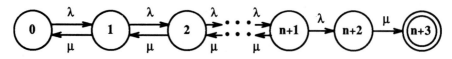

(c) : Buffer capacity = n

Figure 3.43 CTMC models for the system of Figure 3.42

If there is a buffer of capacity $= 1$, then the CTMC will have five states as shown in Figure 3.43(b). The interpretation of these states is left to the reader. Figure 3.43(c) gives the CTMC if the buffer capacity $= n$ (where $n \geq 0$). Note that there are $n + 4$ states, with a single absorbing state [state $(n + 3)$] corresponding to the situation where the buffer is filled with raw parts, robot is holding a raw part, and the machine is waiting to unload a finished part.

In the sequel of this section we will examine some interesting performance issues that can be studied using this class of Markov chains.

3.8.2 Analysis of Markov Chains with Absorbing States

Let the state space of a finite DTMC $\{X_n : n = 0, 1, 2, ...\}$ be given by

$$S = \{1, 2, ..., m, \ m + 1, \ m + 2, ..., m + n\}$$

where $m > 0$, $n > 0$, the first m states are transient states, and the rest of the states are absorbing states. The TPM of the above DTMC may be partitioned as

$$P = \begin{bmatrix} T & C \\ 0 & I \end{bmatrix}$$

In the above, T is an $(m \times m)$ matrix that describes single-step transitions among transient states; I is the identity matrix of order n; 0 is an $(n \times m)$ zero matrix; and C is an $(m \times n)$ matrix that describes transitions from transient states into absorbing states. The k-step TPM can be seen to be

$$P^k = \begin{bmatrix} T(k) & C(k) \\ 0 & I \end{bmatrix}$$

where

$$T(k) = T^k$$

and

$$C(k) = \left(T^{k-1} + T^{k-2} + \dots + T + I \right) C$$

Note that $\left[T^k \right]_{ij}$, $1 \le i, j \le m$, is the probability of arriving in transient state j, starting from transient state i, after exactly k steps.

It can be shown that $\left(\lim\limits_{t \to \infty} \sum\limits_{k=0}^{t} T^k \right)$ exists and is given by the matrix

$$F = (I - T)^{-1} \tag{64}$$

F is called the *fundamental matrix* and is a rich source of information about the given Markov chain with absorbing states. We now state and prove an important result.

Result: The $(i, j)^{\text{th}}$ element of the fundamental matrix gives the mean number of times transient state j is visited, starting from transient state i, before the Markov chain reaches any absorbing state.

Proof: Let X_{ij}, $1 \le i, j \le m$, be a discrete random variable that represents the number of times state j is visited, starting from state i, before reaching any absorbing state. Let Y be the state reached from state i after exactly one time step. Note that

$$P\{Y = k\} = p_{ik} \quad \text{for } 1 \le k \le m + n$$

For $k = m + 1, m + 2, \dots, m + n$, we have

$$X_{ij} = 1 \quad \text{with probability } p_{ik}, \text{ for } i = j$$
$$= 0 \quad \text{with probability } p_{ik}, \text{ for } i \ne j$$

In other words, if k is any absorbing state, $X_{ij} = \delta_{ij}$ with probability p_{ik}, where δ_{ij} is the Kronecker δ function. For $k = 1, 2, ..., m$, we have

$$X_{ij} = X_{kj} + 1 \quad \text{with probability } p_{ik}, \text{ for } i = j$$
$$= X_{kj} \quad \text{with probability } p_{ik}, \text{ for } i \neq j$$

In general, the above may be written as

$$X_{ij} = \delta_{ij} + X_{kj} \quad \text{with probability } p_{ik}, \text{ where } 1 \leq k \leq m$$

Now consider $E[X_{ij}]$. By the theorem of total expectation, we have

$$E[X_{ij}] = \sum_{k=1}^{m+n} E[X_{ij} \mid Y = k] \, P\{Y = k\}$$

$$= \sum_{k=1}^{m} E[X_{ij} \mid Y = k] \, p_{ik} + \sum_{k=m+1}^{m+n} E[X_{ij} \mid Y = k] \, p_{ik}$$

$$= \sum_{k=1}^{m} E[X_{kj} + \delta_{ij}] \, p_{ik} + \sum_{k=m+1}^{m+n} \delta_{ij} p_{ik}$$

$$= \sum_{k=1}^{m} E[X_{kj}] \, p_{ik} + \sum_{k=1}^{m+n} \delta_{ij} p_{ik}$$

Denote $f_{ij} = E[X_{ij}]$ and $F = [f_{ij}]$. Then we get

$$f_{ij} = \delta_{ij} + \sum_{k=1}^{m} p_{ik} \, f_{kj}$$

In matrix form, the above becomes

$$F = I + TF \quad \text{or } F = (I - T)^{-1}$$

Thus, $F = [f_{ij}] = [E[X_{ij}]]$. This proves the result that the $(i, j)^{\text{th}}$ element of the fundamental matrix gives the average number of times state j is visited, starting from state i, before an absorbing state is reached.

Computation of Fundamental Matrix

Equation (64) can also be written as

$$F(I - T) = I$$

This implies

$$F = I + TF \qquad (65)$$

Thus the matrix F can be computed by solving the above system of linear simultaneous equations.

Mean Time before Absorption

Let state 1 be the initial (transient) state. Then for $j = 1, 2, ..., m$, f_{1j} would give the mean number of visits to state j before absorption. If m_j is the mean sojourn time in state j, then the mean time to absorption is given by

$$\sum_{j=1}^{m} f_{1j}\, m_j$$

More generally, let transient state j be the initial state with probability p_j where $\sum_{j=1}^{m} p_j = 1$. Then, the mean number of visits to state j before absorption will be $\sum_{i=1}^{m} p_i f_{ij}$. In this case, the mean time to absorption is given by

$$\sum_{j=1}^{m} \left(\sum_{i=1}^{m} p_i\, f_{ij} \right) m_j$$

Note that the above results would hold for a CTMC by interpreting the above DTMC as an embedded Markov chain.

Probability of Absorbing States

Let us look at the matrix

$$C(k) = \left(T^{k-1} + T^{k-2} + ... + T + I \right) C$$

The $(i, j)^{\text{th}}$ element of the above matrix, $1 \leq i \leq m$, $1 \leq j \leq n$, gives the probability that the Markov chain would reach the absorbing state $m + j$, starting from transient state i, in exactly k steps.

Let us now look at the matrix G, where

$$G = (I - T)^{-1} C = FC \qquad (66)$$

g_{ij}, the $(i,j)^{\text{th}}$ element of G, can be interpreted as the long-run probability that the Markov chain reaches the absorbing state $m + j$, starting from transient state i.

Therefore, if state 1 is the initial state, then $g_{11}, g_{12}, ..., g_{1n}$ would give the long-run probabilities of the Markov chain ending up in the absorbing states $m + 1, m + 2, ..., m + n$, respectively.

3.8.3 Application to Examples

We shall now illustrate the above analysis for the examples discussed earlier.

Example 3.45

The DTMC of Figure 3.39 has a TPM given by

$$P = \begin{bmatrix} 0 & 1 & 0 & 0 & 0 \\ 0 & q & 1-p-q & 0 & p \\ 0 & 0 & q & 1-p-q & p \\ 0 & 0 & 0 & 1 & 0 \\ 0 & 0 & 0 & 0 & 1 \end{bmatrix}$$

The matrices T and C can be easily obtained from the above. The fundamental matrix is given by

$$F = (I - T)^{-1} = \frac{1}{(1-q)^2} \begin{bmatrix} (1-q)^2 & 1-q & 1-p-q \\ 0 & 1-q & 1-p-q \\ 0 & 0 & 1-q \end{bmatrix}$$

The initial state here is state 0. Therefore, from the above matrix, we have the mean number of times states 0, 1, and 2 are visited before getting absorbed given by

$$f_{00} = 1; \quad f_{01} = \frac{1}{1-q}; \quad f_{02} = \frac{1-p-q}{(1-q)^2}$$

For example, if $q = 0.5$ and $p = 0.1$, we have the numerical values as $1, 2$, and 1.6, respectively. The G matrix is given by

$$G = FC = \begin{bmatrix} \left(\frac{1-p-q}{1-q}\right)^2 & \frac{2p-2pq-p^2}{(1-q)^2} \\ \left(\frac{1-p-q}{1-q}\right)^2 & \frac{2p-2pq-p^2}{(1-q)^2} \\ \frac{1-p-q}{1-q} & \frac{p}{1-q} \end{bmatrix}$$

Since state 0 is the initial state, we obtain the long-run probabilities of the absorbing states as

$$\left(\frac{1-p-q}{1-q}\right)^2 \quad \text{for state } 3$$

$$\left(\frac{2p-2pq-p^2}{(1-q)^2}\right) \quad \text{for state } 4$$

If $q = 0.5$ and $p = 0.1$, we have these probabilities as 0.64 and 0.36, respectively. That means, 64% parts are processed successfully.

Example 3.46

Consider the DTMC of Figure 3.41. The fundamental matrix in this case can be computed to be given by (see Problem 1 in this section)

$$F = \begin{bmatrix} \frac{1}{q_0} & \frac{q_1}{q_0} & \frac{q_2}{q_0} & \cdots & \frac{q_m}{q_0} \\ \frac{1}{q_0} & 1+\frac{q_1}{q_0} & \frac{q_2}{q_0} & \cdots & \frac{q_m}{q_0} \\ \frac{1}{q_0} & \frac{q_1}{q_0} & 1+\frac{q_2}{q_0} & \cdots & \frac{q_m}{q_0} \\ \cdot & \cdot & \cdot & \cdots & \cdot \\ \cdot & \cdot & \cdot & \cdots & \cdot \\ \cdot & \cdot & \cdot & \cdots & \cdot \\ \frac{1}{q_0} & \frac{q_1}{q_0} & \frac{q_2}{q_0} & \cdots & 1+\frac{q_m}{q_0} \end{bmatrix}$$

Thus, assuming state 0 as the initial state, we have $\frac{1}{q_0}$ giving the mean number of times AGV is used by a typical part, and $\frac{q_i}{q_0}$ giving the mean number of operations on machine M_i, $i = 1, 2, ..., m$. The above expressions can be used to compute the lead time of a typical part.

Example 3.47

We now study the system of Example 3.44. In this case we have seen that the lone absorbing state [see Figure 3.43(a)] corresponds to a deadlock in the system evolution. The Markov chain here is a CTMC, and we can analyze this system through its embedded Markov chain. The TPM of the EMC is given by

$$P = \begin{bmatrix} 0 & 1 & 0 & 0 \\ p & 0 & 1-p & 0 \\ 0 & 0 & 0 & 1 \\ 0 & 0 & 0 & 1 \end{bmatrix}$$

where $p = \frac{\mu}{\lambda+\mu}$. Here the fundamental matrix can be computed to be given by

$$F = \begin{bmatrix} \frac{1}{1-p} & \frac{1}{1-p} & 1 \\ \frac{1}{1-p} & \frac{1}{1-p} & 1 \\ 0 & 0 & 1 \end{bmatrix}$$

Thus, state 0 and state 1 are each visited $\frac{1}{1-p}$ times before the occurrence of a deadlock. That is, on an average, $\frac{1}{1-p}$ parts are produced by the system before the deadlock. If $\mu = 8$ parts per hour and $\lambda = 2$ parts per hour, then $p = 0.8$ and hence, on an average 5 parts are produced before deadlock.

The mean sojourn times, m_j $(j = 0, 1, 2)$, in the states $0, 1,$ and 2 can be seen to be

$$m_0 = \frac{1}{\lambda}; \quad m_1 = \frac{1}{\lambda + \mu}; \quad m_2 = \frac{1}{\mu}$$

Therefore the mean time to deadlock is given by

$$\left(\frac{1}{1-p}\right)\left(\frac{1}{\lambda}\right) + \left(\frac{1}{1-p}\right)\left(\frac{1}{\mu+\lambda}\right) + 1\left(\frac{1}{\mu}\right)$$

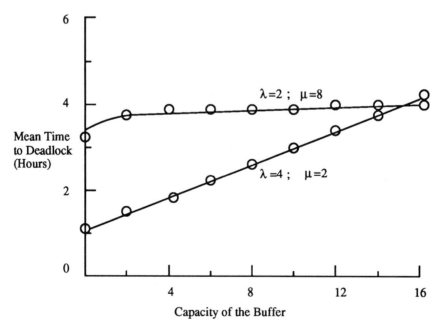

Figure 3.44 Variation of mean time to deadlock with buffer size

If $\lambda = 2$ parts per hour and $\mu = 8$ parts per hour, the mean time to deadlock turns out to be 3.125 hours. From this we can compute the utilization of the machine. If the machine is utilized 100%, then the throughput rate is 8 parts per hour. However, since only 5 parts are produced, the machine is utilized for a mean total of 5/8 hours out of 3.125 hours. Hence, machine utilization turns out to be 20%.

If we want to increase the mean time to deadlock, thereby increasing the number of parts produced before deadlock, then we can introduce a buffer where raw parts and/or finished parts are deposited. The resulting CTMC has already been shown in Figure 3.43(c). It will be interesting to solve this CTMC for different values of n and to notice that the mean time to deadlock is an increasing function of the capacity of the buffer. Figure 3.44 shows a graph of the mean time to deadlock versus the capacity of the buffer.

PROBLEMS

1. For the central server model with one AGV, m machines, and one absorbing state (Example 3.43), compute the fundamental matrix.
2. Figure 3.P.4 represents the transition diagram of the CTMC model of a system with deadlocks.

   (a) Compute the fundamental matrix F of the above chain.
   (b) Compute the expected time to deadlock, assuming (i) 0 as the initial state, and (ii) 1 as the initial state.
   (c) What should be the minimum value of p to ensure that the mean time to deadlock is greater than 10 h, given that $\lambda = 4/$ h; $\mu = 5/$ h.

3. Write a computer program to compute the fundamental matrix of a CTMC with absorbing states, given the TPM of the embedded Markov chain (EMC). This program will be useful in solving the rest of the problems in this section.

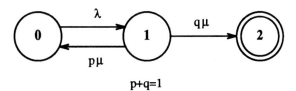

Figure 3.P.4

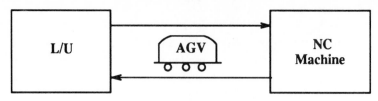

Figure 3.P.5

4. Figure 3.43(c) gives the CTMC diagram for Example 3.44, with a buffer of capacity n. Write down the TPM of the EMC and compute the fundamental matrix. For different values of n, say $n = 0, 1, 2, 3, 4$, and 5, find the mean time to deadlock and the mean number of parts produced before deadlock and draw a graph, for different values of λ and μ. What conclusions can be drawn from the graph?

5. Consider the AMS shown in Figure 3.P.5. A fresh part is picked up by an AGV at the load/unload station (L/U) and taken to the NC machine. The machine does some processing and the finished part is unloaded by the AGV. Assume that the AGV times and processing times are exponentially distributed with rates λ and μ, respectively. A deadlock here would occur when the AGV is holding a raw part and waits near the machine, and the machine holding a finished part waits for the AGV. Assume that raw parts are always available and develop and analyze a Markov model with absorbing states.

6. In the above problem, a buffer in front of the NC machine to hold finished and unfinished parts would increase the time until which a deadlock occurs. Develop a Markov chain model with buffer capacity = 1 and compare the mean number of parts before deadlock for this system with the previous one. Here also, the variation of the number of finished parts before deadlock can be studied as a function of the capacity of the buffer.

3.9 SEMI-MARKOV PROCESSES IN MANUFACTURING

To obtain a CTMC formulation of an AMS, we have necessarily to assume that the processing times, material handling times, setup times, etc., are exponential random variables. In real-life systems, however, these parameters are often deterministic even though some amount of variation is exhibited. The nonexponential nature of these random variables can sometimes be handled in the Markovian framework by using the theory of semi-Markov processes. In this section we explore the use of semi-Markov processes in the modeling of AMSs.

3.9.1 Definition and Examples

Definition: *A semi-Markov process* is a continuous time stochastic process $\{X(t) : t \geq 0\}$ such that

1. the embedded discrete time stochastic process $\{X_n : n \in \mathsf{N}\}$ where X_n is the state of the process at the instant of the nth transition is a DTMC, and

2. the sojourn time in each state of the process is a continuous random variable or a deterministic duration, and the sojourn times are mutually independent.

The embedded stochastic process of a semi-Markov process is called its embedded Markov chain. The embedded structure need not correspond to state transition epochs alone. The observations can be at any of a set of appropriately chosen epochs of time. Note that if all the sojourn times are exponential random variables, then a semi-Markov process becomes a CTMC. Recall that we have already discussed the embedded Markov chain of a CTMC in Section 3.4.6.

Example 3.48

Recall Example 3.11 (Figure 3.7) where a single NC machine processes three different types of parts. Let the processing time of a part of type i be a continuous random variable with mean m_i or a deterministic duration m_i. First assume that the parts are processed in a cyclic way (type 1, type 2, and type 3 in a cyclic sequence). The state space of the stochastic process here has three states $\{1, 2, 3\}$ where i $(i = 1, 2, 3)$ corresponds to the part type currently undergoing processing. If we sample the stochastic process at the time of entering a new state, then we have a DTMC with TPM given by

$$P = \begin{bmatrix} 0 & 1 & 0 \\ 0 & 0 & 1 \\ 1 & 0 & 0 \end{bmatrix}$$

The state transition diagram of this DTMC was earlier shown in Figure 3.8(a). Since condition 2 of the above definition is also satisfied, we have a semi-Markov process.

Now assume that the next part type to be processed is selected probabilistically with probabilities q_1, q_2, and q_3 ($q_1 + q_2 + q_3 = 1$). If we examine the stochastic process at each instant of time that the machine finishes processing a part, the embedded process will be a DTMC with TPM given by

$$P = \begin{bmatrix} q_1 & q_2 & q_3 \\ q_1 & q_2 & q_3 \\ q_1 & q_2 & q_3 \end{bmatrix}$$

The state diagram of this DTMC was earlier shown in Figure 3.8(b). Here again the stochastic process is a semi-Markov process.

Example 3.49

An $M/G/1$ queue is a single-server queuing system with Poisson arrivals and with job service times that are independent and identically distributed continuous random variables. We will study this queue in Chapter 4. If $X(t)$ denotes the number of jobs in the queue plus any in service, then $\{X(t) : t \geq 0\}$ is a semi-Markov process. An embedded Markov chain in this case may be obtained by taking a snapshot of the system at instants of departure of jobs. The sojourn times in this case are nonexponential unless the service times are independent and identical exponential random variables. In the latter case, we get the well-known $M/M/1$ queue (discussed in Section 4.2). If the job service times are assumed to be a constant, then we have the $M/D/1$ queue.

3.9.2 Analysis of Semi-Markov Processes

Consider a semi-Markov process $\{X(t) : t \geq 0\}$ which has an embedded Markov chain $\{X_n : n \in \mathbb{N}\}$ that is irreducible and positive recurrent. Let P be the TPM of the EMC. If $Y = (y_1, y_2, ...)$ is the vector of limiting probabilities of the EMC, then we know that Y can be computed using (22), reproduced below for ready reference:

$$YP = Y, \quad \text{and} \quad \sum_{i=0}^{\infty} y_i = 1$$

The probabilities y_i would give the relative number of times the respective states are visited. To compute the steady-state probabilities π_j of the semi-Markov process, which give the fraction of resident time in the states, we proceed as follows.

Let m_i be the mean sojourn time of state i $(i = 0, 1, ...)$ in the semi-Markov process. Let us fix i. Since y_i is the relative number of visits to state i, $1/y_i$ would give the average number of states visited between successive visits to state i and hence y_j/y_i for $j = 0, 1, 2, ...$, would give the average number of visits to state j between successive visits to state i. Also, $\frac{y_j}{y_i} m_j$ would give the average total time spent in state j between successive visits to state i and hence the average time between successive visits to state i is $\sum_k \frac{y_k}{y_i} m_k$. Hence, the average proportion of residence time in state j is given by

$$\pi_j = \frac{\frac{y_j}{y_i} m_j}{\sum_k \frac{y_k}{y_i} m_k} = \frac{y_j m_j}{\sum_k y_k m_k} \qquad j = 0, 1, 2, ... \tag{67}$$

Equation (67) gives the steady-state probabilities of the states of the semi-Markov process. Note that in deriving the above expression, we have crucially used the irreducibility and positive recurrence of the EMC. Also notice that (67) is identical to (49) which was obtained while analyzing a CTMC via its EMC.

3.9.3 Application to Examples

We now consider the analysis of some typical semi-Markov models.

Example 3.50

We examine the semi-Markov processes presented in Example 3.48. For cyclic sequencing, the limiting probabilities of the EMC can be seen to be $y_1 = y_2 = y_3 = \frac{1}{3}$. It is to be noted that m_1, m_2, and m_3, are the mean processing times for part types 1, 2, and 3, respectively. Therefore they would give the mean sojourn times also. Hence, using (67), we get the steady-state probabilities of the semi-Markov process as

$$\pi_i = \frac{m_i}{m_1 + m_2 + m_3} \qquad i = 1, 2, 3$$

For probabilistic selection, we have $y_i = q_i$ for $i = 1, 2, 3$. Hence the probabilities π_i are given from (67) as

$$\pi_i = \frac{q_i m_i}{q_1 m_1 + q_2 m_2 + q_3 m_3} \qquad i = 1, 2, 3$$

It is important to note that the probabilities π_1, π_2, and π_3, in the current example, depend only on the mean processing times and not on the processing time distributions. Thus, whether the mean processing times are

exponential with rate $\frac{1}{m_i}$ or deterministic durations m_i or arbitrary continuous random variables with means m_i, we get the same values for π_i. This
happens only in very special situations such as in the above example.

Example 3.51

The system considered here is the single-machine system of Example 3.28
(resume policy) and (discard policy). Recall that there are three states:

    1: Machine being set up

    2: Machine processing a part

    3: Machine down, getting repaired.

In the CTMC formulation, it was assumed that the setup time, processing
time, time to failure, and repair time are independent exponential random
variables with rates s, p, f, and r, respectively. Since setup and processing
operations consume more or less constant time, it will be interesting
to investigate the performance assuming the following parameter values:
Setup time $= S$ (constant); processing time $= D$ (constant); time to
failure and repair time as before (that is, exponential with rates f and r,
respectively). The performance model now will be a semi-Markov process.

First, consider the discard policy. We obtain an EMC by observing
the process only at instants of state change. Let the TPM of the EMC, P,
be given by

$$P = \begin{bmatrix} p_{11} & p_{12} & p_{13} \\ p_{21} & p_{22} & p_{23} \\ p_{31} & p_{32} & p_{33} \end{bmatrix}$$

We know that $p_{12} = 1$ and hence $p_{11} = p_{13} = 0$. Also, $p_{31} = 1$ and
hence $p_{32} = p_{33} = 0$. Further, $p_{22} = 0$. Note that p_{21} is equal to the
probability that processing by the machine finishes before the occurrence
of a failure. Let the random variable F denote the time to failure. We
know that $F = EXP(f)$. Therefore,

$$p_{21} = P\{F > D\} = e^{-fD}$$
$$p_{23} = 1 - p_{21} = 1 - e^{-fD}$$

Thus the TPM is given by

$$P = \begin{bmatrix} 0 & 1 & 0 \\ q & 0 & 1-q \\ 1 & 0 & 0 \end{bmatrix}$$

where $q = e^{-fD}$. It is easy to verify that the EMC is irreducible and positive recurrent. The limiting probabilities y_1, y_2, and y_3 of the EMC can be computed to be

$$y_1 = y_2 = \frac{1}{3-q}; \quad y_3 = \frac{1-q}{3-q}$$

We now compute the mean sojourn times m_1, m_2, and m_3. Note that $m_1 = S$ and $m_3 = 1/r$. To compute m_2, we look at the random variable T_2, the sojourn time in state 2. It can be seen that $T_2 = min(D, F)$. Therefore, the density of T_2 can be computed to be (see Problem 1 in this section)

$$f_{T_2}(t) = \frac{1}{1 - e^{-fD}} f e^{-ft} \qquad \text{for} \ \ 0 < t < D$$
$$= 0 \qquad\qquad\qquad \text{otherwise}$$

It can be shown that the mean of T_2 is given by

$$m_2 = \frac{1}{f} - \left(\frac{q}{1-q}\right) D$$

We can now compute the steady-state probabilities π_1, π_2, and π_3 of the semi-Markov process, using (67). It will be interesting to compare these values with the ones obtained using the CTMC formulation (Example 3.29). For the sake of comparison, we can assume $S = 1/s$ and $D = 1/p$.

For resume policy, the TPM of the EMC would be given by

$$P = \begin{bmatrix} 0 & 1 & 0 \\ q & 0 & 1-q \\ 0 & 1 & 0 \end{bmatrix}$$

The mean sojourn times remain the same as for the discard policy. The steady-state probabilities can again be computed using (67) and compared with those obtained in Example 3.28.

Note that the analysis of the above system becomes quite nontrivial if we consider two identical machines instead of a single machine. This is a generic problem with all semi-Markov processes, which manifests when two or more nonexponential activities are concurrently in progress.

PROBLEMS

1. Given a constant $D > 0$ and an exponential random variable $F = EXP(f)$, show that the pdf of the random variable $X = min(D, F)$ is given by

$$f_X(x) = \frac{1}{1 - e^{-fD}} f \; e^{-fx} \qquad 0 < x < D$$
$$= 0 \qquad\qquad\qquad\qquad \text{otherwise}$$

Derive that the expectation of X is given by

$$E[X] = \frac{1}{f} - \left(\frac{e^{-fD}}{1 - e^{-fD}} \right) D$$

2. For the case of probabilistic selection in Example 3.50, another EMC can be visualized in the following way: Observe the system when it starts processing a part of type different from the type of the previous part (and not when it starts processing any part). What is the TPM of this EMC and what are the mean sojourn times of the three states? Obtain the steady-state probabilities of the semi-Markov process and verify that they are the same as obtained in Example 3.50.

3. Consider an NC machine processing three types of parts as in Example 3.50. Cyclic rule or probabilistic rule can be used to select the next part type to be processed. Assume that no setups are required. Processing times are constant and equal to m_i for part type i. Failures are exponential with rate λ and repair times are exponential with rate r. Resume policy is used after repair. Formulate semi-Markov models and evaluate the throughput for (a) cyclic rule and (b) probabilistic selection. Can you generalize the results to the case of n part types?

4. Other popular nonexponential distributions for modeling processing times and setup times are the uniform and the normal random variables. Solve the semi-Markov processes discussed in Example 3.51 assuming that

(a) setup time and processing time are uniformly distributed.

(b) setup time and processing time are normally distributed.

In both the above cases, time to failure and repair time are to be taken as exponential random variables.

5. In Example 3.30, assume that the AGV service time is constant, equal to $\frac{1}{\mu_0}$. If all other details remain the same, solve the resulting semi-Markov process and compare the results with those obtained in that example.

6. Recall the interpretation of the machine repairman model as presented in Example 3.37. Now assume that the service time on the AGV is constant, equal to $1/\mu$. Rest of the details are identical. Solve the resulting semi-Markov process and compare the results with those obtained in Example 3.37.

7. This problem shows that the results of Section 3.8 can be applied to semi-Markov processes with absorbing states. In Example 3.44, a robot cell was described. Assume that the processing time on the machine is constant, equal to $1/\mu$ and that the arrivals are Poisson with rate λ (as earlier). Formulate a semi-Markov model, and compute the EMC and mean sojourn times for buffer capacities zero and one. Compute the mean time to deadlock and the mean number of completed parts before deadlock.

3.10 TRANSIENT ANALYSIS OF MANUFACTURING SYSTEMS

Thus far we have been concerned with the steady-state analysis of Markov and semi-Markov models of AMSs. The models we have considered so far correspond mostly to positive recurrent, irreducible chains, for which the existence of a unique steady-state probability distribution is guaranteed. There are certain situations – for example, chains with absorbing states – where the long-run or steady-state analysis holds no significance because of the presence of transient states. Also, even in ergodic chains, we may often be interested in looking at the performance of the system much before the onset of the steady-state or during a finite observation period. For example, in an AMS in which disruptions in the system, such as tool breakages, machine breakdowns, deadlocks, and change of part mixes, are frequent, steady-state analysis is unlikely to give a complete picture of the system performance. This is because we may be interested in evaluating the performance of an AMS over an 8-hour shift but the system may not reach a steady-state by that time. In such situations, transient analysis will be more meaningful. In this section we discuss transient analysis of CTMCs with several examples drawn from manufacturing situations.

3.10.1 Solution of Forward and Backward Equations

We have seen that the dynamical evolution in time of a CTMC can be described in terms of the forward and backward differential equations.

Recall that for a homogeneous CTMC $\{X(t) : t \geq 0\}$, the forward equations and the backward equations are respectively given by

$$\frac{dH(t)}{dt} = H(t)Q, \quad \text{and}$$

$$\frac{dH(t)}{dt} = QH(t), \quad \text{where}$$

$$H(t) = [p_{ij}(t)], \quad \text{with}$$

$$p_{ij}(t) = P\{X(t) = j \mid X(0) = i\}.$$

Note that Q is the infinitesimal generator of the CTMC and that the initial conditions are given by $H(0) = I$. Also recall that the above equations expressed in terms of the individual matrix elements are given by

$$\frac{dp_{ij}(t)}{dt} = q_{jj}p_{ij}(t) + \sum_{k \neq j} q_{kj}p_{ik}(t) \tag{68}$$

$$\frac{dp_{ij}(t)}{dt} = q_{ii}p_{ij}(t) + \sum_{k \neq i} q_{ik}p_{kj}(t) \tag{69}$$

It is important to recall that the forward and backward equations have the same unique solution given by

$$H(t) = \exp(Qt) \tag{70}$$

If we are interested in computing the state probabilities, that is,

$$\Pi(t) = [\, p_0(t) \quad p_1(t) \quad p_2(t) \quad ...]$$

where $p_j(t) = P\{X(t) = j\}$, then we need to solve the equation

$$\frac{d\Pi(t)}{dt} = \Pi(t)Q$$

whose solution is given by

$$\Pi(t) = \Pi(0)\exp(Qt)$$

We shall get a feel for the forward and backward equations and their solution by using the following examples.

Example 3.52

Let us look at a single-machine system with failure rate $= \lambda$; repair rate $= \mu$; and two states:

    0: Machine working

    1: Machine undergoing repair, after failing.

For this example,

$$H(t) = \begin{bmatrix} p_{00}(t) & p_{01}(t) \\ p_{10}(t) & p_{11}(t) \end{bmatrix}; \quad Q = \begin{bmatrix} -\lambda & \lambda \\ \mu & -\mu \end{bmatrix}$$

The forward equations (68) in this case are given by

$$\frac{dp_{00}(t)}{dt} = p_{00}(t) q_{00} + p_{01}(t) q_{10}$$

$$\frac{dp_{01}(t)}{dt} = p_{01}(t) q_{11} + p_{00}(t) q_{01}$$

$$\frac{dp_{10}(t)}{dt} = p_{10}(t) q_{00} + p_{11}(t) q_{10}$$

$$\frac{dp_{11}(t)}{dt} = p_{11}(t) q_{11} + p_{10}(t) q_{01}$$

The backward equations (69) are given by

$$\frac{dp_{00}(t)}{dt} = q_{00} p_{00}(t) + q_{01} p_{10}(t)$$

$$\frac{dp_{01}(t)}{dt} = q_{01} p_{11}(t) + q_{00} p_{01}(t)$$

$$\frac{dp_{10}(t)}{dt} = q_{10} p_{00}(t) + q_{11} p_{10}(t)$$

$$\frac{dp_{11}(t)}{dt} = q_{11} p_{11}(t) + q_{10} p_{01}(t)$$

First, we solve for $p_{00}(t)$ and $p_{10}(t)$ using backward equations:

$$\frac{dp_{00}(t)}{dt} = -\lambda p_{00}(t) + \lambda p_{10}(t) \tag{71}$$

$$\frac{dp_{10}(t)}{dt} = \mu p_{00}(t) - \mu p_{10}(t) \tag{72}$$

Multiplying (71) by μ and (72) by λ and summing, we get

$$\mu \frac{dp_{00}(t)}{dt} + \lambda \frac{dp_{10}(t)}{dt} = 0$$

Integration of the above yields

$$\mu p_{00}(t) + \lambda p_{10}(t) = C$$

where C is a constant. Since $p_{00}(0) = 1$ and $p_{10}(0) = 0$, we obtain $C = \mu$ and hence we have

$$\mu p_{00}(t) + \lambda p_{10}(t) = \mu \tag{73}$$

Using (73) in (71), we get

$$\frac{dp_{00}(t)}{dt} = -\lambda p_{00}(t) + \mu - \mu p_{00}(t)$$
$$= \mu - (\lambda + \mu) p_{00}(t)$$

That is, we have the differential equation

$$\frac{dp_{00}(t)}{dt} + (\lambda + \mu) p_{00}(t) = \mu \tag{74}$$

Equation (74) is a linear differential equation with solution given by

$$p_{00}(t) = \frac{\mu}{\lambda + \mu} + \left(\frac{\lambda}{\lambda + \mu}\right) e^{-(\lambda + \mu)t} \tag{75}$$

Using (73) in (75), we obtain

$$p_{10}(t) = \frac{\mu}{\lambda}[1 - p_{00}(t)]$$
$$= \frac{\mu}{\lambda + \mu} - \left(\frac{\mu}{\lambda + \mu}\right) e^{-(\lambda + \mu)t}$$

Proceeding in a similar way, it can be shown that

$$p_{11}(t) = \frac{\lambda}{\lambda + \mu} + \left(\frac{\mu}{\lambda + \mu}\right) e^{-(\lambda + \mu)t}$$
$$p_{01}(t) = \frac{\lambda}{\lambda + \mu} - \left(\frac{\lambda}{\lambda + \mu}\right) e^{-(\lambda + \mu)t}$$

Figure 3.45 shows the evolution of the probabilities $p_{ij}(t)$. Note that

$$\lim_{t \to \infty} p_{00}(t) = \lim_{t \to \infty} p_{10}(t) = \frac{\mu}{\lambda + \mu}$$

$$\lim_{t\to\infty} p_{11}(t) = \lim_{t\to\infty} p_{01}(t) = \frac{\lambda}{\lambda + \mu}$$

The above limiting probabilities are precisely the steady-state probabilities π_0 and π_1 of the states 0 and 1, respectively.

We shall now compute, for $j = 0, 1$,

$$
\begin{aligned}
p_j(t) &= P\{X(t) = j\} \\
&= P\{X(t) = j \mid X(0) = 0\} + P\{X(t) = j \mid X(0) = 1\} \\
&= p_{0j}(t)\, p_0(0) + p_{1j}(t)\, p_1(0)
\end{aligned}
$$

If we assume that the initial state is state 0, then we have $p_0(0) = 1$ and $p_1(0) = 0$. Therefore

$$p_0(t) = \frac{\mu}{\lambda + \mu} + \left(\frac{\lambda}{\lambda + \mu}\right) e^{-(\lambda+\mu)t}$$

$$p_1(t) = \frac{\lambda}{\lambda + \mu} - \left(\frac{\lambda}{\lambda + \mu}\right) e^{-(\lambda+\mu)t}$$

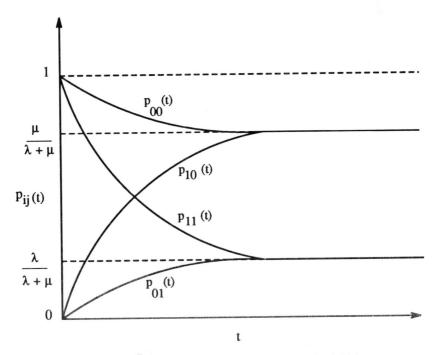

Figure 3.45 Evolution of transition probabilities

Example 3.53

Consider an NC machine as in Example 3.11, processing parts of two types, following a probabilistic policy for selecting part types. In this case, the two states are 1 and 2 depending on which part type is being processed. If q_1 and q_2 are the selecting probabilities, and μ_1 and μ_2 the processing rates for the two part types, we have

$$Q = \begin{bmatrix} -q_2\mu_1 & q_2\mu_1 \\ q_1\mu_2 & -q_1\mu_2 \end{bmatrix}$$

This system is similar to the one we have just now studied and we can use the expressions derived there. In particular, using (75) with suitable substitutions, we get

$$p_{11}(t) = \frac{q_1\mu_2}{q_1\mu_2 + q_2\mu_1} + \left(\frac{q_2\mu_1}{q_1\mu_2 + q_2\mu_1}\right) e^{-(q_1\mu_2 + q_2\mu_1)t}$$

If $\mu_1 = \mu_2 = \mu$ and $q_1 = q$, so that $q_2 = 1 - q$, the above simplifies to

$$p_{11}(t) = q + (1 - q) e^{-\mu t}$$

From the above, one can compute the variation of $p_{11}(t)$ with q. Note that $p_{11}(t) \to q$ as $t \to \infty$. The other transition probabilities can also be similarly computed.

3.10.2 Distribution of Time to Deadlock

Here we show how transient analysis can be used for computing the cumulative distribution function (CDF) of the time to deadlock in AMSs with deadlock.

Example 3.54

We have seen in Section 3.8 that Markov chains with absorbing states provide a natural model for manufacturing systems with deadlocks. If the state space of such a chain is given by $\{1, 2, ..., m, m + 1, ..., m + n\}$ where the first m states are transient states and the rest absorbing states, then recall that $\pi_1 = \pi_2 = ... = \pi_m = 0$, where $\pi_i, i = 1, 2, ..., m$, are the limiting probabilities of state i. Also recall that the Markov chain will permanently reside in any absorbing state it reaches first. In such a scenario, the performance exhibited by the system before the occurrence of a deadlock can only be evaluated by conducting a transient analysis.

From Section 3.8, let us consider the robot cell of Figure 3.42, where raw parts are supplied to an NC machine by a robot which also removes the finished parts to an output conveyor. We have seen that a deadlock here occurs when the machine waits for the robot to unload a finished part and the robot arrives with a raw part. The transition rate diagram of a Markov chain model of this was shown in Figure 3.43(a). This chain comprises three transient states $0, 1,$ and $2,$ and one absorbing state 3. We have seen that the mean time to deadlock, τ, starting from state 0, is given by

$$\tau = \left(\frac{1}{1-p}\right)\left(\frac{1}{\lambda}\right) + \left(\frac{1}{1-p}\right)\left(\frac{1}{\lambda+\mu}\right) + \frac{1}{\mu}$$

where $p = \frac{\mu}{\lambda+\mu}$; μ = rate of processing; and λ = rate of arrival of raw parts.

Also, it can be observed that the mean number of parts produced before deadlock $= \frac{1}{1-p}$.

We shall now look at the transient behavior of the above system. For this, we shall compute $p_{03}(t)$. The backward equation for $p_{03}(t)$ is given by

$$\frac{dp_{03}(t)}{dt} = q_{00}p_{03}(t) + q_{01}p_{13}(t) + q_{02}p_{23}(t) + q_{03}p_{33}(t)$$

We know that $q_{00} = -\lambda$; $q_{01} = \lambda$; $q_{02} = 0$; and $q_{03} = 0$. Therefore we have

$$\frac{dp_{03}(t)}{dt} = -\lambda p_{03}(t) + \lambda p_{13}(t) \tag{76}$$

The backward equation for $p_{13}(t)$ is given by

$$\frac{dp_{13}(t)}{dt} = q_{10}p_{03}(t) + q_{11}p_{13}(t) + q_{12}p_{23}(t) + q_{13}p_{33}(t)$$

Since $q_{10} = \mu$; $q_{12} = \lambda$; $q_{11} = -(\lambda+\mu)$; and $q_{13} = 0$, the above simplifies to

$$\frac{dp_{13}(t)}{dt} = \mu p_{03}(t) - (\mu+\lambda)p_{13}(t) + \lambda p_{23}(t) \tag{77}$$

The backward equation for $p_{23}(t)$ is

$$\frac{dp_{23}(t)}{dt} = -\mu p_{23}(t) + \mu p_{33}(t)$$
$$= -\mu p_{23}(t) + \mu \tag{78}$$

We shall solve for $p_{03}(t)$ by the Laplace transform method. Let $P_{ij}(s)$ denote the Laplace transform of $p_{ij}(t)$. Taking the Laplace transform on both sides of (76), (77), and (78), we get, respectively,

$$sP_{03}(s) = -\lambda P_{03}(s) + \lambda P_{13}(s) \tag{79}$$

$$sP_{13}(s) = \mu P_{03}(s) - (\lambda + \mu) P_{13}(s) + \lambda P_{23}(s) \tag{80}$$

$$sP_{23}(s) = -\mu P_{23}(s) + \frac{\mu}{s} \tag{81}$$

From (81), we have

$$P_{23}(s) = \frac{\mu}{s(s+\mu)} \tag{82}$$

Using (80), (81), and (82), we obtain

$$P_{23}(s) = \frac{\lambda\mu}{s(s+\mu)(s+\lambda+\mu)} + \frac{\mu}{(s+\lambda+\mu)}P_{03}(s) \tag{83}$$

Using (83) in (79), and simplifying, we get

$$P_{03}(s) = \frac{\lambda^2\mu}{s(s+\mu)(s^2 + s(2\lambda+\mu)+\lambda^2)} \tag{84}$$

Equation (84) can further be simplified as

$$P_{03}(s) = \frac{k}{s(s+\mu)(s+a)(s+b)}$$

where the constants k, a, and b depend on λ and μ and can be evaluated easily. Thus, the solution can be written as

$$p_{03}(t) = A + Be^{-\mu t} + Ce^{-at} + De^{-bt}$$

where A, B, C, and D are constants. Since we know that

$$p_{03}(t) = 0 \qquad \text{at } t = 0$$
$$= 1 \qquad \text{at } t = \infty,$$

we have $A = 1$ and $A + B + C + D = 0$. Thus,

$$p_{03}(t) = 1 + Be^{-\mu t} + Ce^{-at} + De^{-bt},$$

where $B + C + D = -1$. Now let T be a continuous random variable that represents the time to deadlock, starting in state 0. The CDF of T can be derived as

$$F_T(t) = P\{T \leq t\} = p_{03}(t) \qquad t \geq 0.$$

Thus, using transient analysis, we are able to compute the distribution of the time to deadlock, whereas using the fundamental matrix approach of Section 3.8 we can only compute the mean time to deadlock.

So far, we have discussed the symbolic computation of the time-dependent transition probabilities. Symbolic computation is feasible only for simple Markov chains, as in Examples 3.52 and 3.54. Numerical methods have to be used in order to handle real-life models. Section 3.11.5 deals with this problem.

PROBLEMS

1. Refer to Figure 3.P.4 of Problem 2 in Section 3.8, which represents the transition diagram of a CTMC with absorbing states. This can be visualized as a model of a system comprising a machine and an inspection facility. λ is the processing rate of the machine and μ is the inspection rate. Every part undergoes an inspection after processing. If the finished part is of acceptable quality, the next raw part is taken up for processing by the machine. p is the probability with which a finished part satisfies the quality requirement. It is assumed that the system reaches absorbing state 2 when a part is rejected by the inspection machine. For the above system, formulate the backward and forward equations for $p_{00}(t), p_{01}(t)$, and $p_{02}(t)$ and solve for these time-dependent probabilities. What is the distribution of

   (a) time to reach the absorbing state (time for which the system works until the first rejected part), and

   (b) number of parts produced by the system before the first rejection?

   Verify that the mean values of these agree with the ones computed in Problem 2 of Section 3.8.

2. In Example 3.54, compute the distribution of the number of parts produced before deadlock. Also, if there is a buffer in front of the machine, with capacity of 1, attempt to deduce the distribution of the number of parts produced before deadlock.

3. Assume a two-machine system with a single repair facility of rate μ. The failure rate of each machine is λ. When both machines have failed, the system is considered to have failed and no recovery is possible. The state space of the system is $\{0, 1, 2\}$ where i $(i = 0, 1, 2)$ denotes the number of failed machines, and the transition rate diagram is given by Figure 3.P.6(a). Formulate the backward equations for $p_{00}(t)$, $p_{01}(t)$, and $p_{02}(t)$, and solve for them. The reliability of the system can be defined by

$$R(t) = 1 - p_{02}(t)$$

If T is the time to failure, then note that $R(t) = P\{T > t\}$. Show, that

$$f_T(t) = \frac{2\lambda^2}{a - b}\left(e^{-bt} - e^{-at}\right)$$

where

$$a, b = \frac{(3\lambda + \mu)}{2} \pm \frac{1}{2}\sqrt{\lambda^2 + 6\lambda\mu + \mu^2}$$

Obtain the mean time to failure of the above system. Repeat the analysis for a system in which there is no repair facility, i.e., with the transition diagram given by Figure 3.P.6(b).

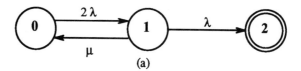

(a)

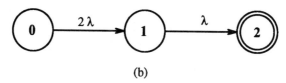

(b)

Figure 3.P.6

4. Consider a pure birth process, with state space $\{0, 1, 2, ...\}$ and with transition rates given by

$$q_{ij} = -\lambda \qquad \text{for } i = j$$
$$= \lambda \qquad \text{for } j = i + 1$$
$$= 0 \qquad \text{otherwise}$$

for all i, j. Show, using transient analysis, that the above process is the same as the Poisson process with rate λ.

5. Formulate the forward and backward equations for a birth and death process. If $p_k(t)$ is the probability of the process being in state k ($k = 0, 1, 2, \ldots$) at time $t \geq 0$, obtain a differential equation for $p_k(t)$ and attempt to solve it.

6. Consider two machines M_1 and M_2. M_i operates for an exponential time with rate λ_i and then fails; it is immediately repaired with repair time being exponential with rate μ_i. The machines act independently of each other. Define a four-state CTMC which describes the above system. Write down the forward and backward equations for the above chain. Assuming both the machines are up initially, obtain an expression for the instantaneous availability of the system.

3.11 COMPUTATIONAL ISSUES IN MARKOV ANALYSIS

Numerical evaluation of performance measures using Markovian models proceeds in two stages. First, the transition probability matrix P or the transition rate matrix Q of the Markov model is derived starting from the physical system. Second, steady-state or transient analysis is carried out using P or Q. The first stage can become a highly nontrivial exercise for complex real-life manufacturing systems. In Chapter 5 we will show that stochastic Petri net models provide an effective tool to generate the Markov chain model. In this section we shall look at the computational issues that arise when we seek a steady-state or transient solution to the given Markov chain model. In analyzing the Markov model of a real-life manufacturing system, we are beset with two problems: (1) large number of states in the Markov chain model and (2) orders of magnitude difference in the transition rates or transition probabilities in Markov models where failures are also modeled alongside machine operations and material handling. Since the matrices involved are sparse, the computational methods should attempt to use the sparsity to advantage.

First we treat the computational issues in steady-state analysis and then we go on to the computational issues in transient analysis.

3.11.1 Computational Issues in Steady-State Analysis

Let us look at the typical problems that are solved in Markov chain steady-state analysis.

(i) Given an ergodic DTMC model with state space $\{0, 1, 2, ..., N\}$ and transition probability matrix P, solve for the limiting probability vector $Y = (y_0, y_1, ..., y_N)$ using the equations

$$YP = Y \quad \text{and} \quad \sum_{i=0}^{N} y_i = 1 \tag{85}$$

(ii) Given an ergodic CTMC model with state space $\{0, 1, 2, ..., N\}$ and transition rate matrix Q, compute the limiting probability vector $\Pi = (\pi_0, \pi_1, ..., \pi_N)$, given by

$$\Pi Q = 0 \quad \text{and} \quad \sum_{i=0}^{N} \pi_i = 1 \tag{86}$$

Often, we wish to evaluate the sensitivity of the vector Π with respect to one of the transition rate parameters, say λ, which could be a part of many entries in Q. Differentiating the equation $\Pi Q = 0$ with respect to λ, we get

$$\frac{d\Pi}{d\lambda} Q + \Pi \frac{dQ}{d\lambda} = 0$$

If Π is known, then $\Pi \frac{dQ}{d\lambda}$ is known and therefore the above can be put in the form

$$xQ = -b \tag{87}$$

where $x = \frac{d\Pi}{d\lambda}$ gives the required sensitivity and $b = \Pi \frac{dQ}{d\lambda}$. Computing x is now a problem of solving a non-homogeneous system of linear simultaneous equations. Note that Q is the coefficient matrix in both (86) and (87).

(iii) For Markov chains with absorbing states, we will be interested in computing the fundamental matrix F given by $F = (I - T)^{-1}$ where T is the matrix of transition probabilities for all the transient states in the chain. We have

$$F(I - T) = I \tag{88}$$

which means that F is the solution of a non-homogeneous system of linear simultaneous equations.

Equations (85), (86), (87), and (88) represent the generic computational problems encountered in the steady-state analysis of Markov chains. Note in all cases that we have a homogeneous or a non-homogeneous system of linear simultaneous equations. In solving these systems of equations, we have to keep in mind the following factors:

1. **Largeness**: The matrices involved are typically large. Real-life AMS models may have tens of thousands of states.

2. **Sparseness**: The matrices are necessarily sparse. The problem of state space explosion can be alleviated to some extent by using sparse matrix storage techniques.

3. **Multiple Time Scales**: The typical activities in an AMS to be captured by a Markov chain model include machine setups, machine operations, transport of parts across machines, machine breakdowns, and machine repairs. The durations of these activities could fall into several different orders of magnitude. This leads to orders of magnitude difference in the transition probabilities or transition rates. Therefore, if all these operations are to be captured in the same Markov chain model, we are confronted with the problem of multiple time scales. Such Markov chains are said to be *stiff*.

4. **Ill-Conditioning**: A matrix is said to be *ill-conditioned* if it is possible for small changes in the matrix to produce large changes in the solution. The condition number of a matrix provides an estimate of the numerical difficulty (ill-conditioning) encountered when computing the solution. Small perturbations in matrices with large condition numbers can produce large changes in the solution. The matrices of Markov models of manufacturing systems may sometimes turn out to be ill-conditioned.

3.11.2 Solution Methods for Steady-State Analysis

There are basically two principal classes of solution methods for Markov chain analysis. These are *direct methods* and *iterative methods*. Direct methods are those in which the coefficient matrix is transformed using a series of elementary operations. LU decomposition for solving linear systems of equations and the QR algorithm for computing eigenvalues and eigenvectors are examples of direct methods. In iterative methods, a carefully chosen initial solution vector is refined through successive iterations to arrive at the actual solution vector. Principal iterative methods include: (a) the Power method, (b) Gauss-Seidel Iteration and Successive Overrelaxation, (c) The Symmetric Successive Overrelaxation method, (d) Preconditioned power iteration, (e) Subspace iteration, (f) Arnoldi's method, and (g) Unsymmetric Lanczos. A detailed discussion of these individual methods has been presented in the paper by Philippe, Saad, and Stewart [1989]. Without going into the details of these methods, we shall only compare the relative merits of direct methods and iterative methods for solving Markov models in the context of manufacturing systems. Iterative methods are by far the most commonly used methods for obtaining solutions for (85), (86), (87), and (88). The following are the advantages of the iterative methods.

(i) In iterative methods, the only operation in which the matrices are involved are multiplications with one or more vectors. These operations do not alter the form of the matrix and hence compact storage schemes may be conveniently implemented. Since the matrices involved are usually large and very sparse, the savings made by such schemes are considerable. With direct solution methods, the elimination of one non-zero element of the matrix during the reduction phase often results in the creation of several non-zero elements in positions that previously contained zeros. This is called *fill-in*. Fill-in makes the organization of compact storage schemes very difficult since provision must be made for the deletion and insertion of elements. Also, the amount of fill-in can often be so extensive that available memory may not be enough.

(ii) In iterative methods, good initial approximations to the solution vector can lead to fast and accurate computation of the solution vector. This is especially beneficial when a series of related experiments is being conducted. In such experiments, it will often happen that the solution to a new experiment is close to that of the previous one and so the latter solution may be used as the new initial approximation.

(iii) An iterative process may be halted once a prespecified tolerance criterion has been satisfied. Often the tolerance specification may be as high as 5–10% because we may be interested in a quick, approximate evaluation rather than a detailed, precise prediction of performance. In such cases, the iteration method will be very fast. Direct solution methods are obligated to continue until the final specified operation has been carried out.

(iv) With iterative methods, the coefficient matrix is never altered and the buildup of rounding error is minimal.

The drawback of iterative methods is that they often require a large number of iterations and hence a large amount of computer time to converge to the desired solution. There is no way of estimating, a priori, the number of iterations for convergence. Direct methods have the advantage that an upper bound on the time required to obtain the solution may be determined before the calculation is initiated. In some cases, the direct methods compute the solution in less time, but in all cases they require more memory than do iterative methods. When the state space is small (say < 100), or even for moderately sized problems in which the non-zero elements lie close to the diagonal, then a direct method is recommended. Otherwise, iterative methods are preferred. Among the iterative methods, extensive experiments have showed that the most robust method is the preconditioned Arnoldi method. However, when the matrix is reasonably well conditioned, all of the iterative methods perform equally well.

3.11.3 Time Scale Analysis Technique

In a typical manufacturing system, there are several activities that occur at markedly different rates, such as setup operations, machining operations, material handling, failures, and repairs. If all these activities are to be captured in the same model then there will be several orders of magnitude difference in the transition rates or transition probabilities. In such situations, the analysis of the Markov chain can be carried out efficiently using a technique called *aggregation* or *time scale decomposition*. Aggregation is basically a means of breaking up the model into models of lower complexity, each of which represents the system at a different time scale. Essentially, one can think of the chain as displaying a certain type of transition behavior if examined over short time intervals and a behavior that is quite different when examined over very long time intervals. To see a simple example, consider a single-machine system that produces an average of 50 parts per hour. If the machine is observed to fail after an average of 20 hours of operation and the repair takes an average of 5 hours, then we can easily perceive the existence of two different time scales in this system. For instance, if the system is examined over a 10-minute interval, we will see individual operations completed, but the machine will remain either failed or working with a very high probability. On the other hand, if we observe the machine over a one-week period, then the focus will shift to failures and repairs rather than individual operations. The technique of aggregation or time scale decomposition is often used in such contexts. To illustrate the idea of aggregation, we present the following Example.

Example 3.55

Consider a manufacturing facility comprising a high precision NC machine M_1 and a conventional, low precision machine M_2. The latter is used only when the former is down and getting repaired. We assume that M_2 is reliable enough not to fail during the repair of the high precision machine. The system produces two different part types, with raw parts of either type always available. The high precision machine takes an average of 3 min and 4 min, respectively, for processing parts of type 1 and type 2. The other machine spends 10 min on type 1 parts and 15 min on type 2 parts. The first machine fails once in 20 h on an average, and it takes an average of 5 h for its repair. As assumed earlier, the second machine does not fail. Each machine while in operation produces type 1 and type 2 parts alternately, in batches of one each. The above system can be formulated as a CTMC with the state space comprising the states $1, 2, 3,$ and 4, having the following interpretation:

    1: M_1 processing a type 1 part; M_2 idle

    2: M_1 processing a type 2 part; M_2 idle

    3: M_2 processing a type 1 part; M_1 down

    4: M_2 processing a type 2 part; M_1 down.

Let us assume that as soon as machine M_1 is repaired, the operations on M_2 are stopped and M_1 will resume the processing of the same part type. Figure 3.46 shows the state transition diagram of the CTMC model. The transition rates are given in units of per hour. The transitions between 1 and 2, and between 3 and 4 are designated as fast transitions, whereas the transitions between 1 and 3, and between 2 and 4 are designated as slow transitions.

In Figure 3.46, the failure rate is 0.05 and the repair rate is 0.2. We denote $\epsilon = 0.05$ and call ϵ as the perturbation parameter. In general, ϵ is a small positive number. Application of time scale decomposition will now proceed in two steps. In step 1, we obtain a model of the form shown in Figure 3.47, for short time scales. This is obtained by setting to zero

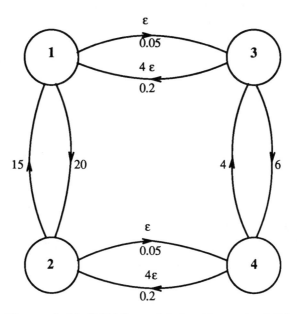

Figure 3.46 CTMC model for Example 3.55

the probability that a slow transition occurs. Or equivalently by setting $\epsilon = 0$ so that the slow transitions do not occur. We now have two CTMCs comprising, respectively, states 1 and 2 and states 3 and 4. The steady-state

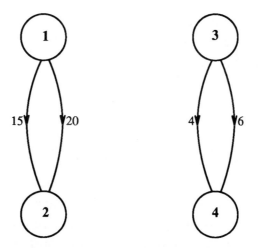

Figure 3.47 CTMC model for fast transitions

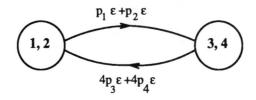

Figure 3.48 CTMC model for slow transitions

probabilities for the individual CTMCs may be computed easily as

$$p_1 = \frac{3}{7}; \quad p_2 = \frac{4}{7}; \quad p_3 = \frac{2}{5}; \quad p_4 = \frac{3}{5}$$

In step 2, we obtain the model for long time scales. This is done by observing that a large number of fast transitions will occur between two successive slow transitions. Therefore it can be assumed that the two CTMCs in Figure 3.47 would reach a steady-state between successive slow transitions. Now we can treat states 1 and 2 as an aggregated state and the states 3 and 4 as another aggregated state. This results in the CTMC model of Figure 3.48, which represents the model for long time scales. Note that the aggregated state $(1,2)$ corresponds to processing by machine 1 and the aggregated state $(3,4)$ to processing by machine 2. The transition rate from $(1,2)$ to $(3,4)$ is given by $p_1 q_{13} + p_2 q_{24}$ and the transition rate from $(3,4)$ to $(1,2)$ is given by $p_3 q_{31} + p_4 q_{42}$, where q_{ij} have the usual significance. It has been shown that the combination of the slow dynamics of Figure 3.48 and the fast dynamics of Figure 3.47 constitutes an asymptotically exact description of the original dynamics as $\epsilon \to 0$.

It is to be noted that in our example, we have reduced the analysis of a 4-state CTMC to that of three lower-order models, each comprising two states. For chains with a large number of states, it is possible to obtain using time scale decomposition, significant reduction in dimensionality. In the literature, algorithms are available for obtaining the steady-state performance of any general Markov chain using the time scale decomposition approach (see Bibliographic Notes).

Time scale decomposition or aggregation cannot, however, sufficiently reduce the size of the state space for models of complex systems with many types of dynamics. In such cases, a technique called *lumping* is often used to further reduce the size of the state space. The reader is referred to the thesis work by Caromicoli [1987] for more details about the application of aggregation and lumping to the analysis of Markov models of FMSs.

3.11.4 Computational Issues in Transient Analysis

We have seen in Section 3.10 the significance of transient analysis of Markov models of manufacturing systems. Consider a CTMC $\{X(t) : t \geq 0\}$ with state space $\{0, 1, 2, ..., N\}$. We recall the notation

$$H(t) = [\, p_{ij}(t) \,] \qquad i, j = 0, 1, 2, ..., N$$
$$\Pi(t) = [\, p_0(t) \quad p_1(t) \quad p_2(t) \,...\, p_N(t) \,]$$

where

$$p_{ij}(t) = P\{X(t) = j \mid X(0) = i\} \quad \text{and}$$
$$p_j(t) = P\{X(t) = j\}$$

We reproduce here the differential equations governing the evolution in time of a CTMC:

$$\frac{dH(t)}{dt} = H(t)Q; \qquad H(0) = I \tag{89}$$

$$\frac{dH(t)}{dt} = QH(t); \qquad H(0) = I \tag{90}$$

$$\frac{d\Pi(t)}{dt} = \Pi(t)Q \tag{91}$$

Equation (89) gives the forward equations, equation (90) gives the backward equations, and (91) gives the differential equation for state probabilities. The solution is known to be given by

$$H(t) = \exp(Qt) \tag{92}$$

$$\Pi(t) = \Pi(0)\exp(Qt) \tag{93}$$

where $\exp(Qt)$ is the matrix exponential defined by the Taylor series

$$\exp(Qt) = \sum_{i=0}^{\infty} \frac{(Qt)^i}{i!} \tag{94}$$

Note that (92) is the same unique solution of (89) and (90). Measures of system performance can be derived using weighted sums of the state probabilities. In the transient analysis of Markov models, we are confronted, as in the case of steady-state analysis, with three problems: size, ill-conditioning, and stiffness. The models of interest are usually large, often having more than 10,000 states. Also, the number of states in the model grows exponentially with the number of resources in the given AMS. A transient solution method should necessarily preserve sparsity of the coefficient matrix, as otherwise we may run out of storage. The second difficulty is ill-conditioning, which means that small changes in the coefficient matrix can lead to large changes in the solution vector. The third difficulty – stiffness – is a consequence of having transition rates of greatly different orders of magnitude.

To find the state probabilities or the transition probabilities as a function of time, we need to solve (89), (90), or (91), which correspond to a system of first-order linear differential equations with constant coefficients. For small models, a general solution is often found by deriving and symbolically inverting Laplace transforms. Analytic Laplace transform inversion requires that the eigenvalues of the transition rate matrix be accurately determined. With a state space size of N, this method has a worst-case computational complexity $O\left(N^5\right)$. A second approach is to evaluate the matrix exponential series (94) directly. But this approach is beset with numerical instabilities such as severe round-off errors even for small models.

Both the above approaches become infeasible for large Markov models and also cannot handle ill-conditioning and stiffness. There are mainly two general approaches that are practical for the numerical transient analysis of large Markov models. These are:

1. Uniformization

2. Numerical ODE (ordinary differential equation) solution.

A commonly used explicit ODE solution technique is the fourth-fifth order Runge-Kutta Fehlberg (RKF45) method. It is found that RKF45 performs very satisfactorily for non-stiff problems with normal accuracy requirements. However, for stiff problems, RKF45 has poor performance. Linear multi-step methods for numerical ODE solutions are in general satisfactory for stiff problems also. A particular linear multi-step method called the TR-BDF2 (Trapezoid Rule – 2nd Order Backward Difference) has been shown to be particularly suitable for stiff problems. A detailed discussion of the above methods is beyond the scope of this book.

For typical transient analysis, the method of uniformization has now become the method of choice. We now discuss this numerical technique.

3.11.5 Uniformization

Consider a CTMC $\{X(t) : t \geq 0\}$ in which the mean sojourn time in all the states is the same, say $(1/v)$. The sojourn time in each state is therefore exponentially distributed with rate v. If $N(t)$ denotes the number of transitions by time t, then it can be seen that $\{N(t) : t \geq 0\}$ is a Poisson process with rate v.

Let p_{ij} as usual denote the transition probabilities of the embedded Markov chain of the CTMC. Let $p_{ij}^{(n)}$ be the n-step transition probabilities of the embedded Markov chain. Since $\{N(t) : t \geq 0\}$ is a Poisson process, we have for any state i,

$$P\{N(t) = n \mid X(0) = i\} = \frac{e^{-vt}(vt)^n}{n!}$$

Also, we have

$$P\{X(t) = j \mid X(0) = i, N(t) = n\} = p_{ij}^{(n)}$$

To compute $p_{ij}(t)$, we proceed as follows.

$$
\begin{aligned}
p_{ij}(t) &= P\{X(t) = j \mid X(0) = i\} \\
&= \sum_{n=0}^{\infty} P\{X(t) = j \mid X(0) = i, N(t) = n\}\, P\{N(t) = n \mid X(0) = i\} \\
&= \sum_{n=0}^{\infty} p_{ij}^{(n)}\, \frac{e^{-vt}(vt)^n}{n!}
\end{aligned}
$$

$$(95)$$

Equation (95) is quite useful from a computational viewpoint since it enables us to compute $p_{ij}(t)$. However, it is applicable to only CTMCs with the same mean sojourn time in all the states.

Uniformization is a technique that transforms an arbitrary CTMC into one having identical mean sojourn times in all the states so that (95) can be employed to compute $p_{ij}(t)$. Consider a CTMC $\{Y(t) : t \geq 0\}$ in which $(1/v_i)$ represents the mean sojourn time of state i $(i = 0, 1, ...)$. Let the v_i's be bounded and let v be any number such that $v_i \leq v$ for all i. When in state i, the CTMC leaves the state at rate v_i. This is equivalent to supposing that transitions occur at rate v, but only the fraction (v_i/v) of transitions are real ones and the remaining fraction$\left(1 - \frac{v_i}{v}\right)$ are fictitious transitions which leave the CTMC in state i, returning immediately to state i. This idea is depicted in Figure 3.49.

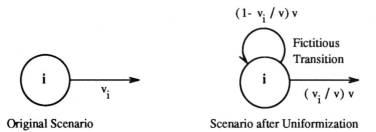

Original Scenario　　　　　　　　Scenario after Uniformization

Figure 3.49 Fictitious transitions in uniformization

The CTMC $\{Y(t) : t \geq 0\}$ can now be thought of as being a process which spends an exponential amount of time with rate v in state i and makes a transition to j with probability p_{ij} given by

$$
\begin{aligned}
p_{ij} &= 1 - \frac{v_i}{v} & j = i \\
&= \frac{v_i}{v}\, r_{ij} & j \neq i
\end{aligned}
$$

where r_{ij} are the transition probabilities in the embedded Markov chain of the CTMC. Note that p_{ij} are the transition probabilities of the embedded Markov chain when uniformization is applied to the CTMC $\{Y(t) : t \geq 0\}$. If $p_{ij}^{(n)}$ are the n-step transition probabilities of this latter EMC, then equation (95) can be used to compute $p_{ij}(t)$. We illustrate uniformization with the following example.

Example 3.56

Consider a single-machine system that can be in two states: 0 (up) and 1 (down). Let λ be the failure rate and μ the repair rate. This system is the same as in Example 3.52. For this example, we have $v_0 = \lambda$, $v_1 = \mu$, and the transition probabilities of the EMC are given by $r_{00} = 0$, $r_{01} = 1$, $r_{10} = 1$, and $r_{11} = 0$.

Letting $v = \lambda + \mu$, the uniformized version of the above is a CTMC with two states 0 and 1, pictorially shown in Figure 3.50.

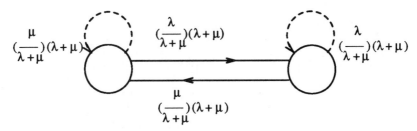

Figure 3.50 Uniformized CTMC model for Example 3.56

For the uniformized version, we have $v_0 = \lambda + \mu$, $v_1 = \lambda + \mu$, and the transition probabilities are given by

$$p_{00} = 1 - p_{01} = \frac{\mu}{\lambda + \mu}$$

$$p_{10} = 1 - p_{11} = \frac{\lambda}{\lambda + \mu}$$

It can be shown that the n–step transition probabilities are given by

$$p_{00}^{(n)} = p_{10}^{(n)} = \frac{\mu}{\lambda + \mu} \quad n \geq 1$$

$$p_{01}^{(n)} = p_{11}^{(n)} = \frac{\lambda}{\lambda + \mu} \quad n \geq 1$$

Further, note that $p_{00}^{(0)} = p_{11}^{(0)} = 1$ and $p_{01}^{(0)} = p_{10}^{(0)} = 0$. Now we can use (95) to compute the transition probabilities $p_{00}(t)$, $p_{01}(t)$, $p_{10}(t)$, and $p_{11}(t)$. It can be derived that

$$p_{00}(t) = \frac{\mu}{\lambda + \mu} + \frac{\lambda}{\lambda + \mu} \, e^{-(\lambda + \mu)t}$$

$$p_{11}(t) = \frac{\lambda}{\lambda + \mu} + \frac{\mu}{\lambda + \mu} \, e^{-(\lambda + \mu)t}$$

$$p_{01}(t) = \frac{\lambda}{\lambda + \mu} \left\{ 1 - e^{-(\lambda + \mu)t} \right\}$$

$$p_{10}(t) = \frac{\mu}{\lambda + \mu} \left\{ 1 - e^{-(\lambda + \mu)t} \right\}$$

These were computed earlier in Example 3.52 by solving the backward equations.

Reibman and Trivedi [1988] have given a detailed comparison of three methods, namely uniformization, RKF45, and TR-BDF2. They have concluded that off-the-shelf ODE solution techniques such as RKF45 perform well only for non-stiff problems with normal accuracy requirements. Uniformization is usually more accurate and efficient than RKF45. It exploits the natural probabilistic structure of the problem and allows more accurate error control. Uniformization is the preferred method for typical problems. For stiff problems, stable algorithms such as TR-BDF2 are well suited.

PROBLEMS

1. Figure 3.P.7 represents a generalized version of the CTMC model for Example 3.55. Conduct a steady-state analysis of the above system, using the aggregation technique. Assume that the λ's and μ's are much smaller compared to a's and b's.

2. Consider a single machine producing n different part types. The machine can fail while processing a part, and after repair will resume the processing of that part. If for $i = 1, 2, ..., n$, P_i denotes the processing of part type i, and

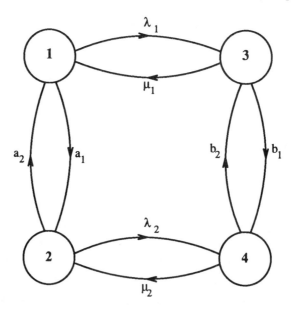

Figure 3.P.7

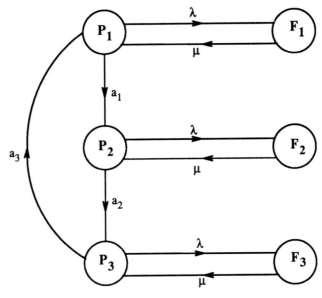

Figure 3.P.8

F_i denotes the machine down while processing part type i, then the CTMC for $n = 3$ will be as shown in Figure 3.P.8. Apply the aggregation technique to the above CTMC model to obtain the steady-state probabilities.

3. In a manufacturing system, there are two identical failure-prone machines which fail with rate λ each. The system has three states: both working, one working, and neither working. The repair time is exponential with rate μ. Use the uniformization technique to obtain the transition probabilities $p_{ij}(t)$ for $i, j = 0, 1, 2$, in the following cases:

(a) There is no repair facility.

(b) There is one repair facility.

(c) There are two repair facilities.

4. Develop a software package to compute time-dependent transition probabilities using uniformization.

3.12 BIBLIOGRAPHIC NOTES AND BIBLIOGRAPHY

The topic of Markov chains is the subject of several celebrated textbooks, and we can only list here a few of these books that have influenced the treatment and presentation found in this chapter. These are the works by Bhat [1984], Cinlar [1975], Kleinrock [1975], Parzen [1962], Ross [1985],

Tijms [1986], Trivedi [1982], and Wolff [1989]. Several of the examples and problems presented in this chapter are culled from the above works, and we have adapted them here by providing a novel interpretation in the manufacturing setting. The first four sections of this chapter and Section 3.6 (Memoryless Random Variables, Stochastic Processes, Discrete Time Markov Chains, Continuous Time Markov Chains, and Birth and Death Processes) have been carved out of the above studies. In other sections, also, we have found the above works useful as references.

The case study on the two-stage transfer line of Section 3.5 is based on the paper by Gershwin and Berman [1981]. Important performance studies on transfer lines can also be found in the contributions of Ammar [1987], Buzacott [1982], Buzacott and Hanifin [1978], Buzacott and Shantikumar [1980], Dallery, David, and Xie [1988, 1989], Gershwin [1987], Gershwin and Schick [1983], Terracol and David [1987], and Wiley [1981].

The important topic of time reversibility of Markov chains has been examined in several works. As further reading, we would suggest the classic study by Kelly [1979]. Wolff [1989] has also discussed this topic in a very interesting way. The paper by Yao and Buzacott [1987] identifies an important class of manufacturing systems whose Markov models are time reversible.

The treatment of Markov chains with absorbing states in Section 3.8 is modeled on the lines given by Trivedi [1982]. Transient analysis of such chains has been discussed by Marie *et al* [1987]. The discussion of semi-Markov processes in Section 3.9 follows the organization given by Ross [1985].

Transient analysis of Markov chains forms the subject matter of a classic survey by Grassman [1977]. There is a survey on methods for transient analysis by Reibman and Trivedi [1988]. Another paper by Reibman and Trivedi [1989] discusses important recent research in the transient analysis of Markov chains. Currently, this topic is an active research area.

Computational methods for analyzing Markov chains constitute another important area of research interest. The theory of aggregation and decomposition is classically dealt with by Curtois [1977, 1985]. Some of the important papers in this context are by Cao and Stewart [1985], Choong and Gershwin [1987], and Schweitzer [1983]. The thesis of Caromicoli

[1987] specifically discusses aggregation methods for FMS models. Matrix methods are well surveyed by Golub and Van Loan [1983]. Specific issues arising in dealing with sparse matrices are covered by Barker [1989] and Duff *et al* [1986]. The computation of matrix exponential has been surveyed by Van Loan [1977] and by Moler and Van Loan [1978]. Numerical methods for differential equations have been discussed in the text by Lambert [1973]. A review of numerical methods in Markov chain analysis has been presented by Stewart [1978] and Philippe *et al* [1989]. The solution of large models has been discussed by Stewart and Goyal [1985]. A survey of software tools available for Markov chain analysis appears in the work by Johnson and Malek [1988]. The technique of uniformization has been discussed thoroughly in Gross and Miller [1984]. Parametric sensitivity analysis using uniformization is the topic of the recent paper by Heidelberger and Goyal [1988]. A survey of numerical techniques for transient analysis has been provided by Reibman and Trivedi [1988]. The Matrix-Geometric methods in Markov chain analysis have been presented in the classic text by Neuts [1981].

Several researchers have used Markov chains as the modeling tool for FMSs. Besides the papers mentioned earlier on transfer line modeling, we mention here the works by Alam *et al* [1985], Davis and Kennedy [1987], Feigin and Proth [1989], Foster and Garcia-Diaz [1983], Seidmann and Schweitzer [1984], and Shantikumar and Tien [1983]. Solberg [1977] is the originator of the central server FMS model, which was discussed repeatedly in this chapter.

Performability, which is a composite measure of performance and reliability, is an issue that can be addressed by Markov chain models. Meyer [1980, 1982] has discussed this issue in the context of computer systems. It is of great importance in the AMS context also. We treat this topic in some detail in Section 4.14.

BIBLIOGRAPHY

1. **Alam, M., D. Gupta, S.I. Ahmad, and A. Raouf** [1985]. Performance Modeling and Evaluation of Flexible Manufacturing Systems Using Semi-Markov Approach, in *Flexible Manufacturing*, (Ed.) Raouf, A., and S.I. Ahmad, Elsevier, New York, pp. 87–118.

2. **Ammar, M.H.** [1987]. Performance of a Two-Stage Manufacturing System with Control and Communication Overhead, *IEEE Transactions on Systems, Man, and Cybernetics*, Vol. SMC-17, No. 4, July-August 1987, pp. 661–665.

3. **Barker, V.A.** [1989]. Numerical Solution of Sparse Singular Systems of Equations Arising from Ergodic Markov Chains, *Communications of Statistics and Stochastic Models*, Vol. 5, No. 3, pp. 335–381.

4. **Bhat, U.N.** [1984]. *Elements of Applied Stochastic Processes*, 2nd edition, John Wiley, New York.

5. **Buzacott, J.A.** [1982]. Optimal Operating Rules for Automated Manufacturing Systems, *IEEE Transactions on Automatic Control*, Vol. AC-27, No. 1, pp. 80–86.

6. **Buzacott, J.A., and L.E. Hanifin** [1978]. Models of Automatic Transfer Lines with Inventory Banks: A Review and Comparison, *AIIE Transactions*, Vol. 10, No. 2, pp. 197–207.

7. **Buzacott, J.A., and J.G. Shantikumar** [1980]. Models for Understanding Flexible Manufacturing Systems, *AIIE Transactions*, Vol. 12, No. 4, pp. 339–350.

8. **Cao, W.-L., and W.J. Stewart** [1985]. Iterative Aggregation/Disaggregation Techniques for Nearly Decomposable Markov Chains, *Journal of the ACM*, Vol. 32, No. 3, pp. 702–719.

9. **Caromicoli, C.A.** [1987]. *Time Scale Analysis Techniques for Flexible Manufacturing Systems*, M.S. Thesis, Department of Electrical Engineering and Computer Science, Massachusetts Institute of Technology, Cambridge, Massachusetts, December 1987.

10. **Choong, Y.F., and S.B. Gershwin** [1987]. A Decomposition Method for the Approximate Evaluation of Capacitated Transfer Lines with Unreliable Machines and Random Processing Times, *IIE Transactions*, Vol. 19, pp. 150–159.

11. **Cinlar, E.** [1975]. *Introduction to Stochastic Process*, Prentice-Hall, Englewood Cliffs, New Jersey.

12. **Curtois, P.J.** [1977]. *Decomposability: Queuing and Computer System Applications*, Academic Press, New York.

13. **Curtois, P.J.** [1985]. On Time and Space Decomposition of Complex Structures, *Communications of the ACM*, Vol. 28, No. 6, June 1985, pp. 590–603.

14. **Dallery, Y., R. David, and X.L. Xie** [1988]. An Efficient Algorithm for Analysis of Transfer Lines with Unreliable Machines and Finite Buffers, *IIE*

Transactions, Vol. 20, pp. 280–283.

15. **Dallery, Y., R. David, and X.L. Xie** [1989]. Approximate Analysis of Transfer Lines with Unreliable Machines and Finite Buffers, *IEEE Transactions on Automatic Control*, Vol. 34, No. 9, September 1989, pp. 943–953.

16. **Davis, R.P., and W.J. Kennedy, Jr.** [1987]. Markovian Modeling of Manufacturing Systems, *International Journal of Production Research*, Vol. 25, No. 3, pp. 337–351.

17. **Duff, I.S., A.M. Erisman, and J.K. Reid** [1986]. *Direct Methods for Sparse Matrices*, Clarendon Press, Oxford, UK.

18. **Feigin, G., and J.M. Proth** [1989]. Performance Analysis of a Flexible Manufacturing Cell Feeding Several Machines with Finite Buffer Capacity, INRIA Research Report, No. 1127, December 1989.

19. **Foster, J.W., and A. Garcia-Diaz** [1983]. Markovian Models for Investigating Failure and Repair Characteristics of Production Systems, *IIE Transactions*, Vol. 15, pp. 202–211.

20. **Gershwin, S.** [1987]. An Efficient Decomposition Method for the Approximate Evaluation of Tandem Queues with Finite Storage Space and Blocking, *Operations Research*, Vol. 35, No. 2, March-April 1987, pp. 291–305.

21. **Gershwin, S.B., and O. Berman** [1981]. Analysis of Transfer Lines Consisting of Two Unreliable Machines with Random Processing Times and Finite Storage Buffers, *AIIE Transactions*, Vol. 13, No. 1, March 1981, pp. 2–11.

22. **Gershwin, S., and I.C. Schick** [1983]. Modeling and Analysis of Three-Stage Transfer Lines with Unreliable Machines and Finite Buffers, *Operations Research*, Vol. 31, No. 2, pp. 354–380.

23. **Grassman, W.K.** [1977]. Transient Solution in Markovian Queuing Systems, *Computers and Operations Research*, Vol. 4, pp. 47–56.

24. **Golub, G.H., and C.F. Van Loan** [1983]. *Matrix Computations*, Johns Hopkins University Press, Baltimore.

25. **Gross, D., and D.R. Miller** [1984]. The Randomization Technique as a Modeling Tool and Solution Procedure for Transient Markov Processes, *Operations Research*, Vol. 32, No. 2, pp. 343–361.

26. **Heidelberger, P., and A. Goyal** [1988]. Sensitivity Analysis of Continuous Time Markov Chains Using Uniformization, in *Computer Performance and Reliability*, (Ed.) Iazeolla, G., P.J. Curtois, and O.J. Boxma, Elsevier Science Publishers B.V., North-Holland, Amsterdam.

27. **Johnson, Jr., A.M., and M. Malek** [1988]. Survey of Software Tools for Evaluating Reliability, Availability, and Serviceability, *ACM Computing*

Surveys, Vol. 20, No. 4, December 1988, pp. 227–269.

28. **Kelly, F.P.** [1979]. *Reversibility and Stochastic Networks*, John Wiley, New York.

29. **Kleinrock, L.** [1975]. *Queuing Systems, Vol. I: Theory*, John Wiley, New York.

30. **Lambert, J.D.** [1973]. *Computational Methods in Ordinary Differential Equations*, John Wiley, London.

31. **Marie, R.A., A.L. Reibman, and K.S. Trivedi** [1987]. Transient Solution of Acyclic Markov Chains, *Performance Evaluation*, Vol. 7, pp. 175–194.

32. **Meyer, J.F.** [1980]. On Evaluating the Performability of Degradable Computer Systems, *IEEE Transactions on Computers*, Vol. C-29, No. 8, August 1980, pp. 720–731.

33. **Meyer, J.F.** [1982]. Closed Form Solutions for Performability, *IEEE Transactions on Computers*, Vol. 31, No. 7, July 1982, pp. 648–657.

34. **Moler, C., and C.F. Van Loan** [1978]. Nineteen Dubious Ways to Compute the Exponential of a Matrix, *SIAM Review*, Vol. 20, pp. 801–835.

35. **Neuts, M.F.** [1981]. *Matrix-Geometric Solutions in Stochastic Models — An Algorithmic Approach*, Johns Hopkins University Press, Baltimore.

36. **Parzen, E.** [1962]. *Stochastic Processes*, Holden-Day, San Francisco.

37. **Philippe, B., Y. Saad, and W.J. Stewart** [1989]. *Numerical Methods in Markov Chain Modeling*, INRIA Research Report, No. 1115, INRIA, Rennes, France, November 1989.

38. **Reibman, A., and K.S. Trivedi** [1988]. Numerical Transient Analysis of Markov Models, *Computers and Operations Research*, Vol. 15, No. 1, pp. 19–36.

39. **Reibman, A., and K.S. Trivedi** [1989]. Transient Analysis of Cumulative Measures of Markov Model Behavior, *Stochastic Models*, Vol. 5, No. 4, pp. 683–710.

40. **Ross, S.M.** [1985]. *Introduction to Probability Models*, 3rd edition, Academic Press, Orlando, Florida.

41. **Schweitzer, P.J.** [1983]. Aggregation Methods for Large Markov Chains, in *Mathematical Computer Performance and Reliability*, (Eds.) Iazeolla, G., P.J. Curtois, and A. Hordijk, Elsevier Science Publishers, North-Holland, Amsterdam.

42. **Seidmann, A., and P. Schweitzer** [1984]. Part Selection Policy for a Flexible Manufacturing Cell Feeding Several Production Lines, *IIE Transactions*, Vol. 16, No. 4, pp. 355–362.

43. **Shantikumar, J.G., and C.C. Tien** [1983]. An Algorithmic Solution to Two Stage Transfer Lines with Possible Scrapping of Units, *Management Science*, Vol. 29, pp. 1069–1086.

44. **Solberg, J.J.** [1977]. A Mathematical Model of Computerized Manufacturing Systems, Proceedings of *Fourth International Conference on Production Research*, Tokyo, August 1977, pp. 22–30.

45. **Stewart, W.J.** [1978]. A Comparison of Numerical Techniques in Markov Modeling, *Communications of the ACM*, Vol. 21, pp. 144–151.

46. **Stewart, W.J., and A. Goyal** [1985]. Matrix Methods in Large Dependability Models, *Research Report RC-11485*, IBM Thomas J. Watson Research Center, Yorktown Heights, New York.

47. **Terracol, C., and R. David** [1987]. An Aggregation Technique for Performance Evaluation of Transfer Lines with Unreliable Machines and Finite Buffers, Proceedings of *IEEE Conference on Robotics and Automation*, Raleigh, North Carolina, March 1987, pp. 1333–1338.

48. **Tijms, H.C.** [1986]. *Stochastic Modeling and Analysis: A Computational Approach*, John Wiley, New York.

49. **Trivedi, K.S.** [1982]. *Probability and Statistics with Reliability, Queuing, and Computer Science Applications*, Prentice-Hall, Englewood Cliffs, New Jersey.

50. **Van Loan, C.F.** [1977]. The Sensitivity of the Matrix Exponential, *SIAM Journal of Numerical Analysis*, Vol. 14, pp. 971–981.

51. **Wiley, R.P.** [1981]. *Analysis of a Tandem Queue Model of a Transfer Line*, M.S. Thesis, Department of Electrical Engineering and Computer Science, Massachusetts Institute of Technology, Cambridge, Massachusetts, September 1981.

52. **Wolff, R.W.** [1989]. *Stochastic Modeling and the Theory of Queues*, Prentice-Hall, Englewood Cliffs, New Jersey.

53. **Yao, D.D., and J.A. Buzacott** [1987]. Modeling a Class of FMSs with Reversible Routing, *Operations Research*, Vol. 35, No. 1, pp. 87–92.

Chapter 4
QUEUING MODELS

Queues and queuing systems have been the subject of considerable research ever since the appearance of the first telephone system. In the years immediately following World War II, several problems of operations research (OR), such as inventory and production control, spurred renewed interest in this subject area. Also, problems relating to reliability and availability were formulated using queuing theory. Abundant literature grew on analysis, design, and optimization of queuing systems in the OR literature in the 1950s and 60s.

The modeling of computer systems and data transmission systems using queues and queuing networks has led to studies on queuing systems with complex service disciplines and has created the need for analyzing interconnected queuing systems. Several new results have been obtained in the area of performance analysis of large computer systems and computer communication systems. Several software packages such as RESQ, QNA, and PANACEA are now available for automated solution of queuing systems. Further, CAN-Q, MANUPLAN, and MVAQ are queuing-based packages designed exclusively for manufacturing system applications. Most researchers in the area of analytical modeling of automated manufacturing systems have focused interest on queuing models. The reason is that queues and queuing networks constitute a natural model for resource contention in manufacturing systems. This chapter is devoted to queue models and queuing network models of automated manufacturing systems. Our presentation here follows the same pattern as in earlier chapters. We present the theory of queues and queuing networks and illustrate by automated manufacturing system examples. Logically, this chapter is organized as two parts. The first part deals with queues and the second part with networks of queues.

Notation for queues and examples of manufacturing situations that can be modeled as queues are presented in Section 4.1. In this section we identify the generic performance measures that can be associated with a queuing system and present the important Little's result. Section 4.2 is on the $M/M/1$ queue while Section 4.3 is on the multiserver $M/M/m$ queue. We discuss the steady-state analysis of these queues and investigate the steady-state waiting-time distributions and departure process. In Section 4.4 we look at batch arrival queuing systems, which are of much relevance to AMSs. Section 4.5 is devoted to queues with general distributions. We discuss in detail the analysis of the $M/G/1$ queue. Queues with server breakdowns are discussed in Section 4.6. In Section 4.7 we focus on the versatile machine center problem and discuss the applicability of polling models in the manufacturing context.

Section 4.8 starts with several examples of queuing network models in manufacturing and discusses the application of Little's formula for queuing networks. In Section 4.9 we present the analysis of open queuing networks. After investigating three generic open queuing network examples — tandem network, tandem network with feedback, and open central server model — we present Jackson's theorem, which is concerned with open queuing networks having product form solution. Section 4.10 on closed queuing networks is organized on the same lines as Section 4.9. We first discuss two generic examples, that of a closed transfer line and the closed central server network, before presenting the product form structure of the Gordon-Newell networks. We then discuss the convolution algorithm and the mean value analysis algorithm, which are the two main computational methods for analyzing closed queuing networks. In Section 4.11 we look at the wider class of Baskett, Chandy, Muntz, and Palacios-Gomez (BCMP) networks, where we focus on multiple job classes and present computational algorithms. Section 4.12 is on the topic of queuing networks with blocking. Here we present generic examples of transfer line with blocking and central server model with blocking, and survey the important results. The importance of queuing network approximations is brought out in Section 4.13, where we discuss, with illustrative manufacturing examples, the principal approximations available in the literature for non-product form networks. Finally, in Section 4.14, we discuss the important topic of performability. We formulate the notion of performability in the AMS context and present computational methods for obtaining performability distributions.

4.1 QUEUES: NOTATION AND EXAMPLES

A queue is a system into which *customers* arrive to receive *service*. When the servers in the system are busy, incoming customers *wait* for their turn. Upon completion of a service, the customer to be served next is selected according to some *queuing discipline*.

Figure 4.1 provides a pictorial representation of a queue. It comprises three basic elements: the arrivals, the service mechanism, and the queuing discipline. The arrivals can occur at regular intervals arising from a predetermined schedule or they could be stochastic with a given statistical description of the inter-arrival times. The arrivals can occur singly or in groups. The arrivals may belong to the same class requiring identical service or they can belong to different classes requiring different kinds of service. The service mechanism will be described by the number of servers available for service at any particular time and the time taken by each to serve a customer class. The service time may be deterministic or a random variable with a specified distribution. The queuing discipline is a rule for selecting the customer for the next service from among the set of waiting customers. This could be either *First-In-First-Out* (FIFO) or *Last-Come-First-In* (LCFI) or *Shortest Processing Time* (SPT) or any other conceivable discipline.

Most queuing networks, i.e., telephone networks, computer networks, manufacturing networks, are stochastic service systems and fast response time and short waiting time could yield customer satisfaction. Typical measures of congestion which are performance indicators include number

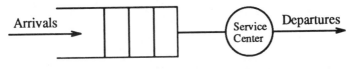

Figure 4.1 A queue

in the system, waiting time, busy period of the servers, response time, and throughput.

4.1.1 Notation for Queues

In connection with queues, a convenient shorthand notation has been developed by Kendall. In its simplest form it is a three-part descriptor $A/S/m$, where A designates arrival process, S the service distribution for the arriving customers, and m the number of servers. For example, $M/M/1$ indicates Poisson arrival of customers, an exponentially distributed service time and a single server. The letter M stands for memoryless (or Markovian) in both arrival process and service time. Occasionally, some other specifically defined symbols are used. We may need to specify the size of the waiting space or size of the customer population. Thus a five-part descriptor $A/S/m/K/M$ denotes a m server queue with arrival process A, service time S, storage space K, and customer population M.

Let $C_1, C_2, \ldots$ be an arbitrary arrival stream of customers with
t_j = arrival epoch of C_j $(0 \le t_1 \le t_2 \le \ldots < \infty)$ and
$T_j = t_{j+1} - t_j$ (inter-arrival time between C_j and C_{j+1}).

Each customer needs to undergo service. A customer who has arrived but not yet departed is said to be *in the system*. While in the system, a customer may be either *in service* or *in the queue*. Let
S_j = Service time of C_j
D_j = Delay in queue of C_j (waiting time in queue)
$W_j = D_j + S_j$ = waiting time in system of C_j.

The number of customers in the system at epoch t is given by $N(t)$, which can be written as

$$N(t) = N_q(t) + N_s(t)$$

where $N_q(t)$ = number of customers in the queue at time t; $N_s(t)$ = number of customers in service at time t.

The number of arrivals by time $t, n_A(t)$, and the number of departures by time $t, n_D(t)$, are given by

$$n_A(t) = \max\{j: \ t_j \le t\}$$
$$n_D(t) = n_A(t) - N(t)$$

The process $\{n_A(t): \ t \ge 0\}$ is called the *arrival process* and the process $\{n_D(t): \ t \ge 0\}$ is called the *departure process*.

4.1.2 Examples of Queues in Manufacturing Systems

We now give some examples illustrating modeling of manufacturing systems using queues.

Example 4.1

Consider an NC machine center, as depicted in Figures 2.9 and 2.10. The tool magazine is loaded with all the tools necessary to process the assigned workload. Here, fixtured workpieces wait in the pallet storage area from where a transporter carries a fixtured workpiece to the machine worktable. Assume that fixtured workpieces arrive into the storage area according to a Poisson process and that the service times of the workpieces are i.i.d. exponential random variables. If there is infinite storage space for fixtured raw parts, then the above system can be viewed as an $M/M/1$ queue by neglecting the transportation and fixturing times. If at most $N - 1$ fixtured raw parts can be accommodated in the pallet storage area, this would correspond to an $M/M/1/N$ queue. Performance measures of interest would be manufacturing lead time (total time a fixtured part spends in the system from the instant it enters the system to the instant of departing from the system), throughput (the number of parts produced in a given time), utilization of the machine center (proportion of time the machine center is kept busy), and work-in-process (average number of fixtured parts waiting in the pallet storage area).

Example 4.2

In the above example, let there be two identical machines in the machine center. As soon as a machine becomes free, it will pick a waiting fixtured part, if any. In this case, the model is an $M/M/2$ queue. By having two identical machines instead of a single machine, it may be reasonable to expect that lead time, utilization, and work-in-process would get halved whereas throughput would increase twofold. That it does not happen can be shown in precise terms by queuing theory.

$M/M/\infty$ queue represents the extreme case of a multiserver queue. Here there is no queuing at all since there is an infinite number of servers. A conveyor system that can accommodate all parts inside a manufacturing system provides a physical example of such an infinite server queue.

Example 4.3

Exponentiality for the service time random variable is usually assumed for reasons of analytical tractability. In real life, however, service times are usually constant. Normal and uniform random variables are also more appropriate models of service time than the exponential random variable. The NC machine center of Example 4.1 with processing times generally distributed will correspond to an $M/G/1$ queue. Using the theory of $M/G/1$ queues, discussed in Section 4.5, one can compute performance measures for such a system.

Example 4.4

Consider an inspection facility in a manufacturing system in which parts for inspection are found to arrive according to a Poisson process. Currently, inspection operation is performed manually, with inspection time *normally* distributed with a given mean and standard deviation. It is proposed to install a fully automated CMM (Coordinate Measurement Machine), in which case the inspection time is a constant. If it is required to compare the performance in these two cases, we again need to model by an $M/G/1$ queue. In the former case, we have an $M/G/1$ queue with normally distributed service time, and in the latter case we have an $M/D/1$ queue (which is a special case of $M/G/1$ queue).

Example 4.5

Let us now consider the same NC machine center processing batches of a particular product. Let batches of size b arrive following a Poisson process with rate of λ batches per week. Batch size b may be a constant or a positive discrete random variable. If the processing time of each part in the batch is exponentially distributed, then we have what is called a *bulk arrival queue*, denoted in this case by $M^b/M/1$. This model can be made more realistic by including a setup time for the machine before processing a next batch. We can compute the performance measures as a function of the batch size. The above analysis would be useful, for example, in finding the optimal batch size for which the total cost (setup cost + inventory cost) is minimum.

Example 4.6

So far we have considered the processing of a single part type. We now consider the most general single-machine manufacturing system. We have a versatile NC machine center capable of producing N different types of parts. Raw parts of type j $(j = 1, 2, ..., N)$ arrive at the machine center, according to a general, independent, and identically distributed inter-arrival time with rate λ_j. If the machine is busy, an arriving raw part joins a

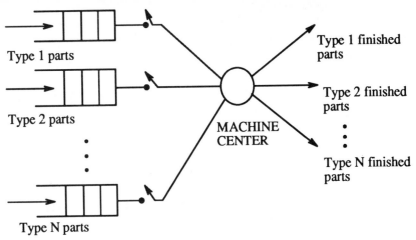

Figure 4.2 Versatile machine center

queue that is dedicated to its type (that is, there are N different queues). The maximum allowed queue length is K_j for $j = 1, 2, ..., N$. The scenario is depicted in Figure 4.2. Note that this system is similar but not identical to the one presented in Section 3.3 (Figure 3.7).

We now complete the description of the above system. For processing a part of type j, the machine has to be set up and the setup time s_j is a generally distributed random variable. The machine requires a setup only if a different part type is going to be machined next. Processing times for parts of type j are assumed to be general i.i.d. random variables. When the machine finishes processing, it can select the next part type to process, in many different ways, as will be detailed in Section 4.7. For example, we have already considered two policies – cyclic and probabilistic – in Example 3.8.

We shall refer to this as the flexible machine center problem and discuss it in detail in Section 4.7.

Example 4.7

Assembly operations are among the most common type in manufacturing systems. A typical assembly operation involves the joining of two or more component parts into a single component. The typical scenario in front of an assembly machine is depicted in Figure 4.3. The different components to be assembled wait in separate queues. When the assembly station is ready to do the next assembly operation, it will wait until a component part becomes available in each queue and starts the assembly operation. Thus in

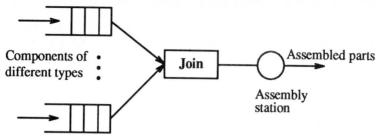

Figure 4.3 Queue representation of an assembly operation

this queuing situation, a part from each queue is removed simultaneously. In this sense, this is an unconventional queue. This also corresponds to the problem of *synchronization*, which is indicated by the *join* block in Figure 4.3. This queue is a special case of *fork-join* queues.

Example 4.8

We now consider a very practical situation of a machine center with breakdowns. In each of the examples above, assume that the machine is prone to failures. The failure times can be described by continuous random variables, such as the exponential random variable. When the machine fails, it is repaired, where the repair time is a random variable with known distribution. During repair, the machine may or may not fail. Also, after repair is over, the machine may resume the interrupted processing on the original workpiece or may start processing a fresh raw part (that is, the semi-finished part is discarded). A treatment of queues with breakdowns appears in Section 4.6.

4.1.3 Performance Measures

The performance of a queue will be defined in terms of properties of one or more of the following stochastic processes:

$$\{N(t): t \geq 0\}, \{N_q(t): t \geq 0\}, \{W_j: j \in \mathbb{N}\}, \text{ and } \{D_j: j \in \mathbb{N}\}.$$

We will be concerned primarily with *long-run* behavior where measures of performance are defined as limits that are averages over either time or customers. We define the following parameters first:

$$\lambda = \text{Arrival rate} = \lim_{t \to \infty} \frac{n_A(t)}{t}$$

$$\frac{1}{\mu} = \text{Average time in service} = \lim_{n \to \infty} \frac{1}{n} \sum_{j=1}^{n} S_j$$

where μ is called the *service rate*. We now define generic measures of performance for a queue. Let m be the number of identical servers in the queuing system.

Average number of customers in system:

$$L = \lim_{t \to \infty} \frac{1}{t} \int_0^t N(u)\, du \qquad (1)$$

Average number in queue (mean queue length):

$$Q = \lim_{t \to \infty} \frac{1}{t} \int_0^t N_q(u)\, du \qquad (2)$$

Average number in service:

$$B = \lim_{t \to \infty} \frac{1}{t} \int_0^t N_s(u)\, du \qquad (3)$$

Average server utilization:

$$U = \frac{B}{m} \qquad (4)$$

Average waiting time in system:

$$W = \lim_{n \to \infty} \frac{1}{n} \sum_{j=1}^n W_j \qquad (5)$$

Average waiting time in queue:

$$D = \lim_{n \to \infty} \frac{1}{n} \sum_{j=1}^n D_j \qquad (6)$$

In the above, the measures L, Q, B, and U are averages over *time*, whereas the measures W and D are averages over *customers*. If we regard the quantities on the right hand side (RHS) as random variables, then the above performance measures are average values of the following random variables: number of customers in system, number of customers in queue, number in service, server utilization, waiting time in system, and waiting time in queue, respectively. Often, waiting time is also referred to as delay. In the most general case, we may be interested in computing the distributions of these random variables. If a manufacturing system is modeled as a queue, the above measures of performance would enable us to compute the work-in-process, machine/AGV utilizations, lead time, throughput, etc.

4.1.4 Little's Result

A closer look at equations (1)-(6) reveals strong interdependence among these performance measures. A remarkable result in this context is the Little's result (also referred to as Little's law, Little's formula, Little's equation, and Little's rule), which is probably the simplest and yet the most significant result in queuing theory. The result states that, given a queue, if the limits

$$\lambda = \lim_{t \to \infty} \frac{n_A(t)}{t} \quad \text{and} \quad W = \lim_{n \to \infty} \frac{1}{n} \sum_{j=1}^{n} W_j$$

exist, with $\lambda < \infty$ and $W < \infty$, then the following limit

$$L = \lim_{t \to \infty} \frac{1}{t} \int_0^t N(u)\, du$$

exists, where $L < \infty$ and

$$L = \lambda W \tag{7}$$

A consequence of Little's result is that if the limits defining λ and D exist, with $\lambda < \infty$, $D < \infty$, then the limit defining Q exists, with $Q < \infty$ and $Q = \lambda D$. Note that this enables the result to be applied to parameters connected with the queue alone.

Example 4.9

This example illustrates Little's result. Consider a system with a single machine processing parts. Raw parts are always available but there are

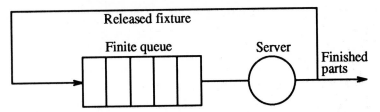

Figure 4.4 A simple feedback queue

only N fixtures in the system. As a result, exactly N fixtured parts are inside the system. There is a buffer of capacity $N - 1$ to hold the fixtured raw parts waiting for processing. After the machine finishes processing a part, the fixture is released and is used for a waiting raw part. The newly fixtured part joins the end of the queue. The scenario is depicted in Figure 4.4. Assume that defixturing and fixturing are instantaneous operations. Let $1/\mu$ be the average service time of the parts. Therefore, the throughput of the system is μ. Consequently, arrival rate of parts is also μ. Since there are always N parts in the system, Little's law gives the delay in the system as

$$W = \frac{N}{\mu}$$

The above can be seen very easily from the simple physics of the system.

PROBLEMS

1. Consider a single server system in which there is no queue. That is, arriving customers have no space to wait, so they leave the system if they find the server busy. Let the arrival rate be λ and the mean service time $1/\mu$. The successive inter-arrival times constitute i.i.d. random variables and also the service times are i.i.d. random variables. This system can only be in two states: 0 (none in the system) and 1 (one in the system). Use Little's law to show that the steady-state probabilities are given by

$$\pi_0 = \frac{\mu}{\lambda + \mu} \quad \text{and} \quad \pi_1 = \frac{\lambda}{\lambda + \mu}$$

2. Verify Little's law for the $M/M/\infty$ queue, in which there is an infinite number of servers, arrivals are Poisson, and service times are i.i.d. exponential random variables.

3. Verify Little's law for the $M/M/m/m$ queue in which there are m identical servers and no queuing space. Arriving customers who find all servers busy leave the system immediately, without service.

4. Parts arrive in Poisson fashion to a machine shop with two NC machine centers. The service times of the parts are independent exponential random variables.

   (a) If an AGV transports the processed parts to an unload station, model the AGV as a queue.

   (b) If the above AGV is also involved in loading raw parts onto the machine centers, model the AGV as a queue.

5. AGVs, conveyors, and robots are typical material handling devices in an AMS. Discuss what type of queuing models $A/S/m/K/M$ describe their working best. Also identify the significance of the performance measures and the consequences of Little's result for these queues.

6. Identify an appropriate queuing model for

   (a) an inspection station, and

   (b) a central storage facility, such as AS/RS (automated storage and retrieval facility).

7. Interpret the machine centers of Figures 2.9, 2.10, and 2.11 as appropriate queuing models.

4.2 THE M/M/1 QUEUE

In the $M/M/1$ queue, the arrivals occur following a Poisson process with rate λ, i.e., the customer inter-arrival times are i.i.d. exponential random variables with mean $1/\lambda$. Service times of customers are i.i.d random variables following exponential distribution with mean $1/\mu$. If the customers denote the workpieces arriving for processing before an NC machine center, then the server represents the NC machine. In the context of local area networks, the customers may be messages and the server the communication channel.

4.2.1 Steady-State Analysis of the M/M/1 Queue

Let $N(t)$ as usual denote the number of customers in the $M/M/1$ queue at time t. Then, it is easy to see that $\{N(t): t \geq 0\}$ is a CTMC. In fact, it is a special case of the birth and death process discussed in Section 3.6 with

$$\lambda_k = \lambda \quad k \geq 0$$
$$\mu_k = \mu \quad k \geq 1$$

The ratio $\rho = \lambda/\mu$ is an important parameter called the *traffic intensity* of the system. It can be verified (see Problem 1) that this process is *irreducible*

1. with positive recurrent states when $\rho < 1$;
2. with null recurrent states when $\rho = 1$; and
3. with *transient* states when $\rho > 1$.

We assume here that $\rho < 1$, which means that the mean inter-arrival time of customers is greater than the mean service time. From equations (52) and (53) in Chapter 3, we get the steady-state probabilities as

$$\pi_0 = \frac{1}{\sum_{k \geq 0} \rho^k} = (1 - \rho) \tag{8}$$

$$\pi_k = \rho^k (1 - \rho); \quad k \geq 0 \tag{9}$$

We notice that the distribution of the number of customers in the system is a modified geometric random variable with parameter $(1 - \rho)$. (X is called a modified geometric random variable with parameter p if $X + 1$ is a geometric random variable with parameter p.) The probability of an empty system is given by $(1 - \rho)$. Thus ρ represents the proportion of the time the server is busy. This is called the *utilization U* of the server or the *traffic intensity* of the queue. The probability π_k is to be treated as the proportion of time in the steady-state the system has exactly k customers. As a consequence of the PASTA (Poisson Arrivals See Time Averages) property, π_k is also the probability that, in the steady-state, a randomly arriving customer finds exactly k customers in the system. Furthermore, π_k is the probability that a departing customer leaves behind exactly k customers in the system. For more details on the PASTA property, see Wolff [1989]. The mean number of customers in the system, L, is found as the expected value of the random variable N, where

$$P\{N = k\} = \lim_{t \to \infty} P\{N(t) = k\} = \pi_k$$

Thus, we have

$$L = E[N] = \sum_{k=0}^{\infty} k\pi_k = (1 - \rho) \sum_{k=0}^{\infty} k\rho^k \tag{10}$$

It is a simple matter to show that

$$\sum_{k=0}^{\infty} k\rho^k = \frac{\rho}{(1-\rho)^2} \tag{11}$$

Combining (10) and (11), we have

$$L = \frac{\rho}{(1-\rho)} = \frac{\lambda}{\mu - \lambda} \tag{12}$$

The mean number of customers, Q, in the queue is similarly given as

$$Q = \sum_{k=1}^{\infty} (k-1)\pi_k = \sum_{k=1}^{\infty} k\pi_k - \sum_{k=1}^{\infty} \pi_k$$

$$= L - (1 - \pi_0) = L - \rho$$

$$= \frac{\rho^2}{1-\rho} = \frac{\lambda^2}{\mu(\mu - \lambda)} \tag{13}$$

We can also rewrite as

$$L = Q + \rho$$

Other steady-state performance measures of interest are: W, the mean waiting time in the system or the mean response time, and D, the mean waiting time in the queue. It is easy to note that

$$W = D + \frac{1}{\mu} \tag{14}$$

To obtain an explicit formula for W, we use Little's formula discussed in Section 4.1.4. Since λ is the arrival rate, we have by Little's formula

$$L = \lambda W \tag{15}$$

Using (15), we can obtain expressions for W and D for the $M/M/1$ queue. From (12) and (15), we have

$$W = \frac{L}{\lambda} = \frac{1}{\mu(1-\rho)} = \frac{1}{\mu - \lambda} \tag{16}$$

and

$$D = \frac{1}{(\mu - \lambda)} - \frac{1}{\mu} = \frac{\lambda}{\mu(\mu - \lambda)} \tag{17}$$

Example 4.10

Consider an NC machine center processing raw parts one at a time in $M/M/1$ fashion. Let $\lambda = 8$ parts/ h and $\mu = 10$ parts/ h. Then we see that $\rho < 1$ and the performance measures are given by

$$\text{Machine utilization} = \rho = \frac{\lambda}{\mu} = 0.8$$

$$\text{Mean number of customers in system} = \frac{\rho}{1 - \rho} = 4.0$$

$$\text{Mean number of customers in queue} = \frac{\rho^2}{1 - \rho} = 3.2$$

$$\text{Mean waiting time in system} = \frac{1}{\mu - \lambda} = \frac{1}{2} \text{ h}$$

$$\text{Mean waiting time in queue} = \frac{\lambda}{\mu(\mu - \lambda)} = \frac{2}{5} \text{ h.}$$

Example 4.11

Let us try to compare the following two $M/M/1$ systems. The first system has an NC machine with production rate 10 parts/ h and the second has an NC machine with rate 20 parts/ h. The maintenance cost of the first system is 100 units per month and that of the second system, 180 units per month. The arrival rate of raw parts is 8/ h. The inventory cost of parts is 1 unit per part per hour. It would interesting to see which of the systems is more cost-effective.

Let us assume 200 working hours per month. Let μ_1 and μ_2 be the respective service rates; ρ_1 and ρ_2, the traffic intensities; L_1 and L_2, the mean numbers in the system, and C_1 and C_2, the maintenance costs. We have

$$C_1 = 100; \qquad C_2 = 180$$

$$\rho_1 = \frac{8}{10} = 0.8; \qquad \rho_2 = \frac{8}{20} = 0.4$$

$$L_1 = \frac{\rho_1}{1 - \rho_1} = 4; \quad L_2 = \frac{\rho_2}{1 - \rho_2} = \frac{2}{3}$$

Total expected cost per hour of system i $(i = 1, 2)$ is given by

$$L_i + \frac{C_i}{200}$$

This works out to 4.5 units/ h for model 1 and 1.567 units/ h for system 2. Thus model 2 is more cost-effective.

If the arrival rate of raw parts is 2 parts/ h, then $\rho_1 = 0.2$ and $\rho_2 = 0.1$ and we get the total cost per hour of model 1 as 0.75 and that of model 2 as 0.911. In this case, system 1 is more cost-effective. Thus a lower rate of arrival of raw parts makes system 2 less cost-effective.

Stability of the M/M/1 Queue
From (8), we see that

$$\pi_0 \left(\sum_{k=0}^{\infty} \rho^k \right) = 1$$

We can solve for π_0 using the above equation if and only if the series in the equation converges. This occurs when $\rho < 1$, in which case we see that

$$\pi_0 = \frac{1}{1 - \rho}$$

When $\rho \geq 1$, the series diverges, which means that the queue grows without bound and the values of $L, Q, W,$ and D would be infinity. We say the queue is *stable* for $\rho < 1$ and *unstable* for $\rho \geq 1$. The stability condition $\rho < 1$ physically means that the arrival rate must be strictly less than the service rate. When ρ is close to 1, queues become very long and as $\rho \to 1$, the number in the system grows without bound, as shown in Figure 4.5. Transient analysis (see Section 3.10) reveals system behavior as $\rho \to 1$ or short-term behavior when $\rho > 1$. Here we concern ourselves with steady-state analysis.

4.2.2 Waiting-Time Distributions

We have been concerned so far with the computation of W and D, the mean steady-state waiting times in system and in queue, respectively. W and D are the mean values of the random variables w and d, whose distributions can be defined by

$$F_w(t) = \lim_{n \to \infty} \frac{1}{n} \sum_{j=1}^{n} P\{W_j \leq t\}$$

$$F_d(t) = \lim_{n \to \infty} \frac{1}{n} \sum_{j=1}^{n} P\{D_j \leq t\}$$

In this section we will compute $F_w(t)$ and $F_d(t)$, assuming that the customers are serviced in FIFO order.

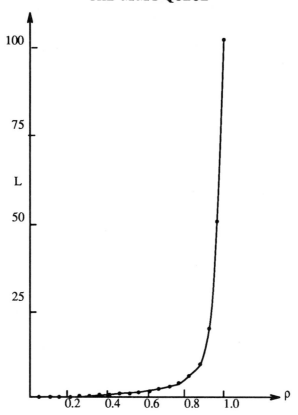

Figure 4.5 Variation of mean number in system in steady-state

First note that d is a continuous random variable except that there is a nonzero probability, π_0, that $d = 0$ and the customer enters service immediately on arrival. We have

$$F_d(0) = P\{d \leq 0\} = P\{d = 0\}$$
$$= P\{\text{System is empty on arrival}\}$$

By virtue of the PASTA property, the above probability is equal to π_0, the steady-state probability of an empty system. Therefore,

$$F_d(0) = \pi_0 = 1 - \rho \tag{18}$$

We now find $F_d(t)$ for $t > 0$. Consider the probability of a customer waiting time being less than or equal to t. If there are k customers in the system upon arrival, for the customer to get into service between 0 and t, all the k units must be serviced by the time t. Since the service

time distribution is memoryless, the distribution of the time required for
k service times is independent of the time of the current arrival and is
the convolution of k exponential random variables, which is an Erlang-k
distribution. The probability that an arrival finds k in the system in the
steady-state is simply the probability π_k. Thus we have

$$F_d(t) = P\{d \le t\}$$

$$= F_d(0) + \sum_{k=1}^{\infty} [P\{0 < d \le t \mid k \text{ in the system}\} \pi_k]$$

We know that $F_d(0) = 1 - \rho$ from (18). Also

$$P\{0 < d \le t \mid k \text{ in the system}\} = P\{\text{sum of } k \text{ service times} \le t\}$$

$$= \int_0^t \frac{\mu(\mu x)^{k-1}}{(k-1)!} e^{-\mu x} dx$$

Therefore we get, for $t > 0$,

$$F_d(t) = (1-\rho) + (1-\rho) \sum_{k=1}^{\infty} \rho^k \int_0^t \frac{\mu(\mu x)^{k-1}}{(k-1)!} e^{-\mu x} dx$$

$$= (1-\rho) + (1-\rho)\rho \int_0^t \mu e^{-\mu x} \left(\sum_{k=1}^{\infty} \frac{(\mu x \rho)^{k-1}}{(k-1)!} \right) dx$$

$$= (1-\rho) + (1-\rho)\rho \int_0^t \mu e^{-\mu x(1-\rho)} dx \qquad (19)$$

Simplifying (19), we get

$$F_d(t) = 1 - \rho e^{-\mu(1-\rho)t} \qquad (t > 0)$$

The distribution of waiting time in queue is then

$$F_d(t) = 1 - \rho \qquad\qquad (t = 0)$$
$$= 1 - \rho e^{-\mu(1-\rho)t} \qquad (t > 0) \qquad (20)$$

From (20), we can compute the mean waiting time in queue as

$$D = E[d] = \frac{\lambda}{\mu(\mu - \lambda)} \qquad (21)$$

Let us now compute the distribution of w, following similar arguments as above. We have, for $t \geq 0$,

$$F_w(t) = \sum_{k=0}^{\infty} P\{w \leq t \mid k \text{ in the system}\} \pi_k$$

$$= \sum_{k=0}^{\infty} P\{\text{sum of } (k+1) \text{ service times } \leq t\} \pi_k$$

$$= \sum_{k=0}^{\infty} \left(\int_0^t \frac{\mu(\mu x)^k}{k!} e^{-\mu x} dx \right) \rho^k (1-\rho)$$

$$= (1-\rho) \int_0^t \mu e^{-\mu x} \sum_{k=0}^{\infty} \frac{(\mu x \rho)^k}{k!} dx$$

$$= (1-\rho) \int_0^t \mu e^{-\mu x(1-\rho)} dx$$

$$= 1 - e^{-\mu(1-\rho)t}$$

$$= 1 - e^{-(\mu-\lambda)t}$$

Thus we have

$$F_w(t) = 0 \qquad\qquad\qquad (t < 0)$$
$$= 1 - e^{-(\mu-\lambda)t} \qquad (t \geq 0) \qquad (22)$$

Therefore w is exponentially distributed with mean given by

$$W = \frac{1}{\mu - \lambda}$$

It is to be noted that the mean values D and W are independent of the queuing discipline, whereas the distributions of d and w depend on the queuing discipline.

4.2.3 The M/M/1/N Queue

This is an $M/M/1$ queue in which the waiting room or the queue can accommodate no more than $N - 1$ customers. Customers arrive at rate λ as long as there are less than N customers in the system. When the waiting room is full, no customers are allowed into the system. This may be represented as

$$\lambda_k = \lambda \qquad k = 0, 1, ..., N - 1$$
$$= 0 \qquad k \geq N$$

The service rate $\mu_k = \mu$ for all $k \geq 1$. The state diagram is shown in Figure 4.6. The CTMC here is a finite birth and death process with $N + 1$ states.

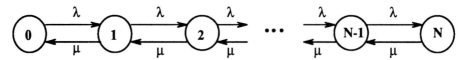

Figure 4.6 State diagram for M/M/1/N queue

The steady-state probabilities are given by

$$\pi_k = \frac{(1 - \rho)\,\rho^k}{1 - \rho^{N+1}} \qquad k = 0, 1, ..., N$$
$$= 0 \qquad\qquad k > N \tag{23}$$

Note that a system with finite population such as the above will always be stable for all values of ρ.

The performance measures can be verified to be given by

$$U = 1 - \pi_0 = \frac{\rho\left(1 - \rho^N\right)}{1 - \rho^{N+1}} \tag{24}$$

$$Q = \frac{\rho^2\left[1 - \rho^N - N\rho^{N-1}(1 - \rho)\right]}{(1 - \rho)(1 - \rho^{N+1})} \tag{25}$$

$$L = \frac{\rho\left[1 - \rho^N - N\rho^N(1 - \rho)\right]}{(1 - \rho)(1 - \rho^{N+1})} \tag{26}$$

$$W = \frac{1 - \rho^N - N\rho^N(1 - \rho)}{\mu(1 - \rho)(1 - \rho^N)} \tag{27}$$

$$D = \frac{\rho\left[1 - \rho^N - N\rho^{N-1}(1 - \rho)\right]}{\mu(1 - \rho)(1 - \rho^N)} \tag{28}$$

Example 4.12

It would be interesting to study the performance measures of a single server queuing system for various queue capacities. First, consider the $M/M/1$ queue of Example 4.10, where we had $\lambda = 8$ parts/ h and $\mu = 10$ parts/ h. We have seen that $U = 0.8$; $L = 4$; $Q = 3.2$; $W = 0.5$ h, and $D = 0.4$ h.

At the other extreme, we have the $M/M/1/1$ system in which no queuing is allowed. In this case, there are only two states, 0 and 1, and

$$\pi_0 = \frac{\mu}{\lambda + \mu} = 0.556; \qquad \pi_1 = 0.444$$

Here, $U = 0.444$; $L = Q = 0.444$; and $W = D = 0.1$ h.

Example 4.13

Consider a machine center modeled as an $M/M/1/N$ queue with parameters λ and μ. Let $C\mu$ be the cost of operating the machine at a rate of μ and let a profit of q accrue for every finished part produced. We can use the results for the $M/M/1/N$ queue to find the service rate that maximizes the total profit, in the following way.

Production rate of the machine center $= U\mu$

$$= \frac{\rho\left(1 - \rho^N\right)}{1 - \rho^{N+1}}\mu \qquad \text{from (24)}$$

$$= \frac{\lambda\mu\left(\mu^N - \lambda^N\right)}{\mu^{N+1} - \lambda^{N+1}}$$

The above is the number of parts produced in one time unit (for example, one hour, if μ is expressed in terms of parts per hour). The corresponding total profit is given by

$$P = \frac{\lambda\mu\left(\mu^N - \lambda^N\right)}{\mu^{N+1} - \lambda^{N+1}}q - C\mu$$

The service rate μ that maximizes the profit can now be obtained in the usual way.

PROBLEMS

1. Let $N(t)$ be the number of customers at time t of an $M/M/1$ queue with traffic intensity ρ. Show that $\{N(t) : t \geq 0\}$ is a CTMC which is irreducible. Show that the chain is

(a) positive recurrent for $\rho < 1$
(b) null recurrent for $\rho = 1$
(c) transient for $\rho > 1$.

2. Let $N_q(t)$ be the number of customers at time t in the queue of an $M/M/1$ queue. Show that $\{N_q(t): \ t \geq 0\}$ is not a Markov chain.

3. Consider a machine center modeled as an $M/M/1$ queuing system. Let λ and μ be the parameters. At the end of an operation, the part undergoes an inspection operation and it is found that the probability of a processed part passing the inspection is α, where $0 < \alpha < 1$, independent of whether that part had failed the inspection one or more times before. The inspection operation is an instantaneous operation. Bad parts are recycled and subsequent service times on a *bad* part are also independent and exponential with rate μ.

   (a) Show that the total time spent in service of a part, until the part passes the inspection, is exponentially distributed with rate $\alpha\mu$.

   (b) Suppose the part that fails the inspection is processed again immediately, until it passes the inspection and that the order of service is FIFO. What are the conditions for the queue to be stable? Under these conditions, find the expected total waiting time of a part in the system.

   (c) Suppose the parts are processed in the order in which they join the queue, and bad parts join the tail of the queue. How will the answers to (b) change now?

4. A machine center has unlimited waiting space. Parts arrive at a rate λ and service times are exponentially distributed with parameter μ. The machine center becomes active only when K parts are present. Once active it services one at a time until all K units, and all subsequent arrivals, are serviced. The machine center then switches to another part only when K new arrivals have occurred.

   (a) Define an appropriate state space and set up the balance equations.

   (b) In terms of the limiting probabilities, what is the average time a customer spends in queue?

   (c) What conditions on λ and μ are necessary for stability?

5. Let X denote the time between successive departures in a stationary $M/M/1$ queue with $\lambda < \mu$. Show by conditioning on whether or not a departure has left the system empty, that X is $EXP(\mu)$.

6. Consider an NC machine modeled as an $M/M/1$ queue. It is desirable to maximize the machine utilization and minimize the MLT; however, this is not possible for obvious reasons. On the other hand, one can try to minimize the product of MLT and $(1 - \rho)$ where ρ is the machine utilization. Find the value of arrival rate that would achieve this objective.

4.3 THE M/M/m QUEUE

Consider a queuing system with Poisson arrival rate λ as before, but where $m \ (\geq 1)$ exponential servers, with rate μ each, share a common queue. This is referred to as the $M/M/m$ queue and is illustrated in Figure 4.7.

If the number of customers in the system is greater than the number of servers, then a queue forms.

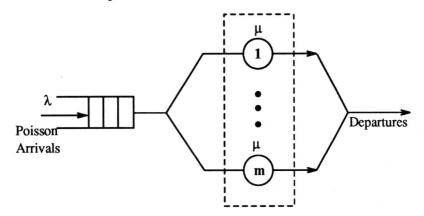

Figure 4.7 An M/M/m queue

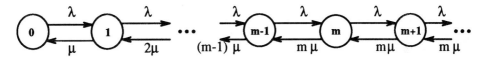

Figure 4.8 State diagram for M/M/m queue

4.3.1 Steady-State Analysis

The $M/M/m$ queue is also a special case of the birth and death model with rates

$$\lambda_k = \lambda; \qquad k = 0, 1, 2, \ldots \qquad (29)$$

$$\begin{aligned} \mu_k &= k\mu & k &= 0, 1, \ldots, m \\ &= m\mu & k &> m \end{aligned} \qquad (30)$$

The state transition diagram is shown in Figure 4.8. The steady-state probabilities could be obtained by using (29) and (30) in the equations (52,53) of Chapter 3. We find that

$$\begin{aligned} \pi_k &= \frac{\pi_0 (m\rho)^k}{k!} & k &= 0, 1, \ldots, m \\ &= \frac{\pi_0 m^m \rho^k}{m!} & k &> m \end{aligned} \qquad (31)$$

where ρ is defined as

$$\rho = \frac{\lambda}{m\mu} \qquad (32)$$

Equation (31) is valid for determining the steady-state probabilities whenever $\rho < 1$, i.e., the stability condition holds. The expression for π_0 can now be obtained using (31) and the fact that the steady-state probabilities sum up to 1. Thus

$$\pi_0 = \left[\frac{(m\rho)^m}{m!\,(1-\rho)} + \sum_{k=0}^{m-1} \frac{(m\rho)^k}{k!} \right]^{-1} \qquad (33)$$

To compute the different performance measures, we first consider N_s, the number of busy servers in the steady-state. N_s is a discrete random variable with range $\{0, 1, 2, ..., m\}$ and with pmf given by

$$P\{N_s = k\} = \pi_k \qquad k = 0, 1, ..., m-1$$

$$= \sum_{j=m}^{\infty} \pi_j \qquad k = m$$

The average number of busy servers in the steady-state, B, can be immediately obtained as

$$B = E[N_s] = \sum_{k=0}^{m} kP\{N_s = k\} = \frac{\lambda}{\mu} \qquad (34)$$

The mean utilization U of each server is simply the ratio of B to the total number of servers and hence

$$U = \frac{\lambda}{m\mu} = \rho \qquad (35)$$

We now compute Q, the average number of customers waiting in queue:

$$Q = \sum_{k=m}^{\infty} (k-m)\,\pi_k = \frac{\rho\,(m\rho)^m\,\pi_0}{m!\,(1-\rho)^2} \qquad (36)$$

The average number L in the system is given by

$$L = Q + B = \frac{\rho\,(m\rho)^m\,\pi_0}{m!\,(1-\rho)^2} + \frac{\lambda}{\mu} \qquad (37)$$

We can now use Little's law to compute the average waiting time in the system. We have

$$W = \frac{L}{\lambda} = \frac{\rho (m\rho)^m \pi_0}{m!\lambda (1-\rho)^2} + \frac{1}{\mu} \tag{38}$$

The average waiting time in queue can now be obtained as

$$D = W - \frac{1}{\mu} = \frac{\rho (m\rho)^m \pi_0}{m!\lambda (1-\rho)^2} \tag{39}$$

Example 4.14

Here we compare the three different queuing organizations shown in Figure 4.9. In Figure 4.9(a), we have two separate, identical $M/M/1$ queues with parameters $\lambda/2$ and μ, respectively. In Figure 4.9(b), the individual Poisson streams are superposed to form a common stream with rate λ, thus forming a single $M/M/1$ queue with parameters λ and 2μ, respectively. Finally, we have in Figure 4.9(c), a common stream with rate λ, serviced by two servers as an $M/M/2$ queue with parameters λ and μ. Note that in all three cases, the effective arrival rate is λ and the effective service rate is 2μ. All three organizations have interesting analogs in manufacturing systems. Let us investigate as to which organization leads to the least lead time.

Let W_1, W_2, and W_3 be the average lead times for the organizations (a), (b), and (c), respectively. It can be verified that

$$W_1 = \frac{2}{2\mu - \lambda}$$

$$W_2 = \frac{1}{2\mu - \lambda}$$

$$W_3 = \frac{4\mu}{4\mu^2 - \lambda^2}$$

For stability of the queues above, $\lambda < 2\mu$. We have

$$W_3 = \left(\frac{4\mu}{2\mu + \lambda}\right) \left(\frac{1}{2\mu - \lambda}\right) > \frac{1}{2\mu - \lambda} = W_2$$

$$W_3 = \left(\frac{2\mu}{2\mu + \lambda}\right) \left(\frac{2}{2\mu - \lambda}\right) < W_1$$

Thus $W_1 > W_3 > W_2$. [This means that organization (b) leads to the minimum lead time, followed by (c) and (a), in that order.]

4.3.2 Departure Process of M/M/m Queue

Here we present the important result that the departures of customers from an $M/M/m$ queue occur according to a Poisson process when the queue

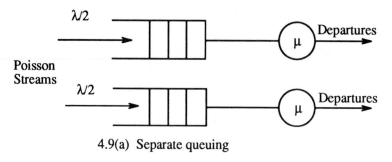

4.9(a) Separate queuing

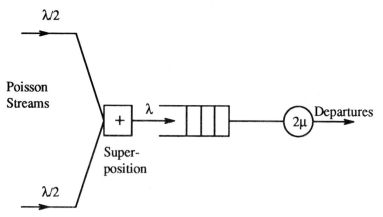

4.9(b) Common queue with a single server

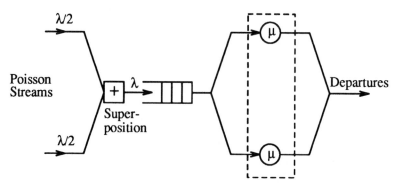

4.9(c) Common queue with two servers

Figure 4.9 Three different organizations with the same service capacity

is in steady-state. This important result is due to Burke [1956]. If $N(t)$ is the number in the queuing system at time t, then recall the notation

$$N(t) = n_A(t) - n_D(t)$$

where $n_A(t)$ and $n_D(t)$ are the number of arrivals into the system and the number of departures from the system by time t, respectively. Recall that the process $\{n_A(t): \ t \geq 0\}$ is called the *arrival process* whereas the process $\{n_D(t): \ t \geq 0\}$ is called the *departure process* of the queue. Consider an $M/M/m$ queue in steady-state so that

$$P\{N(t) = k\} = \pi_k \qquad k = 0, 1, 2, \dots$$

Let X represent the inter-departure time, i.e., the time between successive departures from the queue. Let us condition on the event that a departure leaves the $M/M/m$ queue with k customers in the system ($k = 0, 1, 2, \dots$).

If $k \geq m$, that is, if a departure leaves the system with at least m customers left behind, then the time until next departure is $EXP(m\mu)$. If $1 \leq k \leq m$, then the time until next departure is $EXP(k\mu)$. Finally, if $k = 0$, the time until the next departure will be the sum of the time until next arrival and the service time, i.e., $EXP(\lambda) + EXP(\mu)$. Since the system is in steady-state, we can therefore write that

$$X = EXP(m\mu) \text{ with probability } \sum_{j=m}^{\infty} \pi_j$$

$$= EXP(k\mu) \text{ with probability } \pi_k, \quad k = 1, 2, \dots, m-1$$

$$= EXP(\lambda) + EXP(\mu) \text{ with probability } \pi_0$$

Now, using the total probability theorem, we have

$$X = \left(\sum_{j=m}^{\infty} \pi_j\right) EXP(m\mu) + \sum_{k=1}^{m-1} [\pi_k EXP(k\mu)] \qquad (40)$$
$$+ \pi_0 [EXP(\lambda) + EXP(\mu)]$$

From the above, it can be shown that

$$X = EXP(\lambda)$$

It is also true that the random variables $N(t)$ and X are independent and furthermore that successive inter-departure times are i.i.d. Thus the successive departures from an $M/M/m$ queue in steady-state constitute a Poisson process with rate λ.

The above result plays an important role in the analysis of queuing networks. A more fundamental proof of this result uses the time reversibility property of birth and death processes.

PROBLEMS

1. Assuming FIFO queuing discipline, derive the cumulative distribution functions of w, the total waiting time, and d, the waiting time in queue, of an $M/M/m$ queue in steady-state.

2. Investigate whether the conclusions of Example 4.14 can be generalized when there are three independent arrival streams. Other conditions remain the same as appropriate to this case.

3. The performance measure that was used as the basis for comparing the three configurations of Example 4.14 was the mean manufacturing lead time. If throughput rate is taken as the basis, investigate the relative performance of the three configurations. What would happen if the performance measure is

   (a) mean number in system

   (b) mean number in queue.

4. Consider again Example 4.14. Assume that the individual arrival streams are Poisson with rates λ_1 and λ_2, instead of being λ each. Assume no change in the service rates. Will the conclusions of Example 4.14 still hold in this case?

5. Consider configurations (b) and (c) of Example 4.14. In the general case, we have m servers of rate μ each in case (b), and a single server of rate $m\mu$ in case (c). The arrival rate is λ in either case. If L_1 and Q_1; L_2 and Q_2, are the mean number in system and mean number in queue, for configurations (b) and (c), respectively, show that $L_2 > L_1$ but $Q_2 < Q_1$.

6. Formulate the $M/M/\infty$ queue as a Markov chain. Compute the relevant performance measures for this queue assuming an arrival rate of λ and a service rate of μ for each server.

7. Solve the $M/M/m/m$ queuing system in which there is no queuing space. Arriving customers who find all the servers busy leave the system immediately, without service.

8. There is a warehouse where semi-finished parts in a manufacturing system arrive to wait for an AGV to transport them to different parts of the system. The parts needing AGVs arrive at the warehouse as a Poisson process with rate λ, while the AGVs arrive at the warehouse in Poisson fashion, with rate μ. An arriving part that finds an available AGV leaves immediately on the AGV. Each AGV can only carry one part at a time. An arriving AGV that finds parts waiting in the warehouse will leave immediately with a part. If an arriving part finds no AGV, it will queue up in the warehouse, up to a limit of N parts, i.e., arriving parts that find N other parts waiting leave immediately without service (for example, they may continue to circulate on a conveyor belt). The AGVs can queue up to a limit of m AGVs.

   (a) Define a state space and compute the corresponding state probabilities. In terms of these probabilities, find:

   - The average number of parts and the average number of AGVs in queue.

- The average delay of parts before leaving in an AGV
- The average delay of AGVs before leaving with a part

(b) What are the conditions for the stability of the queue, if

- there is a queue limit on AGVs but not on parts,
- there is a queue limit on parts but not on AGVs,
- there is no queue limit on either customers or AGVs ?

9. Consider an $M/M/2$ queue with arrival rate λ and service rate μ per server, where each server has his own queue. Arrivals join the shortest queue (number in queue plus service), but cannot switch later (no jockeying).

   (a) Formulate the Markov chain and write down the balance equations. Note that it is difficult to solve these equations.

   (b) Would you expect the average customer delay for this model to be greater, less, or the same as that for the standard $M/M/2$ model?

10. Poisson arrivals with rate λ join a queue in front of two parallel servers, namely machines M_1 and M_2, which have processing rates μ_1 and μ_2, respectively. When the system is empty, a fresh arrival is routed to M_1 with probability α and to M_2, with probability $1 - \alpha$. Otherwise, the head of the queue takes the first free server.

    (a) Define a suitable state space and set up the balance equations.

    (b) In terms of the above state probabilities, what is the average number in the system and the average number of idle servers? What is the probability that an arbitrary arrival will get serviced by M_1?

11. Complete the proof of the result that the departures from an $M/M/m$ queue in steady-state constitute a Poisson process with rate equal to the arrival rate. You can start with Equation (40) and use the technique of Laplace transforms. We have shown in Section 3.7 that birth and death processes are time reversible. Can you use this fact to obtain an alternative proof for the above result?

4.4 BATCH ARRIVAL QUEUING SYSTEMS

There exist variations of $M/M/1$ queuing situations that are very important in the manufacturing context. In a typical manufacturing situation, the workpieces arrive at a machine center in batches and they leave in batches. A batch generally consists of two or more identical workpieces that are processed and then transported in batches for further processing. Such a situation can be modeled as queues with bulk arrivals.

In this section we consider the following queue: Workpieces arrive at a machine center in batches of fixed size b with a Poisson arrival rate of λ. The workpieces are processed individually by the machine center

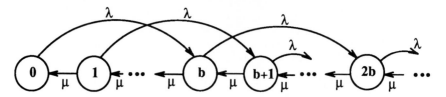

Figure 4.10 State transition diagram of a bulk arrival queue

at an exponential rate of μ. Such a queue is designated as $M^b/M/1$, the bulk arrival queue with bulk size b.

Figure 4.10 shows the state transition diagram for the above bulk arrival queue. Assuming that steady-state exists, let π_0, π_1, ..., be the steady-state probabilities. The rate balance equations can be written down as follows.

$$(\lambda + \mu)\,\pi_k = \lambda\pi_{k-b} + \mu\pi_{k+1}; \quad k \geq b \tag{41}$$

$$(\lambda + \mu)\,\pi_k = \mu\pi_{k+1}; \qquad k = 1, 2, ..., b-1 \tag{42}$$

$$\lambda\pi_0 = \mu\pi_1 \tag{43}$$

We solve the above equations for the steady-state probabilities using generating functions. Multiply equation (42) by z^k and sum from $k = 1$ to $(b-1)$. Next multiply (41) by z^k and sum from b to ∞. Combining these with (43), we obtain

$$\sum_{k=b}^{\infty}\left[\mu z^k \pi_{k+1}\right] - \sum_{k=b}^{\infty}\left[(\lambda + \mu)\,z^k \pi_k\right] + \sum_{k=b}^{\infty}\left[\lambda z^k \pi_{k-b}\right]$$
$$+ \sum_{k=1}^{b-1}\left[\mu z^k \pi_{k+1}\right] - \sum_{k=1}^{b-1}\left[(\lambda + \mu)\,z^k \pi_k\right] + (\mu\pi_1 - \lambda\pi_0) = 0 \tag{44}$$

Collecting terms and factoring powers of z in (44), we obtain

$$\sum_{k=1}^{\infty}\mu z^k \pi_{k+1} - \sum_{k=1}^{\infty}(\lambda + \mu)\,z^k \pi_k + z^b \sum_{k=b}^{\infty}\lambda z^{k-b}\pi_{k-b} + (\mu\pi_1 - \lambda\pi_0) = 0 \tag{45}$$

We now define

$$G(z) = \sum_{k=0}^{\infty}z^k \pi_k \tag{46}$$

and use this definition in (45), to obtain

$$\mu z^{-1}\left[G\left(z\right)-\pi_0-z\pi_1\right]-\left(\lambda+\mu\right)\left[G\left(z\right)-\pi_0\right]+\lambda z^b G\left(z\right)+\mu\pi_1-\lambda\pi_0=0$$

Solving the above for $G\left(z\right)$, we get

$$
\begin{aligned}
G\left(z\right) &= \frac{\mu\left(1-z\right)\pi_0}{\mu-\left(\lambda+\mu\right)z+\lambda z^{b+1}} \\
&= \frac{\mu\pi_0}{\mu-\lambda z\left(\displaystyle\sum_{j=0}^{b-1}z^j\right)}
\end{aligned}
\tag{47}
$$

From (46), we note that

$$G\left(z\right)|_{z=1}=\sum_{k=0}^{\infty}\pi_k=1 \tag{48}$$

From (47) and (48) we get

$$\frac{\mu\pi_0}{\mu-\lambda b}=1 \tag{49}$$

Define

$$\rho=\frac{b\lambda}{\mu} \tag{50}$$

Equation (49) now yields

$$\pi_0=\left(1-\rho\right)$$

Thus $\rho=\frac{b\lambda}{\mu}$ gives the utilization of the server. As usual, $\rho<1$ will be the condition for the existence of steady-state for this queuing system. With this, $G\left(z\right)$ can be simplified as

$$G\left(z\right)=\frac{\mu\left(1-\rho\right)}{\mu-\lambda z\left(\displaystyle\sum_{j=0}^{b-1}z^j\right)} \tag{51}$$

From (51), we can obtain all the performance measures of the system. The mean number in the system L is given by

$$L=\sum_{k=0}^{\infty}k\pi_k=\frac{dG\left(z\right)}{dz}|_{z=1}=\frac{\rho\left(1+b\right)}{2\left(1-\rho\right)} \tag{52}$$

Using Little's result, we can obtain the mean waiting time in the system as

$$W = \frac{L}{\lambda b} = \frac{1+b}{2\mu(1-\rho)} \tag{53}$$

The average number in the queue is given by

$$Q = L - \rho = \frac{\rho(b-1+2\rho)}{2(1-\rho)} \tag{54}$$

The average waiting time in the queue is

$$D = W - \frac{1}{\mu} = \frac{b+2\rho-1}{2\mu(1-\rho)} \tag{55}$$

Example 4.15

Consider the machine center in Example 4.10. Suppose parts arrive in batches of 2 at a rate of 4 batches/ h. Since $\mu = 10$ parts/ h, we have using (52) – (53),

$$\rho = \frac{\lambda b}{\mu} = 0.8$$

and

$$L = 6; W = \frac{3}{4}\text{h} ; Q = 5.2; D = \frac{13}{20}\text{h}$$

We note that in the case of batch arrivals the waiting time and queue lengths are higher than in the case of the $M/M/1$ queue. The deterioration in performance is because the waiting of a typical part starts as soon as the batch containing it arrives.

Example 4.16

At an inspection station in a manufacturing system, boxes of parts arrive following a Poisson process at a rate of 12/ h. Each box contains 100 parts and 10 parts are drawn and inspected separately. Inspection time is exponentially distributed with a mean of 20 sec. We note that

$\lambda = 12$ batches/ h; $b = 10$; $\mu = 180$ parts/ h.

Then from (52) and (53), we have

$$\rho = \frac{\lambda b}{\mu} = \frac{2}{3}; \ \ L = 11 \text{ parts}; \ \ W = \frac{11}{120} \text{ h} = 5.5 \text{ min.}$$

PROBLEMS

1. Consider the $M^b/M/m$ queue in which b customers arrive in a batch and there are m identical servers. Determine $G(z)$ when $m < b$ and $m \geq b$.

2. Consider the $M^{(b)}/M/m$ queue where b is a random variable with generating function $B(z)$ and mean $E[b]$. Show that

$$G(z) = \frac{[\mu - \lambda E(b)][1 - z]}{[\mu(1 - z) - \lambda z(1 - B(z))]}$$

3. Consider a machine center at which identical batches of size b queue up. Each batch requires a setup. Each part is processed separately. Suppose τ is the average setup time per batch and $1/\mu$ is the average part processing time. Further, both setup time and part processing time are exponentially distributed and independent. Find the distribution of the batch service time.

4. A fixture used in an NC machine center can accommodate r parts. Parts arrive at the machine center at a rate of λ in Poisson fashion. The fixturing is done for r parts and all of them are processed collectively. If r parts are not available, fixturing process waits until r parts accumulate in the queue.

   (a) Draw the state diagram for the above situation.

   (b) Find the generating function and other performance measures for this system.

5. Consider the $M/E_b/1$ queue where the service time is b-Erlang distributed. Define a suitable state space for this queue, for which the state diagram is the same as that for an $M^b/M/1$ queue. Explain why this happens.

6. For the batch arrival queue $M^4/M/2$ with batch arrival rate λ, exponential service at rate μ, and server utilization $\rho = 2\lambda/\mu < 1$, show the following:

$$G(z) = \frac{(1 - z)(1 - \rho)(16 + 4\rho z)}{[\rho z^5 - (\rho + 4)z + 4](4 + \rho)}$$

$$L = \frac{\rho}{4 + \rho} + \frac{5\rho}{2(1 - \rho)}$$

4.5 QUEUES WITH GENERAL DISTRIBUTIONS

The queuing models studied until now have assumed Poisson arrivals and exponential service. In this section we look at queues where the memoryless property is violated by arrivals or by service or by both. The analysis of such queues is more formidable than that of the earlier queues, mainly because of the lack of memoryless property.

We first analyze the $M/G/1$ queue in some detail and later summarize the important known results for the $GI/M/1$ and $GI/G/1$ queues.

4.5.1 The M/G/1 Queue

The $M/G/1$ queue is a single-server system with Poisson arrivals (with rate, say λ) and arbitrary service time with a general distribution. Let T be the service time random variable, and F_T and f_T, its CDF and pdf, respectively. The service times are assumed to be mutually independent. Let $E[T] = 1/\mu$ and let $V[T]$ be the variance of T. We can define the utilization factor as $\rho = \lambda/\mu$. In this section we derive the well-known *Pollaczek-Khinchin* (P-K) mean-value formula for the mean number of customers in the system. This formula is given by

$$L = \rho + \frac{\lambda^2 V[T] + \rho^2}{2(1-\rho)} \qquad (56)$$

From (56), we can obtain the mean waiting time in the system using Little's law as

$$W = \frac{1}{\mu} + \frac{\lambda\left(V[T] + \frac{1}{\mu^2}\right)}{2(1-\rho)} \qquad (57)$$

We can obtain D and Q by using the relationships $D = W - 1/\mu$ and $Q = \lambda D$. These are given by

$$Q = \frac{\lambda^2\left(V[T] + \frac{1}{\mu^2}\right)}{2(1-\rho)} \qquad (58)$$

$$D = \frac{\lambda\left(V[T] + \frac{1}{\mu^2}\right)}{2(1-\rho)} \qquad (59)$$

We thus see that if we derive any one of the above four formulae (56)-(59), the others can be easily obtained.

The Embedded Markov Chain

Let $N(t)$ as usual denote the number of jobs in the system at time t. If $N(t) \geq 1$, then a job is in service and we need to know the time spent by the job in service to predict the behavior of the system. Thus $\{N(t) : t \geq 0\}$ is not a Markov chain. Suppose we take a snapshot of the system at the departure epochs, i.e., the time instants at which a job has been serviced and is departing from the system. Let t_i, $i = 1, 2, ...,$

be the time instant at which the ith job departs from the system. Let q_i be the number of customers left behind in the system at time t_i, i.e.,

$$q_i = N(t_i); \qquad i = 1, 2, \ldots \tag{60}$$

We show that the stochastic process $\{q_i : i = 1, 2, \ldots\}$ is a DTMC, so we can call it the *embedded Markov chain* (EMC). If $\{N(t) : t \geq 0\}$ has a unique limiting distribution, then we can use the limiting distribution of the EMC as a measure of the original process $N(t)$ since it is known that

$$\lim_{t \to \infty} P\{(N(t) = k)\} = \lim_{i \to \infty} P\{q_i = k\}; \quad k = 0, 1, \ldots \tag{61}$$

We first prove that $\{q_i : i = 1, 2, \ldots\}$ is a DTMC. For the moment, assume that $q_i > 0$. The epoch for the service of $(i+1)$st job starts at t_i. During the service period of this job, new arrivals can occur. We denote by a_{i+1} the number of arrivals that occur during the service time of job $(i+1)$. The random variables $a_1, a_2, \ldots$, are independent and identically distributed with probability mass function given by, say,

$$P\{a_i = k\} = b_k \quad \text{with} \quad \sum_{k=0}^{\infty} b_k = 1$$

Further, each a_i is independent of $q_0, q_1, \ldots, q_{i-1}$. The state of the system at the $(i+1)$st departure time t_{i+1} is given by

$$q_{i+1} = q_i - 1 + a_{i+1} \quad (q_i > 0) \tag{62}$$

If the departure of the ith job leaves the queue empty, a slightly different equation describes the process. If the $(i+1)$st departing job arrived into an empty queue, it would leave behind only those jobs that arrived during its service period. Therefore, we have

$$q_{i+1} = a_{i+1} \quad (q_i = 0) \tag{63}$$

We can combine equations (62) and (63) to obtain the fundamental relationship between the random variables q_{i+1}, q_i, and a_{i+1} as

$$q_{i+1} = q_i - U(q_i) + a_{i+1} \tag{64}$$

where $U(q_i)$ is a unit step function defined by

$$U(q_i) = 1 \qquad (q_i > 0)$$
$$= 0 \qquad (q_i = 0)$$

Since a_{i+1} is independent of $q_0, q_1, ..., q_i$, it follows that for a given value of q_i, the probabilistic behavior of q_{i+1} depends only on q_i and not on $q_0, q_1, ..., q_{i-1}$. Thus, $\{q_i : i = 1, 2, ...\}$ is a Markov chain.

Derivation of Pollaczek-Khinchin Formula

Equation (64) is the key for the study of the $M/G/1$ queue. Define the probability generating function or the z-transform of q_i as

$$H_i(z) = \sum_{k=0}^{\infty} P\{q_i = k\} z^k \tag{65}$$

We note from the definition of expectation that

$$E[z^{q_i}] = H_i(z) \tag{66}$$

We start with (64) and write down the obvious equations

$$z^{q_i+1} = z^{q_i - U(q_i) + a_{i+1}} \tag{67}$$

Taking expectation on both sides of (67), we get

$$E[z^{q_i+1}] = E\left[z^{q_i - U(q_i) + a_{i+1}}\right]$$
$$= E\left[z^{q_i - U(q_i)} z^{a_{i+1}}\right] \tag{68}$$

As we observed earlier, the random variable a_{i+1} is independent of the random variable q_i (which represents the number of customers left behind upon departure of the ith customer). Since functions of independent random variables are also independent, we can write the expectation of the product as product of expectations. Hence, from (68),

$$H_{i+1}(z) = E\left[z^{q_i - U(q_i)}\right] E[z^{a_{i+1}}] \tag{69}$$

We now calculate the two expectations in (69). First, we calculate $E[z^{a_{i+1}}]$.

Computation of $E[z^{a_{i+1}}]$

Recall that a_{i+1} is the number of arrivals during the service time of the $(i + 1)$st job and that T is the random variable denoting the service time. Then

$$P\{a_{i+1} = k \mid T = t\} = \frac{e^{-\lambda t} (\lambda t)^k}{k!}$$

The unconditional distribution of a_{i+1} is given by

$$P\{a_{i+1} = k\} = \int_0^\infty \frac{e^{-\lambda t}(\lambda t)^k}{k!} f_T(t)\, dt \qquad (70)$$

Let $A_{i+1}(z)$ be the generating function of a_{i+1}, i.e.,

$$A_{i+1}(z) = \sum_{k=0}^\infty P\{a_{i+1} = k\} z^k$$

Then, from (70) we have

$$A_{i+1}(z) = \int_0^\infty e^{-\lambda t}\left(\sum_{k=0}^\infty \frac{(\lambda t)^k z^k}{k!}\right) f_T(t)\, dt$$

$$= \int_0^\infty e^{-\lambda t(1-z)} f_T(t)\, dt$$

$$= F_T^*(s)|_{s=\lambda(1-z)}$$

where $F_T^*(s)$ is the Laplace transform of $f_T(t)$. Thus the generating function $A_{i+1}(z)$ of the number of arrivals during $(i+1)$th service interval can be expressed in terms of the Laplace transform of the service-time distribution. Indeed, recalling

$$E[z^{a_{i+1}}] = E[z^{a_i}] = A(z) \text{ and } A_{i+1}(z) = A_i(z)$$

we have in the steady-state,

$$A(z) = F_T^*(s)|_{s=\lambda(1-z)} \qquad (71)$$

From this generating function, we can compute the average number of arrivals during one service time interval:

$$E[a_{i+1}] = \frac{dA(z)}{dz}\Big|_{z=1}$$

$$= \frac{dF_T^*(s)}{ds}\frac{ds}{dz}\Big|_{s=\lambda(1-z);\ z=1} \qquad (72)$$

$$= \lambda E[T] = \lambda/\mu = \rho$$

Thus from (72), we have the conclusion that the expected number of arrivals in a service interval equals ρ. Further, from (64) and (72), in the steady-state (i.e., $E[q_{i+1}] = E[q_i]$), we have

$$E[U(q_i)] = E[a_{i+1}] = \rho \tag{73}$$

Noting that $E[U(q_i)] = 1 - P\{q_{i+1} = 0\}$ and using (73), we get

$$P\{q_{i+1} = 0\} = 1 - \rho \tag{74}$$

Thus the probability that an arriving customer does not have to wait is given by $(1 - \rho)$.

Computation of $E\left[z^{q_i - U(q_i)}\right]$

We note that

$$E\left[z^{q_i - U(q_i)}\right] = z^{0 - U(0)}P\{q_i = 0\} + z^{1 - U(1)}P\{q_i = 1\}$$

$$+ \dots + z^{k - U(k)}P\{q_i = k\} + \dots$$

$$= P\{q_i = 0\} + \sum_{k=1}^{\infty} P\{q_i = k\}\, z^{k-1}$$

$$= (1 - \rho) + z^{-1}\left[H_i(z) - (1 - \rho)\right] \tag{75}$$

Recall that, in the steady-state, $A_{i+1}(z) = A_i(z) = A(z)$ and $H_{i+1}(z) = H_i(z) = H(z)$. Now using (69) in (75) we get

$$H(z) = \frac{(1 - \rho)(1 - z)A(z)}{(A(z) - z)} \tag{76}$$

where $A(z)$ is given by (71). We can derive the P-K formula (56) by differentiating (76) two times. From (76), we have

$$H'(z)[A(z) - z] + H(z)[A'(z) - 1] \\ = (1 - \rho)(-1)A(z) + (1 - \rho)(1 - z)A'(z) \tag{77}$$

$$H''(z)[A(z) - z] + 2H'(z)[A'(z) - 1] + H(z)[A''(z)] \\ = 2(1 - \rho)(-1)A'(z) + (1 - \rho)(1 - z)A''(z) \tag{78}$$

From (71), we have

$$\begin{aligned} A(1) &= 1 \\ A'(1) &= E[T] = \rho \\ A''(1) &= \lambda^2 V[T] + \rho^2 \end{aligned} \tag{79}$$

From (78), we have

$$L = \frac{dH(z)}{dz}\Big|_{z=1}$$
$$= \frac{(1-\rho)A'(1)}{1-A'(1)} + \frac{A''(1)}{2(1-A'(1))} \qquad (80)$$

Equations (79) and (80) now immediately lead to the following P-K formula:

$$L = \rho + \frac{\lambda^2 V[T] + \rho^2}{2(1-\rho)}$$

Waiting-Time Distribution

Let w be the random variable denoting the total time spent by a customer in the system in the steady-state. If we consider FCFS (first come, first served) discipline, it follows that those present upon arrival of the ith customer must depart before he does; consequently, those customers that were left behind (total of q_i) at the departure of ith customer must be precisely those who arrived during his waiting time w in the system. Therefore,

$$P\{q_i = k\} = P\{k \text{ customers arrive in } w\}$$
$$= \int_0^\infty \frac{e^{-\lambda t}(\lambda t)^k}{k!} f_w(t)\, dt$$

Thus, we have

$$H(z) = \sum_{k=0}^\infty z^k P\{q_i = k\} = \sum_{k=0}^\infty z^k \left(\int_0^\infty \frac{e^{-\lambda t}(\lambda t)^k}{k!} f_w(t)\, dt \right)$$
$$= \int_0^\infty e^{-\lambda t} \left(\sum_{k=0}^\infty \frac{z^k(\lambda t)^k}{k!} \right) f_w(t)\, dt$$

The above yields

$$H(z) = \int_0^\infty e^{-\lambda t(1-z)} f_w(t)\, dt$$
$$= F_w^*(s)\big|_{s=\lambda(1-z)} \qquad (81)$$

where $F_w^*(s)$ is the Laplace transform of $f_w(t)$.

From (76) and (81), we have

$$F_w^*(s)\big|_{s=\lambda(1-z)} = \frac{(1-\rho)(1-z)(A(z))}{A(z)-z} \tag{82}$$

We can rewrite (82) in terms of $F_T^*(s)$ and s, using the definition of $A(z)$ in (71):

$$F_w^*(s) = \frac{s(1-\rho)F_T^*(s)}{\lambda F_T^*(s) - \lambda + s} \tag{83}$$

Equation (83) is also called the *Pollaczek-Khinchin equation* and is important for computing the distribution of the waiting time in the system.

Example 4.17

Let us assume that the service time is a constant, say, $1/\mu$, for all work-pieces. This gives rise to an $M/D/1$ queue. In this case, $V[T] = 0$ and therefore the mean performance measures, given by (56–59), become:

$$L = \rho + \frac{\rho^2}{2(1-\rho)}; \quad Q = \frac{\rho^2}{2(1-\rho)}$$

$$W = \frac{1}{\mu} + \frac{\lambda}{2\mu^2(1-\rho)}; \quad D = \frac{\lambda}{2\mu^2(1-\rho)}$$

where $\rho = \lambda/\mu$, λ being the Poisson arrival rate. To compare with an $M/M/1$ queue, let us recall Example 4.10 where we had an $M/M/1$ queue with $\lambda = 8$ parts/ h and $\mu = 10$ parts/ h. Treating the system as an $M/D/1$ queue, we get

$$\rho = 0.8; \quad L = 2.4; \quad Q = 1.6$$
$$W = 18 \text{ min}; \quad D = 12 \text{ min}$$

Note that the values of L, Q, W, and D above are less compared to the $M/M/1$ values. However, the average throughput is the same in both the cases.

Example 4.18

Here we consider a machine center as in Examples 4.10 and 4.17 and assume Poisson arrivals at rate $\lambda = 8$ parts/ h and investigate the performance of the system assuming various service time distributions. In Example 4.10, the service time was $EXP(10)$, whereas in Example 4.17, the service time was constant, equal to 0.1 h (6 min). Let us look at the following cases, which are also relevant in the AMS context.

Case 1. Service time normally distributed with mean 6 min and standard deviation, say 1 min.

Case 2. Service time uniformly distributed over the interval [5 min, 7 min].

Case 3. Service time is the sum of 6 i.i.d. exponential random variables of mean 1 min each (6–Erlang with mean 6 min). This case is appropriate when each fixture can accommodate 6 raw parts and fixtured parts arrive at rate $\lambda = 8$ parts/ h.

The following table gives the performance measures for the above cases.

Service time distribution	L	Q	W (h)	D (h)
Exponential	4.0	3.2	0.5	0.4
Constant	2.4	1.6	0.3	0.2
Normal	2.44	1.64	0.305	0.205
Uniform	2.42	1.62	0.3025	0.2025
Erlang-6	2.65	1.85	0.331	0.231

4.5.2 The GI/M/1 Queue

We consider the system in which customers arrive singly with inter-arrival times identically and independently distributed with distribution function $B(t)$ and a mean time between arrivals of $1/\lambda$. Service times are i.i.d. exponentially distributed with a mean of $1/\mu$. Define the utilization factor as $\rho = \lambda/\mu$ and $\rho < 1$. Let $B^*(s)$ be the Laplace transform of the inter-arrival time density function. Let N as usual denote the steady-state number of customers in the system.

Let x be the unique solution less than 1 of the equation

$$x = B^*(\mu(1-x)) \tag{84}$$

Then it can be shown that

$$P\{N = k\} = 1 - \rho \qquad\qquad k = 0$$
$$= \rho x^{k-1}(1-x) \qquad k = 1, 2, \ldots \tag{85}$$

The average number of customers in the system and the average waiting time in system are then given by

$$L = \frac{\rho}{1 - x} \tag{86}$$

$$W = \frac{1}{\mu(1 - x)} \tag{87}$$

The CDF of w, the steady-state waiting time in the system is given by

$$\begin{aligned} F_w(t) &= 0 && (t \leq 0) \\ &= 1 - e^{-\mu(1-x)t} && (t > 0) \end{aligned} \tag{88}$$

Example 4.19

Consider the $(M/M/1)$ queue. Here we have

$$B^*(s) = \frac{\lambda}{s + \lambda}$$

Using (84), x must satisfy

$$x = \frac{\lambda}{\mu(1 - x) + \lambda}$$

which yields

$$(x - 1)(\mu x - \lambda) = 0$$

Of the two solutions, the case $x = 1$ is not acceptable and therefore the only acceptable solution is $x = \rho$. Other results of $M/M/1$ system follow immediately.

Example 4.20

Consider $E_2/M/1$ queuing system, in which the inter-arrival times are i.i.d. 2–Erlang distributed. We have

$$B^*(s) = \frac{2\mu^2}{(s + \mu)(s + 2\mu)}$$

From (84), we have

$$x = \frac{2\mu^2}{(\mu - \mu x + \mu)(\mu - \mu x + 2\mu)}$$

which leads us to the cubic equation $x^3 - 5x^2 + 6x - 2 = 0$, which has roots at $x = 1$, $x = 2 + \sqrt{2}$ and $x = 2 - \sqrt{2}$. Clearly $x = 2 - \sqrt{2}$ is the acceptable solution. Now performance measures of the system can be easily obtained.

Example 4.21

Consider the unconventional queuing situation depicted in Figure 4.11. Here, the assembly station assembles m component parts in time $EXP(\mu)$. The m component parts are produced from m raw parts by the machine centers $M_1, M_2, ..., M_m$. When all these m machines finish processing the respective component parts, the component parts are moved instantaneously into a queue where they wait for the assembly station. After assembly, the finished part leaves the system as shown. When the group of m component parts moves to the queue at the assembly station, the m machine centers are free and start working on fresh raw parts simultaneously. We are making an assumption that raw parts are always available. The processing times on the machine centers are independent exponential random variables with rates $\mu_1, \mu_2, ...,$ and μ_m. Machine centers which finish earlier than some others will wait until all the centers finish processing. Thus the machine centers are synchronized for commencing the processing of the next parts. This explains the fork-join blocks in Figure 4.11.

    It is easy to see that the inter-arrival time of assembly groups into the queue is given by the random variable

$$\max_{1 \leq i \leq m} EXP(\mu_i)$$

Also, these arrivals are independent and so we have a $GI/M/1$ queue.

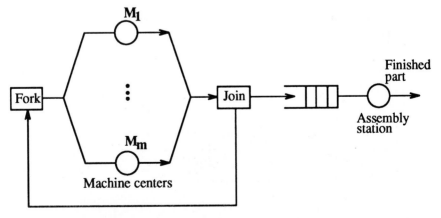

Figure 4.11 Example for GI/M/1 queue

4.5.3 The GI/G/1 Queue

In Sections 4.5.1 and 4.5.2 we have considered queuing models in which either the service times or the inter-arrival times are exponentially distributed. When both the inter-arrival times and service times have general distributions, there are very few results available. However, bounds can be obtained for the steady-state values of average number in the system and the average waiting time in system. The upper bounds are given by

$$L \leq \rho + \frac{\lambda^2 (V_a + V_s)}{2 (1 - \rho)} \tag{89}$$

$$W \leq E[t_s] + \frac{\lambda (V_a + V_s)}{2 (1 - \rho)} \tag{90}$$

where t_a and t_s are inter-arrival and service times, V_a and V_s are the variances of inter-arrival and service times, respectively, with

$$\rho = E[t_s] / E[t_a]$$

Example 4.22

Let us consider the system of Example 4.21 (depicted in Figure 4.11) with the only variation that the assembly time is deterministic with value equal to $1/\mu$. Let $m = 2$ so that inter-arrival time is given by $max (EXP(\mu_1), EXP(\mu_2))$. This now represents a $GI/G/1$ queue.

PROBLEMS

1. For an $M/G/1$ queue, it would be interesting to study the variation of average number in system as a function of server utilization ρ for various service time distributions. Assuming the distributions considered in Example 4.18, draw a graph of average number versus ρ.

2. Consider an $M/D/1$ queue with a finite capacity N. Can you solve this problem using the EMC approach, assuming that arrivals that find the queue full, leave without service?

3. In the machine repairman model discussed in Section 3.6, assume that the repair time is generally distributed. Attempt a solution of this model using the methodology of analyzing an $M/G/1$ queue.

4. In a manufacturing center with one machine, raw parts arrive in batches of constant size b according to a Poisson process. They are instantaneously fixtured onto a pallet and the machine processes the parts one by one. Each pallet can accommodate exactly b parts. The processing time for each part is a normal random variable with mean μ and standard deviation σ. Solve this problem as an $M/G/1$ queue.

5. Consider Problem 3 in Section 4.4. Model the system described therein as an $M/G/1$ queue and obtain relevant performance measures.

6. Using the P-K equation (83), derive the distribution of waiting time in system, for

   (a) $M/M/1$ queue
   (b) $M/D/1$ queue.

4.6 QUEUES WITH BREAKDOWNS

Traditional queuing analysis is performed under the assumption that all servers provide failure-free service. In the manufacturing context, however, failures and repairs are common occurrences and performance analysis conducted in the presence of failures and repairs is therefore more realistic.

In classical studies, reliability/availability models are used to predict the performance of the system in the presence of failures. Here we investigate the performance of the $M/M/1$ queuing system in the presence of server failures.

4.6.1 Problem Formulation

Consider a server such as a machine center processing parts of a single type. Let λ be the rate of arrival of the workpieces at the machine center and μ the service rate. The machine breaks down at random and the failure time is exponentially distributed with parameter f. The repair time is also assumed to be exponential with parameter r. The inter-arrival times, service times, times to failure, and repair times are all mutually independent.

To formulate the problem precisely we need to make the following assumptions regarding the failure process.

1. When the machine is under repair, no further failures can occur.

2. The machine can fail when it is idle or when it is serving a customer.

There are different types of service interruption interactions. In all cases the service is interrupted immediately on failure. After the machine is repaired, there are two possibilities:

1. Pre-emptive resume (PRS): The customer service is resumed from the point at which it was interrupted.

2. Pre-emptive repeat (PRT): The workpiece is discarded and service is repeated from the beginning on a fresh workpiece.

4.6.2 Steady-State Analysis

Here we conduct steady-state analysis assuming the PRS policy. Let the stochastic process $\{(X(t), Y(t)) : t \geq 0\}$ describe the state of the system at time t, where $X(t)$ is the state of the server and $Y(t)$ is the number of customers present in the system at time t. We write $X(t) = 1$ when machine is in the up state and $X(t) = 0$ when the machine is in the down state. Let $\pi(i, j)$ be the steady-state probability that the system is in state (i, j), $i = 0, 1$; $j = 0, 1, 2, \ldots$.

Figure 4.12 shows the Markov chain associated with this system. The steady-state balance equations of the system are

$$(\lambda + i\mu + if + (1 - i)r)\,\pi(i, k) = \lambda\pi(i, k - 1) + i\mu\pi(i, k + 1)$$
$$+ir\pi(1 - i, k) + (1 - i)\,f\pi(1 - i, k) \tag{91}$$
$$i = 0, 1; \quad k \geq 1$$

$$(\lambda + if + (1 - i)r)\,\pi(i, 0) = i\mu\pi(i, 1) + ir\pi(1 - i, 0)$$
$$+(1 - i)\,f\pi(1 - i, 0); \quad i = 0, 1 \tag{92}$$

Define the generating functions $G_i(z)$ by

$$G_i(z) = \sum_{j=0}^{\infty} \pi(i, j)\,z^j \quad i = 0, 1 \tag{93}$$

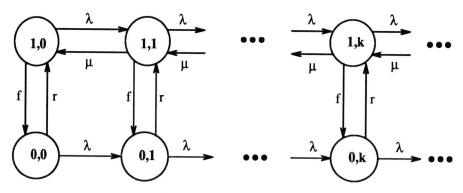

Figure 4.12 State diagram for M/M/1 queue with breakdowns

Multiplying both sides of equations (91) and (92) by z^j and summing over all j, we obtain

$$[\lambda z (1 - z) - i\mu (1 - z) + ifz + (1 - i) rz] G_i (z)$$
$$= (1 - i) fz G_{1-i} (z) + irz G_{1-i} (z) - (1 - z) i\mu \pi (i, 0); \quad i = 0, 1 \tag{94}$$

We can rewrite (94) for $i = 0, 1$ as follows:

$$(-\lambda (z - 1) + r) G_0 (z) - f G_1 (z) = 0 \tag{95}$$

$$[-\lambda z (z - 1) + \mu (z - 1) + fz] G_1 (z) - rz G_0 (z) = \mu (z - 1) \pi (1, 0) \tag{96}$$

Solving these two equations for $G_0 (z)$ and $G_1 (z)$, we get

$$G_0 (z) = \frac{f \mu \pi (1, 0)}{\lambda (\lambda z - \mu) (z - 1) - \lambda (f + r) z + r\mu} \tag{97}$$

$$G_1 (z) = \frac{[r - \lambda (z - 1)] \mu \pi (1, 0)}{\lambda (\lambda z - \mu) (z - 1) - \lambda (f + r) z + r\mu} \tag{98}$$

To compute $\pi (1, 0)$, we use the fact that $G_0 (1) + G_1 (1) = 1$. This yields

$$\pi (1, 0) = \frac{r\mu - \lambda (f + r)}{\mu (f + r)} \tag{99}$$

Thus the generating function $G (z) = G_0 (z) + G_1 (z)$ can be computed in terms of the parameters λ, μ, f, and r. The expected number in the system is given by

$$L = \frac{d\pi (z)}{dz} \Big|_{z=1}$$
$$= \frac{\lambda \left[(f + r)^2 + \mu f \right]}{(f + r) [r (\mu - \lambda) - \lambda f]} \tag{100}$$

The expected waiting time in the system can be obtained by using Little's law as

$$W = \frac{L}{\lambda} = \frac{(f + r)^2 + \mu f}{(f + r) [r (\mu - \lambda) - \lambda f]} \tag{101}$$

From (100) and (101), it is easy to derive the condition under which this queuing system is stable. The condition is

$$\mu > \lambda \left(1 + \frac{f}{r}\right) \qquad (102)$$

Example 4.23

Let the machine center of Example 4.10 be failure-prone with failure rate $f = 0.1/h$ and repair rate $r = 1/h$. We see that the stability conditions of (102) are satisfied. Using (100) and (101), we obtain the expected number of customers and the expected delay as

$$L = 13.39$$
$$W = 1.674 \text{ h}$$

Example 4.24

In the above example, let λ, μ, and f be as before. Now we can determine the minimum value of r that ensures stability of the queuing system. From (102), we have

$$r > \frac{\lambda f}{\mu - \lambda} = 0.4/h$$

If μ, f, and r are as given in the above example, then we can compute the maximum arrival rate λ for stability as

$$\lambda < \mu - \frac{\lambda f}{r} = 9.2/h.$$

PROBLEMS

1. Consider the $M/M/1$ queuing system with breakdowns considered in this section. Suppose we assume that the breakdowns can only occur when in service and not when the machine is idle. Consider the following approach to analyzing this system: Define the completion time of a workpiece as the total time taken for finishing the processing on the workpiece. Note that during the completion time of a workpiece, the machine may fail and get repaired, an arbitrary number of times. Compute the distribution of completion time and treat the system as an $M/G/1$ queue. Obtain the steady-state performance measures using the above approach.

2. Consider the $M/M/1$ queuing system considered above with the following restrictions:

   (a) Failures can only occur when in service
   (b) Failures do not occur when the machine is in repair
   (c) Arrivals cannot occur when the machine is under repair

Write down the state transition diagram for this case and obtain the steady-state performance measures. What is the condition for the stability of this queuing system?

3. Consider the $M/M/1$ system with breakdowns considered in this section. Suppose now that we follow the pre-emptive repeat policy, i.e., the workpiece is discarded and a fresh workpiece is used for processing. Write down the Markov chain for this case. Find the generating function and compare the results with equations (100), (101), and (102).

4. Consider the $M/M/2$ system with breakdowns and having one repair facility. Find the generating function and the performance characteristics of such a system.

5. Analyze the $M/D/1$ queuing system with exponential failures and exponential repairs, assuming the pre-emptive repeat policy, using the completion time approach suggested in Problem 1.

4.7 ANALYSIS OF A FLEXIBLE MACHINE CENTER

A machine center is the prime component of an automated manufacturing system. Machine centers are equipped with automatic tool changing capabilities and also pallet pools where fixtured parts are stored and from where they are transported to the machine whenever it is free. A typical machine center was shown in Figure 2.10. A machine center can produce a wide variety of part types, each with different processing and tooling requirements.

In our analysis thus far, we have considered only single-part-type situations. Here we consider a machine center processing multiple part types with different processing and setup time requirements.

4.7.1 Problem Formulation

In this section we present a case study of a highly versatile machine center capable of processing a wide variety of part types and analyze its performance using queuing models. We consider specifically the following problem.

There are parts of N different types waiting in different queues for processing by a machine center. Workpieces of part type i arrive at the machine center following a Poisson process with rate λ_i. The machine has to be set up for processing each part type. The machine setup time required for processing ith part type is an independent random variable which is generally distributed. Let r_i and $\delta_i^{(2)}$ denote the mean and variance of the setup time. Once set up, the machine can process subsequent workpieces without incurring additional setup time. The machine processing time for the ith type is an independent random variable denoted by B_i following a general distribution. Let b_i and $b_i^{(2)}$ denote the mean and second moment of the processing time for part type i.

To complete the description of the model, we need to specify the *scheduling policy* (how the machine chooses the next part type) and the *service policy* (how much service is carried out on each part type).

Scheduling Policy: There are two common scheduling policies for which results are available in the literature.

1. Cyclic Scheduling: Here part types are labeled $1, 2, ..., N$, and a separate queue is maintained for each part type. Processing of part types is taken up in cyclic order $1, 2, ..., N, 1, 2, ...$ The processing of each part type is preceded by a corresponding setup operation. This type of scheduling is also called *cyclic service or polling*.

2. Probabilistic Scheduling: Here, also, there are separate queues for part types. Whenever the machine finishes processing the required number of a part type, it chooses part type i next with probability $p_i, 0 < p_i < 1, i = 1, 2, ..., N$ and these probabilities add up to 1. Each service is preceded by an appropriate setup.

Service Policy: Once the machine selects the part type for processing next, it has to follow a rule to decide how many parts of that type it will process before switching over to another part type. The service policies considered include:

1. Exhaustive: Once the machine center is set up for a particular part type, say type i, machining is done on all type i workpieces waiting in the queue at the beginning of the service period and those which arrive during the service period.

2. Gated: Here the machine center selects the part type i following the scheduling policy and services all those workpieces found in the queue at the beginning of the service period. However, none of the workpieces that arrived during the service period will be served during the current service.

3. Limited: The machine center would perform service on a fixed number of workpieces and then switch over to another part type.

Here we discuss the cyclic scheduling policy with exhaustive and gated service policies.

4.7.2 Performance Measures

Here we present expressions for two performance measures: (i) Delay in the queue, and (ii) Cycle time. The *Delay Time* is the time that elapsed between the arrival of the workpiece into the system and the time instant the machine starts servicing the workpiece. In order to find MLT, the time the workpiece spends in the system, we simply have to add the workpiece processing time to the delay time. *Cycle Time* is the time required to visit all the queues and process all the workpieces following the stipulated service policy. Let r_i be the setup time for the ith part type and T_i the time required to process all parts in the ith queue. Consider cyclic scheduling. Then the cycle time, T_c, is given by

$$T_c = \sum_{i=1}^{N} r_i + \sum_{i=1}^{N} T_i \tag{103}$$

Notice that $T_1, T_2, ..., T_N$ are random variables and are not independent. By linearity of the expectation operator, we have

$$E[T_c] = \sum_{i=1}^{N} E[r_i] + \sum_{i=1}^{N} E[T_i] \tag{104}$$

If we follow the exhaustive service policy, T_i is the time required to process all the workpieces of type i that arrived during the cycle time. Assuming infinite buffer capacity and Poisson arrivals, we have

$$E[T_i] = \lambda_i E[T_c] b_i$$
$$= \rho_i E[T_c] \tag{105}$$

where b_i is the average processing time and $\rho_i = \lambda_i b_i$ is the utilization factor for the ith queue. From (104) and (105), we have

$$E[T_c] = \frac{\sum\limits_{i=1}^{N} E[r_i]}{1 - \sum\limits_{i=1}^{N} \rho_i} \tag{106}$$

The numerator in the above equation is the sum of all setup times. Note that the machine does not process any parts during setup.

We also define another random variable called the inter-visit time denoted by I_i for part type i. I_i is the time duration elapsing between the instant the machine leaves queue i and the instant the machine starts setup for part type i in the next cycle. It is easy to see that

$$I_i = T_c - T_i$$

and

$$E[I_i] = (1 - \rho_i) E[T_c]$$

4.7.3 Analysis for Exhaustive Service and Gated Service

Now we consider two cases, Exhaustive Service and Gated Service, and discuss their analysis.

Exhaustive Service

The system may be solved for the mean waiting times as follows: recall that b_i and $b_i^{(2)}$ denote the mean and second moment of the processing time B_i for part i. Let $\rho_i = \lambda_i b_i$ be the utilization of the machine by part type i, and let $\rho = \sum_{i=1}^{N} \rho_i$ be the total utilization of the machine (the utilization values exclude the time spent on setups). The mean of the total time spent on setup in each cycle is $R = \sum_{i=1}^{N} r_i$, and the variance of this time is $\Delta^2 = \sum_{i=1}^{N} \delta_i^{(2)}$. The system is assumed stable, i.e., the queue lengths for each part type do not build up to infinity, if $\rho < 1$.

The waiting time in queue of a type i workpiece is given by

$$W_i = \frac{E\left[I_i^2\right]}{2E[I_i]} + \frac{\lambda_i b_i^{(2)}}{2(1 - \rho_i)} \tag{107}$$

where I_i is the inter-visit time for the queue corresponding to part type i. The mean $E[I_i]$ and the variance $Var[I_i]$ of the inter-visit time are given by

$$E[I_i] = \frac{(1 - \rho_i) R}{2(1 - \rho)}$$

and

$$Var\,[I_i] = \delta_i^{(2)} + \frac{1 - \rho_i}{\rho_i} \sum_{j=1, j \neq i}^{N} r_{ij}$$

where $\{r_{ij}\}$, $1 \leq i, j \leq N$, are the covariances for the station times of the queues for part types i and j. The station time for queue i is defined as the time interval between successive instants the machine starts setup for part types i and $i + 1$. The values of the covariances r_{ij} are obtained by solving the set of the following $O\left(N^2\right)$ linear equations

$$r_{ij} = \frac{\rho_i}{1 - \rho_i} \left(\sum_{m=i+1}^{N} r_{jm} + \sum_{m=1}^{j-1} r_{jm} + \sum_{m=j}^{i-1} r_{mj} \right), \quad \text{for } j < i;$$

$$r_{ij} = \frac{\rho_i}{1 - \rho_i} \left(\sum_{m=i+1}^{j-1} r_{jm} + \sum_{m=j}^{N} r_{mj} + \sum_{m=1}^{i-1} r_{mj} \right), \quad \text{for } j > i;$$

and

$$r_{ii} = \frac{\delta_i^{(2)}}{(1 - \rho_i)^2} + \frac{\lambda_i b_i^{(2)} E\,[I_i]}{(1 - \rho_i)^3} + \frac{\rho_i}{1 - \rho_i} \sum_{j=1, j \neq i}^{N} r_{ij}$$

Gated Service

We follow the same notation as in the exhaustive service case. The mean waiting times in queue are obtained by solving a set of $O\left(N^2\right)$ linear equations. The mean waiting time for a workpiece of part type i is given by

$$W_i = (1 + \rho_i) \frac{E\left[C_i^2\right]}{2E\,[C]} \tag{108}$$

where C_i is the random variable denoting the cycle time for part type i, defined as the time interval between successive instants of setup initiation for part type i. The expected value of the cycle time is independent of the part type and is given by

$$E\,[C] = E\,[C_i] = \frac{R}{1 - \rho} \tag{109}$$

To obtain $E\left[C_i^2\right] = \left(E\left[C_i\right]\right)^2 + Var\left[C_i\right]$, we solve for $Var\left[C_i\right]$ from:

$$Var\left[C_i\right] = \frac{1}{\rho_i} \sum_{j=1, j\neq i}^{N} r_{ij} + \sum_{j=1}^{N} r_{ji}$$

The values $\{r_{ij}; 1 \leq i, j \leq N\}$ are again the set of covariances of station times. Here the station time for part type i is defined as the time interval between the successive instants the setups for part types i and $i+1$ are completed. The values of r_{ij} are obtained by solving the following set of linear equations

$$r_{ij} = \rho_i \left(\sum_{m=i}^{N} r_{jm} + \sum_{m=1}^{j-1} r_{jm} + \sum_{m=j}^{i-1} r_{mj} \right), \quad \text{for } j < i;$$

$$r_{ij} = \rho_i \left(\sum_{m=i}^{j-1} r_{jm} + \sum_{m=j}^{N} r_{mj} + \sum_{m=1}^{i-1} r_{mj} \right), \quad \text{for } j > i;$$

and

$$r_{ii} = \delta_{i+1}^{(2)} + \lambda_i b_i^{(2)} E\left[C\right] + \rho_i \sum_{j=1, j\neq i}^{N} r_{ij} + \rho_i^2 \sum_{j=1}^{N} r_{ji}$$

Example 4.25

Consider a machine center processing three part types. Mean arrival times for part types 1, 2, and 3 are given by 10, 16, and 20 min, respectively. The mean setup times are 15, 10, and 8 min, respectively, for part types 1, 2, and 3. Similarly, mean processing times are given by 3, 2, and 5 min. Arrival and setup times are exponentially distributed. Service time is 3-stage Erlang. Then the mean waiting times in minutes for part types are given in the table below.

Part type	Exhaustive service	Gated service
1	45.39	76.76
2	56.91	67.06
3	49.21	74.79

PROBLEMS

1. A machine center processes workpieces from N pallet stations where fixtured workpieces belonging to N families wait for processing. Each pallet buffer station can hold only one batch containing α workpieces. Fixed batch sizes of α, of different classes, arrive at a Poisson rate, λ, i.e., we assume that the batch arrival rate is the same for all families of workpieces. Since station buffers can hold only one batch, any batch arriving at the pallet station when the buffer is full is not admitted. In other words, the arrival time to an empty buffer is exponentially distributed and there are no arrivals to full buffers. Assuming processing and setup requirements are identical for all workpieces, find the mean cycle time and the mean waiting time.
   [Hint: see Takagi (1988), pp. 7–9.]

2. Consider the NC machine center considered in Section 4.7.1. Suppose workpieces arrive in batches of fixed size b at a Poisson rate of λ_i. Derive the expressions for cycle time and waiting time as a function of b.

3. Consider the following optimization problem: N different workpieces are processed by a machine center and they wait following fixturing in separate pallet pools. The number of fixtures available for each part type is limited and equals β. After processing, the workpiece is defixtured and fixture is used for a fresh workpiece. In other words, fixtured parts of type i; $i = 1, 2, ..., N$ arrive at Poisson rate of λ until number in the pallet pool is β and zero for full buffers. Find β, the number of fixtures of each type, such that the waiting time W_i is less than W_d. Also find β such that the total cost = setup cost + waiting cost + fixture cost is a minimum.

4. Consider the machine center in Section 4.7.1 with the difference that jobs are selected probabilistically rather than cyclically. Calculate the mean cycle time and the mean waiting time.
   [Hint: see Kleinrock and Levy (1988)].

5. Consider a two-part-type machine center problem when all random variables representing the setup, processing, and arrival times are exponentially distributed. Let $\lambda_1 = 3$; $\lambda_2 = 2$; $b_1 = 1/6$; $b_2 = 1.5$; $r_1 = 1/2$; $r_2 = 1/3$. Find the performance measures of the system under cyclic processing. Compare this result with the situation when both the part types share the same queue and jobs are processed in FCFS manner.

4.8 QUEUING NETWORKS

In modeling manufacturing systems, queuing networks (QNs) provide a much greater degree of detail and fidelity than models containing only one service center. In an AMS, we have seen that workpieces belonging to various classes are transported from the load station to various machine centers and finally to the unload station for defixturing and unloading. A job joins a queue if the machine center or transporter is busy and is served when its turn comes by. After completion of service at a service center the job either moves to another service center for further service or leaves the system. The contention for resources and the service requirements can be faithfully represented by queuing networks.

We shall consider two types of queuing networks: *open* and *closed*. An *open queuing network* is characterized by one or more sources of job arrivals and correspondingly one or more sinks that absorb jobs departing from the network. In a *closed queuing network*, on the other hand, jobs neither enter nor depart from the network, and the number of customers circulating among the service centers is fixed. A QN may contain *several classes* of customers. Customers of a particular class have identical service requirements. In the manufacturing context, customer classes correspond to part types. A QN is said to be a *mixed* QN if some customer classes are closed (i.e., fixed number of customers of these classes circulate in the network) and other classes are open. The individual queues in a QN may have finite or infinite waiting space.

4.8.1 Examples of QN Models in Manufacturing

We now present typical situations in manufacturing systems that can be modeled by queuing networks.

Example 4.26

    Consider a transfer line comprising m machine centers (Figure 4.13). Suppose a single part type is manufactured on this transfer line. Raw parts enter the queue at M_1 and go through m operations at the m machine centers in a sequence. The finished parts leave after an operation by M_m. There is a buffer (finite or infinite) in front of each machine. Such an open queuing network is called a tandem network. The tandem network with infinite buffers is discussed in Section 4.9 while the network with finite buffers is considered in Section 4.12. Performance measures of interest here would

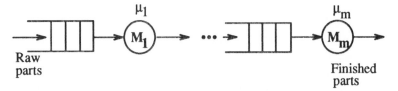

Figure 4.13 A tandem network of machines

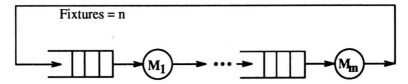

Figure 4.14 A closed tandem network of machines

be: MLT, throughput, in-process inventory, and machine utilizations.

Example 4.27

The tandem network with a limited number of fixtures can be modeled as the closed network in Figure 4.14. Here, if n is the number of fixtures, then the system has always n jobs circulating inside the system. The assumptions to be made are: raw parts are always available and released fixtures are instantaneously used up for waiting raw parts. In this model, it is enough for each buffer to be of capacity $n - 1$ in order to eliminate the possibility of blocking. If even one buffer has capacity less than $n - 1$, blocking will occur. Closed QNs are covered in Section 4.10.

Example 4.28

Figure 4.15 depicts a highly aggregated closed QN model of an AMS. The system here has a set of m identical machine centers (see Figure 2.11) and a set of r identical AGVs. Each part visits any of the m machines and then is unloaded by any AGV. The machine subsystem can be modeled as an $M/M/m$ queue whereas the AGV subsystem is like an $M/M/r$ queue. In this model, contention for machines and also AGVs has been captured.

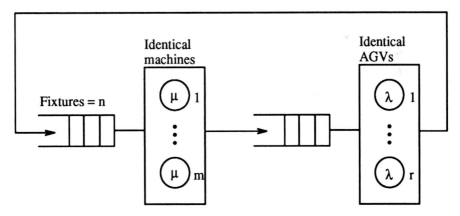

Figure 4.15 An aggregated closed QN model of an AMS

One can compute MLT, throughput, etc., using the results of Section 4.10. This model is also a birth and death process (Section 3.6).

Example 4.29

Figures 3.9 and 3.40 depict the familiar central server models of an FMS. The former is an open network while the latter is a closed network. Details of these models have been covered at several places earlier in the book.

Example 4.30

A generalization of the closed central server network is shown in Figure 4.16. In this model, there are r AGV nodes and m machine nodes. The numbers $q_1, q_2, ..., q_m$ represent the routing probabilities for the machines and $p_1, p_2, ..., p_r$ represent the routing probabilities for the AGVs. Each machine node corresponds to a machine center with one or more identical machines. The buffers may be finite or infinite. Note that to eliminate blocking, it is adequate if each buffer is of capacity at least $n - 1$ where n is the population of the network. The routing probabilities may be static or dynamic. For example, if we want to assign a part to the shortest queue, then these probabilities become dynamic.

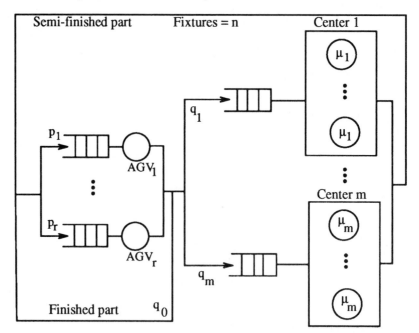

Figure 4.16 A generalized central server model of an AMS

Example 4.31

Consider an AMS processing two part types. The system has an AGV that loads a part onto a machine. Each part type requires exactly one operation. There are three machines, M_1, M_2, and M_3. Type 1 parts can be handled by M_1 or M_2 while type 2 parts require M_2 or M_3. We assume limited number of fixtures for each type, say, n_1 and n_2 respectively. After undergoing the designated operation, the parts are automatically unloaded from the system (AGV not required) and the released fixtures are recirculated. The resulting model, shown in Figure 4.17, is a closed QN model, with two part types. The routing tables are given by

$$
\text{Type 1:} \begin{bmatrix} 0 & q_{11} & q_{21} & 0 \\ 1 & 0 & 0 & 0 \\ 1 & 0 & 0 & 0 \\ 0 & 0 & 0 & 0 \end{bmatrix} ; \text{Type 2:} \begin{bmatrix} 0 & 0 & q_{12} & q_{22} \\ 0 & 0 & 0 & 0 \\ 1 & 0 & 0 & 0 \\ 1 & 0 & 0 & 0 \end{bmatrix}
$$

If we look at M_2, the buffer at M_2 can contain parts of both types. It may choose to process them in FIFO order, or according to some priorities, or any other policy. To solve this model, i.e., to derive performance measures such as MLT and throughput, one has to specify these decision policies.

Example 4.32

Figure 4.18 shows a queuing network of four machines and three part types. Part type p₁ follows the route M₁ → M₂ → M₃; part type p₂ follows the route M₄ → M₁ → M₃; and part type p₃ follows the route M₄ → M₂. In this diagram, queues are not explicitly represented and only the routes are shown. Note that at each machine, there could be contention between two part types.

Example 4.33

Suppose an assembly facility works as follows. There is a fixturing station F and an assembly station A. There are m machines $M_1, ..., M_m$, which produce m components which are assembled by A into a single finished product. Assume that loading, unloading, and transporting are immediate. Typically, raw parts arrive into the queue of F and wait for F. After fixturing by F, a typical part is routed to one of the m machines. When a processed component is available at all the machines, all the m components are put onto a special fixture and wait in front of A for assembly. A QN model of this system is shown in Figure 4.19.

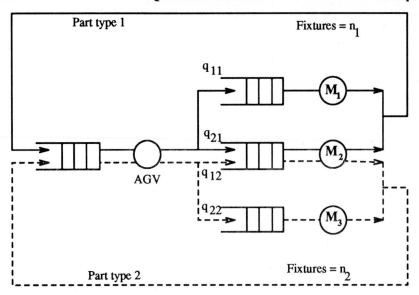

Figure 4.17 A simple QN model of an AMS with two part types

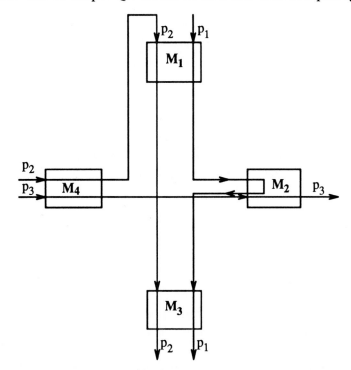

Figure 4.18 A network of 4 machines with 3 part types

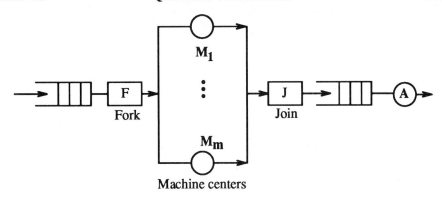

Figure 4.19 An assembly network

4.8.2 Little's Law in Queuing Networks

Consider a manufacturing system consisting of m machine centers, $M_1, M_2, ..., M_m$. Workpieces from an external source arrive at the system, move from machine center to machine center following a routing table and eventually depart from the system. Let λ be the average arrival rate of raw parts at the system, L the average number of workpieces present in the system (work-in-process), and W the average manufacturing lead time. Applying Little's law to this situation we have

$$L = \lambda W \tag{110}$$

This equation shows the relationship between MLT and WIP (work-in-process) at the manufacturing system level. At the machine center M_i, let λ_i denote the arrival rate, L_i the average WIP, and W_i the average MLT (average time spent on each visit to M_i). Applying Little's law to each machine center, we have

$$L_i = \lambda_i W_i \quad i = 1, 2, ..., m \tag{111}$$

Assume that the WIP at the system level is the sum of the WIPs at the individual machine centers. Then, we have

$$L = L_1 + ... + L_m \tag{112}$$

The above assumption is reasonable in most manufacturing situations. However, in assembly networks where two or more parts may join into a single product, the above may not hold. From equations (110–112), we have the system level MLT given by

$$W = \frac{\sum\limits_{i=1}^{m} \lambda_i W_i}{\sum\limits_{i=1}^{m} \lambda_i}$$

i.e., the manufacturing lead time at the system level is expressible directly in terms of the MLTs at the individual machine centers.

A workpiece may visit a machine center more than once. Let T_i be the total time spent by the workpiece at the ith machine center, in all its visits. Then Little's law gives

$$L_i = \lambda T_i \qquad i = 1, 2, ..., m \tag{113}$$

From (110) and (113), we get

$$\frac{T_i}{W} = \frac{L_i}{L} \tag{114}$$

The above equation implies that the fraction of MLT at any machine center is equal to the fraction of WIP at the same center.

It is thus clear that MLT and WIP are directly related. Attempts to minimize WIP will almost certainly bring down the MLT.

In the above discussion, note that we did not make any assumptions about the distributions of the inter-arrival times, service times, etc. We now present three examples which use the above discussion and further highlight the usefulness of Little's law.

Example 4.34

Consider the manufacturing system just discussed, except that the system operates in a closed loop mode, i.e., a new part enters the system only when a finished part departs and the total number of workpieces in the system is constant (say N). Thus the total number of customers in the system is always equal to N, implying that the system-level WIP is always equal to N. The MLT, W, is the time spent by the workpiece in the system. Let λ be the rate of arrival of raw parts into the system (which in this case is the rate at which finished parts are produced). Then Little's formula yields $N = \lambda W$. Usually, λ is obtained from a detailed analysis of the system and W is obtained from this formula. The equations (111) – (114) hold in this case also, with L replaced by N.

As a special case, consider a synchronous transfer line with N stages and a perennial supply of raw parts. Each stage has a constant delay of τ. At intervals of every τ, a fresh part enters the first stage, a semi-finished part will move from each stage to the next stage except from the final stage, and a finished part gets unloaded from the final Nth stage. It is easy to see that $\lambda = 1/\tau$ and that each workpiece stays in the system for exactly N stage delays. Therefore, $W = N/\tau$. The same may be obtained from Little's law also, since N is the total number in the system.

Example 4.35

Suppose a flexible manufacturing system is currently producing a part-mix consisting of three types of parts. Let λ_i, L_i, and W_i denote the arrival rate, WIP, and MLT for the ith type of parts. Then

$$L_i = \lambda_i W_i, \quad i = 1, 2, 3$$

Also, Little's formula holds for the entire system without regard to part types so that $L = \lambda W$, where

$$L = L_1 + L_2 + L_3$$
$$\lambda = \lambda_1 + \lambda_2 + \lambda_3$$

We have from the above equations

$$W = \frac{\sum_{i=1}^{3} \lambda_i W_i}{\sum_{i=1}^{3} \lambda_i}$$

The average system MLT for all types of customers is the linear combination of average MLTs for each type of customer. A similar result holds for each individual machine center.

Example 4.36

Similar results as in Example 4.35 hold for the closed FMS model. Suppose the number of customers in the system is fixed at N. Let n_i be the total number of ith type customers, so that $\sum_{i=1}^{3} n_i = N$. We have by Little's result

$$n_i = \lambda_i W_i \quad i = 1, 2, 3$$
$$N = \lambda W; \quad \text{Hence,}$$

$$W = \frac{\sum_{i=1}^{3} \lambda_i W_i}{\sum_{i=1}^{3} \lambda_i} = \frac{N}{\sum_{i=1}^{3} \lambda_i}$$

PROBLEMS

1. In a particular FMS, there are five machines M_1, M_2, M_3, M_4, and M_5. The FMS produces parts of a single type. Each part undergoes two operations, in any arbitrary order (operation flexibility). One operation may be on M_1 or M_2 and the other operation may be on M_3 or M_4 or M_5 (routing flexibility). Assuming a limited number of fixtures, formulate a closed QN model for the above system, assuming that all other operations (loading, fixturing, defixturing, unloading, etc.) are instantaneous.

2. An FMS with four machines and an AGV produces two types of products. Product 1 undergoes two operations, the first on M_1 or M_2, and the second on M_2 or M_3. Product 2 undergoes three operations, the first on M_1 or M_2 or M_3, the second on M_4, and the third on M_1 or M_3. Formulate a closed central server model with two part types for the above system. You are required to give the routing probabilities for the two part types. Assume that for any operation, a designated machine is chosen from the list of alternative machines, with equal probability.

4.9 OPEN QUEUING NETWORKS

In this section we present the theory and application of open queuing network models in manufacturing. Our treatment mainly focuses on the so-called *Jackson queuing networks*, which are open queuing networks that admit product form solutions.

4.9.1 The Tandem Queue

A simple special case of a queuing network is the tandem queue in which service facilities are arranged in strict serial order (Figure 4.13). Assembly lines in factories and sequence of traffic intersections are some common examples.

Consider a simple model of a tandem queue with two servers. Customers arrive according to a Poisson process with rate λ and get service from the first and second servers in that order with independent exponential service times having rates μ_1 and μ_2, respectively. Queues are allowed to build up in front of both servers.

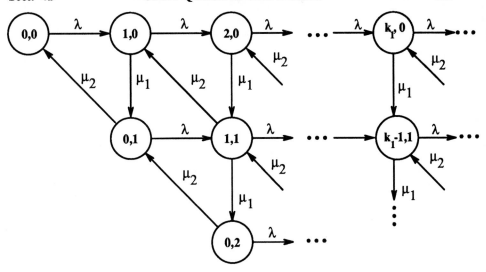

Figure 4.20 State diagram for a two-stage tandem network

Let $N_1(t)$ and $N_2(t)$ be the number of customers at the first and second nodes, respectively, at time t. As a consequence of the Poisson arrivals and exponential service times, the stochastic process $\{X(t) = (N_1(t), N_2(t)) : t \geq 0\}$ is a CTMC with state space $\{(k_1, k_2) : k_1, k_2 = 0, 1, ...\}$.

Let N_1 and N_2 denote the steady-state averages for the queue length values and let

$$\pi(k_1, k_2) = P\{N_1 = k_1; N_2 = k_2\} \tag{115}$$

Then $\pi(k_1, k_2)$ is the joint probability of finding k_1 jobs at server 1 and k_2 jobs at server 2 in the steady-state. The state changes occur upon a completion of service at one of the servers or upon an external arrival. Figure 4.20 shows the state diagram of the CTMC. For the sake of clarity, we show, in Figure 4.21, the in-flow and out-flow for node (k_1, k_2). From Figure 4.21 we obtain the following global balance equations

$$(\lambda + \mu_1 + \mu_2)\pi(k_1, k_2) = \mu_1 \pi(k_1 + 1, k_2 - 1)$$
$$+ \mu_2 \pi(k_1, k_2 + 1) + \lambda \pi(k_1 - 1, k_2); \quad k_1 > 0, \quad k_2 > 0 \tag{116}$$

For the states $(0, 0), (k_1, 0)$, and $(0, k_2)$, where $k_1 > 0$ and $k_2 > 0$,

$$\lambda \pi(0, 0) = \mu_2 \pi(0, 1)$$
$$(\mu_1 + \lambda)\pi(k_1, 0) = \mu_2 \pi(k_1, 1) + \lambda \pi(k_1 - 1, 0)$$
$$(\mu_2 + \lambda)\pi(0, k_2) = \mu_1 \pi(1, k_2 - 1) + \mu_2 \pi(0, k_2 + 1) \tag{117}$$

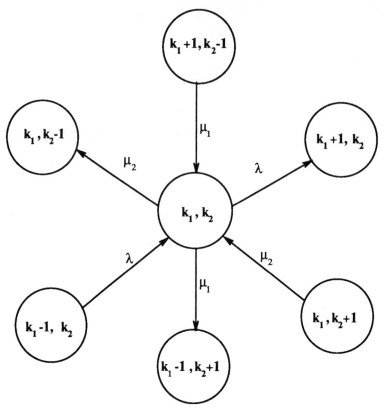

Figure 4.21 In-flow and out-flow for a typical node

The normalization is provided by

$$\sum_{k_1 \geq 0} \sum_{k_2 \geq 0} \pi\left(k_1, k_2\right) = 1 \tag{118}$$

Define $\rho_1 = \lambda/\mu_1$ and $\rho_2 = \lambda/\mu_2$, then the condition for stability is that both ρ_1 and ρ_2 should be less than unity. It can easily be shown by direct substitution that

$$\pi\left(k_1, k_2\right) = \left(1 - \rho_1\right) \rho_1^{k_1} \left(1 - \rho_2\right) \rho_2^{k_2} \tag{119}$$

$$\pi\left(0, 0\right) = \left(1 - \rho_1\right)\left(1 - \rho_2\right) \tag{120}$$

Equation (119) is a *product form* solution. Observe that node 1 has a Poisson arrival source of rate λ and exponentially distributed service time. Thus node 1 is an $M/M/1$ queue. It follows that

$$P\left\{N_1 = k_1\right\} = \pi_1\left(k_1\right) = \left(1 - \rho_1\right) \rho_1^{k_1}$$

We have shown earlier in Section 4.3 that the departure process of a stable $M/M/1$ queue is a Poisson process with the same rate as the arrival rate. Thus node 2 is also an $M/M/1$ queue with server utilization ρ_2. Hence, the steady-state number of jobs at node 2 is given by

$$P\{N_2 = k_2\} = \pi_2(k_2) = (1 - \rho_2)\rho_2^{k_2}$$

Thus the joint probability $\pi(k_1, k_2)$ is the product of the marginal probabilities $\pi_1(k_1)$ and $\pi_2(k_2)$; hence, the steady-state random variables N_1 and N_2 are independent of each other.

The measures of performance for this system can be easily computed as under:

$$\text{Utilization of } M_1 = \rho_1 = \lambda/\mu_1$$
$$\text{Utilization of } M_2 = \rho_2 = \lambda/\mu_2$$
$$\text{Throughput Rate } = \lambda$$

$$\text{Mean number in the system } = \frac{\rho_1}{1 - \rho_1} + \frac{\rho_2}{1 - \rho_2}$$

$$\text{MLT} = \frac{1}{\lambda}\left[\frac{\rho_1}{1 - \rho_1} + \frac{\rho_2}{1 - \rho_2}\right]$$

The product form solution of (119) and the computation of performance measures can be generalized in a straightforward way to the case of an m-stage tandem queue, $m \geq 3$.

It may be noted that the product form nature of the solutions disappears under practical situations such as finite buffers and machine breakdowns. One may have to resort to direct Markov chain analysis in such instances.

Example 4.37

A transfer line has two machines M_1 and M_2 with unlimited buffer space in between. Parts arrive at the transfer line at a rate of 1 part every 2 min. The processing rates of M_1 and M_2 are 1 per min and 2 per min, respectively.

Given $\lambda = 0.5$; $\mu_1 = 1$; $\mu_2 = 2$, we have $\rho_1 = 0.5$ and $\rho_2 = 0.25$. The average number of parts at station i (those in the queue and in service) is given by

$$L_1 = \frac{\rho_1}{1 - \rho_1} = 1$$
$$L_2 = \frac{\rho_2}{1 - \rho_2} = \frac{1}{3}$$

Using Little's formula the queuing delay at stations 1 and 2 is given by

$$W_1 = \frac{L_1}{\lambda} = 2 \text{ min}$$

$$W_2 = \frac{L_2}{\lambda} = \frac{2}{3} \text{ min}$$

Therefore, MLT $= W = W_1 + W_2 = \frac{8}{3}$ min. Observe that $W = (L_1 + L_2)\lambda$.

4.9.2 An Open Queuing Network with Feedback

Consider the model of a simple manufacturing system shown in Figure 4.22. Jobs arrive at the machine center in Poisson fashion at a rate of λ. After getting processed at the machine center, they go in for inspection. A job passes the inspection with probability p_a and goes for rework to the machine with probability p_r. Thus, $p_a + p_r = 1$. Arrivals at the machine center occur either from the outside world at the rate λ or from the rejects of the inspection station at a rate of λ_r. The total arrival rate to the machine center is

$$\lambda_m = \lambda + \lambda_r$$

In the steady-state, the arrival rate at the inspection station is the same as the departure rate at the machine center, which is λ_m. The rate of departures from the inspection station is λ_m and the rate of arrival of rejected parts is given by

$$\lambda_r = \lambda_m p_r$$

Thus, we have

$$\lambda_m = \frac{\lambda}{(1 - p_r)} = \frac{\lambda}{p_a}$$

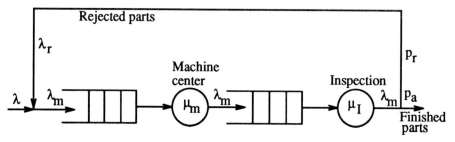

Figure 4.22 An open queuing network with feedback

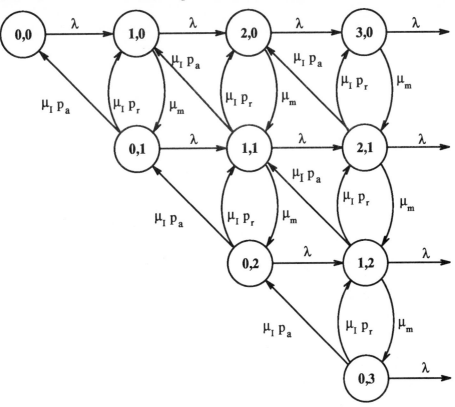

Figure 4.23 Markov chain for the system shown in Figure 4.22

It is important to note that the arrival processes at the machine center and at the inspection station are not Poisson. In the above system, only external arrivals are Poisson. This implies that the relative utilizations are given by

$$\rho_m = \frac{\lambda_m}{\mu_m} = \frac{\lambda}{p_a \mu_m}$$

and

$$\rho_I = \frac{\lambda_m}{\mu_I} = \frac{\lambda}{p_a \mu_I}$$

where μ_m and μ_I are the processing rates at the machine center and inspection station, respectively.

We analyze the Markov chain whose states are given by pairs (k_1, k_2), $k_1 \geq 0$, $k_2 \geq 0$, where k_1 and k_2 are the numbers of jobs at machine center and inspection station, respectively. Figure 4.23 shows

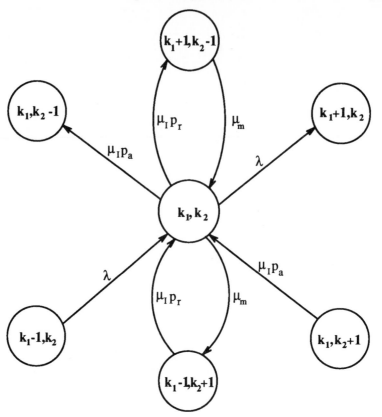

Figure 4.24 In-flow and out-flow for a typical node

the Markov chain model and Figure 4.24 depicts the in-flow and out-flow for a typical state. For the state (k_1, k_2), $k_1, k_2 > 0$, the steady-state balance equation is obtained by equating the rate of flow into the state with the rate of flow out of the state:

$$(\lambda + \mu_I + \mu_m) \, \pi \, (k_1, k_2) = \lambda \pi \, (k_1 - 1, k_2) + \mu_m \pi \, (k_1 + 1, k_2 - 1)$$
$$+ \mu_I p_a \pi \, (k_1, k_2 + 1) + \mu_I p_r \pi \, (k_1 - 1, k_2 + 1)$$
$$\lambda \pi \, (0, 0) = \mu_I p_a \pi \, (0, 1)$$
$$(\lambda + \mu_m) \, \pi \, (k_1, 0) = \lambda \pi \, (k_1 - 1, 0) + \mu_I p_a \pi \, (k_1, 1)$$
$$+ \mu_I p_r \pi \, (k_1 - 1, 1), \quad k_1 > 0$$
$$(\lambda + \mu_I) \, \pi \, (0, k_2) = \mu_m \pi \, (1, k_2 - 1) + \mu_I p_a \pi \, (0, k_2 + 1), \quad k_2 > 0$$

We can easily verify that the expression

$$\pi \, (k_1, k_2) = (1 - \rho_m) \, \rho_m^{k_1} \, (1 - \rho_I) \, \rho_I^{k_2} \tag{121}$$

satisfies the rate balance equations and the normalization condition when $\rho_m < 1$ and $\rho_I < 1$. Equation (121) again displays a product form structure and signifies that the machine center and the inspection station behave as if they are two independent $M/M/1$ queues with traffic intensities ρ_m and ρ_I, respectively.

We can easily compute the average numbers of jobs at the machine center and at the inspection station using the expressions

$$L_m = \frac{\rho_m}{1 - \rho_m}$$

$$L_I = \frac{\rho_I}{1 - \rho_I}$$

The work-in-process is given by $L = L_I + L_m$ and the manufacturing lead time is the ratio of L to λ.

4.9.3 An Open Central Server Model for FMS

Consider the familiar open central server model of an FMS shown in Figure 4.25. The configuration represents the parts flow through the system and may not represent the physical layout. The transport mechanism is central in the sense that every workpiece must pass through it before and after each operation. We have m machine centers, $M_1, M_2, ..., M_m$, and infinite buffer space is available at each machine center to store the workpieces to be processed. The transporter, either an AGV system or any other, is the station marked 0. Let q_i $(i = 1, 2, ..., m)$ be the probability

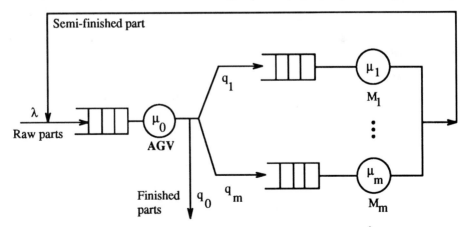

Figure 4.25 Open central server model of an FMS

that the transporter delivers the part to the ith machine center. Let the processing on the workpiece be completed and thus a finished part delivered with probability q_0. We have, thus, $\sum_{i=0}^{m} q_i = 1$.

The flow of a single tagged workpiece inside this network can be modeled as a DTMC with $m+2$ states, $\{0, 1, 2, ..., m + 1\}$. The state transition diagram of the DTMC is shown in Figure 4.26. State i $(i = 1, 2, ..., m)$ indicates that the workpiece is with node i and state $(m + 1)$ is an absorbing state that indicates a finished part.

Let Q be the leading $(m + 1) \times (m + 1)$ submatrix of P, where P is the transition probability matrix of the DTMC in Figure 4.26. That is,

$$Q = \begin{bmatrix} 0 & q_1 & \cdots & q_m \\ 1 & 0 & \cdots & 0 \\ \cdot & \cdot & \cdots & \cdot \\ \cdot & \cdot & \cdots & \cdot \\ \cdot & \cdot & \cdots & \cdot \\ 1 & 0 & \cdots & 0 \end{bmatrix}$$

Then Q is referred to as the routing matrix of the network. We are interested in computing the average number of visits or visit counts v_j that a job makes to station j. It can be shown that

$$v_j = \frac{1}{q_0} \quad j = 0$$

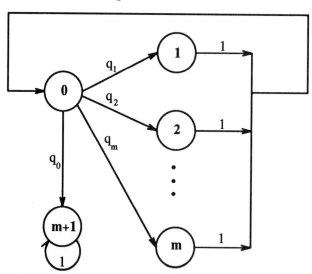

Figure 4.26 Markov model for the flow of a tagged workpiece

$$vj = \frac{q_j}{q_0} \qquad j = 1, 2, ..., m \tag{122}$$

In other words, the average number of times a typical workpiece visits the jth machine center ($j = 1, 2, ..., m$) is q_j/q_0. At each node we can compute the average number of arrivals as

$$\begin{aligned} \lambda_j &= \frac{\lambda}{q_0} & j = 0 \\ &= \frac{\lambda q_j}{q_0} & j = 1, 2, ..., m \end{aligned} \tag{123}$$

where λ is the Poisson arrival rate into the system. Note that the arrival processes into individual nodes are not Poisson. We define the utilization of station j and the AGV as

$$\rho_j = \frac{\lambda_j}{\mu_j} = \lambda \frac{v_j}{\mu_j}; \qquad j = 0, 1, ..., m \tag{124}$$

We assume that the stability condition $\rho_j < 1$ is satisfied at each node. Jackson showed that the joint probability of having k_j customers at the jth node, $j = 0, 1, ..., m$, is given by

$$\pi(k_0, k_1, ..., k_m) = \prod_{j=0}^{m} \pi_j(k_j) \tag{125}$$

where

$$\pi_j(k_j) = P\{N_j = k_j\} = (1 - \rho_j)\rho_j^{k_j} \tag{126}$$

with N_j being the steady-state number of customers at station j. The above result implies that:

1. the numbers of jobs present in the steady-state at various nodes are mutually independent random variables, and
2. node i behaves as if it is subjected to a Poisson arrival stream with rate λ_i. This is surprising because the arrival rate into node i is λ_i but the stream is not Poisson in general. Yet the distribution of the number of jobs present is the same as with a Poisson input stream.

The average queue length L_j and the waiting time W_j are given by

$$L_j = \frac{\rho_j}{1 - \rho_j} \text{ and } W_j = \frac{1}{\lambda_j} \left(\frac{\rho_j}{1 - \rho_j} \right)$$

From this, the average number of jobs in the system is given by

$$L = \sum_{j=0}^{m} \left(\frac{\rho_j}{1 - \rho_j} \right)$$

and the average MLT by

$$W = \frac{1}{\lambda} \sum_{j=0}^{m} \frac{\rho_j}{1 - \rho_j}$$

4.9.4 Jackson's Network

We have seen that typical open QN models of manufacturing display a product form structure. Jackson's result [1957, 1963] serves to generalize the class of open QN models with product form structure. A Jackson network is an open QN consisting of m machine centers or nodes, indexed $1, 2, ..., m$. Machine center i comprises c_i identical exponential servers with mean service time $1/\mu_i$. Jobs arrive into the network following a Poisson stream, with the arrival rate α_i jobs per unit time at center i; let the total arrival rate be λ. If we let $q_i = \alpha_i/\lambda$; $i = 1, 2, ..., m$, so that $\sum_{i=1}^{m} q_i = 1$, then an arriving job will enter the network at node i with probability q_i. Upon service completion at machine center i, the job is routed to machine center j with probability p_{ij} or completes processing with (exit) probability $\left(1 - \sum_{j=1}^{m} p_{ij} \right)$. The $(m \times m)$ matrix $P = [p_{ij}]$ is called the *routing matrix*.

Here the network parameters are the external arrival rates α_i, the average service times $1/\mu_i$, the number c_i of servers at different nodes, and the routing matrix P. At least one of the external arrival rates is non-zero and at least one of the exit probabilities p_{io} is non-zero. Therefore, it is an open QN. Moreover, the routing matrix is such that from every node there is a sequence of moves leading out of the network with a non-zero probability. This completes the description of a Jackson network.

We are interested in computing the average arrival rate of customers to a given machine center in the steady-state. Let λ_i denote the arrival rate of jobs at the ith machine center. Some of the incoming jobs are external arrivals and some come from other nodes including node i. Thus λ_i is the total average number of jobs arriving into (and leaving) node i per unit time. On the average, λ_j jobs leave node j per unit time; of these a fraction p_{ji} go to the node i. Therefore, the rate of traffic from node j to node i is $\lambda_j p_{ji}$; $j = 1, 2, ..., m$. It can thus be seen that

$$\lambda_i = \alpha_i + \sum_{j=1}^{m} \lambda_j p_{ji}; \quad i = 1, 2, ..., m \tag{126}$$

We shall call (126) as the *traffic equations* of the network. Since at least one of the exit probabilities is non-zero, the matrix power series $\left(\sum_{k=0}^{\infty} P^k \right)$ converges and therefore the matrix $(I - P)$ is invertible.

We can obtain the above equations in another way. Recall that $\lambda = \sum_{i=1}^{m} \alpha_i$ and $q_i = \alpha_i / \lambda$, $i = 1, 2, ..., m$. We can then say that a job enters the network at node i, with probability q_i. We can analyze a tagged job through the network as a DTMC. Let v_i denote the average number of visits the tagged job makes to the ith machine center, then we have

$$v_i = q_i + \sum_{k=1}^{m} p_{ki} v_k; \quad i = 1, 2, ..., m \tag{127}$$

Equation (126) can be recovered from (127) by multiplying it by λ and noting that $\lambda v_i = \lambda_i$ and $\lambda q_i = \alpha_i$. The relation $\lambda v_i = \lambda_i$ can be obtained by observing that on the average, a total of λ jobs enters the network from outside per unit time. Each of these jobs makes an average of v_i visits to the ith machine center. Therefore the total average number of arrivals into machine center i is λv_i which is by definition λ_i.

The system of equations (127) has a unique solution if we assume that there is at least one node j such that $\alpha_j > 0$ and that the matrix power series $\sum_{k=0}^{n} P^k$ converges as $n \to \infty$. This is true in a Jackson network.

Let us now return to the question of computing the steady-state probability distribution of a Jackson network. We have seen that when the steady-state exists, the machine center i is subjected to a total stream of jobs arriving at a rate λ_i determined by the traffic equations (126). The load at machine center i, i.e., the average amount of service demanded per unit time, is $\rho_i = \frac{\lambda_i}{c_i \mu_i}$. This load should be less than 1, for stability. Thus we assume $\rho_i < 1$. Let $\pi(k_1, k_2, ..., k_m)$ be the steady-state probability that there are k_1 jobs at center 1, k_2 jobs at center 2, and so on. Let $\pi_i(k_i)$ be the probability that there are k_i jobs in an isolated $M/M/c_i$ queuing system with traffic intensity ρ_i. Then Jackson's theorem states that

$$\pi(k_1, k_2, ..., k_m) = \prod_{i=1}^{m} \pi_i(k_i) \tag{128}$$

The proof of this result involves writing down the state balance equations of the Markov process and verifying that (128) indeed holds.

Jackson's theorem allows us to derive many network performance measures by a straightforward application of standard queuing theory results. To keep the exposition simple, we shall assume that all nodes contain a single server, i.e., $c_i = 1$; $i = 1, 2, ..., m$. Every node can now be treated as an independent $M/M/1$ queue. Suppose, $\rho_i < 1$ for all i, so that steady-state exists.

The average number of jobs at node i, L_i, is given by,

$$L_i = \frac{\rho_i}{1 - \rho_i}; \quad i = 1, 2, ..., m \tag{129}$$

The total number of jobs in the network, L, is the sum of these averages over all nodes:

$$L = \sum_{i=1}^{m} \frac{\rho_i}{1 - \rho_i} \tag{130}$$

Denote by W the average time that a job spends in the network, i.e., the average time interval between the arrival of a job from outside and its departure to the outside. Applying Little's result to the entire network, we get

$$L = \lambda W \tag{131}$$

where λ is the external arrival rate defined earlier. Thus we get

$$W = \frac{1}{\lambda} \sum_{i=1}^{m} \frac{\rho_i}{(1 - \rho_i)} \tag{132}$$

One may be interested in various other sojourn times in the network. Let W_i be the average time a job spends at node i on each visit to that node. An application of Little's result to node i gives $L_i = \lambda_i W_i$ or

$$W_i = \frac{1}{\mu_i(1-\rho_i)}; \quad i = 1, 2, ..., m \tag{133}$$

Now consider the average time, R_i, between the arrival of a job at node i and its subsequent departure from the network. Because of the memoryless routing, it does not matter whether the job arrived at node i from the outside or from another node. First, the job has to pass through node i, which takes W_i on the average. If it next goes to node j (with probability p_{ij}), its average remaining sojourn time will be R_j. Hence we can write a set of linear equations

$$R_i = W_i + \sum_{j=1}^{m} p_{ij} R_j \tag{134}$$

Equation (134) determines R_i uniquely for the same reasons that the traffic equations determine arrival rates uniquely.

Every time a job visits node i, it requires an amount of service equal to $1/\mu_i$, on the average. The total average service time, D_i, that a job requires from node i during its stay in the network is therefore equal to

$$D_i = \frac{v_i}{\mu_i} = \frac{\rho_i}{\lambda}; \quad i = 1, 2, ..., m \tag{135}$$

Thus ρ_i can be interpreted as the average amount of load destined to node i that enters the network from outside per unit time. Similarly, total average time, B_i, that a job spends at node i during its life in the network can also be obtained:

$$B_i = v_i W_i = \frac{v_i}{\mu_i(1-\rho_i)} = \frac{D_i}{(1-\rho_i)}; \quad i = 1, 2, ..., m \tag{136}$$

The results we have presented above can easily be rederived for networks with more than one server.

Example 4.38

Consider an FMS consisting of a loading station (L), unload station (U), three identical machine centers (MC), two vertical turret lathes (VTL), and

Table 4.1 Routing table for Example 4.38

From	To		
	MC	VTL	U
L	0.50	0.50	-
MC	-	0.40	0.60
VTL	0.70	-	0.30

a transport system made up of two AGVs. The routing matrix is given by Table 4.1.

The input rates for different stations are computed as follows.

$$\lambda_{MC} = 0.50\lambda_L + 0.70\lambda_{VTL}$$

$$\lambda_{VTL} = 0.50\lambda_L + 0.40\lambda_{MC}$$

$$\lambda_U = 0.60\lambda_{MC} + 0.30\lambda_{VTL}$$

$$\lambda_{AGV} = \lambda_L + \lambda_{MC} + \lambda_{VTL}$$

We note that load and unload stations are $M/M/1$ queues; machine center is $M/M/3$ queue and lathe center and AGV system form $M/M/2$ queues. Given that $\lambda_L = 15$; $\mu_L = 20$; $\mu_{MC} = 7$; $\mu_{VTL} = 10$; $\mu_{AGV} = 25$; we get the performance characteristics shown in Table 4.2:

PROBLEMS

1. Consider a two-station production system in which fresh parts arrive at station 1 at a Poisson rate of 10/h; production time at stage 1 is exponentially distributed with a mean of 4 min including inspection. If a unit is defective and can be reworked, it is placed at the end of the queue and is reprocessed at station 1. It is found that 20% of the items inspected are reworked, 10%

Table 4.2 Performance results for Example 4.38

Station	Mean queue length (parts)	Mean waiting time (h) in the queue
Load Station	2.25	0.15
Machine centers (3)	3.87	0.22
VTL (2)	1.65	0.23
Unload station	2.25	0.15
AGVs (2)	25.71	0.54

to station 2. Processing time at station 2 is exponentially distributed with a mean of 6 min. All items processed by station 2 leave the system. Determine L_1, W_1, and W_2. Also determine work-in-process and MLT.

2. A transfer line has six stations with unlimited amount of buffer in-between them. Parts arrive at the rate of 1 every hour. The mean processing times at the six stations are 30, 15, 20, 25, 54, and 30 min, respectively. The processing times are independent exponential random variables. Calculate the output rate, waiting times, queue lengths, and machine utilizations at each station. Also find the MLT of the system.

3. Consider a three-station transfer line with two inspection stations between stations 1 and 2 and stations 2 and 3. Jobs enter at station 1 at rate λ and are processed with rates μ_1, μ_2, and μ_3 at the stations. Parts are rejected at inspection stations 1 and 2 with probabilities $(1-\alpha_1)$ and $(1-\alpha_2)$, respectively. Find the performance measures.

4. Derive expressions for the performance measures of a Jackson network with multiple servers in each node.

5. Consider the model of a machine center shown in Figure 4.P.1. The queue is infinite; the service time is exponential with rate μ and the parts for reworking join the tail of the queue.

(a) Can the above be considered as an $M/M/1$ queue?

(b) Apply Jackson's theorem for the network and compute performance measures.

(c) Under stability conditions, what can you say about the departure process (of accepted parts)?

(d) Compute the distribution of waiting time of an accepted part.

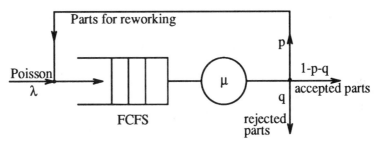

Figure 4.P.1

6. Figure 4.P.2 depicts a two-node Jackson network.

(a) For what values of p_1, q_1, p_2, and q_2, does the network cease to be a Jackson network?

(b) Set up the traffic equations and deduce the conditions for the stability of the above network.

(c) Assuming stability, compute the steady-state probability distribution for the network.

(d) Compute the

- mean time a job spends in node i, $(i = 1, 2)$ on each visit to node i
- mean time a job spends in the network before leaving the network
- mean time a job spends in the network, after finishing a service in node 1.

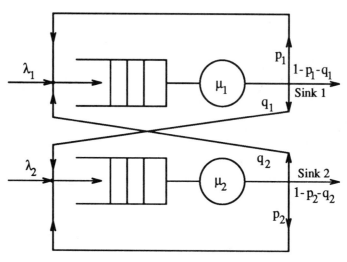

Figure 4.P.2

4.10 CLOSED QUEUING NETWORKS

Next we consider closed queuing networks (CQN) in which the total number n of jobs circulating in the system is constant. In the AMS context the fixed population n represents the pallet constraint. Suppose the AMS has n pallets so that n jobs are circulating within the system at any time. Whenever a job finishes all its processing operations and leaves the system, another job is immediately released into the system to occupy the available pallet. One important assumption is that raw parts are always available whenever a pallet is available and they are immediately released into the system. Thus a release of job into the system is triggered solely by another job's departure from the system and not based on the system state. To fix ideas, we go through the analysis of two typical CQN models encountered in the manufacturing context.

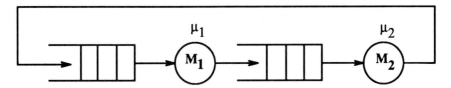

Figure 4.27 A closed queuing network with feedback

4.10.1 A Closed Transfer Line

Let us consider a transfer line with two machine centers M_1 and M_2 (Figure 4.27). We assume that only n fixtures are available and hence the total number of jobs allowed in the system is n. As before, the pair (k_1, k_2) represents the state of the system where k_1 is the number of jobs with M_1 and k_2 is the number of jobs with M_2. We note that k_1 and k_2 are constrained such that $k_1 + k_2 = n$. The jobs processed by the machine center M_1 queue up before M_2. From M_2, they go out of the system, after releasing the pallet, and a new job enters the system. We assume that the processing times at M_1 and M_2 are exponentially distributed with service rates μ_1 and μ_2, respectively. We assume that the two buffers have a capacity of at least $n - 1$ so that there is no blocking. The state diagram is shown in Figure 4.28.

The balance equations are given by

$$
\begin{aligned}
(\mu_1 + \mu_2)\, \pi\, (k, n - k) &= \mu_1 \pi\, (k + 1, n - k - 1) \\
&\quad + \mu_2 \pi\, (k - 1, n - k + 1); \quad k \neq 0, \quad k \neq n \\
\mu_2 \pi\, (0, n) &= \mu_1 \pi\, (1, n - 1) \\
\mu_1 \pi\, (n, 0) &= \mu_2 \pi\, (n - 1, 1)
\end{aligned}
\tag{137}
$$

Suppose we define $\rho_1 = a/\mu_1$ and $\rho_2 = a/\mu_2$ where a is an arbitrary constant, then it can be verified by direct substitution that $\pi\,(k_1, k_2)$ has the following product form solution:

$$
\pi\,(k_1, k_2) = \frac{1}{C\,(n)} \rho_1^{k_1} \rho_2^{k_2}
$$

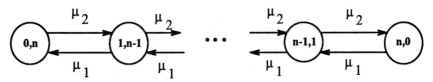

Figure 4.28 State diagram for the CQN of Figure 4.27

where $C(n)$, the normalizing constant is chosen such that

$$\sum_{k=0}^{n} \pi(k, n-k) = 1 \qquad (138)$$

The choice of the constant a is quite arbitrary. A choice of $a = \lambda_1$ will give the usual interpretation of utilization factors to ρ_1 and ρ_2, if λ_1 is the rate of arrival of jobs into M_1. Note that $\lambda_1 = \mu_2(1 - \pi(n, 0))$.

Example 4.39

Two popular choices for a are $a = 1$ and $a = \mu_1$. The latter choice would yield $\rho_1 = 1$ and $\rho_2 = \mu_1/\mu_2$. Then

$$\pi(k, n-k) = \frac{1}{C(n)} \rho_2^{n-k}; \qquad k = 0, 1, ..., n$$

Then we can compute $C(n)$ using the normalization condition, i.e.,

$$\frac{1}{C(n)} \sum_{k=0}^{n} \rho_2^{n-k} = \frac{1}{C(n)} \frac{\left(1 - \rho_2^{n+1}\right)}{(1 - \rho_2)} = 1$$

This yields

$$C(n) = \frac{\left(1 - \rho_2^{n+1}\right)}{(1 - \rho_2)} \qquad \mu_1 \neq \mu_2$$
$$= n + 1 \qquad \mu_1 = \mu_2$$

Assume that $\mu_1 \neq \mu_2$. Then the machine center utilizations are given by

$$U_1 = 1 - \pi(0, n) = 1 - \frac{\rho_2^n}{C(n)} = 1 - \frac{(1 - \rho_2)\rho_2^n}{\left(1 - \rho_2^{n+1}\right)} = \frac{(1 - \rho_2^n)}{\left(1 - \rho_2^{n+1}\right)}$$

$$U_2 = 1 - \pi(n, 0) = 1 - \frac{1}{C(n)} = \frac{\rho_2(1 - \rho_2^n)}{\left(1 - \rho_2^{n+1}\right)}$$

The throughput of the system is given by $U_2\mu_2$, which in this case should also be equal to $U_1\mu_1$. This can be easily verified.

4.10.2 The Closed Central Server Model

Consider the familiar closed central server network model shown for ready reference in Figure 4.29. We define the state of the network by an $(m+1)$–tuple, $(k_0, k_1, ..., k_m)$ where $k_i \geq 0$ is the number of jobs at

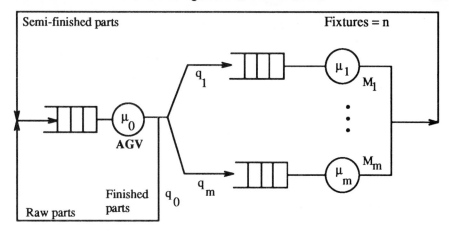

Figure 4.29 Closed central server model of an AMS

server i including those in service. We assume that the number of jobs in the system is fixed, i.e., $\sum_{i=0}^{m} k_i = n$. A fresh job enters the system only when a job leaves the system. As a consequence, the state space is finite, the number of states being equal to the number of partitions of n objects among $(m+1)$ cells, i.e., $\binom{n+m}{m} = \frac{(n+m)!}{n!m!}$. If the service times are independent and exponentially distributed, the behavior of the network corresponds to that of a finite CTMC, which is irreducible and positive recurrent provided $0 < q_i < 1$ for $i = 0, 1, 2, ..., m$. It is important to recall that the CTMC here is time reversible (Example 3.41) and the network satisfies the so-called local balance property.

To proceed, we first analyze the behavior of a tagged workpiece modeled as a DTMC with $m+1$ states. The transition probability matrix is given by

$$P = \begin{bmatrix} q_0 & q_1 & \cdots & q_m \\ 1 & 0 & \cdots & 0 \\ 1 & 0 & \cdots & 0 \\ \cdot & & & \\ \cdot & & & \\ \cdot & & & \\ 1 & 0 & \cdots & 0 \end{bmatrix}$$

We can obtain the steady-state visit count vector $V = (v_0, v_1, ..., v_m)$ by solving

$$V = VP \tag{139}$$

The variable v_i gives the visit count at node i. For the central server model, we have

$$v_0 = v_0 q_0 + \sum_{i=1}^{m} v_i \qquad (140)$$

$$v_i = q_i v_0; \qquad i = 1, 2, ..., m \qquad (141)$$

Only m out of these $(m + 1)$ equations are linearly independent; hence, we can choose v_0 arbitrarily and determine v_i using (141). The usual choices of v_0 are $1/q_0, \mu_0$, and 1.

If we choose $v_0 = 1/q_0$, then $v_i = q_i/q_0$, the average number of visits a workpiece makes to station i in order to complete the processing. If we choose $v_0 = \mu_0$, then $\rho_0 = 1$ and all machine center utilizations are scaled up by the AGV utilization.

Gordon and Newell [1967] have shown that the steady-state probabilities are given by

$$\pi(k_0, k_1, ... k_m) = \frac{1}{C(n)} \prod_{i=0}^{m} \rho_i^{k_i}$$

$$= \frac{1}{C(n)} \prod_{i=0}^{m} \left(\frac{v_i}{\mu_i}\right)^{k_i} \qquad (142)$$

Here the normalization constant $C(n)$ is evaluated using the normalizing condition that the sum of all the steady-state probabilities is unity.

Example 4.40

If we have just two nodes in the closed central server model, then (142) yields

$$\pi(k_0, k_1) = \frac{1}{C(n)} \rho_0^{k_0} \rho_1^{k_1}$$

where $k_0 + k_1 = n$; $\rho_0 = v_0/\mu_0$; $\rho_1 = v_1/\mu_1$ where $v_1 = q_1 v_0$. Choosing $v_0 = \mu_0$, we have $\rho_0 = 1$ and $\rho_1 = \mu_0 q_1/\mu_1$. This means that

$$\pi(k_0, k_1) = \frac{1}{C(n)} \rho_1^{k_1}$$

Using the normalization condition, it can be shown that

$$C(n) = \frac{1 - \rho_1^{n+1}}{1 - \rho_1} \qquad \rho_1 \neq 1$$

$$= n + 1 \qquad \rho_1 = 1$$

The utilization of the AGV can be computed as

$$U_{AGV} = 1 - \pi\left(0, n\right) = 1 - \frac{\rho_1^n}{C\left(n\right)}$$

The average number R of parts produced per unit time is obtained as

$$R = \mu_0 q_0 U_{AGV}$$

4.10.3 Gordon-Newell Networks

Let us now consider an arbitrary closed queuing network with $(m+1)$ nodes, each with a single exponential server having service rate μ_i, $i = 0, 1, 2, ..., m$. The transition probability matrix is P, i.e., after completing the service at node i, a job goes to node j with probability p_{ij}. The routing probabilities satisfy

$$\sum_{j=0}^{m} p_{ij} = 1; \quad i = 0, 1, 2, ..., m \tag{143}$$

Thus no job ever leaves the network. There are no external arrivals, either. The number of jobs is constant and is equal to n. Further, P is a stochastic matrix. We denote the state of the system by $(k_0, k_1, ..., k_m)$ where k_i is the number of jobs at machine center i. Since there are only n jobs in the system, the state space I contains $\binom{n+m}{m}$ states and is described by

$$I = \left\{ (k_0, k_1, ..., k_m) : k_i \geq 0, \sum_{i=0}^{m} k_i = n \right\} \tag{144}$$

The class of CQNs described above was shown to have product form solution by Gordon and Newell [1967].

Denote by λ_i, $i = 0, 1, 2, ..., m$, the total average number of jobs arriving into node i per unit time. These jobs can only come from other nodes in the network. Following the same reasoning as in the case of an open network, we can obtain a set of traffic equations that the arrival rates must satisfy:

$$\lambda_i = \sum_{j=0}^{m} \lambda_j p_{ji} \quad i = 0, 1, ..., m \tag{145}$$

These equations are homogeneous because of the absence of external arrival rates. The coefficient matrix $(I - P)$ is singular. Also, as in the closed central server model, we can model the behavior of a tagged workpiece through the network as a DTMC and obtain the average number of visits of each job to each of the nodes. We can obtain these visit counts by solving the set of linear equations

$$v_i = \sum_{j=0}^{m} v_j p_{ji} \tag{146}$$

Only m out of the above $(m + 1)$ equations are linearly independent and hence the system of equations has a unique solution up to a multiplying constant. As before, we can choose v_0 arbitrarily.

To obtain the balance equations, we have to equate the rate of flow out of a state to the rate of flow into the state. For any state $(k_0, k_1, ..., k_m)$, we have

$$\pi (k_0, k_1, ..., k_m) \left(\sum_{j:k_j>0} \mu_j \right) \tag{147}$$
$$= \sum_{i} p_{ij} \mu_i \pi (k_0, k_1, ..., k_i + 1, ..., k_j - 1, ..., k_m)$$

The equations have a product form solution

$$\pi (k_0, k_1, ..., k_m) = \frac{1}{C(n)} \prod_{i=0}^{m} \rho_i^{k_i} \tag{148}$$

where

$$\rho_i = \frac{v_i}{\mu_i}; \quad i = 0, 1, ..., m$$

The normalization constant $C(n)$ is given by

$$C(n) = \sum \prod_{i=0}^{m} \rho_i^{k_i} \tag{149}$$

where the summation is over the entire state space I.

There are obvious similarities between the above result and Jackson's theorem; however, there is an important difference that should be pointed out and that is, the numbers of jobs present at the stations in the CQN case are not independent random variables. For example, if all n jobs are at node 1, then the other nodes are empty.

Example 4.41

Figure 4.30 shows a CQN model of an FMS in which each part undergoes two operations. Operation 1 can be carried out only on machine M_0 whereas the second operation can be carried out on machine M_1 or machine M_2. There are n fixtures in the system. The processing time on M_i $(i = 0, 1, 2)$ is $EXP(\mu_i)$ and these times are mutually independent. A given workpiece can be routed to M_1 or M_2 for the second operation, the routing probabilities being q and $1 - q$, respectively. Let

$$q = \frac{\mu_1}{\mu_1 + \mu_2}$$

That is, the routing probability is dependent directly on the processing rates of the machines. Such a choice of routing probabilities has the load balancing effect. The routing matrix can be seen to be

$$P = \begin{bmatrix} 0 & q & 1-q \\ 1 & 0 & 0 \\ 1 & 0 & 0 \end{bmatrix}$$

The visit counts can be easily computed from the above as

$$v_0 = a; \quad v_1 = qa; \quad v_2 = (1 - q)a$$

for any arbitrary real constant a. The relative utilizations are given by

$$\rho_0 = \frac{a}{\mu_0}; \quad \rho_1 = \frac{qa}{\mu_1}; \quad \rho_2 = \frac{(1-q)a}{\mu_2}$$

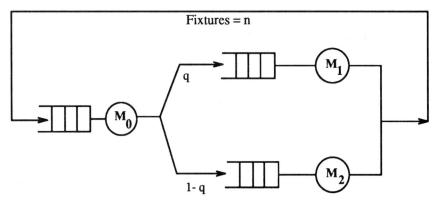

Figure 4.30 A CQN model of a simple FMS

Using $q = \frac{\mu_1}{\mu_1+\mu_2}$, we get

$$\rho_0 = \frac{a}{\mu_0}; \quad \rho_1 = \frac{a}{\mu_1 + \mu_2}; \quad \rho_2 = \frac{a}{\mu_1 + \mu_2}$$

The load balancing effect of the above routing probabilities is shown by the fact that $\rho_1 = \rho_2$.

Let us choose $a = \mu_0$. This yields $\rho_0 = 1$; $\rho_1 = r$ and $\rho_2 = r$ where $r = \frac{\mu_0}{\mu_1+\mu_2}$. Assume for convenience that $\mu_0 \neq \mu_1 + \mu_2$ so that $r \neq 1$. Since the above is a Gordon-Newell network and $k_1 + k_2 + k_3 = n$ the steady-state probabilities are given by

$$\pi(k_0, k_1, k_2) = \frac{1}{C(n)} \rho_0^{k_0} \rho_1^{k_1} \rho_2^{k_2} = \frac{1}{C(n)} r^{k_1+k_2}$$

Using the normalization condition, we have that

$$\sum_{k_0+k_1+k_2=n} \frac{1}{C(n)} r^{k_1+k_2} = 1$$

i.e., $C(n) = \{(n+1)r^n + nr^{n-1} + ... + 2r + 1\}$

Thus

$$C(n) = \sum_{k=0}^{n} (k+1)r^k$$

4.10.4 Computation of Normalization Constant

Since the number of states of the network grows exponentially with the number of customers and the number of service centers, it is computationally expensive to evaluate $C(n)$ by direct summation as in (149). Buzen [1973] derived an efficient algorithm to obtain the normalization constant. We obtain here his results using the generating function approach.

Consider the following polynomial

$$G(z) = \prod_{i=0}^{m} \frac{1}{(1 - \rho_i z)} \tag{150}$$
$$= \left(1 + \rho_0 z + \rho_0^2 z^2 + ...\right) ... \left(1 + \rho_m z + \rho_m^2 z^2 + ...\right)$$

It is clear that the coefficient of z^n in $G(z)$ is equal to the normalization constant $C(n)$, since the coefficient is just the sum of all the terms of the form $\rho_0^{k_0} \rho_1^{k_1} ... \rho_m^{k_m}$ with $\sum\limits_{i=0}^{m} k_i = n$. In other words, $G(z)$ is the generating function of the sequence $C(1), C(2), ...,$ and hence

$$G(z) = \sum_{n=0}^{\infty} C(n) z^n; \quad G(0) = 1 \tag{151}$$

We note that $G(1) \neq 1$ since $C(n)$ is not a probability.

We now derive a recursive relation to compute $C(n)$. Define

$$G_i(z) = \prod_{k=0}^{i} \frac{1}{(1 - \rho_k z)}; \quad i = 0, 1, ..., m$$

$$= \sum_{j=0}^{\infty} C_i(j) z^j; \quad i = 0, 1, ..., m \tag{152}$$

From (152), it is clear that $G_m(z) = G(z)$ and $C_m(n) = C(n)$. Now,

$$G_i(z) = \frac{1}{(1 - \rho_i z)} G_{i-1}(z); \quad i = 1, 2, ..., m \tag{153}$$

$$G_0(z) = \frac{1}{(1 - \rho_0 z)} \tag{154}$$

Equation (153) can be rewritten as

$$G_i(z) = \rho_i z G_i(z) + G_{i-1}(z)$$

Equating coefficients of z^j on both sides, we have a recursive formula for the computation of the normalization constant.

$$C_i(j) = C_{i-1}(j) + \rho_i C_i(j-1); \quad i = 1, 2, ..., m; \quad j = 1, 2, ..., n \tag{155}$$

The initialization is obtained using (154) as

$$C_0(j) = \rho_0^j; \quad j = 0, 1, 2, ..., n$$
$$C_i(0) = 1; \quad i = 0, 1, ..., m$$

Example 4.42

Consider the CQN of Example 4.41. We shall use the recursion of (155) and compute the constant $C(4)$, which in this case is $C_2(4)$. The initial conditions are

$$C_0(j) = \rho_0^j; \quad j = 0, 1, 2, 3, 4$$
$$C_i(0) = 1; \quad i = 0, 1, 2$$

In our case, $\rho_0 = 1$ and $\rho_1 = \rho_2 = r$ where $r = \frac{\mu_0}{\mu_1 + \mu_2}$. Let $n = 4$. The following shows the calculation of the normalization constant $C_2(4)$.

$j\backslash i$	0	1	2
0	1	1	1
1	1	$1+r$	$1+2r$
2	1	$1+r+r^2$	$1+2r+3r^2$
3	1	$1+r+r^2+r^3$	$1+2r+3r^2+4r^3$
4	1	$1+r+r^2+r^3+r^4$	$1+2r+3r^2+4r^3+5r^4$

It can be seen that the above pattern corresponds to the $C(n)$ we had derived in Example 4.41. In fact, it is easy to see that

$$C(n) = \sum_{k=0}^{n} r^k + \sum_{k=0}^{n} kr^k = \sum_{k=0}^{n} (k+1) r^k$$

4.10.5 Computation of Performance Measures

We now derive expressions for the performance measures: server utilization, probability of k or more jobs at a node, and expected queue length. Let n be the population of the network. We will use the notation $U_i(n)$ for the utilization of server at node i, $N_i(n)$ for the steady-state number of jobs at node i, and $L_i(n)$ for the expected number of jobs in the steady-state at node i. We shall derive the following relations.

$$U_i(n) = \frac{\rho_i C(n-1)}{C(n)} \tag{156}$$

$$P\{N_i(n) \geq k\} = \rho_i^k \frac{C(n-k)}{C(n)} \tag{157}$$

$$L_i(n) = E[N_i(n)] = \frac{1}{C(n)} \sum_{j=1}^{n} \rho_i^j C(n-j) \tag{158}$$

The waiting times can be obtained using Little's formula.

To derive the formula (156), first note that

$$U_i(n) = P\{N_i(n) \geq 1\} \tag{159}$$

Now define

$$u_i(n) = \sum_{k_i \geq 1} \rho_0^{k_0} \rho_1^{k_1} \dots \rho_m^{k_m} \tag{160}$$

where, as usual, $k_0 + k_1 + \dots + k_m = n$. Then from (148), (159), and (160), we have

$$U_i(n) = \frac{u_i(n)}{C(n)} \tag{161}$$

To compute $u_i(n)$, define

$$H(z) = \rho_i z G(z) \tag{162}$$

Note that the coefficient of z^n in $H(z)$ is precisely $u_i(n)$. Further from (162), the coefficient of z^n in $H(z)$ is simply ρ_i times the coefficient of z^{n-1} in $G(z)$. We have thus shown that

$$u_i(n) = \rho_i C(n-1) \tag{163}$$

The expression for $U_i(n)$ now follows from (161) and (163). Following exactly similar arguments, we can show that

$$P\{N_i(n) \geq k\} = \frac{\rho_i^k C(n-k)}{C(n)} \tag{164}$$

To get an expression for average queue length at node i, we observe that

$$
\begin{aligned}
L_i(n) &= \sum_{k=1}^{n} k P\{N_i(n) = k\} \\
&= \sum_{k=1}^{n} k P\{N_i(n) \geq k\} - \sum_{k=1}^{n} k P\{N_i(n) \geq k+1\} \\
&= \sum_{k=1}^{n} k P\{N_i(n) \geq k\} - \sum_{j=2}^{n+1} (j-1) P\{N_i(n) \geq j\} \\
&= \sum_{k=1}^{n} k P\{N_i(n) \geq k\} - \sum_{j=2}^{n+1} j P\{N_i(n) \geq j\} + \sum_{j=2}^{n+1} P\{N_i(n) \geq j\} \\
&= P\{N_i(n) \geq 1\} - (n+1) P\{N_i(n) \geq n+1\} + \sum_{j=2}^{n+1} P\{N_i(n) \geq j\} \\
&= \sum_{j=1}^{n} P\{N_i(n) \geq j\} \quad [\text{since } P\{N_i(n) \geq n+1\} = 0]
\end{aligned}
$$

Now, using (157), we have

$$L_i(n) = \frac{1}{C(n)} \sum_{j=1}^{n} \rho_i^j C(n-j)$$

Example 4.43

Let us consider the CQN model of Example 4.41 for which we computed the normalization constant in Example 4.42. For $n = 4$, let us compute typical performance measures. Recall that

$$\rho_0 = 1; \quad \rho_1 = \rho_2 = r = \frac{\mu_0}{\mu_1 + \mu_2}$$

$$C(0) = 1$$
$$C(1) = 1 + 2r$$
$$C(2) = 1 + 2r + 3r^2$$
$$C(3) = 1 + 2r + 3r^2 + 4r^3$$
$$C(4) = 1 + 2r + 3r^2 + 4r^3 + 5r^4$$

Let us delete $n = 4$ from the notation, for the sake of convenience. Using (156), we can obtain the utilizations U_i of machine M_i, $(i = 0, 1, 2)$ as

$$U_0 = \frac{\rho_0 C(3)}{C(4)} = \frac{1 + 2r + 3r^2 + 4r^3}{1 + 2r + 3r^2 + 4r^3 + 5r^4}$$

$$U_1 = U_2 = \frac{r\left(1 + 2r + 3r^2 + 4r^3\right)}{1 + 2r + 3r^2 + 4r^3 + 5r^4}$$

The average number of jobs with machine center M_0 is

$$L_0 = \frac{1}{C(4)} \left\{ \rho_0 C(3) + \rho_0^2 C(2) + \rho_0^3 C(1) + \rho_0^4 C(0) \right\}$$

$$= \frac{C(3) + C(2) + C(1) + C(0)}{C(4)}$$

$$= \frac{4 + 6r + 6r^2 + 4r^3}{1 + 2r + 3r^2 + 4r^3 + 5r^4}$$

Similarly, we can see that

$$L_1 = L_2 = \frac{rC(3) + r^2 C(2) + r^3 C(1) + r^4 C(0)}{C(4)}$$

$$= \frac{r + 3r^2 + 6r^3 + 10r^4}{1 + 2r + 3r^2 + 4r^3 + 5r^4}$$

Little's result can now be used to compute the average waiting times at the machine centers. We see that the average arrival rates into the three machines are given by

$$\lambda_0 = U_1\mu_1 + U_2\mu_2$$
$$\lambda_1 = U_0\mu_0\mu_1/(\mu_1 + \mu_2)$$
$$\lambda_2 = U_0\mu_0\mu_2/(\mu_1 + \mu_2)$$

The average delays in each machine center are thus given by

$$W_0 = \frac{L_0}{\lambda_0}; \quad W_1 = \frac{L_1}{\lambda_1}; \quad W_2 = \frac{L_2}{\lambda_2}$$

4.10.6 Mean Value Analysis

In computing the normalization constant $C_m(n)$ on a digital computer, numerical difficulties could arise, especially when n and m are large. Specifically, there could be overflow or underflow depending on the choice of the visit count v_0. Mean value analysis (MVA) is an alternative approach to the computation of performance measures, specially designed to mitigate such numerical difficulties. As the name implies, MVA yields mean values of performance measures.

We assume that all stations have single server queues, that they have independent exponential service times, and that their service discipline is FCFS. The results, however, extend to the whole class of product form networks that we discuss in Section 4.11.

MVA is based on the *arrival theorem*. Let n be the total number of jobs circulating in the system. Then the theorem states that the distribution of the network state seen by a job arriving at any node in the network is the same as the distribution of the network state a random observer would see with $(n - 1)$ jobs circulating in the network. In other words, a job about to join a node behaves as a random observer of a network whose job population is less by one. We define the following quantities of interest:

n = Number of jobs circulating in the network

$L_i(n)$ = Average number of jobs at node i

$W_i(n)$ = Average time a job spends at node i

v_i = Average number of visits a job makes to node i

$T(n)$ = Throughput, i.e., average number of jobs leaving the network per unit time.

Using (156) and (158), we get

$$
\begin{aligned}
L_i(n) &= \frac{1}{C(n)} \left[\rho_i C(n-1) + \rho_i^2 C(n-2) + \dots + \rho_i^n C(0) \right] \\
&= \frac{\rho_i C(n-1)}{C(n)} + \frac{\rho_i}{C(n)} \left[\rho_i C(n-2) + \dots + \rho_i^{n-1} C(0) \right] \\
&= U_i(n) + \frac{\rho_i C(n-1)}{C(n)} \frac{1}{C(n-1)} \left[\rho_i C(n-2) + \dots + \rho_i^{n-1} C(0) \right] \\
&= U_i(n) + U_i(n) L_i(n-1) \\
&= U_i(n) \mu_i \left[1 + L_i(n-1) \right] \frac{1}{\mu_i}
\end{aligned}
$$

Thus we get

$$
\frac{L_i(n)}{U_i(n)\mu_i} = \left[1 + L_i(n-1) \right] \frac{1}{\mu_i}
$$

But by Little's law,

$$
W_i(n) = \frac{L_i(n)}{U_i(n)\mu_i}
$$

Thus we have

$$
W_i(n) = \frac{1}{\mu_i} \left[1 + L_i(n-1) \right]; \quad i = 0, 1, \dots, m \tag{165}
$$

Note how the above expression exemplifies the arrival theorem. Since $T(n)$ is the throughput, on an average, $T(n)$ jobs arrive into the network per unit time and each of them makes an average of v_i visits to node. Therefore, the arrival rate into node i is

$$
\lambda_i = T(n) v_i \quad i = 0, 1, \dots, m \tag{166}
$$

Now, $L_i(n)$ can be easily obtained as

$$
L_i(n) = T(n) v_i W_i(n); \quad i = 0, 1, \dots, m \tag{167}
$$

Summing over all nodes, equation (167) yields

$$
\sum_{i=0}^{m} L_i(n) = n = T(n) \sum_{i=0}^{m} v_i W_i(n) \tag{168}
$$

Then we have

$$T(n) = \frac{n}{\displaystyle\sum_{i=0}^{m} v_i W_i(n)} \tag{169}$$

Equations (165), (167), and (169) form the basis for the iterative procedure, with the initial conditions:

$$L_i(0) = 0; \quad i = 0, 1, 2, ..., m \tag{170}$$

The first application gives $W_i(1), T(1)$, and $L_i(1)$; the second application gives $W_i(2), T(2)$, and $L_i(2)$; and so on.

Example 4.44

We shall use MVA to obtain the performance measures for the system of Example 4.41 (Figure 4.30). From (170), we have the initialization conditions as

$$L_0(0) = L_1(0) = L_2(0) = 0$$

Also, from Example 4.41, we have

$$v_0 = \mu_0; \quad v_1 = \frac{\mu_0 \mu_1}{\mu_1 + \mu_2} = \mu_1 r; \quad v_2 = \frac{\mu_0 \mu_2}{\mu_1 + \mu_2} = \mu_2 r$$

From (165), we get

$$W_0(1) = \frac{1}{\mu_0}; \quad W_1(1) = \frac{1}{\mu_1}; \quad W_2(1) = \frac{1}{\mu_2}$$

We have

$$v_0 W_0(1) = 1; \quad v_1 W_1(1) = v_2 W_2(1) = r$$

Therefore, from (169), we have

$$T(1) = \frac{1}{1 + 2r}$$

Equation (167) now gives us

$$L_0(1) = \frac{1}{1 + 2r}; \quad L_1(1) = L_2(1) = \frac{r}{1 + 2r}$$

This marks the end of the first iteration. Note that we have computed $W_i(1)$ for $i = 0, 1, 2$; $T(1)$; and $L_i(1)$ for $i = 0, 1, 2$. Applying (165), we now get

$$W_0(2) = \frac{1}{\mu_0}\left[1 + \frac{1}{1+2r}\right] = \frac{1}{\mu_0}\left[\frac{2+2r}{1+2r}\right]$$

$$W_1(2) = \frac{1}{\mu_1}\left[1 + \frac{r}{1+2r}\right] = \frac{1}{\mu_1}\left[\frac{1+3r}{1+2r}\right]$$

$$W_2(2) = \frac{1}{\mu_2}\left[1 + \frac{r}{1+2r}\right] = \frac{1}{\mu_2}\left[\frac{1+3r}{1+2r}\right]$$

We thus have

$$v_0 W_0(2) = \frac{2+2r}{1+2r}$$

$$v_1 W_1(2) = v_2 W_2(2) = \frac{r(1+3r)}{1+2r}$$

Applying (169), we now get

$$T(2) = \frac{2(1+2r)}{2+4r+6r^2} = \frac{1+2r}{1+2r+3r^2}$$

Equation (167) therefore yields

$$L_0(2) = \frac{2+2r}{1+2r+3r^2}$$

$$L_1(2) = L_2(2) = \frac{r(1+3r)}{1+2r+3r^2}$$

We have now finished iteration 2 and we have now computed $W_0(2), W_1(2), W_2(2), T(2), L_0(2), L_1(2)$, and $L_2(2)$. By applying (165), (169), and (167) in that order in repeated fashion, we can derive the values of these performance measures for any n.

PROBLEMS

1. In Example 4.39, the value of the arbitrary constant a was assumed to be μ_0. Compute the normalization constant $C(n)$, assuming $a = 1$. Show that the performance measures are the same though the normalization constant is different. Repeat for Examples 4.40 and 4.41. Can you generalize this property and prove it?

2. Write software to compute the normalization constant using Buzen's algorithm for closed queuing networks with a single job class. Devise a storage efficient scheme.

3. Design software to implement the mean value analysis algorithm.

4. Note that the normalization constant $C(n)$ is a function of the relative utilizations $\rho_0, \rho_1, ..., \rho_m$. Show that

$$C_n(c\rho_0, c\rho_1, ..., c\rho_m) = c^n C_n(\rho_0, \rho_1, ..., \rho_m)$$

for any arbitrary constant c. When will this property be useful?

5. Obtain the performance measures of the closed tandem network of Figure 4.14 using the convolution method and the MVA algorithm.

6. Complete the MVA iterations in Example 4.44.

7. Consider the closed tandem network of Figure 4.P.3.

   (a) Show that the network satisfies the local balance property, when the capacity of each queue is at least 2.

   (b) Using the time reversibility of the underlying CTMC, derive a product form structure for the steady-state probabilities.

   (c) Use Buzen's algorithm to obtain a normalization constant and compute the performance measures.

   (d) Now use the MVA iterations to rederive the expressions for the above performance measures.

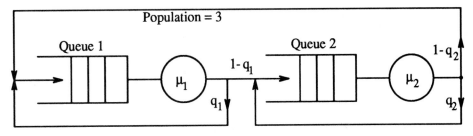

Figure 4.P.3

4.11 PRODUCT FORM QUEUING NETWORKS

Jackson networks and Gordon-Newell networks are widely used for modeling manufacturing systems because of their product form structure. These networks assume that exponential distributions describe the random event occurrences in the network. The class of product form queuing networks (PFQNs) was extended substantially and presented in a unified fashion by Baskett, Chandy, Muntz, and Palacios-Gomez (BCMP) in 1975. This class of queuing networks, now commonly known as the BCMP networks, has been very widely applied in practice and includes, as special cases, many previous developments in the area of queuing networks. We summarize these results in the next section. Kelly [1976] also obtained essentially the same results as those presented in the BCMP Theorem.

In an FMS, several part types are simultaneously produced following distinct routing tables. The material in this section is in a sense very important since it presents models that capture simultaneous presence of several part types produced via different routes and with different service requirements.

4.11.1 Types of Service Centers

Jackson networks (Section 4.9) and Gordon and Newell networks (Section 4.10) work with two crucial assumptions: (1) all customers are identical; and (2) all the service time distributions are exponential. In BCMP networks, multiple classes of customers are considered and service time distributions other than exponential are also treated. Service stations in a BCMP network can be any of the following four types.

Type 1 node: At this node the customers are served in the order of arrival, following the FCFS discipline. The service time at this node is exponentially distributed with the same mean for all classes of customers. The service rate can be state dependent with $\mu = \mu(k)$ denoting the service rate when k customers are at the node.

Type 1 service centers are appropriate for modeling machine centers, assembly stations, and AGVs. In all these cases, preemption is not possible and exponential service time assumption yields results with reasonable accuracy. As in Section 4.10, we are interested in determining only the mean values of the performance measures: throughput, server utilization, queue length, and waiting time. Only mean service times are used in the calculation of these performance measures. Further, it is known that the performance measures are not overly sensitive to the exponential assumption.

In real-life FMSs, the number of parts waiting at a node cannot influence the speed of the service center. Hence, the type of state dependent service rates that arise is similar to the case when multiple servers process from a single queue. Hence, in this section we assume identical servers following FCFS discipline.

In practice, however, the service rates for different part types would be different. While modeling a service station as a type 1 node, one has to determine a mean service time by an averaging calculation. This approximation may induce errors in the calculations.

Type 2 node: Here there is a single server at the station; the service discipline is processor sharing (i.e., when there are n customers in the service center, each is receiving service at the same rate $1/n$). All customers receive a small quota of their respective service time in turns. Each class of customers may have a distinct service time distribution. The service time distribution may be arbitrary but should have a rational Laplace transform.

A number of common distributions have rational Laplace transforms. These include exponential, hyperexponential, hypoexponential, and Erlang. Cox [1955] has shown that any distribution with rational Laplace transform can be represented as a network of exponential stages.

Type 2 service centers are appropriate models for certain material handling systems in cell environments such as a tending robot in a machine cell (see Example 2.12). For an external observer, the robot would be time shared between loading, transfer from machine to machine, and unloading operations for several parts. In a symmetric cell with balanced workloads, the robot operation can be modeled by processor sharing discipline. Each job receives a quantum of service from the robot for performing one of the above operations.

Type 3 node: These are also called *infinite server* (IS) nodes. Here the number of servers in the service center is greater than or equal to the maximum number of customers that can queue up, and each class of customers can have a distinct service time distribution. The service time distributions can be arbitrary but should have rational Laplace transforms.

Conveyor systems generally could be modeled as IS nodes. Also, the failure process in a manufacturing system where each subsystem can fail independently following an appropriate distribution is also modeled as an IS node as in the *machine-repairman* model.

Type 4 node: There is a single server at the station, the queuing discipline is pre-emptive resume, last-come-first-served (LCFS). Each customer of a separate class can have a distinct service time distribution that has a rational Laplace transform. This type of node does not seem to have much practical significance in the AMS context.

4.11.2 Closed Networks with Multiple Job Classes

Let the closed network consist of r classes of customers and m nodes. Let class j, $j = 1, 2, ..., r$, customer have a routing matrix X_j and its service rate at node i, $i = 1, 2, ..., m$, be denoted by μ_{ij}. Let k_{ij} be the number of jobs of type j at node i and $k_i = \sum_{j=1}^{r} k_{ij}$, the total number of jobs at node i. Also let n_j be the total number of jobs of type j in the network, then $\sum_{i=1}^{m} k_{ij} = n_j$. For type 1 nodes, μ_{ij} will be the same for all $j = 1, 2, ..., r$, and call it μ_i. Define the population vectors:

$$K_i = (k_{i1}, k_{i2}, ..., k_{ir}); \quad i = 1, 2, ..., m \tag{171}$$

$$K = (K_1, K_2, ..., K_m) \tag{172}$$

First, we solve for the visit counts v_{ij}, $j = 1, 2, ..., r$, from the equation

$$v_{ij} = \sum_{h=1}^{m} v_{hj} x_{hij} \tag{173}$$

In the above, v_{ij} is the visit count of class j jobs at node i; x_{hij} is the probability that a class j job, after finishing service at node h, goes next to node i.

The steady-state joint probability is given by

$$\pi(K_1, K_2, ..., K_m) = \frac{1}{C(n_1, ..., n_r)} \prod_{i=1}^{m} g_i(K_i) \tag{174}$$

where the value of $g_i(K_i)$ is given by

$$g_i(K_i) = k_i! \prod_{j=1}^{r} \frac{1}{k_{ij}!} \left(\frac{v_{ij}}{\mu_i} \right)^{k_{ij}} \quad \text{for type 1 nodes} \tag{175}$$

$$g_i(K_i) = k_i! \prod_{j=1}^{r} \frac{1}{k_{ij}!} \left(\frac{v_{ij}}{\mu_{ij}} \right)^{k_{ij}} \quad \text{for type 2 or type 4 nodes} \tag{176}$$

$$g_i(K_i) = \prod_{j=1}^{r} \frac{1}{k_{ij}!} \left(\frac{v_{ij}}{\mu_{ij}} \right)^{k_{ij}} \quad \text{for type 3 nodes} \tag{177}$$

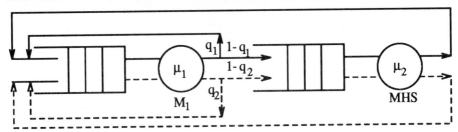

Figure 4.31 Multiclass network for Example 4.45

Example 4.45

To illustrate the product form solution for a closed network with multiple job classes, we examine an AMS comprising a machine M_1 and an automated MHS. The system produces two classes of parts. A part of class 1 undergoes an operation on M_1 (exponential time with rate μ_1) and is subjected to a quality control inspection (negligible inspection time). If the quality is acceptable, it is unloaded by the MHS (unloading time is exponential with rate μ_2). If the quality is unacceptable, the part goes back and joins the tail of the queue at M_1. It is found that the probability of acceptance after any operation is $1 - q_1$, independent of the number of operations undergone by the part in question. Parts of class 2 have identical characteristics as those of class 1, except that the acceptance probability is $1 - q_2$.

Under fixed pallet constraint for each part type, the above AMS can be modeled as a two-class CQN with both node 1 (M_1) and node 2 (MHS)

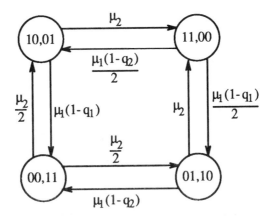

Figure 4.32 CTMC model of the network in Figure 4.31

considered as type 1 nodes, and with routing matrices given by

$$X_1 = \begin{bmatrix} q_1 & 1 - q_1 \\ 1 & 0 \end{bmatrix}; \quad X_2 = \begin{bmatrix} q_2 & 1 - q_2 \\ 1 & 0 \end{bmatrix}$$

Figure 4.31 shows the flow of parts inside this network. The flow of class 1 parts is represented by solid lines and that of class 2 parts by dotted lines. Assume that n_1 and n_2 are the numbers of pallets of class 1 and class 2, respectively. We shall investigate the case $n_1 = n_2 = 1$. Following the state description in equations (171) and (172), we have four states in this network given by $[(10), (01)]$, $[(01), (10)]$, $[(11), (00)]$, and $[(00), (11)]$. For example, the state $[(10), (01)]$ means that there is one part of class 1 and no part of class 2 at node 1, and one part of class 2 and no part of class 1 at node 2. Figure 4.32 represents the CTMC model with these four states, underlying the given CQN model. The reader is urged to carefully develop the above CTMC model and confirm the transition rates in the model. It is easy to verify that the CTMC model is irreducible and positive recurrent. The unique steady-state probabilities are given by

$$\pi(10, 01) = \frac{\mu_1 \mu_2 (1 - q_2)}{\mu_1 \mu_2 (2 - q_1 - q_2) + 2\mu_2^2 + 2\mu_1^2 (1 - q_1)(1 - q_2)} \quad (178)$$

$$\pi(01, 10) = \frac{\mu_1 \mu_2 (1 - q_1)}{\mu_1 \mu_2 (2 - q_1 - q_2) + 2\mu_2^2 + 2\mu_1^2 (1 - q_1)(1 - q_2)} \quad (179)$$

$$\pi(11, 00) = \frac{2\mu_2^2}{\mu_1 \mu_2 (2 - q_1 - q_2) + 2\mu_2^2 + 2\mu_1^2 (1 - q_1)(1 - q_2)} \quad (180)$$

$$\pi(00, 11) = \frac{2\mu_1^2 (1 - q_1)(1 - q_2)}{\mu_1 \mu_2 (2 - q_1 - q_2) + 2\mu_2^2 + 2\mu_1^2 (1 - q_1)(1 - q_2)} \quad (181)$$

From the above probabilities, one can easily verify that the CTMC is time reversible. Let us now see how we can express the above as product form expressions. For this, we use equations (174) and (175). A typical state of the system is given by $[(k_{11}, k_{12}), (k_{21}, k_{22})]$, where k_{ij} is the number of class j $(j = 1, 2)$ jobs at node i $(i = 1, 2)$. We denote $K_i = (k_{i1}, k_{i2})$ for $i = 1, 2$. By the product form structure of (174), we have

$$\pi(K_1, K_2) = \frac{1}{C(n_1, n_2)} g_1(K_1) g_2(K_2) \quad (182)$$

In this case $n_1 = n_2 = 1$ and so $C(n_1, n_2)$ becomes $C(1, 1)$. Also, both are type 1 nodes and therefore equation (175) applies, yielding

$$g_i(K_i) = k_i! \prod_{j=1}^{2} \frac{1}{(k_{ij})!} v_{ij}^{k_{ij}} \left(\frac{1}{\mu_i}\right)^{k_{ij}} \quad (183)$$

where the v_{ij} values are to be obtained using (173). We have

$$[v_{11} \quad v_{21}] = [v_{11} \quad v_{21}] \begin{bmatrix} q_1 & 1 - q_1 \\ 1 & 0 \end{bmatrix}$$

$$[v_{12} \quad v_{22}] = [v_{12} \quad v_{22}] \begin{bmatrix} q_2 & 1 - q_2 \\ 1 & 0 \end{bmatrix}$$

The above equations yield the values

$$v_{21} = v_{11} (1 - q_1); \quad v_{22} = v_{12} (1 - q_2)$$

Choosing $v_{11} = 1$ and $v_{12} = 1$, we get $v_{21} = 1 - q_1$ and $v_{22} = 1 - q_2$. Using (183), we get

$$g_1 (10) = \frac{1}{\mu_1}; \quad g_2 (01) = \frac{1 - q_2}{\mu_2}$$

Therefore, using (182), we get

$$\pi (10, 01) = \frac{1}{C (1,1)} \frac{1 - q_2}{\mu_1 \mu_2} \tag{184}$$

Also we get

$$g_1 (01) = \frac{1}{\mu_1}; \quad g_2 (10) = \frac{1 - q_1}{\mu_2}; \quad g_1 (00) = 1; \quad g_2 (00) = 1;$$

$$g_1 (11) = \frac{2}{\mu_1^2}; \quad g_2 (11) = \frac{2 (1 - q_1)(1 - q_2)}{\mu_2^2}$$

Therefore, we get

$$\pi (01, 10) = \frac{1}{C (1,1)} \frac{1 - q_1}{\mu_1 \mu_2} \tag{185}$$

$$\pi (11, 00) = \frac{1}{C (1,1)} \frac{2}{\mu_1^2} \tag{186}$$

$$\pi (00, 11) = \frac{1}{C (1,1)} \frac{2 (1 - q_1)(1 - q_2)}{\mu_2^2} \tag{187}$$

Using the normalization condition, we get

$$\frac{1}{C (1,1)} \left\{ \frac{1 - q_2}{\mu_1 \mu_2} + \frac{1 - q_1}{\mu_1 \mu_2} + \frac{2}{\mu_1^2} + \frac{2 (1 - q_1)(1 - q_2)}{\mu_2^2} \right\} = 1$$

This yields

$$C(1,1) = \frac{(1-q_1)\mu_1\mu_2 + (1-q_2)\mu_1\mu_2 + 2\mu_2^2 + 2\mu_1^2(1-q_1)(1-q_2)}{\mu_1^2\mu_2^2}$$

(188)

Substituting (188) in (184)–(187), we get the same expressions as (178)–(181). This illustrates the product form of the solution.

Example 4.46

Let us consider the same system as in Example 4.45 with the only difference that node 2 (MHS) is now an infinite server, i.e., type 3 node. Physically, this is quite realistic since a conveyor type of MHS would simultaneously carry several workpieces at a time. Since node 2 is type 3 node, the service rates at node 2 for class 1 and class 2 parts, can be different and we assume these as μ_2 and μ_3, respectively. The CTMC model will now be different from that of Figure 4.32. The reader is urged to develop this CTMC model (see Problem 2 in this section) and verify its time reversibility. We shall now use (175) and (177) to obtain product form expressions for the steady-state probabilities. Since node 1 is of type 1, we have, as before

$$g_1(10) = \frac{1}{\mu_1}; \; g_1(01) = \frac{1}{\mu_1}; \; g_1(11) = \frac{2}{\mu_1^2}; \; g_1(00) = 1$$

To obtain $g_2(00), g_2(01), g_2(10)$, and $g_2(11)$, we use (177). We get

$$g_2(00) = 1; \; g_2(01) = \frac{1-q_2}{\mu_3}$$

$$g_2(10) = \frac{1-q_1}{\mu_2}; \; g_2(11) = \frac{(1-q_1)(1-q_2)}{\mu_2\mu_3}$$

Also we get $C(1,1)$ as

$$\frac{\mu_1\mu_3(1-q_1) + \mu_1\mu_2(1-q_2) + \mu_1^2(1-q_1)(1-q_2) + 2\mu_2\mu_3}{\mu_1^2\mu_2\mu_3}$$

The steady-state probabilities in this case are

$$\pi(10,01) = \frac{(1-q_2)\mu_1\mu_2}{D}; \; \pi(01,10) = \frac{(1-q_1)\mu_1\mu_3}{D}$$

$$\pi(11,00) = \frac{2\mu_2\mu_3}{D}; \; \pi(00,11) = \frac{\mu_1^2(1-q_1)(1-q_2)}{D}$$

where D is the sum of all the numerators above.

Computation of the Normalization Constant

The recursive formulation for computing the normalization constant is derived in a way analogous to the single class case (Section 4.10.4). We give below the formulation derived using the convolution method. Define the initial conditions

$$C_0(j_1, ..., j_r) = \frac{(j_1 + ... + j_r)!}{j_1! j_2! ... j_r!} \prod_{k=1}^{r} \rho_{ok}^{j_k} \tag{189}$$

$$C_i(0, ..., 0) = 1; \quad i = 1, 2, ..., m \tag{190}$$

Also define

$$C(n_1, n_2, ..., n_r) = C_m(n_1, n_2, ..., n_r)$$

Then $C_i(j_1, j_2, ..., j_r), i = 1, 2, ..., m; j_k = 1, 2, ..., n_k$, where $k = 1, 2, ..., r$, is computed from the following recursion.

$$C_i(j_1, j_2, ..., j_r) = C_{i-1}(j_1, j_2, ..., j_r)$$
$$+ \sum_{k=1; \ j_k \neq 0}^{r} \rho_{ik} C_i(j_1, j_2, ..., j_{k-1}, j_k - 1, j_{k+1}, ..., j_r) \tag{191}$$

Computation of Performance Measures

Define the relative utilization of node i due to jobs of type j by

$$\rho_{ij} = \frac{v_{ij}}{\mu_{ij}}$$

Then the utilization of the node i due to jobs of type j is given by

$$U_{ij} = \frac{\rho_{ij} C(n_1, n_2, ..., n_{j-1}, n_j - 1, n_{j+1}, ..., n_r)}{C(n_1, n_2, ..., n_{j-1}, n_j, ..., n_r)}$$

and utilization at node i is given by

$$U_i = \sum_{j=1}^{r} U_{ij}$$

Other performance measures can be derived as in Section 4.10.5. The computation of the normalization constant as well as the performance measures can be easily implemented in software.

MVA for Closed Networks with Multiple Job Classes

We now consider the MVA algorithm for the network with multiple customer classes. As in the single class MVA algorithm presented in Section 4.10.6, the multiple-class MVA algorithm determines all the mean performance measures directly. The multi-class MVA is also based on the *arrival theorem* and Little's law. According to the arrival theorem, in a closed multi-class queuing network with product form solution, an arriving customer observes the equilibrium solution with one less customer in the arriving customer's class. We present here the mean value analysis results for type 3 nodes and for single server FCFS nodes.

Suppose μ_{ij} is the service rate for part type j at service station i. Then

$$W_{ij}(K) = \text{average time spent by type } j \text{ job at node } i$$

$$= \frac{1}{\mu_{ij}} + \frac{1}{\mu_{ij}} \text{ [mean number of } j\text{th class jobs on arrival at node } i]$$

$$+ \sum_{q=1;q\neq j}^{r} \frac{1}{\mu_{iq}} \text{ [mean number of } q\text{th class jobs on arrival at node } i]$$

$$= \frac{1}{\mu_{ij}} \left[1 + \delta_i \sum_{q=1}^{r} L_{iq}(n - 1_j) \right]$$

where $n = (n_1, ..., n_r)$ is the population size vector, 1_j is a r-dimensional unit vector with jth element as 1, and all other elements as 0 and $L_{iq}(n - 1_j)$ is the mean number of customers of type q at node i for a population vector of $(n - 1_j)$. Also, $\delta_i = 0$ if node i is a delay node and $\delta_i = 1$ if node i is a single server FCFS exponential node.

From Little's law the average number of jobs of type j at node i, L_{ij}, is given by

$$L_{ij}(n) = T_j(n) v_{ij} W_{ij}(n); \quad i = 1, 2, ..., m$$

where $T_j(n)$ is the average throughput of class j and is given by

$$T_j(n) = \frac{n_j}{\sum_{i=1}^{m} v_{ij} W_{ij}(n)}$$

The initial conditions are $L_{ij}(0) = 0; \quad i = 1, 2, ..., m; \quad j = 1, 2, ..., r$. Note that for each population vector, there are $(2m + 1)r$ equations.

PROBLEMS

1. Obtain an expression for the mean number of jobs of each class at station i $(i = 1, 2, ..., m)$, in terms of the normalization constants, for a typical closed BCMP network.
2. Develop the CTMC model for the network considered in Example 4.46 and verify that the steady-state probabilities are the same as derived in that example.
3. Develop a software package for computation of normalization constant and performance measures using the convolution method for closed networks with multiple job classes.
4. Implement the multi-class MVA algorithm as a software package.

4.12 QUEUING NETWORKS WITH BLOCKING

We have thus far modeled manufacturing systems as queues and queuing networks with infinite capacity. In particular, product form networks have proved valuable in faithfully representing many features of flexible manufacturing systems and in analyzing their performance. However, real-world manufacturing systems have finite buffers and these would lead to queuing network models with finite capacity. We study such queuing networks in this section.

Queuing networks with finite capacity are subject to *blocking* (i.e., the transfer of a workpiece that has just finished processing, from one machine to another machine, may be delayed because all the buffers at the destination machine are full). The transfer of a workpiece finally occurs when the destination machine finishes processing the current workpiece and transfers it to another machine and starts processing the job from the head of the queue, creating an empty position in the buffer. The rule that dictates the blocking and unblocking of machines is called the *blocking mechanism*.

Manufacturing systems with blocking are, in general, difficult to analyze. However, queuing networks with certain kinds of blocking have product form solutions. During the 1980s, literature on queuing networks with blocking has grown rapidly. In this section we consider three typical manufacturing configurations: two-node open networks, two-node closed networks, and the central server model. For these situations, we present the procedures for determining the steady-state solution.

4.12.1 Types of Blocking Mechanisms

Three types of blocking mechanisms have been studied in the literature. We consider these below.

Blocked After Service (BAS)

A workpiece upon service completion at a machine i is destined to the input buffer of machine j according to the routing table. If the input buffer at machine j is full at the moment, the job is forced to wait on the machine i until it enters the input buffer of the destination machine j. The machine i remains blocked for this period of time and it cannot process any jobs waiting in its input queue.

In an FMS with versatile machine centers following a complex routing table, several machines may be blocked because the buffer of a destination machine is full. To see this, suppose a part requires two operations: the first operation can be done on either M_1 or M_2 and the second on M_3. Assume that the buffers at these machines are finite. Consider the situation when the buffer of M_3 is full. Suppose now M_1 finishes processing the workpiece before M_3, blocking machine M_1. If M_2 also completes its service before M_3, then both M_1 and M_2 are blocked by machine M_3 in that order. This necessitates imposing an ordering on the blocked nodes to determine which machine, M_1 or M_2, will be unblocked first, when M_3 completes processing and its buffer has an empty slot. One can follow *First-Blocked-First-Unblocked* rule and service workpiece from machine M_1. The workpiece from M_2 has to wait for another service completion from M_3.

It is possible deadlocks might occur in FMSs following BAS blocking. We have also seen that both blocking and deadlocks are undesirable phenomena and result in idle resources. System design should take care to see that both of these situations will not occur. It can be established that closed networks can be operated deadlock-free by regulating the total number of customers in the system to be less than the storage capacity for each cycle in the network. A cycle is a directed path that starts and ends on the same node. Storage capacity of a node is the buffer capacity plus the number of servers, and storage capacity of a cycle is the sum of storage capacities of nodes in the cycle.

Blocked Before Service (BBS)

This type of blocking occurs in manufacturing systems following certain routing and flow control policies with a view to avoid deadlocks.

Suppose a workpiece currently at machine i has to receive service for the next operation at machine j. If the routing policy is "start service on machine i only if buffer space is available at machine j," then if buffers are full at machine j, then machine i gets blocked, i.e., the workpiece cannot receive any service from machine i. If the buffer at destination machine j becomes full during the service of the customer at machine i, the service is interrupted and machine i is again blocked. The service is resumed at the interruption point as soon as the buffer at machine j has free space.

In the literature, two different BBS blocking categories are identified. In one case, the service facility of the blocked node cannot hold a customer, and in the other it can hold a customer.

Repetitive Service (RS)

Suppose a workpiece upon service completion at machine i is destined to machine j. If the buffer at machine j is full then the customer receives another service at machine i. This is repeated until the customer on completing service at machine i finds an empty buffer at machine j. This is called *rejection* blocking. We can visualize two categories of this type of blocking:

1. **RS-FD (fixed-destination)**: Here the route of a given part is fixed and cannot be changed.
2. **RS-RD (random-destination)**: Here adaptive routing is followed, i.e., a destination node is chosen at each service completion independent of the destination node chosen the previous time.

All three types of blocking mechanisms have been studied in the AMS literature.

4.12.2 Two-Node Open Network with BAS Blocking

Here we consider a two-stage manufacturing system with two stations in series, with storage space in front of each machine. Let b_1 and b_2 denote the capacities (buffer size + number of servers) at stations 1 and 2, respectively. The arrivals occur at a Poisson rate of λ at the first station and service rates of stations 1 and 2 are μ_1 and μ_2, respectively. Here we consider BAS blocking although other blocking models are also possible. Also, we consider the case when $b_1 = b_2 = 1$, i.e., no queues are allowed to form at either station 1 or station 2. Arrivals when station 1 is busy are blocked or turned away.

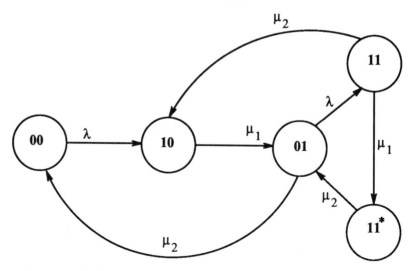

Figure 4.33 State diagram for a two-node QN with blocking

Let $\pi(k_1, k_2)$ denote the steady-state probability that there are k_1 customers at station 1 and k_2 customers at station 2. At the first station we distinguish among three states: empty, busy, and blocked. Let 0 denote the empty state and 1 denote the busy state. A starred state represents the blocked state. The second station could be in either busy state or empty state. The possible states are $(0, 1), (1, 0), (0, 1), (1, 1), (1, 1)^*$, where the starred state represents the blocked state. The state diagram is given in Figure 4.33. The balance equations are

$$\lambda \pi (0, 0) = \mu_2 \pi (0, 1)$$
$$\mu_1 \pi (1, 0) = \mu_2 \pi (1, 1) + \lambda \pi (0, 0)$$
$$(\mu_1 + \mu_2) \pi (1, 1) = \lambda \pi (0, 1)$$
$$(\lambda + \mu_2) \pi (0, 1) = \mu_1 \pi (1, 0) + \mu_2 \pi (1, 1)^*$$
$$\mu_2 \pi (1, 1)^* = \mu_1 \pi (1, 1)$$

Let $\rho_1 = \frac{\lambda}{\mu_1}$ and $\rho_2 = \frac{\lambda}{\mu_2}$. Solving the above balance equations, we can compute expressions for $\pi(k_1, k_2)$. For the special case $\mu_1 = \mu_2$, we have $\rho_1 = \rho_2 = \rho$, and we get

$$\pi (0, 0) = \frac{2}{\alpha}; \; \pi (0, 1) = \frac{2\rho}{\alpha}; \; \pi (1, 0) = \frac{2\rho + \rho^2}{\alpha};$$
$$\pi (1, 1) = \frac{\rho^2}{\alpha}; \; \pi (1, 1)^* = \frac{\rho^2}{\alpha}$$

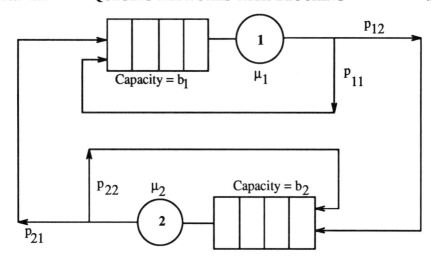

Figure 4.34 Two-node closed network with finite buffers

where $\alpha = 3\rho^2 + 4\rho + 2$. Further, expected queue length L is given by

$$L = \frac{4\rho + 5\rho^2}{\alpha}$$

It is easy to see how the problem becomes more complex when the stations have finite buffers of capacity greater than unity. Conceptually, series queuing situations with finite buffers could be understood by the Markov chain models presented above. However, one has to resort to approximations in such situations, in order to obtain quick solutions.

4.12.3 Two-Node Closed Network with BAS Blocking

We consider here a two node closed queuing network shown in Figure 4.34 serving n single class jobs. Each station has a single server that follows FCFS service discipline and has exponentially distributed service time. For $j = 1, 2$, let k_j denote the number of jobs at station j; b_j the capacity at each station (buffer size + 1); and μ_j the service rate. Let p_{ij} denote the probability that a job, after service at station i, proceeds to station j provided there is room (i.e., $k_j < b_j$). We assume that $n < b_1 + b_2$. Here we solve the network by establishing its equivalence with another two-node closed queuing network with no capacity limits.

First consider the two-node network with no capacity limits, i.e., $b_i = \infty$, for $i = 1, 2$. Suppose (k_1, k_2) denotes the state in which there are k_1 jobs at node 1 and k_2 jobs at node 2. The state diagram with

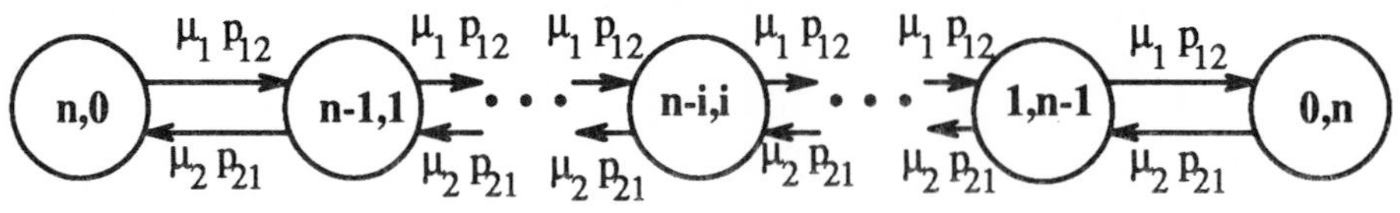

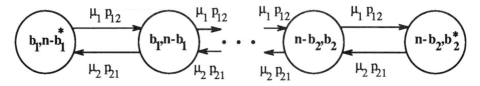

Figure 4.35 State diagram assuming infinite buffers

Figure 4.36 State diagram assuming finite buffers

$(n + 1)$ states is shown in Figure 4.35. In the case when network nodes have limited capacity, not all the $(n + 1)$ states in Figure 4.35 are feasible and only those satisfying the capacity constraint $k_i \leq b_i$ are feasible. In addition, we have two more states $(b_1, n - b_1)^*$ and $(n - b_2, b_2)^*$ representing "server 2 blocked and buffer of server 1 full" and "server 1 blocked and buffer of server 2 full," respectively. The Markov chain diagram for this blocked network is shown in Figure 4.36. As can be seen, the number of states is $[(b_1 + 1) + (b_2 + 1) - n + 1]$.

Obviously, the state graph in Figure 4.36 is a subgraph of the state graph in Figure 4.35. It is easy to observe that the state space diagram in Figure 4.36 has exactly the same structure as the state diagram of a two-node closed network (see Figure 4.35) with no limits on capacity but with a reduced number of customers $\hat{n}$ where $\hat{n} = (b_1 + 1) + (b_2 + 1) - n$. Since the state spaces of the two networks are isomorphic and the transition rates are equal, the equilibrium probabilities in the two cases are identical.

Once the equivalence is established between the two systems, then results of closed networks without blocking could be used to solve the blocking case.

Example 4.47

Consider a network with two stations in which $n = 10$ jobs are circulating. Other parameters include $b_1 = 7$, $b_2 = 5$, $1/\mu_1 = 2.0$, $1/\mu_2 = 0.9$, $p_{11} = 0.3$, $p_{12} = 0.7$, $p_{21} = 1$. With no limit on buffer capacity the system has 11 states. The feasible state diagram is shown in Figure 4.37. It can easily be verified that this state space is identical to the closed network with $\hat{n} = 4$ jobs and unlimited buffer capacities. We can write down the balance equations from Figure 4.38.

$$\mu_1 p_{12} \pi (4,0) = \mu_2 \pi (3,1)$$
$$(\mu_1 p_{12} + \mu_2) \pi (3,1) = \mu_1 p_{12} \pi (4,0) + \mu_2 \pi (2,2)$$
$$(\mu_1 p_{12} + \mu_2) \pi (2,2) = \mu_1 p_{12} \pi (3,1) + \mu_2 \pi (1,3)$$
$$(\mu_1 p_{12} + \mu_2) \pi (1,3) = \mu_1 p_{12} \pi (2,2) + \mu_2 \pi (0,4)$$
$$\mu_2 \pi (0,4) = \mu_1 p_{12} \pi (1,3)$$

If we let $\rho_1 = a/\mu_1$ and $\rho_2 = a p_{12}/\mu_2$, where a is an arbitrary constant, then it can be verified by direct substitution that $\pi (k_1, k_2)$ has the following product form:

$$\pi (k_1, k_2) = \frac{1}{C(4)} \rho_1^{k_1} \rho_2^{k_2}$$

where the normalizing constant $C(4)$ is found such that

$$\pi (4,0) + \pi (3,1) + \pi (2,2) + \pi (1,3) + \pi (0,4) = 1$$

Choosing $a = \mu_1$, we have $\rho_1 = 1$ and $\rho_2 = \mu_1 p_{12}/\mu_2$. We have

$$C(4) = \frac{1 - \rho_2^5}{1 - \rho_2} \qquad \rho_2 \neq 1$$
$$= 5 \qquad \rho_2 = 1$$

From the data we have, $\rho_2 = (0.7)(0.45)$. We can now determine various performance measures such as mean queue lengths, mean waiting times, and utilizations. We can also determine the blocking probabilities for each station. For example,

Probability that station 1 is blocked $= \pi (0,4)$
Probability that station 2 is blocked $= \pi (4,0)$

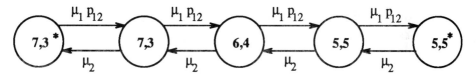

Figure 4.37 State diagram for the blocking network in Example 4.47

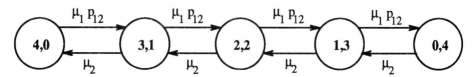

Figure 4.38 State diagram of the unblocked network

4.12.4 Central Server Model with Blocking

We have analyzed the closed central server model with m machine centers for flexible manufacturing systems in Section 4.10.2 under the assumption that the machines and the central server (MHS) have unlimited buffer capacities, i.e., each buffer has a capacity n, the number circulating in the system. On the other hand, FMSs generally have only one or two extra waiting spaces per machine. Here we consider the situation when the local buffers of the machines have limited capacities and the MHS has finite but enough storage capacity to hold all the n circulating parts. In the above situation, two kinds of blocking can occur:

1. Repetitive Service – Random Destination (RS-RD): Here the MHS could be of loop conveyor type and tries to send parts to the machines whose local buffers are already full. The blocked part remains on the MHS and waits for a retry for any one of the machines in the following cycles. The part receives another service by the MHS.

2. Blocking After Service: This kind of blocking models MHS types such as carts, AGVs, etc., where the blocked parts wait in front of the machines until the machine receives the workpiece.

Here we consider the central server model with RS-RD blocking with m machines and n pallets. Let $\pi(k_0, k_1, ..., k_m)$ be the probability of finding k_j jobs at node j $(j = 0, 1, ..., m)$. In the unrestricted buffer case, Equation (142) gives a product form solution for the joint probabilities. It happens that in the limited buffer case also the product form nature of the solution is preserved.

Recall from (144) that I is the state space of the CQN with unlimited buffers. Let b_i, $i = 1, 2, ..., m$, be the buffer size at each local workstation. We assume that $b_i < n$ for each i, and parts attempting entry from the MHS to a machine with full buffer will get blocked. Blocked parts stay in the central buffer or on the conveyor for delivery at a later time. The storage capacity of the central buffer or loop conveyor is assumed to be large enough to accommodate all the n jobs, i.e., $b_0 \geq n$. The state space of this limited buffer network can be described by

$$I_b = \{(k_0, k_1, ..., k_m) : \sum_{i=0}^{m} k_i = n, \ 0 \leq k_i \leq b_i, \ i = 1, 2, ..., m;$$

$$max\left(0, n - \sum_{i=1}^{m} b_i\right) \leq k_0 \leq n\}$$

Obviously I_b is a subset of I. It is known that if the *unblocked* Markov chain with state space I is reversible, then so is the *blocked* Markov chain with state space I_b and further it admits product form equilibrium distribution of the type given by (148)-(149). It is formidable to check the reversibility from the detailed balance equations of Section 3.7. However, it is also known that the reversibility of the CTMC in this case is equivalent to the reversibility of the routing matrix P. A routing matrix P is reversible if P can be written down as the product of a symmetric matrix with non-negative entries and a diagonal matrix. Indeed, we can write P as

$$
P = \begin{bmatrix} q_0 & q_1 & \cdots & q_m \\ 1 & 0 & \cdots & 0 \\ 1 & 0 & \cdots & 0 \\ . & . & . & . \\ . & . & . & . \\ . & . & . & . \\ 1 & 0 & \cdots & 0 \end{bmatrix} = \begin{bmatrix} q_0 & 1 & \cdots & 1 \\ 1 & 0 & \cdots & 0 \\ 1 & 0 & \cdots & 0 \\ . & . & . & . \\ . & . & . & . \\ . & . & . & . \\ 1 & 0 & \cdots & 0 \end{bmatrix} \begin{bmatrix} 1 & 0 & \cdots & . & 0 \\ 0 & q_1 & \cdots & . & 0 \\ 0 & 0 & q_2 & \cdots & 0 \\ . & . & . & . & . \\ 0 & 0 & 0 & \cdots & q_m \end{bmatrix}
$$

In summary, the central server model with limited buffers at the machines and infinite buffer at the MHS has a product form solution of the type (142), i.e.,

$$
\pi(k_0, k_1, ..., k_m) = \frac{1}{C(n)} \prod_{i=0}^{m} \rho_i^{k_i}
$$

where $C(n)$ is the normalization constant, $\rho_i = \frac{v_i}{\mu_i}$ and v_i's are the visit counts. The normalization constant $C(n)$ is given by

$$
C(n) = \sum_{k \in I_b} \prod_{i=0}^{m} \rho_i^{k_i}
$$

where $k = (k_0, k_1, ..., k_m)$.

Example 4.48

Recall the CQN model (Figure 4.30) discussed in Example 4.41. This can be treated as a closed central server model with n jobs, one AGV, two machine centers, and with routing matrix given by

$$
P = \begin{bmatrix} 0 & q & 1-q \\ 1 & 0 & 0 \\ 1 & 0 & 0 \end{bmatrix}
$$

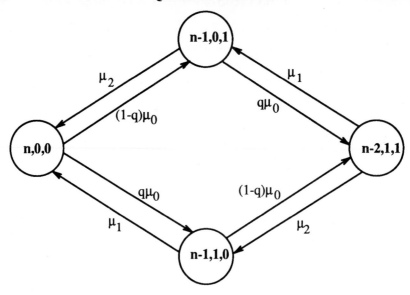

Figure 4.39 CTMC model of the central server model with blocking

where $q = \frac{\mu_1}{\mu_1 + \mu_2}$. Note that $\mu_0, \mu_1,$ and μ_2 are the service rates of the AGV, M_1, and M_2, respectively. Let the buffer capacity at the AGV be n and let there be no buffer at both M_1 and M_2. That is, the AGV can get blocked when either M_1 is busy or M_2 is busy or both are busy. First we observe that P may be written as the product of a symmetric matrix and diagonal matrix:

$$P = \begin{bmatrix} 0 & 1 & 1 \\ 1 & 0 & 0 \\ 1 & 0 & 0 \end{bmatrix} \begin{bmatrix} 1 & 0 & 0 \\ 0 & q & 0 \\ 0 & 0 & 1-q \end{bmatrix}$$

Thus P is a *reversible* routing matrix and we shall now verify the product form solution for this model. For this, we first compute the steady-state probabilities of the possible states, which are given by the set

$$I_b = \{(n,0,0),(n-1,1,0),(n-1,0,1),(n-2,1,1)\}$$

Note that these are the only four possible states for the above network. Further note that the state $(n-1,1,0)$ leads to blocking if a part, on completion of AGV service, is assigned to M_1; similarly, the state $(n-1,0,1)$ will lead to blocking if a part, on completion of AGV service, is assigned to M_2. Also, the state $(n-2,1,1)$ causes blocking as soon as the part on AGV finishes service. Figure 4.39 shows the state diagram for the Markov chain underlying this network.

Using the rate balance equations and normalizing, we get the steady-state probabilities for the above Markov chain as,

$$\pi(n,0,0) = \frac{(\mu_1 + \mu_2)^2}{(\mu_0 + \mu_1 + \mu_2)^2} \tag{192}$$

$$\pi(n-1,1,0) = \pi(n-1,0,1) = \frac{\mu_0(\mu_1 + \mu_2)}{(\mu_0 + \mu_1 + \mu_2)^2} \tag{193}$$

$$\pi(n-2,1,1) = \frac{\mu_0^2}{(\mu_0 + \mu_1 + \mu_2)^2} \tag{194}$$

We shall now verify that the above expressions satisfy product form. For this, we first assume the product form solution

$$\pi(k_0, k_1, k_2) = \frac{1}{C(n)} \rho_0^{k_0} \rho_1^{k_1} \rho_2^{k_2}$$

where ρ_0, ρ_1, and ρ_2 are the relative utilizations that can be computed as in Example 4.41. Assuming the same values as in Example 4.41, we have

$$\rho_0 = 1; \quad \rho_1 = \rho_2 = \frac{\mu_0}{\mu_1 + \mu_2}$$

Thus we obtain

$$\pi(n,0,0) = \frac{1}{C(n)} \tag{195}$$

$$\pi(n-1,1,0) = \pi(n-1,0,1) = \frac{1}{C(n)}\left(\frac{\mu_0}{\mu_1 + \mu_2}\right) \tag{196}$$

$$\pi(n-2,1,1) = \frac{1}{C(n)}\left(\frac{\mu_0}{\mu_1 + \mu_2}\right)^2 \tag{197}$$

To compute $C(n)$, we have to use the normalization condition

$$\pi(n,0,0) + \pi(n-1,1,0) + \pi(n-1,0,1) + \pi(n-2,1,1) = 1$$

Using (195) – (197), we get

$$C(n) = \left(\frac{\mu_0 + \mu_1 + \mu_2}{\mu_1 + \mu_2}\right)^2$$

Using the above in (195) – (197), we get the same expressions as in (192) – (194). This verifies the product form solution.

We have shown here that for the central server model with limited buffers, a product form solution exists. One can extend the convolution and mean value analysis algorithms for the limited buffer case. For details, see the papers by Li Zhuang and Hindi [1990, 1991].

In this section we considered queuing networks with blocking. We have restricted our attention to situations where elegant analytical solutions are available. As one can easily visualize, such nice situations are limited. In most real-world manufacturing examples, one has to resort to approximations.

PROBLEMS

1. Consider a transfer line with two workheads. Under the usual assumptions derive the performance characteristics for the following situations:

   (a) Infinite waiting space at the first station and no waiting space at the second.

   (b) No waiting space at the first and infinite waiting space at the second.

   (c) A buffer space of capacity 1 at each station.

2. Consider a three-stage transfer line with no waiting space in between. Derive expressions for the blocking probabilities.

3. Consider a two-station closed transfer line in which seven jobs circulate. Let $b_1 = 3$; $b_2 = 5$; $\frac{1}{\mu_1} = 3$, and $\frac{1}{\mu_2} = 1$. Find the state space without capacity limits, with capacity limits, and for an equivalent network with no capacity limits.

4. Consider a two-node closed network with the same description as in Section 4.12.3, but with BBS – Server Occupied blocking and derive the performance measures.

5. Consider an automated manufacturing system with four different machines and a load/unload station. Each station has limited local buffer capacity. Workpieces are moved by an AGV from machine to machine. The system can be modeled as a central server queuing network. The service rates of AGV and machines 1,2,3,4 are given by 30, 20, 15, 10, and 5 parts/ h, respectively. The average number of operations a part undergoes is 10, i.e., $q_0 = 0.1$. The routing probabilities q_i are selected in the ratio of the service rate, i.e.,

$$q_i = \frac{\text{service rate of } i\text{th machine}}{\sum\limits_{j=1}^{n} (\text{service rate of } j\text{th machine})}$$

Plot the throughput, response time, and machine utilizations for the following cases:

   (a) The machines have (i) no buffer and (ii) one single buffer each.

   (b) The number of fixtures (jobs) in the system varies from 1 to 10.

6. Consider a central server model with one AGV and one machine center. The machine center has two NC machines but has no buffers. The AGV buffer can hold all the jobs in the system. A job is routed to the machine center with probability q. Derive the performance measures for this system, in the following cases.

   (a) Blocking is of type BAS (blocked after service).
   (b) Blocking is of type RS-RD (repetitive service – random destination).

7. Recall the closed tandem network of Figure 4.P.3 (Problem 7 in Section 4.10). Let the population remain at 3. Assume that there is no buffer at node 2, i.e., the capacity of node 2 is 1. Node 1 continues to have adequate capacity. In this network, node 1 can get blocked. Assume BAS blocking.

   (a) Find an equivalent unblocked closed QN for this network.
   (b) Show that the steady-state solution is product form.
   (c) Use Buzen's algorithm to obtain a normalization constant and compute the performance measures.
   (d) Now use the MVA iterations to rederive the above performance measures.

4.13 APPROXIMATE ANALYSIS OF QUEUING SYSTEMS

Exact analysis of queuing network models of manufacturing systems is feasible and attractive if the models are product form. If a QN model does not have a product form solution and it has too many Markov states for a numerical solution to be feasible, then the alternative is to use simulation or approximations. Approximate analysis is particularly attractive to use if the error from the exact solution is minimal and acceptable. Also, approximate analysis techniques are usually computationally inexpensive compared to simulation.

There is a vast literature on queuing network approximations, and several techniques have been developed for approximate analysis of QN models. We can broadly identify three approaches: aggregation, diffusion approximation, and heuristic methods.

1. In aggregation, the general methodology is to replace a subnetwork by a single *composite* queue which is the *flow-equivalent* of the subnetwork. That is, the composite queue is intended to behave as the entire subnetwork in its interaction with the remaining queues of the network. The resulting network will usually have fewer states and is thus easier to analyze.

2. Diffusion approximation is usually applied to open QN models with heavy traffic. The basic technique is to treat the stochastic process of

a queuing network as a diffusion process which has a continuous state space and then use the theory of diffusion processes.

3. In heuristic methods, a given QN model is approximated by an efficiently solvable QN model by studying the physics of the system and making simplifying assumptions.

In this section we first present AMS features that indicate approximate techniques to be used. We then dwell on the aggregation technique, with typical examples. Finally, we outline the important approximation studies in the AMS context.

4.13.1 Non-Product Form Features in AMSs

Here we list some common characteristics of AMSs which may render the QN models non-product form, thus entailing the use of approximations.

1. **Service Time Distributions**: If the service times are deterministic or in general nonexponential, we have seen that product form solution entails the server to be an infinite server or to use the processor sharing discipline or LCFI discipline. The last two disciplines are not very realistic in the AMS context.

2. **Scheduling Discipline**: FCFS is the most appropriate scheduling discipline for AMS situations. But to obtain product form solution using FCFS discipline, the service time distribution is constrained to be exponential. A more severe constraint appears in the multiple part type case where each part type is constrained to have the same exponential processing time at a given machine.

3. **Priorities**: In AMSs producing multiple types of parts, different priorities are usually tagged with different part types in order to honor production deadlines. Priority queuing very often results in non-product form solutions.

4. **New Production Control Policies**: In pull type of production systems, production control is achieved by employing new schemes such as the Japanese *kanban* scheme. The use of *kanbans* leads to synchronization constraints because a part is taken up for processing only when a corresponding *kanban* is available. Such situations can easily render the solutions non-product form.

5. **Assembly Operations**: A typical assembly operation (see Figure 4.3) involves the joining of two or more subassemblies into a single product. This again induces a synchronization constraint which may lead to non-

product form solutions. QN models that capture assembly operations belong to the realm of fork-join queuing networks which are essentially non-product form networks.

6. **Breakdowns**: Product form QN models assume that the servers, i.e., machines, conveyors, AGVs, etc., are free from interruptions that can be caused by breakdowns or preventive maintenance. In real-world AMSs, breakdown of equipment is an unavoidable situation and hence an AMS model will be realistic only if it can capture failures, repairs, and reconfiguration of equipment.

7. **Dynamic Routing**: Typically, in an AMS, the route a job takes through a network of queues is designed to depend on the state of the system. For example, in shortest queue routing (SQR), a waiting part is routed to a service center having the least number of waiting parts. In shortest expected delay routing (SEDR), a waiting part is routed to a service center that results in the least expected delay. Both SQR and SEDR have a kind of load balancing effect on the system. Such dynamic routing policies often lead to non-product form solution.

8. **Blocking**: Product form QNs assume that all buffers are infinite. In Section 4.12, we have seen that some QNs with finite buffers do result in product form models. However, in general, finite buffers will lead to non-product form solution.

9. **Multiple Resource Holding**: In some AMS situations, a part may hold two or more resources. For example, a part typically needs to be fixtured onto a pallet before undergoing processing. Thus a part needs a fixture, a pallet, a machine, and a set of tools for a particular operation. Such multiple resource holding leads to non-product form models.

4.13.2 Performance Analysis Through Aggregation

We consider here only the single part type case. We can also regard aggregation as the *flow-equivalent* technique since it involves computing the flow-equivalents of subnetworks. By a flow-equivalent of a subnetwork, we mean a *composite* queue that behaves just like the entire subnetwork does in its interaction with the remaining queues of the network. That is, the job flow through the composite queue is equivalent to job flow through the subnetwork. The composite queue is usually a queue with state-dependent service rates.

To illustrate, consider the simple CQN model of Figure 4.40 which represents a single part type AMS with an AGV and two machines

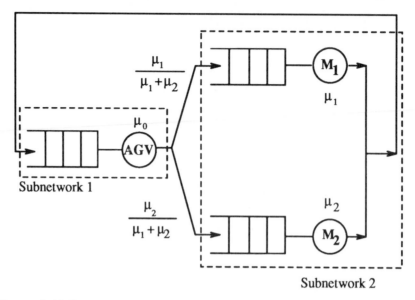

Figure 4.40 Example to illustrate approximate analysis by aggregation

M_1 and M_2. Each part first gets loaded into the system by the AGV and then proceeds to either M_1 or M_2 for an operation. After a single operation, the part leaves the system and is immediately replaced by a fresh raw part. The closed nature of the network is ensured as usual by a limited number of fixtures. As usual, μ_0, μ_1, μ_2 represent the rates of the exponential processing times at the three nodes. The routing is static; however, to balance the load, we choose the probabilities as $\mu_1/(\mu_1 + \mu_2)$ and $\mu_2/(\mu_1 + \mu_2)$ (i.e., route with greater probability to faster machine). This example is similar to the one studied in Section 4.10.

    In the above CQN, we have two natural parts. Subnetwork 1 contains just the AGV node whereas subnetwork 2 comprises M_1 and M_2. To apply aggregation, the first step will be to find a flow-equivalent to subnetwork 2. The resulting network, which comprises subnetwork 1 and the composite queue corresponding to subnetwork 2, is shown in Figure 4.41. It is easy to see that this resulting network has fewer states than the original network. In the general case, aggregation can be repeated until the resulting network has a tractable solution. If it is required to study the effect of the parameters of subnetwork 1 over a wide range, then it takes minimal effort to repeatedly solve the network of Figure 4.41 than the network of Figure 4.40.

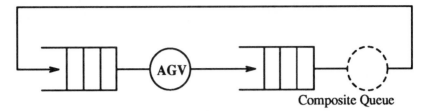

Figure 4.41 Network of Figure 4.40 after applying aggregation

Flow-Equivalence Through Norton's Theorem

To obtain the composite queue from a given subnetwork, several methods could be followed. One characterization is to let the composite queue have a service rate that depends on the queue length. The service rate for a given queue length is the throughput in a network with the corresponding population where the network is obtained by connecting the output of the subnetwork to its input. Figure 4.42 shows the network that should be analyzed in order to obtain the flow-equivalent of subnetwork 2 in Figure 4.40. The process of obtaining flow-equivalents in this fashion is analogous to the Norton's theorem in electrical circuit theory.

It has been shown that the aggregation process as done above can be performed exactly for product form networks. That is, the results produced by the original network and the aggregated network are the same provided the original network is product form. We verify this through the following example.

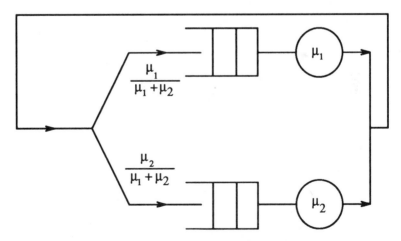

Figure 4.42 Network to be analyzed for obtaining the flow-equivalent

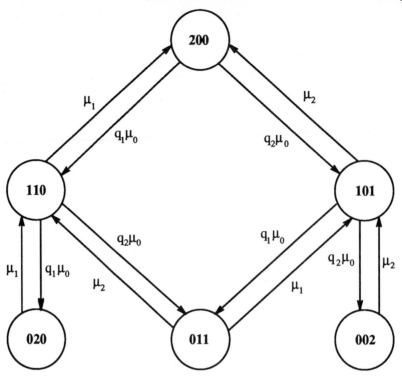

Figure 4.43 CTMC model underlying the CQN of Figure 4.40

Example 4.49

Let there be two jobs circulating in the CQN of Figure 4.40. This CQN will then have six states (200), (110), (101), (011), (020), and (002) where the triple (k_1, k_2, k_3) indicates k_1 jobs in AGV node, k_2 jobs in M_1 node, and k_3 jobs in M_2 node. Figure 4.43 shows the CTMC model underlying this CQN model. This is an irreducible, positive recurrent CTMC and hence there exists a unique steady-state probability distribution that can be computed by writing down the rate balance equations and solving them together with the normalization condition. If $\pi(k_1, k_2, k_3)$ is the steady-state probability of state (k_1, k_2, k_3), it can be easily verified that

$$\pi(200) = \frac{(\mu_1 + \mu_2)^2}{(\mu_1 + \mu_2)^2 + 2\mu_0(\mu_1 + \mu_2) + 3\mu_0^2} \tag{198}$$

$$\pi(110) = \pi(101) = \frac{\mu_0(\mu_1 + \mu_2)}{(\mu_1 + \mu_2)^2 + 2\mu_0(\mu_1 + \mu_2) + 3\mu_0^2} \tag{199}$$

$$\pi\,(011) = \pi\,(020) = \pi\,(002) = \frac{\mu_0^2}{(\mu_1 + \mu_2)^2 + 2\mu_0\,(\mu_1 + \mu_2) + 3\mu_0^2} \tag{200}$$

From the above probabilities, one can compute various steady-state performance measures. For example, the AGV utilization is given by

$$U_{AGV} = \pi\,(200) + \pi\,(110) + \pi\,(101) = \frac{(\mu_1 + \mu_2)^2 + 2\mu_0\,(\mu_1 + \mu_2)}{(\mu_1 + \mu_2)^2 + 2\mu_0\,(\mu_1 + \mu_2) + 3\mu_0^2} \tag{201}$$

The steady-state throughput of the system is given by $R = \mu_0 U_{AGV}$. We may be interested in studying the effect of μ_0 on U_{AGV} and R.

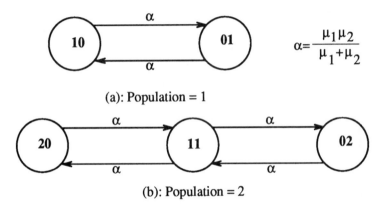

(a): Population = 1

(b): Population = 2

Figure 4.44 Markov chain for populations 1 and 2

We shall now use the method of aggregation to this example. For this we should first compute the parameters of the composite queue. Since the population of the network is 2, the population inside subnetwork 2 is 0,1, or 2. For population 0, the throughput of the network in Figure 4.42 is zero. When the population is 1, this network corresponds to the Markov chain of Figure 4.44(a). Figure 4.44(b) shows the Markov chain corresponding to a population of 2. In these diagrams, the state is indicated by an ordered pair, with the first (second) component showing the number of jobs with M_1 (M_2). From these Markov chains, it can be easily derived that the throughput of the composite queue is $\frac{\mu_1 + \mu_2}{2}$ for a population of 1 and $\frac{2}{3}\,(\mu_1 + \mu_2)$ for a population of 2. Thus we have computed the queue length dependent parameters of the composite queue.

The next step is to solve the aggregated network (shown in Figure 4.41). The aggregated network corresponds to the 3-state Markov chain

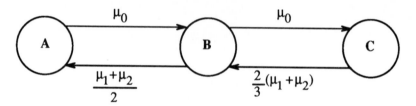

Figure 4.45 Markov chain of the aggregated network

shown in Figure 4.45. The three states A, B, and C have the following interpretation:

A : Both jobs in the AGV node

B : One job in the AGV node, the other in the composite queue

C : Both jobs in the composite queue.

One can easily visualize that state A corresponds to state (200) in the original network. State B is an aggregation of states (110) and (101), whereas state C is an aggregation of states (011), (020), and (002).

Note in Figure 4.45 that the transition rates are written down based on the composite queue characteristics. The steady-state probabilities of states A, B, and C can be derived to be

$$\pi_A = \frac{(\mu_1 + \mu_2)^2}{(\mu_1 + \mu_2)^2 + 2\mu_0 (\mu_1 + \mu_2) + 3\mu_0^2} \tag{202}$$

$$\pi_B = \frac{2\mu_0 (\mu_1 + \mu_2)}{(\mu_1 + \mu_2)^2 + 2\mu_0 (\mu_1 + \mu_2) + 3\mu_0^2} \tag{203}$$

$$\pi_C = \frac{3\mu_0^2}{(\mu_1 + \mu_2)^2 + 2\mu_0 (\mu_1 + \mu_2) + 3\mu_0^2} \tag{204}$$

The utilization of the AGV is given by $\pi_A + \pi_B$ and therefore

$$U_{AGV} = \frac{(\mu_1 + \mu_2)^2 + 2\mu_0 (\mu_1 + \mu_2)}{(\mu_1 + \mu_2)^2 + 2\mu_0 (\mu_1 + \mu_2) + 3\mu_0^2} \tag{205}$$

Comparing (198) – (201) with (202) – (205), one can conclude the aggregated CQN of Figure 4.42 is an *exact* aggregation of the CQN of Figure 4.40.

Example 4.50

The system we consider here is the same as in Figure 4.40 except that the routing of parts to M_1 or M_2 follows the shortest queue routing policy. In

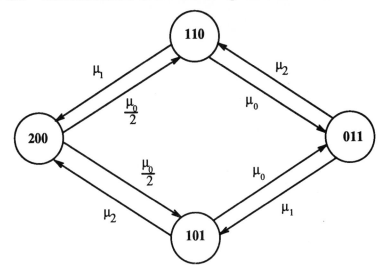

Figure 4.46 CTMC model for a population of 2 and SQR policy

SQR, we route a part to M_1 if the total number of parts in the M_1 node (i.e., in the queue plus getting serviced) is strictly less than that in the M_2 node and to M_2 if the number in the M_2 node is strictly less. When the M_1 node and M_2 node have equal number of parts, the routing is done probabilistically, with equal probability of 0.5 each. For a population of two, the network now has four states (200), (110), (101), and (011). The states (020) and (002) are not feasible because of the SQR policy. Figure 4.46 shows the CTMC model underlying this network.

The steady-state probabilities of this CTMC model can be easily obtained to be

$$\pi(200) = \frac{2\mu_1\mu_2}{\mu_0(\mu_0 + \mu_1 + \mu_2) + 2\mu_1\mu_2}$$

$$\pi(110) = \frac{\mu_0\mu_2}{\mu_0(\mu_0 + \mu_1 + \mu_2) + 2\mu_1\mu_2}$$

$$\pi(101) = \frac{\mu_0\mu_1}{\mu_0(\mu_0 + \mu_1 + \mu_2) + 2\mu_1\mu_2}$$

$$\pi(011) = \frac{\mu_0^2}{\mu_0(\mu_0 + \mu_1 + \mu_2) + 2\mu_1\mu_2}$$

From the above probabilities, it can be seen that the above CTMC model is time reversible and hence the CQN satisfies the local balance property. The throughput rate of the system is given by $\mu_0 U_{AGV}$ where the AGV utilization U_{AGV} is given by

$$U_{AGV} = \frac{2\mu_1\mu_2 + \mu_0\mu_1 + \mu_0\mu_2}{2\mu_1\mu_2 + \mu_0\left(\mu_0 + \mu_1 + \mu_2\right)}$$

In this case, the aggregated model has three states, A, B, and C, as in the previous example. The states A, B, and C have the same interpretation as earlier. The CTMC underlying the aggregated model will be, however, different from the earlier case, since the composite queue has different parameters. Figure 4.47 shows this CTMC.

The steady-state probabilities of this model are given by

$$\pi_A = \frac{2\mu_1\mu_2}{2\mu_1\mu_2 + \mu_0\left(\mu_0 + \mu_1 + \mu_2\right)}$$

$$\pi_B = \frac{\mu_0\left(\mu_1 + \mu_2\right)}{2\mu_1\mu_2 + \mu_0\left(\mu_0 + \mu_1 + \mu_2\right)}$$

$$\pi_C = \frac{\mu_0^2}{2\mu_1\mu_2 + \mu_0\left(\mu_0 + \mu_1 + \mu_2\right)}$$

These are the same as the corresponding probabilities of the original model.

The above two examples show how the technique of aggregation preserves the steady-state probabilities and performance measures of some queuing networks. In general, for product form QNs, the performance measures obtained after aggregation will be exact. However, for an arbitrary non-product form network, the performance measures obtained will be approximate in general. Extensive numerical studies have shown that the performance estimates obtained using aggregation, for non-product form QNs, are quite accurate and the percentage inaccuracies obtained are acceptable in typical modeling situations.

In summary, we can say that the technique of aggregation provides an efficient methodology for exact analysis of large product form QNs and an efficient methodology for approximate analysis of non-product form queuing networks.

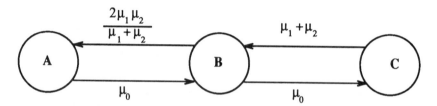

Figure 4.47 Aggregated Markov chain for Figure 4.46

Flow-Equivalence Through Response Time Preservation

In this technique, the flow-equivalent of a subnetwork is computed by obtaining an equivalent server whose response time under an assumed arrival process equals that of the isolated subnetwork. Here, starting from the original network, we first isolate the subnetwork from the original model and study the isolated subnetwork under an assumed arrival process. We replace the subnetwork by a composite queue whose response time under the assumed arrival process is equal to that of the subnetwork. Thus during the aggregation process, we are preserving the response time of the isolated subnetwork; hence, the method is referred to as the *response time preservation* (RTP)-based approximation.

We illustrate the RTP-based approximation by the following example.

Example 4.51

Consider the model of Figure 4.40. Let us make just one change to this model, namely that the AGV node is now an FCFS server with deterministic service time instead of exponential service time. Let the service time be $\frac{1}{\mu_0}$. The network ceases to be product form because of this change. However, if we can replace the deterministic FCFS server by an exponential FCFS server, the network becomes product form. RTP can be made as the basis for doing this replacement. When isolated, the deterministic FCFS server becomes an $M/D/1$ queue.

Recall that the response time of an $M/D/1$ queuing system with service time $\frac{1}{\mu_0}$ and arrival rate λ is given by (see Example 4.17)

$$W = \frac{1}{\mu_0} + \frac{\lambda}{2\mu_0(\mu_0 - \lambda)} \tag{206}$$

Also, recall that the response time W' of a standard $M/M/1$ queue with arrival rate λ' and service rate μ_0' is given by

$$W' = \frac{1}{\mu_0' - \lambda'} \tag{207}$$

For response time preservation, we have $W = W'$. Also, we have $\lambda = \lambda'$ since the isolated subnetwork and the flow-equivalent are with respect to the same arrival process. Equating (206) and (207), we get

$$\mu_0' = \lambda + \frac{2\mu_0(\mu_0 - \lambda)}{2\mu_0 - \lambda} = \frac{2\mu_0^2 - \lambda^2}{2\mu_0 - \lambda}$$

The above gives the effective service rate for the equivalent server.

In the above example, computing the parameters of the equivalent server was straightforward. In the general case, however, an iterative procedure may have to be used for this purpose. Agrawal, Buzen, and Shum [1984] have developed a general methodology for RTP-based approximation in general QN models.

The RTP-based technique for approximate analysis is similar to the Norton theorem approach in the sense that in both techniques we isolate a subsystem, equate its on-line behavior with its off-line behavior, and parameterize an equivalent server. The difference, however, is that in the Norton theorem approach we use the throughput rate as the basic parameter, whereas here we use response time. In this sense, the two approaches are duals of each other. The two techniques are complementary and are not substitutes for one another. They can sometimes be effectively combined to develop solutions for complex systems.

4.13.3 Approximations Employed in the AMS Context

QN literature abounds in a large number of approximation techniques for analyzing non-product form or very large product form networks. In the AMS context, also, several researchers have developed new techniques for approximate analysis of QN models of AMSs. We present a brief overview of some of the major efforts with special reference to AMSs.

Renewal-Approximations

The main idea here is to decompose the given network and analyze each station separately by approximating the arrival process to each station by a renewal process that is characterized by its first two moments.

Shantikumar and Buzacott [1981] have looked at an open QN model with single server stations with general service times and unlimited local buffers. The network is decomposed into a set of $GI/G/1$ queues, with the arrival process formulated using the renewal approximation. The $GI/G/1$ models are individually solved using the approximations proposed by Shantikumar and Buzacott [1980]. Shantikumar and Gocmen [1983] have extended the same approach to closed QN models using an iterative approach. Yao and Buzacott [1985b,1986a] have applied the technique to an open central server model with finite buffers and nonexponential processing times. Kamath and Sanders [1987] have used renewal approximation to evaluate large asynchronous automatic assembly systems.

Exponentialization

In this approach, the given CQN model is transformed into an exponential network where all stations have exponential processing times and all arrival processes are Poisson. Yao and Buzacott [1986b] formulated exponentialization as a fixed point problem and used it to analyze QN models of AMSs with general processing times, limited buffers, and dynamic routing schemes. This approach had earlier been employed by Chandy, Herzog, and Woo [1975b]. This approach, however, is adequate only for CQNs with a small to medium size.

Diffusion Approximation

A diffusion process can be thought of as a Markov process with a continuous state space. Diffusion approximations use the theory of diffusion processes to analyze queuing problems. Diffusion approximations have been found to be suitable for open queuing networks under heavy traffic conditions. Yao and Buzacott [1985a] have looked at an open central server network model of AMSs with limited buffers and general processing times. To obtain an approximate solution, the network is decomposed into a set of finite $GI/G/m$ queues and the individual queues are analyzed using diffusion approximation.

Approximate Mean Value Analysis

Another approach that has been pursued is to formulate MVA equations for non-product form networks employing suitable heuristics. For example, Cavaille and Dubois [1982] have presented an approximate MVA algorithm that can handle QNs with FCFS servers where the various part types may require distinct routing and distinct service time requirements. Shalev-Oren, Seidmann, and Schweitzer [1985] have extended approximate MVA methods to handle priority scheduling discipline.

PROBLEMS

1. In Example 4.49, let the routing probabilities be q and $1 - q$ $(0 < q < 1)$, instead of $\frac{\mu_1}{\mu_1 + \mu_2}$ and $\frac{\mu_2}{\mu_1 + \mu_2}$, respectively. Show that the aggregation is exact, for any arbitrary q.

2. Consider the following variant of the SQR policy in Example 4.50. In the event of a tie, a part is routed to M_1 with probability $\frac{\mu_1}{\mu_1 + \mu_2}$ and to M_2 with probability $\frac{\mu_2}{\mu_1 + \mu_2}$, instead of with equal probabilities. Investigate whether or not aggregation preserves the equilibrium probabilities in this case.

4.14 PERFORMABILITY ANALYSIS

We have seen in Chapter 2 that AMSs are highly capital-intensive and have short process life cycles. These systems have built-in redundancy in terms of flexibility so that the system can effectively cope with demand, design, and product mix changes as well as equipment failures. Guaranteed levels of productivity and payback ratio are essential for survival of such systems in competitive markets. This requires that the system flexibility is managed to achieve low lead times and high throughput. Here we present a combined performance and reliability measure for assessing the productivity either in terms of throughput or lead time over a given time horizon, in the face of failures.

One factor that has a major influence on system performance is the unscheduled down-time of the equipment due to failures. Traditionally, down-time management is done via reliability and availability theories (see Section 2.3). Also, performance and reliability issues have been dealt with separately. Reliability and availability are usually computed using Markov and combinatorial models. Discrete event simulation, Markov chains, stochastic Petri nets, and queuing networks are popular modeling tools for performance evaluation of the failure-free model. However, AMSs have a high degree of fault-tolerance induced by flexibility and can exist in various structure states (modes of operation) during the time intervals of interest, and the performance of the system degrades or enhances as the structure of the system changes with failure and repair. Thus, a combined study of performance and reliability using performability modeling is highly relevant.

4.14.1 Reliability and Availability Measures

An AMS can be considered as an interconnected system of components such as machines, automated guided vehicles (AGVs), robots, and conveyors. These components are typically prone to failures. Usually, manual or automatic repair facilities are available to restore failed components to the normal level of operation. Sometimes, reconfiguration of system resources and layout may be done in order to cope with failures of components. Failures, together with repairs and reconfiguration, constitute three basic events that we need to model, to compute the performance of AMSs in the presence of failures.

An AMS component such as a machine or an AGV can only be in two states: *up* (properly functioning) or *down* (not properly functioning).

We say a given AMS is *properly functioning* if the AMS is able to achieve a given level of performance, i.e., if the throughput exceeds a given lower bound, or the MLT is below a given upper bound, the average machine utilization is above a given threshold, and so on. We will assume that such upper bounds and lower bounds of various measures with respect to which to judge the given AMS as properly functioning are given. Another way of describing an AMS that is not functioning properly is to say that the AMS has reached a *failure state* if the performance lies out of the bounds and is *operational* if the performance is within the bounds.

First, we shall give several definitions to describe the behavior of an AMS, taking into account failures, repair, and reconfiguration.

Definition: A *fault-tolerant system* is one that has inherent capability to adapt automatically, in a well-defined manner, to failures of its components, so as to maintain continuously a specified level of performance.

The above defines a generic fault-tolerant system and includes AMSs as a special case. When the failure of a component occurs in a fault-tolerant system, the performance level can be expected to deteriorate. However, if enough standby components are available, the same level of performance can be maintained by quickly bringing up the standby components.

Definition: A fault-tolerant system is *degradable* if on the occurrence of a failure it is operable at a reduced level of performance, and *non-degradable* if the system continues to operate, producing the same level of performance, in the presence of component failures.

AMSs can be classified as fault-tolerant, degradable systems.

Definition: Given an AMS, a *structure state* of the AMS is a vector whose components describe the condition of individual AMS subsystems as influenced by failures, repairs, and reconfigurations.

The structure state of the system changes as time progresses. The dynamics of the state transitions are captured via the structure state process defined below.

Definition: Let $Z(u)$ be the structure state of an AMS at time $u \geq 0$. Then the family of random variables $\{Z(u) : u \geq 0\}$ is called the *structure state process* (SSP) of the AMS.

The SSP of an AMS essentially characterizes the dynamics of the

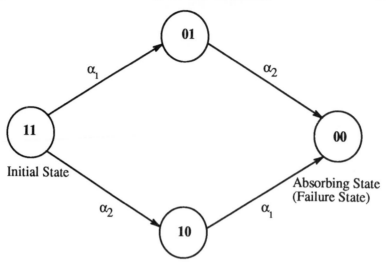

Figure 4.48 SSP for the AMS in Example 4.52 (non-repairable case)

system structure and environmental influences, taking into account only the events concerned with failures, repairs, and reconfigurations.

Example 4.52

Consider an AMS comprising two machines, M_1 and M_2, which are operated in parallel. When up, M_1 can produce parts at a rate of $\mu_1/$ h and M_2 can produce at $\mu_2/$ h. Assume that M_1 is faster than M_2 $(\mu_1 > \mu_2)$. Let the failure times of M_i $(i = 1, 2)$ be exponentially distributed with rate α_i and be independent. The structure state vector has two components here, the first indicating the status of M_1, and the second, the status of M_2. Let the state of M_i $(i = 1, 2)$ be designated 1 if M_i is up, and 0 if M_i is down. Then the AMS has four structure states given by

$$S = \{(11),(10),(01),(00)\}$$

S is the state space of the structure state process. Since the up times of M_1 and M_2 are independent exponential random variables, the SSP is a continuous time Markov chain.

Two cases would arise here, namely the system is non-repairable (failed machines are not repaired) and the system is repairable (failed machines are repaired). In the former case, the Markov chain model for the SSP is shown in Figure 4.48 [note that the state (00) is an absorbing state]. Figure 4.49 shows the Markov SSP model for the repairable case, assuming that: (i) the repair times of M_1 and M_2 are independent exponential random

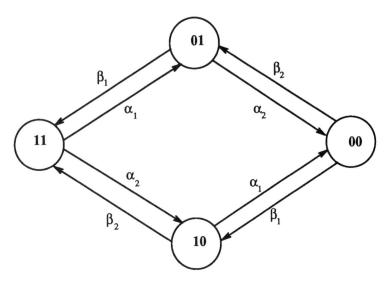

Figure 4.49 SSP for the AMS in Example 4.52 (repairable case)

variables with rates β_1 and β_2, respectively, and (ii) there is a dedicated repair facility for each machine and the repair starts immediately on failure.

Note that this AMS is fault-tolerant and degradable, with a different level of performance in each structure state.

We now define two important measures, *reliability* and *availability*. Note that these definitions are the same as in Section 2.3.7.

Definition: The *reliability* of a system over an observation period $[0, t]$ is the probability that the system is functioning properly throughout the observation period (that is, the system does not reach a failure state during $[0, t]$).

We reiterate that the phrase *functioning properly* is with respect to a certain prespecified performance requirement. For instance, in the above example of two machines, functioning properly may mean both machines working or it may mean at least one machine working.

Example 4.53

In Example 4.52, consider the non-repairable case, where the SSP is described by the Markov chain $\{Z(u) : u \geq 0\}$ of Figure 4.48. Let the state (00) be designated the system failure state. Let $Z(0) = (11)$. If the observation period is $[0, t]$, then the reliability in this case is given by

$$R(t) = P\{T > t\}$$

where T is the time to reach state (00). Note that if

$$p_{ij}(u) = P\{Z(u) = j \mid Z(0) = i\}; \quad i, j \in S$$

give the transition probabilities of the Markov chain model, we have

$$R(t) = 1 - p_{(11),(00)}(t)$$
$$= p_{(11),(11)}(t) + p_{(11),(10)}(t) + p_{(11),(01)}(t)$$

Definition: The *instantaneous availability* $A(u)$ of a system, at time $u \geq 0$, is the probability that the system is properly functioning at time u.

Note that if the system is non-repairable and started in the properly functioning state, then the availability $A(u)$ and the reliability $R(u)$ are identical. However, if the system is repairable, availability and reliability will be different. For, at a given time u, the system may be functioning properly because of two mutually exclusive events: (i) The system was properly functioning throughout the observation period $[0, t]$. (ii) The system was not properly functioning in various subintervals of $[0, t]$, but it is properly functioning at the instant u.

Availability is therefore a better measure than reliability to characterize repairable systems. Availability models usually assume that all failures are recoverable and therefore the SSP will be an irreducible Markov chain. If we assume that some failures are irrecoverable, the system will have an absorbing state (or failure state) and in such cases we study the system reliability, which will be the same as system availability. Often, we are also interested in steady-state availability, defined as follows:

Definition: The *steady-state availability*, A, of a system is the limiting value of availability $A(u)$ as $u \to \infty$. Thus,

$$A = \lim_{u \to \infty} A(u)$$

Note that $A = 0$ for non-repairable systems. For repairable systems, A is the fraction of time the system functions properly.

4.14.2 Performability Measures

Now we present composite measures that combine both performance and reliability aspects, using the notions of *structure state process* and *accumulated rewards*. Let $\{Z(u) : u \geq 0\}$ be the SSP of an AMS. In each structure state, the system can be associated with a performance index that may be MLT, throughput, WIP, machine utilization, etc. In the most general case, the chosen performance index is a random variable. Our discussion in this section centers around MLT and throughput because these are important and encompass other performance measures.

Definition: Given a structure state i, its associated *reward* f_i is a random variable that describes the performance of the system in that structure state.

Let $[0, t]$ be an observation period. In the AMS context, this could be, for example, a shift period. Let $S = \{0, 1, 2, ..., m\}$ be the state space of the SSP. For $i = 0, 1, 2, ..., m$, define τ_i as the total time during $[0, t]$ that the SSP spends in state i. Note that $t = \sum_{i=0}^{m} \tau_i$. The sum $\sum_{i=0}^{m} f_i \tau_i$ would then give the total accumulated reward during the period $[0, t]$.

Definition: Given (i) an AMS with structure state process $\{Z(u) : u \geq 0\}$ having state space $S = \{0, 1, 2, ..., m\}$, and (ii) rewards $f_0, f_1, ..., f_m$ in the individual structure states, the *performability* $Y_t(s)$ over an observation period $[0, t]$ and with initial structure state as $s \in S$, is a random variable given by

$$Y_t(s) = \sum_{i=0}^{m} f_i \tau_i$$

where τ_i is the total time during $[0, t]$ that the SSP stays in state i.

In the performability context, we will be interested in three measures: performability distribution, steady-state performability, and interval performability. These are defined below:

Definition: The *performability distribution* is the cumulative distribution function of performability $Y_t(s)$, i.e., $P\{Y_t(s) \leq x\}$ for $x \in \mathbf{R}$. The limit $\lim_{t \to \infty} Y_t(s)$, if it exists, is called the *steady-state performability*; and the expected value $E[Y_t(s)]$ is called the *interval performability*.

Example 4.54

Consider the system of Example 4.52 and assume that repairs are not possible. The SSP of the system is given in Figure 4.48. Let us relabel the state (00) as state 0, (01) as 1, (10) as 2, and (11) as 3. The state space S of the SSP is then given by $S = \{0, 1, 2, 3\}$. Assume that 3 is the initial state.

First we look at throughput-related performability. For this, we choose reward f_i $(i = 0, 1, 2, 3)$ as the average throughput rate in state i. Assuming that raw parts are always available, we then have

$$f_0 = 0; \quad f_1 = \mu_2; \quad f_2 = \mu_1; \quad f_3 = \mu_1 + \mu_2$$

In an observation period $[0, t]$, let τ_i as usual denote the time spent in state i. We then see that the sum $\tau_1 \mu_2 + \tau_2 \mu_1 + \tau_3 (\mu_1 + \mu_2)$ is the total accumulated average throughput during $[0, t]$. This will be denoted by $Y_t(3)$. By computing the distribution functions of τ_1, τ_2, and τ_3, one can evaluate, for any throughput lower bound x, the probability, $P\{Y_t(3) > x\}$, of exceeding a throughput of x during $[0, t]$. Now, $E[Y_t(3)]$ is the interval performability or average throughput.

Next we look at MLT-related performability. Let W_1, W_2, and W_3 be the average MLTs in states 1, 2, and 3, respectively. Since no parts are produced in state 0, it does not affect the analysis.

Suppose D is a desired upper bound on MLT and we choose the rewards as

$$f_1 = 0; \quad f_i = (W_i - D) Q_i \quad (i = 1, 2, 3),$$

where W_i represents the average MLT and Q_i the average throughput in state i. The accumulated reward is

$$Y_t(3) = \sum_{i=0}^{3} \tau_i (W_i - D) Q_i$$

Now consider

$$P\{Y_t(3) < 0\} = P\left\{\sum_{i=0}^{3} \tau_i (W_i - D) Q_i < 0\right\}$$

$$= P\left\{\sum_{i=0}^{3} \tau_i W_i Q_i < \sum_{i=0}^{3} \tau_i D Q_i\right\}$$

$$= P\left\{\frac{\sum_{i=0}^{3} \tau_i W_i Q_i}{\sum_{i=0}^{3} \tau_i Q_i} < D\right\}$$

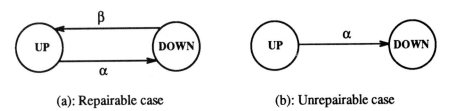

(a): Repairable case   (b): Unrepairable case

Figure 4.50 Structure state processes for a single machine system

The above probability can be interpreted as the probability of the overall average MLT during $[0, t]$ being less than a desired upper bound D.

Thus, by appropriately defining the rewards, one can compute performability measures of various kinds. The above discussion can be extended to the case when the SSP is as described in Figure 4.49.

4.14.3 Machine Center with Infinite Waiting Space

Here we consider an NC machine center consisting of a single, failure-prone NC machine. The architecture of such a system was described earlier in Chapter 2 (Figure 2.10). We shall illustrate the performability concept for the single-part-type case. Generalization to the multiple-part-type case can be easily carried out. Two natural and possibly the simplest queuing models that are applicable to the present problem are:

1. $M/M/1/\infty$ queue with breakdowns.
2. $M/M/1/N$ queue with breakdowns.

For both of the above models, the SSP is the same and has only two states: machine in working condition ("up") and machine in failed condition ("down"). Assuming that the time to next failure and the time to repair are independent exponential random variables, this SSP will be a Markov chain. Figure 4.50(a) shows the state diagram of the SSP assuming the machine is repairable, and Figure 4.50(b) shows the SSP for the unrepairable case. In the latter case, the down state will be an absorbing state.

In our discussion here, we shall restrict to the steady-state performability of the first model, $M/M/1/\infty$ queues with breakdowns, assuming that the system is repairable. Our discussion here is based on the treatment in Section 4.6 and does not use the notions of SSP and accumulated rewards.

Assume that raw parts arrive into the system according to a Poisson process with rate λ and the service times of parts are i.i.d. exponential random variables with mean $1/\mu$. The machine is assumed to break down such that the time between successive failures is an exponential random variable with mean $1/\alpha$. The service is interrupted immediately on a failure and simultaneously the repair commences. Repair times are assumed to be i.i.d. exponential random variables with mean $1/\beta$. As soon as repair finishes, the machine resumes processing on the interrupted workpiece. To complete the model description, we additionally assume the following:

1. The machine can fail when it is idle or when it is processing a part.

2. When the machine is under repair, no further failures can occur.

For this system, we now compute two steady-state performability measures, namely average MLT and average WIP. To this end, we first write down the rate balance equations. Figure 4.12 shows the state diagram of this queuing system. Let $X(u)$ be the state of the machine at time u, and $Y(u)$ the number of parts in the system at time u. We see that the stochastic process $\{(X(u), Y(u)) : u \geq 0\}$ constitutes a continuous time Markov chain. Let 0 indicate the machine down condition, and 1 indicate that the machine is up. The state space of the process is

$$S = \{(i,j) : i \in \{0,1\}, j \in \{0,1,2,...\}\}$$

Let $\pi(i,j)$ be the steady-state probability of state (i,j). The rate balance equations are given by (91) and (92). We have shown that the mean WIP in the steady-state denoted by L, and the mean MLT in the steady-state denoted by W are given by

$$L = \frac{\lambda \left[(\alpha + \beta)^2 + \mu\alpha\right]}{(\alpha + \beta)\left[\beta(\mu - \lambda) - \lambda\alpha\right]} \tag{208}$$

$$W = \frac{L}{\lambda} = \frac{(\alpha + \beta)^2 + \mu\alpha}{(\alpha + \beta)\left[\beta(\mu - \lambda) - \lambda\alpha\right]} \tag{209}$$

The condition for the stability of this queuing system is given by

$$\frac{1}{\lambda} > \frac{1}{\mu}\left(1 + \frac{\alpha}{\beta}\right) \tag{210}$$

The term $1/\left(1 + \frac{\alpha}{\beta}\right)$ is the steady-state probability of the machine being "up" and is therefore the *steady-state availability* of the system.

Further, the quantity $\frac{1}{\mu}\left(1 + \frac{\alpha}{\beta}\right)$ will give the *mean completion time* of a part.

For the above system, performance measures of the associated $M/M/1/\infty$ queue without breakdowns would give the "performance" related measures whereas steady-state availability would give a "reliability" measure. The mean completion time, mean steady-state WIP as given by (208), and mean steady-state MLT as given by (209) would give performability measures.

Example 4.55

Consider a machine center with one machine that can produce 20 parts/ h (mean processing time = 3 min). Fixtured raw parts are found to arrive according to a Poisson process with rate 10/ h (average of 6 min for interarrival time). The machine is assumed to fail randomly and the average repair time is assumed to be 1 h. We can model the above system as an $M/M/1/\infty$ queue with breakdowns. Figure 4.51 shows the variation of mean steady-state MLT as a function of the failure rate α (the average WIP is linearly related to mean MLT, and hence behaves similarly). For an $M/M/1/\infty$ queue without failures, the mean MLT would be 6 min and the mean WIP would be 1. It is observed from the graph in Figure 4.51 that the MLT (as well as WIP) tends to ∞ as α approaches the value of 1/ h. The graph shows that inventory levels and lead times can rise rapidly if the system is prone to increasing rates of failures.

4.14.4 Central Server FMS Without Repair

In this section we look at the computation of the distributions of performability measures using the notions of structure state process and accumulated rewards. The example that we consider is that of a central server FMS, as shown in Figure 4.52.

Here we have one AGV for material handling and there is a single machine center with m identical machines in it. If the AGV and the machines are prone to failure, then the structure state process $\{Z(u) : u \geq 0\}$ for this system will have the state space $\{0, 1, ..., m\}$ where the interpretation of the states is as follows:

0 : AGV failed or all machines failed

i : AGV operating and exactly i machines working $(i = 1, 2, ..., m)$.

Let the time to failure of the AGV and the time to failure of each machine be exponentially distributed with rates α_A and α, respectively, and let the failures be independent of one another. Let us assume that a

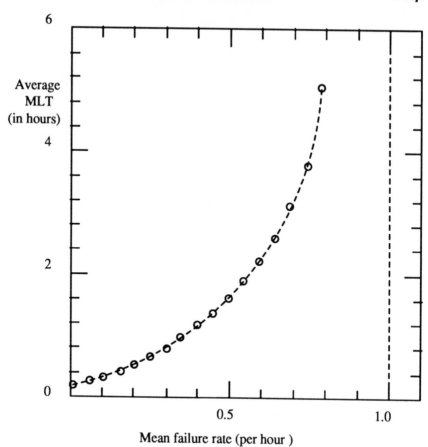

Figure 4.51 Variation of average MLT with failure rate

device (AGV or machine), once failed, is not repaired in the observation period. In such a case, the state transition graph of the SSP is as shown in Figure 4.53.

The SSP depicted in Figure 4.53 is the same as the one considered by Donatiello and Iyer [1987]. We will follow the same approach as presented by Donatiello and Iyer to compute the performability distribution of this FMS. The scenario we consider is the following: the FMS in question has an AGV and m machines which are failure prone. The system has n fixtures. At the end of an observation period, say a shift period of 8 h, the FMS is to meet a minimum production target and also produce the parts in as short a time as possible. Let the observation period be $[0, t]$, the total production during this period $Q(t)$, and the MLT of a typical part, $W(t)$. Also, assume that x is a given production target, w a desired MLT, and p

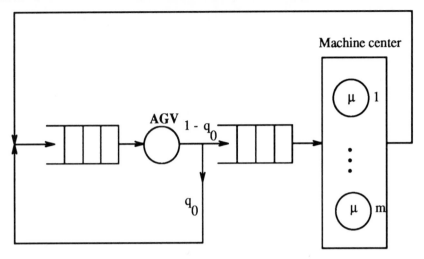

Figure 4.52 Central server FMS with m identical machines

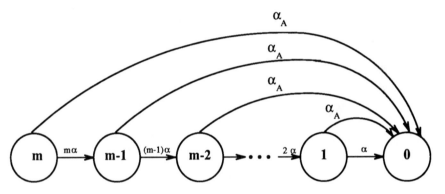

Figure 4.53 SSP for the central server FMS without repair

a desired probability. We would like to answer questions such as:

1. For a given $m, x,$ and $p,$ how many fixtures should we employ, i.e., what should be the value of n in order that

$$P\{Q(t) > x\} > p \qquad (211)$$

$$P\{W(t) < x\} > p \qquad (212)$$

2. For a given $n, x, w,$ and $p,$ how many machines (m) should we employ so as to satisfy (211) or (212)?

3. What are the values of $E[Q(t)]$ and $E[W(t)]$?

4. For a given x, w, p, and n, what should be t (how long should the shift be operated?) so that (211) is satisfied?

All the above questions can be answered by computing over $[0, t]$ the throughput-related and MLT-related performability distributions. To achieve this, we proceed as follows.

Consider the SSP $\{Z(u): u \geq 0\}$ of Figure 4.53. Let f_i be the reward associated with state i ($i = 0, 1, ..., m$). Assume that the initial state is m (i.e., all the machines and the AGV are functioning). In the observation period $[0, t]$, the accumulated reward or the performability is given by

$$Y_t(m) = \sum_{i=0}^{m} f_i \tau_i$$

where τ_i is the total time during $[0, t]$ the SSP stays in state i. Starting from state m, the evolution of the SSP during $[0, t]$ can fall into three different categories.

1. The SSP stays in state m throughout the interval, without making a transition to any other state.

2. The SSP transits to state 0 directly from state m sometime during the interval and will therefore stay in state 0 for the rest of the interval.

3. The SSP transits to state $m - 1$ at some instant during the observation period. Its evolution during the rest of the interval will follow the same pattern as the original process, except that the initial state will be $m - 1$.

The above observations form the basis of a recursive formulation for the evolution of the SSP over $[0, t]$. To write down the recursive formulation, we first introduce some notation. Let C be a general condition. Define the indicator function

$$I(C) = 1 \quad \text{if } C \text{ is true}$$
$$= 0 \quad \text{if } C \text{ is false}$$

Let p_{ij} ($i = 0, 1, ..., m; j \leq i$) denote the probability of a single-step transition from state i to state j. Note that, for $k = 1, 2, ..., m$,

$$p_{k,0} = \frac{\alpha_A}{\alpha_A + k\alpha}$$
$$p_{k,k-1} = \frac{k\alpha}{\alpha_A + k\alpha}$$

For $k = 0, 1, ..., m$, let $c_k = \alpha_A + k\alpha$. It may be verified that the sojourn time in state $k \geq 1$ is exponentially distributed with rate c_k. Therefore, $e^{-c_m t}$ gives the probability that the SSP stays in the initial state m throughout the interval $[0, t]$.

Consider the probability $P\{Y_t(m) < y\}$ where $y > 0$. This can be split into three terms, based on the three observations above. It can be shown, for $m > 1$, that

$$P\{Y_t(m) < y\} = I(f_m t < y)\, e^{-c_m t}$$

$$+ \int_0^t c_m e^{-c_m x} p_{m0} I\left([f_m x + f_0(t - x)] < y\right) dx$$

$$+ \int_0^t c_m e^{-c_m x} p_{m,m-1} P\{Y_{t-x}(m-1) < y - f_m x\} dx$$

$$(213)$$

Equation (213) gives a recursive formulation for computing the distribution of performability. For $m = 1$, this equation applies without the first term in the two integrals and after setting $p_{m,m-1} = 1$. Also, $Y_t(0) = f_0 t$, and $c_0 = 0$ since state 0 is an absorbing state of the SSP. The solution of (213), proposed by Donatiello and Iyer [1987], uses the double Laplace-Stieltjes transform of the distribution $P\{Y_t(m) < y\}$ to unfold the recursion into an efficient computational procedure. We do not present the details of this procedure, but only give some interesting numerical results obtained using the software implementation of the above procedure.

Example 4.56

First we look at a central server FMS with the number of fixtures, $n = 12$. Let the observation period be a shift of 8 h. The other parameters are: number of machines $= m$ (variable); exit probability of a finished part leaving the system (with the simultaneous entry of a new part) is $q_0 = 0.2$, implying that a workpiece undergoes five material handling operations and four machining operations on the average.

The rate of material movement by the AGV (μ_0) is assumed to be 100 parts/h, and the mean processing rate of a machine (μ_1) is 20 parts/h.

Mean time to failure (MTTF) of AGV = 8 h.

MTTF of each machine = 16 h.

Table 4.3 shows the probability that the number of finished parts produced in the shift period exceeds x for $x = 20, 30, 40, 50, 60,$ and 70, for $m =$

Table 4.3 Throughput-related performability distribution

| No. of machines | Probability that the throughput exceeds x, P{Q(t) > x} | | | | | |
| | Target production level, x | | | | | |
	20	30	40	50	60	70
1	0.4724	0.3247	0.0000	0.0000	0.0000	0.0000
2	0.7407	0.6200	0.5126	0.3760	0.2724	0.1941
3	0.8338	0.7525	0.6738	0.5942	0.5137	0.4364
4	0.8675	0.8043	0.7429	0.6831	0.6240	0.5655
5	0.8781	0.8214	0.7671	0.7151	0.6650	0.6163
6	0.8811	0.8265	0.7748	0.7258	0.6792	0.6347
7	0.8819	0.8281	0.7773	0.7294	0.6841	0.6413
8	0.8822	0.8286	0.7781	0.7306	0.6859	0.6438

$1, 2, ..., 8$. Using Table 4.3, we can answer questions such as, "What is the initial number of 'up' machines so that the probability of the total production in the shift exceeding a given number is greater than a given probability?" For example, if it is required that this probability should be greater than 0.75, then we need three machines to surpass a target of 20 parts (and also 30 parts); five machines to surpass a target of 40 parts, etc.

Example 4.57

We now consider MLT-related performability for the central server FMS. Let the shift duration be 8 h, $m = 4$, $1/\alpha_A = 8$ h, $1/\alpha = 16$ h. (Other parameters are the same as in Example 4.56.) For different lower bounds on MLT, and for different numbers of fixtures, Table 4.4 shows the probability values of attaining the lower bounds on MLT. Table 4.4 can be used to answer the question, "What is the maximum number of fixtures that may be employed so that the probability of the MLT being less than a specified value exceeds a desired probability?" For example, if the desired probability is 0.99, then we can employ at most four fixtures for a lower bound of 35 min, at most 12 fixtures for a lower bound of 85 min, etc.

Modern automated manufacturing systems possess characteristics such as flexibility, fault-tolerance, and degradability in performance. Neither pure reliability analysis nor pure performance analysis can accurately

Table 4.4 MLT-related performability

No. of fixtures	Probability that MLT is less than a specified value, P{W(t) < w}						
	Desired MLT, w (min)						
	25.0	35.0	45.0	55.0	65.0	75.0	85.0
4	0.9633	0.9969	1.0000	1.0000	1.0000	1.0000	1.0000
5	0.8625	0.9859	0.9983	1.0000	1.0000	1.0001	1.0000
6	0.6449	0.9636	0.9925	0.9988	0.9999	1.0000	1.0000
7	0.0000	0.9005	0.9814	0.9952	0.9991	0.9999	1.0000
8	0.0000	0.8141	0.9600	0.9883	0.9966	0.9993	0.9999
9	0.0000	0.6258	0.9128	0.9777	0.9920	0.9974	0.9994
10	0.0000	0.4323	0.8506	0.9565	0.9847	0.9940	0.9979
11	0.0000	0.0000	0.7820	0.9184	0.9745	0.9888	0.9954
12	0.0000	0.0000	0.6003	0.8701	0.9535	0.9816	0.9915
13	0.0000	0.0000	0.4582	0.8163	0.9215	0.9711	0.9860
14	0.0000	0.0000	0.0000	0.7220	0.8821	0.9511	0.9790
15	0.0000	0.0000	0.0000	0.5810	0.8381	0.9234	0.9678

capture the behavior of such systems. Integrated performance-reliability or performability studies therefore assume great importance.

In this section we have shown, through illustrative examples of manufacturing systems, the utmost relevance of performability modeling in AMS design. The performability measures we have considered deal with throughput and manufacturing lead time, which essentially decide the competitiveness of a plant.

The presentation in this section is based on the dissertation work of Ram [1991] and the paper by Viswanadham, Narahari, and Ram [1991]. For more details on this topic, the above two references may be consulted.

PROBLEMS

1. Obtain expressions for the steady-state performability measures of an $M/M/1/N$ queue with breakdowns and repair, under the assumptions of Section 4.14.3.
2. Consider the $M/M/1/\infty$ model with breakdowns and no repair. The structure state process was shown in Figure 4.50(b). Obtain the throughput-related and

MLT-related performability measures for this system, over a finite observation period. Attempt to compute these measures if the system is repairable.

3. For the machine repairman model with interpretation as in Example 3.37, write down the state diagram of the structure state process assuming that the system is non-repairable. Obtain a recursive formulation similar to Equation (213).

4. Consider the classical central server AMS model of Figure 4.29. Assuming that all the machines have i.i.d. failure times, exponentially distributed with rate α, and the AGV has a failure time exponentially distributed with rate α_A, obtain the structure state process under the non-repairable case. How will you formulate recursive equations to compute throughput-related and MLT-related performability measures over a finite observation period $[0, t]$?

4.15 BIBLIOGRAPHIC NOTES AND BIBLIOGRAPHY

Performance evaluation and operations research literature abounds in publications related to the theory and applications of queues and queuing networks. Indeed, queuing theory is now a well-developed, well-researched, and mature topic. Putting together the material in this chapter was therefore that much simplified because of the availability of excellent treatises. In particular, we have benefited by looking through the works by Kleinrock [1975], White, Schmidt, and Bennett [1975], Allen [1978], Kelly [1979], Sauer and Chandy [1981], Trivedi [1982], Lavenberg [1983], Bhat [1984], Gross and Harris [1985], Bertsekas and Gallager [1987], Gelenbe and Pujolle [1987], and Wolff [1989]. We have also adapted many examples in these books to fit into the manufacturing setting and also added our own original examples to present the techniques and tools. The book by Bruell and Balbo [1980] deals exclusively with computational methods for queuing networks. Lavenberg [1989] has recently surveyed the important results in this area. There have been a large number of survey articles written in this area over the years but we have not mentioned them here.

The early material in this chapter, on $M/M/1, M/M/m, M/G/1$, and bulk queues, has been compiled from several of the sources above. We would like to mention three fundamental references of interest here: the remarkable result of Little [1961] and the trend-setting work of Burke [1956, 1968]. There is also an informative book by Cohen [1969] on the single server queuing system. The section on queues with breakdowns is based on the papers by Gaver [1962] and Mitrani and Avi-Itzhak [1968]. Nicola, Kulkarni, and Trivedi [1987] have presented a general technique for analyzing single server queues with breakdowns. Doshi [1990] has surveyed the state-of-the-art in the topic of single server queues with vacations.

The flexible machine center problem, discussed in Section 7, is taken from the recent paper by Ram and Viswanadham [1990]. This section is concerned with the application of the polling models of queuing theory in the manufacturing systems context. Two authoritative survey articles on polling models are by Takagi [1988] and Kleinrock and Levy [1988].

Queuing networks have been the most important modeling paradigm for automated and flexible manufacturing systems. A large number of publications exist in this area. The papers by Buzacott [1985], Suri [1985], and Narahari and Viswanadham [1989] are general articles dealing not only with QN models but also other modeling paradigms. The doctoral works of Shantikumar [1979], Hildebrandt [1980], Stecke [1981], and Yao [1983] are concerned exclusively with QN modeling of manufacturing systems. The excellent survey articles by Buzacott and Yao [1986a, 1986b] give an overview of QN modeling of AMSs. Seidmann, Schweitzer, and Shalev-Oren [1987] have evaluated four different computational methods developed for solving closed QN models of AMSs.

In the AMS context, there have been several papers dealing with QN models. The important ones include Solberg [1977] (the first paper to give a closed QN formulation of flexible manufacturing systems); Buzacott and Shantikumar [1980]; Stecke and Solberg [1981]; Shantikumar and Buzacott [1981]; Cavaille and Dubois [1982]; Dallery and David [1983]; Shantikumar and Sargent [1983]; Shantikumar and Gocmen [1983]; Suri and Hildebrandt [1984]; Buzacott and Shantikumar [1985]; Seidmann, Schweitzer, and Shalev-Oren [1987]; Yao and Buzacott [1985a, 1985b, 1986a, 1986b]; Vinod and Altiok [1986]; Suri and Diehl [1986]; Dallery and Yao [1986]; Kamath and Sanders [1987]; Yao and Buzacott [1987]; and Li Zhuang and Hindi [1990, 1991a, 1991b].

The material that we have presented in Sections 8, 9, 10, and 11 has been mainly put together from the textbooks mentioned earlier, whereas the source for Sections 12 and 13 is provided by several papers. Here, again, we would like to mention some sources that are fundamental in nature: Cox [1955], Jackson [1957], Jackson [1963], Gordon and Newell [1967], Baskett, Chandy, Muntz, and Palacios-Gomez [1975], Kelly [1976], and Chandy, Howard, and Towsley [1977]. Computational algorithms have an important place in this area. Buzen [1973] and Reiser and Lavenberg [1980] have contributed the two principal techniques of convolution method and the mean value analysis, respectively. Bruell and Balbo [1980] have collected together many of the computational algorithms. More recently, Conway and Georganas [1989] have given an account of exact computational algorithms for queuing networks. They have discussed many of the recently developed algorithms, such as RE-CAL (Recursion by Chain Algorithm) and MVAC (MVA by Chain). Two other developments in the computational techniques are the tree convolution method of Lam and Lien [1983] and the tree MVA method of Tucci and Sauer [1985]. Several software packages have been developed for aiding system designers to analyze queuing models, including the RESQ package (Chow, MacNair, and Sauer [1984]; Sauer, Reiser, and MacNair [1977]), the QNA package (Whitt [1983]), and the package PANACEA (Ramakrishnan and Mitra [1989]). In the manufacturing systems context, the packages CAN-Q (Solberg [1980]), MANUPLAN (Suri and Diehl [1985]), and MVAQ (Suri and Hildebrandt [1984]) are quite popular. Seidmann, Schweitzer, and Shalev-Oren [1987] have surveyed and compared four existing closed QN analysis packages for manufacturing systems.

On the important topic of QNs with blocking, there is a recent survey by Onvural [1990] and several contributions by Akyildiz [1987, 1988a, 1988b] and Akyildiz and Von Brand [1989]. One of the early contributions was by Boxma and Konheim [1981].

In the section on QN approximations, we have mainly used the papers by Chandy, Herzog, and Woo [1975a, 1975b], the survey paper by Chandy and Sauer [1978], the paper by Agrawal, Buzen, and Shum [1984] (Response time preservation technique) and the unifying book by Agrawal [1985]. There are a number of important papers in this area, which we have omitted here. Also, many of the papers on QN modeling of AMSs deal with approximate analysis techniques.

We have not touched upon the important topics of sensitivity analysis in queuing networks. A survey appears in Liu and Nain [1989]. The technique originated by Ho [1987], called perturbation analysis, is an important landmark in this area. Suri [1989] has given a tutorial introduction to perturbation analysis. Suri and Dille [1985] have used this technique in the AMS context.

The important topic of performability of AMSs is a recent one, first considered by Albino, Okogbaa, and Shell [1990]. Earlier, Kanth and Viswanadham [1989] had considered pure reliability analysis of flexible manufacturing systems. The article by Viswanadham, Narahari, and Ram [1991] presents a comprehensive treatment of the notion of performability in the AMS context. Ram [1991] has also treated this topic in much detail. The notion of performability is an extensively researched subject in the fault-tolerant computing literature. Beaudry [1978] introduced performance-related reliability measures for gracefully degrading fault-tolerant systems. Meyer [1980] used the term *performability* for the first time and pioneered early research work on this topic. Reibman [1990] has given a tutorial introduction to performability modeling in computer systems. In our treatment of $M/M/1/\infty$ queue with breakdowns, we have used the results of Gaver [1962] and of Mitrani and Avi-Itzhak [1968]. Performability analysis of the $M/M/1/N$ queue has been considered by Bobbio and Trivedi [1986]. The treatment of the central server FMS without repair is based on the recursive formulation of Donatiello and Iyer [1987].

BIBLIOGRAPHY

1. **Agrawal, S.C. [1985].** *Metamodeling: A Study of Approximations in Queuing Models*, Research Reports and Notes, Computer Systems Series, The MIT Press, Cambridge, Massachusetts.

2. **Agrawal, S.C., J.P. Buzen, and A.W. Shum [1984].** Response Time Preservation: A General Technique for Developing Approximate Algorithms for Queuing Networks, *Proceedings of 1984 ACM SIGMETRICS Conference on Measurement and Modeling of Computer Systems*, August 1984, pp. 222–258.

3. **Akyildiz, I.F. [1987].** Exact Product Form Solutions for Queuing Networks with Blocking, *IEEE Transactions on Computers*, Vol. C-37, pp. 121–126.

4. **Akyildiz, I.F. [1988a].** On the Exact and Approximate Throughput Analysis of Closed Queuing Networks with Blocking, *IEEE Transactions on Software Engineering*, Vol. SE-14, pp. 62–71.

5. **Akyildiz, I.F. [1988b].** Mean Value Analysis for Blocking Queuing Networks, *IEEE Transactions on Software Engineering*, Vol. SE-14, No. 1, pp. 418–429.

6. **Akyildiz, I.F., and H. Von Brand [1989].** Central Server Models with Multiple Job Classes, State Dependent Routing, and Rejection Blocking, *IEEE Transactions on Software Engineering*, Vol. 15, No. 10, pp. 1305–1312.

7. **Albino, V., G.O. Okogbaa, and R.L. Shell [1990].** Computerized Integrated Performance-Reliability Measure of a Flexible Production System, *Computers and Industrial Engineering*, Vol. 18, No. 4, pp. 547–558.

8. **Allen, A.O. [1978].** *Probability, Statistics, and Queuing Theory with Computer Science Applications,* Academic Press, New York.

9. **Baskett, F., K.M. Chandy, R.R. Muntz, and F. Palacios-Gomez [1975].** Open, Closed, and Mixed Networks of Queues with Different Classes of Customers, *Journal of ACM*, Vol. 22, pp. 248–260.

10. **Beaudry, M. [1978].** Performance-related Reliability Measures for Computer Systems, *IEEE Transactions on Computers*, Vol. 27, No. 6, June 1978, pp. 248–255.

11. **Bertsekas, D., and R. Gallager [1987].** *Data Networks*, Prentice-Hall, Englewood Cliffs, New Jersey.

12. **Bhat, U.N. [1984].** *Elements of Applied Stochastic Processes*, John Wiley, New York.

13. **Bobbio, A., and K.S. Trivedi [1986].** An Aggregation Technique for the Transient Analysis of Stiff Markov Chains, *IEEE Transactions on Computers*, Vol. 35, No. 9, September 1986, pp. 803–814.

14. **Boxma, O., and A. Konheim [1981].** Approximate Analysis of Exponential Queuing Systems with Blocking, *Acta Informatica*, Vol. 15, pp. 19–66.

15. **Bruell, S.C., and G. Balbo [1980].** *Computational Algorithms for Closed Queuing Networks*, Elsevier, North-Holland, New York.

16. **Burke, P.J. [1956].** The Output of Queuing Systems, *Operations Research*, Vol. 4, pp. 699–704.

17. **Burke, P.J. [1968].** The Output Process of a Stationary M/M/s Queuing System, *The Annals of Mathematical Statistics*, Vol. 39, No. 4, pp. 1144–1152.

18. **Buzacott, J.A. [1985].** Modeling Manufacturing Systems, *Robotics and Computer Integrated Manufacturing*, Vol. 2, No. 1, pp. 25–32.

19. **Buzacott, J.A., and J.G. Shantikumar [1980].** Models for Understanding Flexible Manufacturing Systems, *AIIE Transactions*, Vol. 12, pp. 339–350.

20. **Buzacott, J.A., and J.G. Shantikumar [1985].** On Approximate Queuing Models of Dynamic Jobshops, *Management Science*, Vol. 31, pp. 870–887.

21. **Buzacott, J.A., and D.D. Yao [1986a].** On Queuing Network Models of Flexible Manufacturing Systems, *Queuing Systems*, Vol. 1, pp. 5–27.

22. **Buzacott, J.A., and D.D. Yao [1986b].** Flexible Manufacturing Systems: A Review of Analytical Models, *Management Science*, Vol. 32, No. 7, July 1986, pp. 890–905.

23. **Buzen, J.P. [1973].** Computational Algorithms for Closed Queuing Networks with Exponential Servers, *Communications of the ACM*, Vol. 16, pp. 527–531.

24. **Cavaille, J.B., and D. Dubois [1982].** Heuristic Methods Based on Mean Value Analysis for Flexible Manufacturing Systems Performance Evaluation, *Proceedings of 21st IEEE Conference on Decision and Control*, Orlando, Florida, pp. 1061–1065.

25. **Chandy, K.M., U. Herzog, and L. Woo [1975a].** Parametric Analysis of Queuing Networks, *IBM Journal of Research and Development*, Vol. 19, No. 1, January 1975, pp. 43–49.

26. **Chandy, K.M., U. Herzog, and L. Woo [1975b].** Approximate Analysis of General Queuing Networks, *IBM Journal of Research and Development*, Vol. 19, No. 1, January 1975, pp. 36–42.

27. **Chandy, K.M., J.H. Howard, and D.F. Towsley [1977].** Product Form and Local Balance in Queuing Networks, *Journal of ACM*, Vol. 24, pp. 250–263.

28. **Chandy, K.M., and C.H. Sauer [1978].** Approximate Methods for Analyzing Queuing Network Models of Computer Systems, *ACM Computing Surveys*, Vol. 10, No. 3, September 1978, pp. 281–317.

29. **Chow, W.M., E.A. MacNair, and C.H. Sauer [1984].** Analysis of Manufacturing Systems by the Research Queuing Package, *IBM Research Report*, RC 10769, September 1984.

30. **Cohen, J.W. [1969].** *The Single Server Queue*. North-Holland, Amsterdam.

31. **Conway, A.E., and N.D. Georganas [1989].** *Queuing Networks – Exact Computational Algorithms*, The MIT Press, Cambridge, Massachusetts.

32. **Cox, D.R. [1955].** The Analysis of Non-Markovian Stochastic Processes by the Inclusion of Supplementary Variables, *Proceedings of Cambridge Philosophical Society*, Vol. 51, pp. 433–441.

33. **Dallery, Y., and R. David [1983].** A New Approach Based on Operational Analysis for Flexible Manufacturing Systems Performance Evaluation, *Proceedings of 22nd IEEE Conference on Decision and Control*, San Antonio, Texas.

34. **Dallery, Y. and Yao, D.D. [1986].** Modeling a System of Flexible Manufacturing Cells, in *Modeling and Design of FMSs*, (Ed.) Kusiak, A., Elsevier, North-Holland, New York, pp. 289–300.

35. **Donatiello, L., and B.R. Iyer [1987].** Analysis of a Composite Performance Reliability Measure for Fault-Tolerant Systems, *Journal of ACM*, Vol. 34, No. 1, January 1987, pp. 179–199.

36. **Doshi, B. [1990].** Single Server Queues with Vacations, in *Stochastic Analysis of Computer and Communication Systems*, (Ed.) Takagi, H., North-Holland, Amsterdam, pp. 217–265.

37. **Gaver, D.P. [1962].** A Waiting Line with Interrupted Service, Including Priorities, *Journal of Royal Statistical Society*, Vol. B25, pp. 73–90.

38. **Gelenbe, E., and G. Pujolle [1987].** *Introduction to Queuing Networks*, John Wiley, New York.

39. **Gordon, W.J., and G.F. Newell [1967].** Closed Queuing Systems with Exponential Servers, *Operations Research*, Vol. 15, pp. 254–265.

40. **Gross, D., and C.M. Harris [1985].** *Fundamentals of Queuing Theory*, 2nd edition, John Wiley, New York.

41. **Hildebrandt, R.R. [1980].** *Scheduling Flexible Manufacturing Systems When Machines Are Prone to Failure*, Ph.D. Dissertation, Department of Aeronautics and Astronautics, Massachusetts Institute of Technology, Cambridge, Massachusetts.

42. **Ho, Y.C. [1987].** Performance Evaluation and Perturbation Analysis of Discrete Event Dynamic Systems, *IEEE Transactions on Automatic Control*, Vol. AC-32, No. 7, July 1987, pp. 563–572.

43. **Jackson, J.R. [1957].** Networks of Waiting Lines, *Operations Research*, Vol. 5, pp. 518–527.

44. **Jackson, J.R. [1963]**. Jobshop-like Queuing Systems, *Management Science*, Vol. 10, pp. 131–142.

45. **Kamath, M., and J.L. Sanders [1987]**. Analytical Methods for Performance Evaluation of Large Asynchronous Automatic Assembly Systems, *Large Scale Systems*, Vol. 12, pp. 143–154.

46. **Kanth, M.L., and N. Viswanadham [1989]**. Reliability Analysis of Flexible Manufacturing Systems, *International Journal of Flexible Manufacturing Systems*, Vol. 2, pp. 145–162.

47. **Kelly, F.P. [1976]**. Networks of Queues, *Advances in Applied Probability*, Vol. 8, pp. 416–432.

48. **Kelly, F.P. [1979]**. *Reversibility and Stochastic Networks*, John Wiley, New York.

49. **Kleinrock, L. [1975]**. *Queuing Systems, Vol. 1: Theory*, John Wiley, New York.

50. **Kleinrock, L., and H. Levy [1988]**. The Analysis of Random Polling Systems, *Operations Research*, Vol. 36, No. 5, pp. 716–732.

51. **Lam, S.S., and Y.L. Lien [1983]**. A Tree Convolution Algorithm for the Solution of Queuing Networks, *Communications of ACM*, Vol. 26, No. 1, March 1983, pp. 203–215.

52. **Lavenberg, S.S. (Ed.) [1983]**. *Computer Performance Modeling Handbook*, Academic Press, New York.

53. **Lavenberg, S.S. [1989]**. A Perspective on Queuing Models of Computer Performance, *Performance Evaluation*, Vol. 10, pp. 53–76.

54. **Li Zhuang and K.S. Hindi [1990]**. Mean Value Analysis for Multiclass CQN Models of FMSs with Limited Buffers, *European Journal of Operations Research*, Vol. 46, pp. 366–379.

55. **Li Zhuang, and K.S. Hindi [1991a]**. Approximate MVA for Closed Queuing Network Models for FMS with Block-and-Wait Mechanism, *Computers and Industrial Engineering*, Vol. 20, No. 1, pp. 35–44.

56. **Li Zhuang, and K.S. Hindi [1991b]**. Convolution Algorithm for Closed Queuing Network Models of Flexible Manufacturing Systems with Limited Buffers, *Information and Decision Technologies*, Vol. 17, pp. 83–90.

57. **Little, J.D.C. [1961]**. A Proof for the Queuing Formula $L = \lambda W$, *Operations Research*, Vol. 9, pp. 383–385.

58. **Liu, Z., and P. Nain [1989]**. Sensitivity Results in Open, Closed, and Mixed Product Form Queuing Networks, *INRIA Research Report*, No. 1144, INRIA, Le Chesnay, France, December 1989.

59. **Meyer, J.F. [1980]**. On Evaluating the Performability of Degradable Computing Systems, *IEEE Transactions on Computers*, Vol. 29, No. 8, August 1980, pp. 720–731.

60. **Mitrani, I.L., and B. Avi-Itzhak [1968]**. A Many-Server Queue with Service Interruptions, *Operations Research*, Vol. 16, pp. 628–638.

61. **Narahari, Y., and N. Viswanadham [1989]**. Performance Modeling of

Flexible Manufacturing Systems, *Journal of the Institution of Electronics and Telecommunication Engineers*, Vol. 35, No. 4, pp. 221–236.

62. **Nicola, V.F., V.G. Kulkarni, and K.S. Trivedi [1987]**. Queuing Analysis of Fault-Tolerant Computer Systems, *IEEE Transactions on Software Engineering*, Vol. 13, March 1987, pp. 363–375.

63. **Onvural, R.O. [1990]**. Survey of Closed Queuing Networks with Blocking, *ACM Computing Surveys*, Vol. 22, No. 2, June 1990, pp. 83–121.

64. **Ram, R. [1991]**. *Performance and Performability Evaluation of Automated Manufacturing Systems*, Ph.D. Dissertation (to be submitted), Department of Computer Science and Automation, Indian Institute of Science, Bangalore, India.

65. **Ram, R., and N. Viswanadham [1990]**. Stochastic Analysis of Versatile Workcenters, *Sadhana*, Indian Academy Proceedings in Engineering Sciences, Vol. 15, pp. 301–317.

66. **Ramakrishnan, K.G., and D. Mitra [1989]**. PANACEA: An Integrated Set of Tools for Performance Analysis, in *Modeling Techniques and Tools for Performance Analysis*, Elsevier North-Holland, Amsterdam, pp. 25–40.

67. **Reibman, A.L. [1990]**. Modeling the Effect of Reliability on Performance, *IEEE Transactions on Reliability*, Vol. 39, No. 8, August 1990, pp. 314–320.

68. **Reiser, M., and S.S. Lavenberg [1980]**. Mean Value Analysis of Closed Multichain Queuing Networks, *Journal of ACM*, Vol. 27, pp. 313–322.

69. **Sauer, C.H., and K.M. Chandy [1981]**. *Computer Systems Performance Modeling*, Prentice-Hall, Englewood Cliffs, New Jersey.

70. **Sauer, C.H., M. Reiser, and E.A. MacNair [1977]**. RESQ — A Package for Solution of Generalized Queuing Networks, *Proceedings of 1977 National Computer Conference*, pp. 977–986.

71. **Seidmann, A., P.J. Schweitzer, and S. Shalev-Oren [1987]**. Computerized Closed Queuing Network Models of Flexible Manufacturing Systems: A Comparative Evaluation, *Large Scale Systems*, Vol. 12, pp. 91–107.

72. **Shalev-Oren, S., A. Seidmann, and P.J. Schweitzer [1985]**. Analysis of Flexible Manufacturing Systems with Priority Scheduling: PMVA, *Annals of Operations Research*, Vol. 3, pp. 115–139.

73. **Shantikumar, J.G. [1979]**. *Approximate Queuing Models of Dynamic Job Shops*, Ph.D. Thesis, Department of Industrial Engineering, University of Toronto, Canada.

74. **Shantikumar, J.G., and J.A. Buzacott [1980]**. On the Approximations to the Single Server Queue, *International Journal of Production Research*, Vol. 18, pp. 761–770.

75. **Shantikumar, J.G., and J.A. Buzacott [1981]**. Open Queuing Network Models of Dynamic Job Shops, *International Journal of Production Research*, Vol. 19, pp. 255–266.

76. **Shantikumar, J.G., and R.G. Gocmen [1983]**. Heuristic Analysis of Closed Queuing Networks, *International Journal of Production Research*, Vol. 21,

pp. 675–690.

77. **Shantikumar, J.G., and R.G. Sargent [1983]**. A Unifying View of Hybrid Simulation/Analytic Models and Modeling, *Operations Research*, Vol. 31, pp. 1030–1052.

78. **Solberg, J.J. [1977]**. A Mathematical Model of Computerized Manufacturing Systems, *Proceedings of 4th International Conference on Production Research*, Tokyo, pp. 22–30.

79. **Solberg, J.J. [1980]**. *CAN-Q User's Guide*, Report No. 9 (Revised), School of Industrial Engineering, Purdue University, W. Lafayette, Indiana.

80. **Stecke, K.E. [1981]**. *Production Planning Problems for Flexible Manufacturing Systems*, Ph.D. Thesis, School of Industrial Engineering, Purdue University, W. Lafayette, Indiana.

81. **Stecke, K.E., and J.J. Solberg [1981]**. Loading and Control Policies for a Flexible Manufacturing System, *International Journal of Production Research*, Vol. 19, No. 5, pp. 481–490.

82. **Suri, R. [1985]**. An Overview of Evaluative Models for Flexible Manufacturing Systems, *Annals of Operations Research*, Vol. 3, pp. 13–21.

83. **Suri, R. [1989]**. Perturbation Analysis: The State of the Art and Research Issues Explained via the GI/G/I Queue, *Proceedings of the IEEE*, Vol. 77, No. 1, January 1989, pp. 114–137.

84. **Suri, R., and G.W. Diehl [1985]**. MANUPLAN: A Precursor to Simulation for Complex Manufacturing Systems, *Proceedings of 1985 Winter Simulation Conference*, pp. 411–420.

85. **Suri, R., and G.W. Diehl [1986]**. A Variable Buffer Size Model and Its Use in Analytical Closed Queuing Networks with Blocking, *Management Science*, Vol. 32, No. 2, pp. 206–225.

86. **Suri, R., and J.W. Dille [1985]**. On-line Optimization of FMS Using Perturbation Analysis, *Annals of Operations Research*, Vol. 3, pp. 381–391.

87. **Suri, R., and R.R. Hildebrandt [1984]**. Modeling Flexible Manufacturing Systems Using Mean Value Analysis, *Journal of Manufacturing Systems*, Vol. 3, pp. 27–38.

88. **Takagi, H. [1988]**. Queuing Analysis of Polling Models, *ACM Computing Surveys*, Vol. 20, No. 1, pp. 5–28.

89. **Trivedi, K.S. [1982]**. *Probability and Statistics with Reliability, Queuing and Computer Science Applications*, Prentice-Hall, Englewood Cliffs, New Jersey.

90. **Tucci, S., and C.H. Sauer [1985]**. The Tree MVA Algorithm, *Performance Evaluation*, Vol. 5, pp. 187–196.

91. **Vinod, B., and T. Altiok [1986]**. Approximating Unreliable Queuing Networks under the Assumption of Exponentiality, *Journal of Operational Research Society*, Vol. 37, No. 3, pp. 309–316.

92. **Viswanadham, N., Y. Narahari, and R. Ram [1991]**. Performability of Automated Manufacturing Systems, in *Advances in Manufacturing and Automation Systems*, Academic Press, New York, (in press).

93. **White, J.A., J.W. Schmidt, and G.K. Bennett [1975].** *Analysis of Queuing Systems*, New York, Academic Press.

94. **Whitt, W. [1983].** The Queuing Network Analyzer, *Bell Systems Technical Journal*, Vol. 62, pp. 2779–2815.

95. **Wolff, R.A. [1989].** *Stochastic Modeling and the Theory of Queues*, Prentice-Hall, Englewood Cliffs, New Jersey.

96. **Yao, D.D. [1983].** *Queuing Models of Flexible Manufacturing Systems*, Ph.D. Dissertation, Department of Industrial Engineering, University of Toronto, Canada.

97. **Yao, D.D., and J.A. Buzacott [1985a].** Queuing Models for a Flexible Machining Station. Part I: Diffusion Approximations; Part II: The Method of Coxian Phases, *European Journal of Operations Research*, Vol. 19, pp. 233–252.

98. **Yao, D.D., and J.A. Buzacott [1985b].** Modeling a Class of State-Dependent Routing in Flexible Manufacturing Systems, *Annals of Operations Research*, Vol. 3, pp. 153–167.

99. **Yao, D.D., and J.A. Buzacott [1986a].** Models of Flexible Manufacturing Systems with Limited Local Buffers, *International Journal of Production Research*, Vol. 24, pp. 107–118.

100. **Yao, D.D., and J.A. Buzacott [1986b].** The Exponentialization Approach to FMS Models with General Processing Times, *European Journal of Operations Research*, Vol. 24, pp. 410–416.

101. **Yao, D.D., and J.A. Buzacott [1987].** Modeling a Class of FMSs with Reversible Routing, *Operations Research*, Vol. 35, No. 1, pp. 87–92.

Chapter 5
PETRI NET MODELS

This chapter is devoted to Petri net models, which have emerged as a very promising performance modeling tool for systems that exhibit concurrency, synchronization, and randomness. Stochastic Petri nets (SPNs) have now come to play an important role in the modeling of automated manufacturing systems.

An SPN is essentially a high-level model that generates a stochastic process. For example, an SPN under exponential assumptions is isomorphic to a Markov chain. SPN-based performance evaluation basically consists in modeling the given system by an SPN and automatically generating the stochastic process that governs the system behavior. This stochastic process is analyzed using known techniques. SPN is a graphical model and offers great convenience to a modeler in arriving at a credible, high-level model of a system.

SPNs offer the following advantages as a modeling tool: (1) They provide a convenient framework for correctly and faithfully describing an AMS and for generating the underlying stochastic process. (2) Their analysis can be automated and there are available several software tools for this purpose. (3) They can exactly model non-product form features, such as priorities, synchronization, forking, blocking, and multiple resource holding. (4) They can be used as both logical and quantitative models. (5) Even if their analysis is intractable, they serve as a ready simulation model.

Representationally, SPNs have more modeling power than product form queuing networks and, in fact, have the same power as Markov chain models. Computationally, however, they suffer from the problem of state space explosion.

This chapter comprises seven sections. Section 5.1 deals with classical Petri nets, which are introduced with a series of definitions and manufacturing examples. In Section 5.2 we discuss exponential timed Petri nets, which constitute the basic SPN formulation. In Section 5.3 we discuss the most important class of SPNs, namely GSPNs (Generalized SPNs) with several examples. A case study of a Kanban manufacturing system is presented in Section 5.4, using GSPNs, whereas the problem of deadlocks in AMSs is treated in detail using GSPNs in Section 5.5. This section includes discussion of qualitative issues such as deadlock avoidance and quantitative issues such as the performance in the presence of deadlocks. Various extended classes of SPNs are covered in Section 5.6. These include extended stochastic Petri nets, colored Petri nets, and timed Petri nets with both stochastic and deterministic times. Section 5.7 is concerned with an interesting class of *integrated* models that combine GSPNs and product form queuing networks into a single modeling framework.

As in the previous chapters, the theory and the modeling paradigms are illustrated with the help of a large number of examples drawn from manufacturing situations.

A brief note about the notation employed in this chapter: the roman letters M_1, M_2, ..., will denote NC machines or machine centers; the italic letters M_0, M_1, ..., will denote the markings or states of Petri net models.

5.1 CLASSICAL PETRI NETS

Petri nets (PNs), or place-transition nets, are classical models of concurrency, non-determinism, and control flow, first proposed in 1962 by Carl Adam Petri. Petri nets are bipartite graphs and provide an elegant and mathematically rigorous modeling framework for discrete event dynamical systems. In this section an overview of Petri nets is presented with the aid of several definitions and an illustrative example. In the following, N and **R** denote, respectively, the set of non-negative integers and the set of real numbers.

5.1.1 Preliminary Definitions

We start with some elementary definitions in classical Petri nets and illustrate the definitions with some examples.

Definition: A *Petri net* is a four-tuple (P, T, IN, OUT) where

$$P = \{p_1, p_2, p_3, ..., p_n\} \quad \text{is a set of places}$$
$$T = \{t_1, t_2, t_3, ..., t_m\} \quad \text{is a set of transitions}$$
$$P \cup T \neq \phi, \quad P \cap T = \phi$$

$IN : (P \ X \ T) \rightarrow \mathsf{N}$ is an *input function* that defines directed arcs from places to transitions, and

$OUT : (P \ X \ T) \rightarrow \mathsf{N}$ is an *output function* that defines directed arcs from transitions to places.

Pictorially, places are represented by circles and transitions by horizontal or vertical bars. If $IN(p_i, t_j) = k$, where $k > 1$ is an integer, a directed arc from place p_i to transition t_j is drawn with label k. If $IN(p_i, t_j) = 1$, we include an unlabeled directed arc. If $IN(p_i, t_j) = 0$, no arc is drawn from p_i to t_j.

Places of Petri nets usually represent conditions or resources in the system while transitions model the activities in the system. In all subsequent definitions, we assume a Petri net (P, T, IN, OUT) as given in the above definition. Also, we assume that the index i takes on the values $1, 2, ..., n$, while the index j takes on the values $1, 2, ..., m$.

Example 5.1

Let us consider a simple manufacturing system comprising two machines M_1 and M_2 and processing two different types of parts. Each part type goes through one stage of operation, which can be performed on either M_1 or M_2. On completion of processing of a part the part is unloaded from the system and a fresh part of the same type is loaded into the system. Figure 5.1 depicts a PN model of this system and Table 5.1 gives the interpretation of the places and transitions in the model. For this Petri net,

$$P = \{p_1, p_2, ..., p_8\}; \quad T = \{t_1, t_2, ..., t_8\}$$

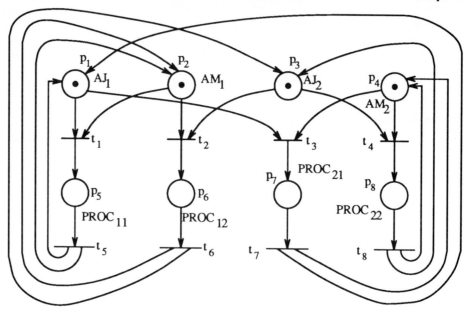

Figure 5.1 Petri net model of a simple manufacturing system

The directed arcs represent the input and output functions IN and OUT, respectively. For example,

$$IN\,(p_1, t_1) = 1; \quad IN\,(p_6, t_2) = 0$$
$$OUT\,(p_5, t_1) = 1; \quad OUT\,(p_6, t_6) = 0$$

Note in the above example that the maximum weight of each arc is 1. Such a Petri net can be adequately described by a simpler notation (P, T, A) where P and T have the usual significance and A is the set of arcs such that

$$A \subseteq (P \; X \; T) \cup (T \; X \; P)$$

Indeed, the use of an arc weight greater than unity is only a matter of convenience since a Petri net with arc weights greater than unity can always be represented by another Petri net having maximum arc weight unity. In the literature, both these notations have been employed. In this book, we shall employ the (P, T, IN, OUT) notation even though most of the examples presented in this text can be described by the (P, T, A) notation.

Table 5.1 Legend for Figure 5.1

Places

AJ_1 : p_1 : Raw parts of type 1
AM_1 : p_2 : Machine M_1 available
AJ_2 : p_3 : Raw parts of type 2
AM_2 : p_4 : Machine M_2 available
$PROC_{11}$: p_5 : M_1 processing a part of type 1
$PROC_{12}$: p_6 : M_1 processing a part of type 2
$PROC_{21}$: p_7 : M_2 processing a part of type 1
$PROC_{22}$: p_8 : M_2 processing a part of type 2

Transitions

TSP_{11} : t_1 : M_1 starts processing a part of type 1
TSP_{12} : t_2 : M_1 starts processing a part of type 2
TSP_{21} : t_3 : M_2 starts processing a part of type 1
TSP_{22} : t_4 : M_2 starts processing a part of type 2
TFP_{11} : t_5 : M_1 finishes processing a part of type 1
TFP_{12} : t_6 : M_1 finishes processing a part of type 2
TFP_{21} : t_7 : M_2 finishes processing a part of type 1
TFP_{22} : t_8 : M_2 finishes processing a part of type 1

Example 5.2

For the PN of Example 5.1, the set A is given by

$$\{(p_1,t_1),(p_2,t_1),(p_2,t_2),(p_3,t_2),(p_1,t_3),(p_4,t_3),(p_3,t_4),(p_4,t_4),$$
$$(p_5,t_5),(p_6,t_6),(p_7,t_7),(p_8,t_8),(t_1,p_5),(t_2,p_6),(t_3,p_7),(t_4,p_8),$$
$$(t_5,p_1),(t_5,p_2),(t_6,p_2),(t_6,p_3),(t_7,p_1),(t_7,p_4),(t_7,p_3),(t_7,p_4)\}$$

Definition: Given a transition t_j, the set of *input places* of t_j, denoted by $IP(t_j)$ and the set of *output places* of t_j, denoted by $OP(t_j)$, are defined by

$$IP(t_j) = \{p_i \in P: \quad IN(p_i,t_j) \neq 0\}$$
$$OP(t_j) = \{p_i \in P: \quad OUT(p_i,t_j) \neq 0\}$$

Definition: Given a place p_i, the set $IT(p_i)$ of *input transitions* of p_i and the set $OT(p_i)$ of *output transitions* of p_i are defined by

$$IT(p_i) = \{t_j \in T: \quad OUT(p_i,t_j) \neq 0\}$$
$$OT(p_i) = \{t_j \in T: \quad IN(p_i,t_j) \neq 0\}$$

Example 5.3

For the Petri net of Figure 5.1, we have

$$IP(t_1) = OP(t_5) = \{p_1, p_2\}; \quad IP(t_5) = OP(t_1) = \{p_5\}$$

The other sets of input places and output places can be obtained similarly. Also,

$$IT(p_1) = \{t_5, t_7\}; \quad OT(p_1) = \{t_1, t_3\}$$

The other sets of input transitions and output transitions can be obtained similarly.

Definition: Let T_1 be a subset of T. The transitions of T_1 are said to be *conflicting* if

$$\bigcap_{t \in T_1} IP(t) \neq \phi$$

and *concurrent* if

$$IP(t_j) \cap IP(t_k) = \phi \quad \forall\, t_j, t_k \in T_1$$

Example 5.4

In the Petri net of Figure 5.1, the sets of transitions that are conflicting are $\{t_1, t_3\}, \{t_1, t_2\}, \{t_2, t_4\}$, and $\{t_3, t_4\}$. Some of the concurrent sets of transitions are $\{t_1, t_4\}, \{t_2, t_3\}, \{t_5, t_8\}$, and $\{t_1, t_8\}$. Petri nets capture concurrency of activities through concurrent transitions and non-deterministic activities through conflicting transitions. Further, they can also model co-existence of concurrency and non-determinism. Elegant representation of such features is an important facet of Petri net modeling.

Definition: A *marking* M of a Petri net is a function $M : P \to \mathbb{N}$. A *marked Petri net* is a Petri net with an associated marking.

A marking of a Petri net with n places is an $(n \times 1)$ vector, associates with each place a certain number of tokens represented by dots, and represents a state of the Petri net. We always associate an initial marking M_0 with a given Petri net model. In the rest of the book we use the words *state* and *marking* interchangeably. Also, unless otherwise specified, a Petri net henceforth will refer to a marked Petri net.

Example 5.5

In Figure 5.1, the marking of the PN is given by

$$M_0 = \begin{bmatrix} M_0\,(p_1) \\ \cdot \\ \cdot \\ \cdot \\ M_0\,(p_8) \end{bmatrix} = \begin{bmatrix} 1 \\ 1 \\ 1 \\ 1 \\ 0 \\ 0 \\ 0 \\ 0 \end{bmatrix}$$

This corresponds to a state of the system when both machines are free and one fresh part of each type is waiting to be processed.

5.1.2 Transition Firing and Reachability

We now introduce the important notion of reachability set for a marked Petri net.

Definition: A transition t_j of a Petri net is said to be *enabled* in a marking M if

$$M\,(p_i) \geq IN\,(p_i, t_j) \quad \forall\, p_i \in IP\,(t_j)$$

An enabled transition t_j can *fire* at any time. When a transition t_j enabled in a marking M fires, a new marking M' is reached according to the equation

$$M'\,(p_i) = M\,(p_i) + OUT\,(p_i, t_j) - IN\,(p_i, t_j) \quad \forall\, p_i \in P \qquad (1)$$

We say marking M' is *reachable* from M and write $M \overset{t_j}{\to} M'$.

We consider that every marking is trivially reachable from itself by firing no transition. Also, if some marking M_j is reachable from M_i and M_k is reachable from M_j, then it is easy to see that M_k is reachable from M_i. Thus reachability of markings is a *reflexive* and *transitive* relation on the set of markings.

Definition: The transitive closure of the reachability relation, which comprises all markings reachable from the initial marking M_0 by firing zero, one, or more transitions, is called the *reachability set* of a Petri net with initial marking M_0. It is denoted by $R[M_0]$.

Definition: For a marked Petri net with initial marking M_0, the *reachability graph* is a directed graph (V, E) where, $V = R[M_0]$ is the set of vertices, and E, the set of directed arcs, is given by: $(M_1, M_2) \in E$ if

(i) $M_1, M_2 \in R[M_0]$ and

(ii) either there exists a transition $t \in T$ such that $M_1 \xrightarrow{t} M_2$ or there exists a set, $T_1 \subseteq T$, such that T_1 is a set of concurrent transitions by firing all of which M_1 reaches M_2.

In the reachability graph, the nodes are labeled by the markings they represent and the directed arcs are labeled by the transition or the set of concurrent transitions whose firing takes the source node to the destination node.

Example 5.6

In the marked Petri net of Figure 5.1, the transitions t_1, t_2, t_3 , and t_4 are all enabled. When t_1 fires, the new marking reached is M_1 where $M_1 = (00111000)^T$. Thus, $M_0 \xrightarrow{t_1} M_1$. Also, $M_0 \xrightarrow{t_4} M_2$, $M_0 \xrightarrow{t_2} M_3$, and $M_0 \xrightarrow{t_3} M_4$ where $M_2 = (11000001)^T$, $M_3 = (10010100)^T$, and $M_4 = (01100010)^T$. It can be shown that $R[M_0] = \{M_0, M_1, ..., M_6\}$, where the details of the markings are given in Table 5.2. Figure 5.2 gives the reachability graph of this Petri net.

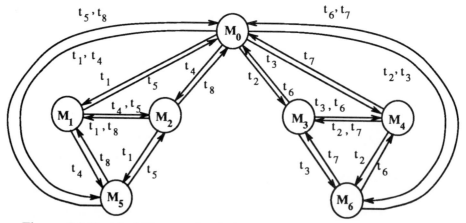

Figure 5.2 Reachability graph of the marked Petri net of Figure 5.1

Table 5.2 Reachable markings of the Petri net of Figure 5.1

Marking	p1	p2	p3	p4	p5	p6	p7	p8
M0	1	1	1	1	0	0	0	0
M1	0	0	1	1	1	0	0	0
M2	1	1	0	0	0	0	0	1
M3	1	0	0	1	0	1	0	0
M4	0	1	1	0	0	0	1	0
M5	0	0	0	0	1	0	0	1
M6	0	0	0	0	0	1	1	0

5.1.3 Representational Power

The typical characteristics exhibited by the activities in an AMS, such as concurrency, decision making, synchronization, and priorities, can be modeled elegantly by PNs. We have already seen in Example 5.4 how concurrency and conflicts are represented. Here we identify Petri net constructs for representing characteristics of AMS activities. Figure 5.3 depicts these constructs.

1. **Sequential Execution**: In Figure 5.3(a), transition t_2 can fire only after the firing of t_1. This imposes the precedence constraint "t_2 after t_1." Such precedence constraints are typical of the execution of parts in an AMS. Also, this PN construct models the causal relationship among activities.

2. **Conflict**: Transitions t_1, t_2, and t_3 are in conflict in Figure 5.3(b). All are enabled but the firing of any leads to the disabling of the other transitions. Such a situation will arise, for example, when a machine has to choose among part types or a part has to choose among several machines. The resulting conflict may be resolved in a purely *non-deterministic* way or in a *probabilistic* way, by assigning appropriate probabilities to the conflicting transitions.

3. **Concurrency**: In Figure 5.3(c), the transitions t_1, t_2, and t_3 are concurrent. Concurrency is an important attribute of AMS interactions. Note that a necessary condition for transitions to be concurrent is the existence of a *forking* transition that deposits a token in two or more output places.

4. **Synchronization**: Often, parts in an AMS wait for resources and

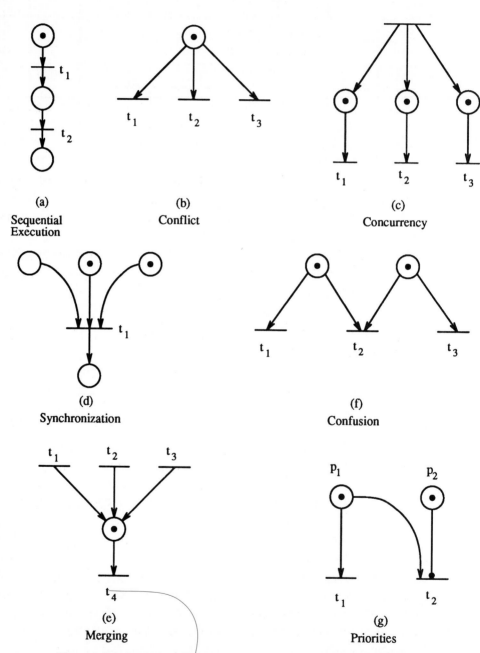

Figure 5.3 Petri net primitives to represent system features

resources wait for appropriate parts to arrive (as in assembly). The resulting synchronization of activities can be captured by transitions of the type shown in Figure 5.3(d). Here, t_1 will be enabled only when a token arrives into the place, currently without token. The arrival of a token into this place could be the result of a possibly complex sequence of operations elsewhere in the rest of the PN model. Essentially, transition t_1 models the *joining* operation.

5. **Merging**: When parts from several streams arrive for service at the same machine, the resulting situation can be depicted as in Figure 5.3(e). Another example is the arrival of several parts from several sources to a centralized warehouse.

6. **Confusion**: Confusion is a situation where concurrency and conflicts co-exist. An example is depicted in Figure 5.3(f). Both t_1 and t_3 are concurrent while t_1 and t_2 are in conflict, and t_2 and t_3 are also in conflict.

7. **Priorities**: The classical PNs discussed so far have no mechanism to represent priorities. *Inhibitor nets* defined below include special arcs called *inhibitor arcs* to model priorities.

Definition: An *inhibitor net* is a five-tuple (P, T, IN, OUT, INH) where (P, T, IN, OUT) is a Petri net and

$$INH \ : \ (P \ X \ T) \rightarrow \{0, 1\}$$

is a function called the *inhibitor* function. In an inhibitor net, a transition t_j is enabled in a marking M if

(i) $M(p_i) \geq IN(p_i, t_j) \quad \forall\, p_i \in IP(t_j)$, and

(ii) $M(p_i) = 0 \quad \forall\, p_i$ for which $INH(p_i, t_j) \neq 0$

On firing t_j, the new marking obtained is computed as in equation (1).

A portion of an inhibitor net is shown in Figure 5.3(g). p_2 is called an inhibitor place of t_2 and we have $INH(p_2, t_2) = 1$. An inhibitor arc from p_2 to t_2 is drawn as shown in Figure 5.3(g). t_2 is enabled if p_1 has a token and p_2 does not have a token. This enables to give priority to t_1 over t_2. It is to be noted that the reachability set of an inhibitor net is a subset of the same net but with the inhibitor arcs removed.

Inhibitor arcs enhance the modeling power of the Petri net model and, indeed, it has been shown that Petri nets with inhibitor arcs are equivalent in power to the classical Turing machines. It has been proved that the classical PNs, i.e., without inhibitor arcs, are less powerful than Turing machines and can only generate a proper subset of context-sensitive languages.

Petri net researchers have found it convenient to work with subclasses of Petri nets in order to study their formal properties. We define three important subclasses below.

Definition: A *state machine* is a PN (P, T, IN, OUT), such that each transition t has exactly one input place and exactly one output place, i.e.,

$$| IP(t) | = | OP(t) | = 1 \quad \forall t \in T$$

Note that a state machine cannot represent synchronization and concurrency.

Definition: A *marked graph* is a PN (P, T, IN, OUT), such that each place p has exactly one input transition and exactly one output transition, i.e.,

$$| IT(p) | = | OT(p) | = 1 \quad \forall p \in P$$

A marked graph cannot model conflicts and merging but can capture concurrency and synchronization. A marked graph is also called a *decision-free PN* and an *event-graph*.

Definition: A *free-choice net* is a PN (P, T, IN, OUT), such that every arc from a place is either a unique outgoing arc or a unique incoming arc to a transition, i.e.,

$$| OT(p) | \leq 1 \quad \text{or} \quad \bigcup_{t \in OT(p)} IP(t) = \{p\} \quad \forall p \in P$$

A free-choice net allows conflicts and concurrency but not confusion. The class of free-choice nets includes both state machines and marked graphs.

In this book we will only occasionally deal with these special classes of PNs. Most of the PN models discussed in this text are the classical PNs or the inhibitor nets.

5.1.4 Properties of Petri Nets

We now define three important desirable properties that Petri net models of physical systems should exhibit.

Definition: A place p_i of a marked Petri net is said to be *k-bounded* ($k > 0$, integer) in marking M_0 if

$$M(p_i) \leq k \quad \forall M \in R[M_0]$$

If $k = 1$, p_i is said to be *safe*. If all places of a PN are k-bounded (safe) in a marking M_0, the PN itself is said to be bounded (safe) in M_0.

Boundedness refers to a finite requirement of resources and also models absence of overflows in buffers. It can be shown (see Problem 3 below) that a bounded PN has a finite reachability set. This is an important requirement for carrying out performance analysis using PN models.

Definition: A marked Petri net with initial marking M_0 is said to be *proper* or *reversible* if

$$M_0 \in R[M] \quad \forall M \in R[M_0]$$

In a proper Petri net, the initial marking is reachable in one or more steps from every reachable marking. Properness implies reinitializability of the system and assumes significance in ensuring recovery from failure states. Properness is often referred to as reversibility and reinitializability. In later sections we will see that properness is often required for carrying out performance analysis. Also, closed queuing networks exhibit this property; so do ergodic Markov chains.

Definition: A transition t_j of a marked Petri net is said to be *live* under a marking M_0 if, for all markings $M \in R[M_0]$, there exists a sequence of transition firings which results in a marking that enables t_j. A Petri net is said to be live if all its transitions are live.

Liveness in a Petri net implies absence of deadlocked states. In Petri net terms, a deadlocked state is a reachable marking in which none of the transitions are enabled. We have already seen in earlier chapters the significance of the issue of deadlocks in the design and operation of AMSs. Thus liveness is a very desirable property of Petri net models.

Example 5.7

It can be seen that the Petri net of Figure 5.1 is bounded in each of the markings M_0, M_1 ,..., M_6 shown in Table 5.1. In fact, it is safe in all these markings. Also, the Petri net is proper and live in each of these markings.

There are many other important properties of PNs such as *fairness* which we are not considering here. Also, there is extensive literature on the existence of necessary and sufficient conditions for boundedness, properness, and liveness of subclasses of Petri nets, such as state machines, marked graphs, and free-choice nets. Since quantitative performance modeling is the main focus of this book, we do not discuss these related issues.

PROBLEMS

1. Show the equivalence between the two Petri net notations (P,T,IN,OUT) and (P,T,A). Exhibit typical situations in automated manufacturing systems where the latter notation is inadequate.

2. In the portion of the Petri net model of Figure 5.P.1, write down the sets of conflicting transitions and the sets of concurrent transitions.

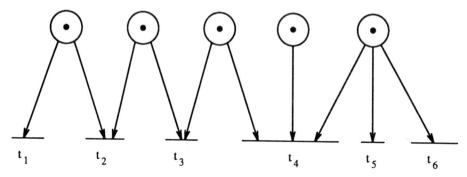

Figure 5.P.1

3. Show that a Petri net (P,T,IN,OUT,M_0) is bounded if and only if the reachability set $R[M_0]$ is finite.

4. Investigate whether or not the notion of liveness is equivalent to absence of deadlocks.

5. Construct realistic examples of Petri net models with the following properties:

   (a) An unbounded PN with two places and two transitions.

   (b) Deadlock-free but not live.

(c) Proper but not live.

(d) Live but not proper.

(e) Neither proper nor live.

6. Write a computer program to construct the reachability graph of a bounded, marked Petri net model.

7. Given the reachability graph of a bounded Petri net, write algorithms to determine whether the Petri net is (a) proper and (b) live.

8. Construct a Petri net model of an AMS in which there are two machines M_1 and M_2. Each part has to undergo two operations, one on M_1 and the other on M_2, in any order (M_1 followed by M_2 or vice versa). Assume that a raw part is always available and neglect loading, fixturing, transporting, etc. When a raw part finds both M_1 and M_2 free, it will be assigned to M_1. After finishing the first operation, the part will go to the next machine if it is available; otherwise it waits on the machine (thus blocking the machine) until the other machine becomes free and then moves to the other machine. If a fresh raw part and an in-process part vie for a machine, the latter will be assigned the machine. Construct the reachability graph of the above model and show that it is bounded, proper, and live.

9. Show that the PN model of a transfer line with no buffers in-between is a marked graph.

5.2 STOCHASTIC PETRI NETS

Classical Petri nets are useful in investigating qualitative or logical properties of concurrent systems, such as mutual exclusion, existence and absence of deadlocks, boundedness, and fairness. However, for quantitative performance evaluation, the concept of time needs to be added to the definition of Petri nets. A natural way of introducing time into a PN is based on its interpretation as a system model in which given a state (marking), a certain amount of time must elapse before an event occurs (i.e., a transition fires). The event is the final result of some activity that is performed by the system when it is in the situation specified by the marking. Time is thus naturally associated with transitions, indicating that they can fire some time after they become enabled. The choice of associating time with transitions is the most frequent in the literature on timed PNs. It may, however, be noted that PNs with timed transitions are equivalent to PNs with timed places. Several researchers such as Ramchandani [1973], Sifakis [1977], and Ramamoorthy and Ho [1980] investigated the use of *timed*

Petri nets in which places or transitions were associated with *deterministic* time durations. The analysis of such timed Petri nets (TPNs) is, however, tractable only in the case of special classes such as marked graphs.

The idea of associating *random* time durations was first explored independently by Natkin [1980] and Molloy [1981], and this was the starting point for the emergence of *stochastic Petri nets* (SPNs) and their extensions as a principal performance modeling tool. In this book, the focus will be on SPNs rather than on deterministic timed Petri nets. Also, we shall consider SPNs in which transitions rather than places are associated with times.

Definition: An SPN is a sex-tuple (P, T, IN, OUT, M_0, F) where (P, T, IN, OUT, M_0) is a Petri net and F is a function with domain $(R[M_0] \ X \ T)$, which associates with each transition in each reachable marking, a random variable.

The above is a very general definition of an SPN. We shall call the function F as the *firing function* and the random variable $F(M, t)$ for $M \in R[M_0]$ and $t \in T$ as the *firing time* of transition t in the marking M. Thus the firing time of a transition in an SPN is in general *marking dependent*. In an SPN, when t is enabled in M, the tokens remain in the input places of t during the firing time of t in M. At the end of the firing time, tokens are removed from the input places of t and tokens are deposited in the output places of t. When a transition t gets enabled, we say t *starts firing* and when the firing time has elapsed, we say t *has finished firing* or also often say t *has fired*. It is, however, possible that t gets disabled at some instant of time before finishing firing, due to the firing of a conflicting transition.

In the SPN literature, most often only continuous random variables have been employed. If only continuous random variables are used, a significant ramification will be that no two concurrently enabled transitions of an SPN can finish firing simultaneously. Also, we make the usual simplifying assumption that these random variables are mutually independent.

If, in addition to random firing times, we allow zero firing times, then we have an interesting class of SPNs, which will be discussed in the next section. Also, there have been SPN proposals in which, besides random or zero firing times, deterministic firing times are also allowed.

Definition: Let (P, T, IN, OUT, M_0, F) be an SPN. Let $X(u)$ represent the marking of the SPN at time $u \geq 0$ and let $X(0) = M_0$. Then $\{X(u) : u \geq 0\}$ is a stochastic process which we shall call the *marking process* of the SPN.

Note that the state space of the marking process of an SPN is $R[M_0]$, the reachability set. The basic philosophy underlying the use of various classes of SPNs in performance evaluation is the equivalence of their marking process, under appropriate distributional assumptions, to a Markov or semi-Markov process with discrete state space. The typical steps in SPN-based performance evaluation include: (1) modeling the given system by an SPN, (2) generating the marking process, (3) computing the steady-state probability distribution of the states of the marking process, and (4) obtaining the required performance measures from the steady-state probabilities. All steps in the SPN-based performance evaluation can be automated, and this constitutes an important reason for the popularity of SPN-based performance modeling.

5.2.1 Exponential Timed Petri Nets

The remainder of this section is devoted to the basic class of SPNs in which all firing times are exponentially distributed. For this reason we shall call this class of SPNs exponential timed Petri nets (ETPNs).

Definition: An ETPN is a sex-tuple (P, T, IN, OUT, M_0, F) in which (P, T, IN, OUT, M_0) is a Petri net and the firing function $F : (R[M_0] \ X \ T) \rightarrow \mathbf{R}$ associates to each transition t in each reachable marking M, an exponential random variable with rate $F(M, t)$.

For the sake of convenience, we shall designate each transition in an ETPN as an *exponential transition* and refer to $F(M, t)$ as the *firing rate* of t in M. A transition of an ETPN is usually represented by a rectangular bar in ETPN diagrams.

Example 5.8

Consider the manufacturing system of Example 3.24, which comprises a single NC machine that works on an inexhaustible supply of raw workpieces one at a time and produces finished parts according to *resume policy* or *discard policy*. The sequence of activities in the above system can be modeled by the ETPNs shown in Figure 5.4. The interpretation of the various elements of these ETPN models is provided in Table 5.3. Note that in the initial marking shown, the machine is being set up for the next

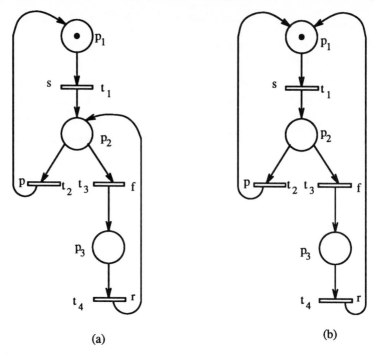

(a)   (b)

Figure 5.4 ETPN models for resume policy and discard policy

part. For this initial marking, the reachability set of each ETPN comprises three markings, and the reachability graphs are shown in Figure 5.5. The three markings are:

$M_0 = (100)$: Machine being set up for the next part

$M_1 = (010)$: Machine processing a part

$M_2 = (001)$: Machine failed, being repaired.

Note that the above markings are identical to the three states of the Markov chain of Example 3.24.

Equivalence Between ETPNs and CTMCs

Natkin [1980] and Molloy [1981] have shown that the marking process of an ETPN is a continuous time Markov chain (CTMC). This establishes a bridge between SPNs and Markov chains. In the following discussion, we outline a proof for showing the equivalence between an SPN and a CTMC. The proof is presented in the form of two lemmata. In the first lemma, we derive the transition probabilities for the states of the equivalent CTMC.

Table 5.3 Description of the ETPN models of Figure 5.4

Places

1 : Machine being set up for the next operation
2 : Machine processing a workpiece
3 : Failed machine being repaired.

Exponential Transitions

1 : Setup operation
2 : Processing of a part by the machine
3 : Failure of the machine
4 : Repair of the machine.

Firing Rates

$F(M, t_1) = s; \ F(M, t_2) = p; \ F(M, t_3) = f; \ F(M, t_4) = r$

Initial Marking

$p_1 : 1; \ p_2 : 0; \ p_3 : 0$

In the second lemma, we show that the sojourn states in the individual states are exponentially distributed.

Lemma: Let (P, T, IN, OUT, M_0, F) be an ETPN. Given $M_i, M_j \in R[M_0]$, there exists a specific probability a_{ij} of reaching M_j immediately after exiting from M_i.

Proof: Let T_i be the set of enabled transitions in M_i and define:

$$T_{ij} = \left\{ t \in T_i : M_i \xrightarrow{t} M_j \right\}$$

There are two possibilities: $T_{ij} = \phi$ and $T_{ij} \neq \phi$. If T_{ij} is empty, we have that M_j cannot be reached from M_i in a single step and hence $a_{ij} = 0$. Now consider the case when T_{ij} is non-empty. Let

$$\lambda_{ij} = \sum_{t_k \in T_{ij}} F(M_i, t_k), \quad \lambda_i = \sum_{t_k \in T_i} F(M_i, t_k)$$

The probability of marking M_i changing to M_j is the same as the probability that one of the transitions in the set T_{ij} fires before any of

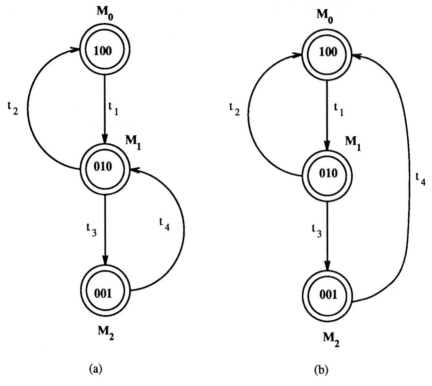

(a)   (b)

Figure 5.5 Reachability graphs of ETPN models of Figure 5.4

the transitions in the set $T \smallsetminus T_{ij}$. Since the firing times in an ETPN are mutually independent exponential random variables, it follows that the required probability has the specific value given by

$$a_{ij} = \frac{\lambda_{ij}}{\lambda_i}$$

In the expression for a_{ij} deduced above, note that the numerator is the sum of the rates of those enabled transitions in M_i, the firing of any of which changes the marking from M_i to M_j; whereas the denominator is the sum of the rates of all the enabled transitions in M_i. Also note that $a_{ij} = 1$ if and only if $T_{ij} = T_i$.

Example 5.9

Let us look at marking $M_1 = (010)$ in the ETPN model of Figure 5.4(a). Following the notation employed in the lemma above, we have

$$T_1 = \{t_2, t_3\}; \quad T_{10} = \{t_2\}; \quad T_{11} = \phi; \quad T_{12} = \{t_3\}$$

$$\lambda_1 = p + f; \quad \lambda_{10} = p; \quad \lambda_{11} = 0; \quad \lambda_{12} = f$$

Thus we have

$$a_{10} = \frac{p}{p+f}; \quad a_{11} = 0; \quad a_{12} = \frac{f}{p+f}$$

In fact, the matrix of transition probabilities can be seen to be

$$\begin{bmatrix} 0 & 1 & 0 \\ \frac{p}{p+f} & 0 & \frac{f}{p+f} \\ 0 & 1 & 0 \end{bmatrix}$$

Similarly, the matrix of transition probabilities for the ETPN model of Figure 5.4(b) can be verified to be

$$\begin{bmatrix} 0 & 1 & 0 \\ \frac{p}{p+f} & 0 & \frac{f}{p+f} \\ 1 & 0 & 0 \end{bmatrix}$$

Note that the first of the above matrices was derived in Example 3.33.

Lemma: The sojourn time of any reachable marking in an ETPN (P, T, IN, OUT, M_0, F) is exponentially distributed.

Proof: Let $M_i \in R[M_0]$ and let T_i be the set of enabled transitions in M_i. Suppose T_i' is the subset of M_i comprising all transitions, the firing of any of which in M_i would lead to a marking other than M_i. Denote

$$\lambda_i' = \sum_{t_k \in T_i'} F(M_i, t_k)$$

The sojourn time in M_i is a random variable given by

$$\min_{t_k \in T_i'} \left(EXP \left(F(M_i, t_k) \right) \right)$$

Then by the mutual independence of the firing times, it follows that the sojourn time of M_i is exponentially distributed with rate λ_i'.

Example 5.10

Considering again the ETPN models depicted in Figure 5.4, the sojourn times of the markings $M_0, M_1,$ and M_2 can be seen to be exponential random variables with rates $s, p + f$, and r, respectively.

Theorem: The marking process of an exponential timed Petri net is a continuous time Markov chain.

Proof: Proof is immediate on applying the two lemmata above and using the fact that the firing time random variables in an ETPN are all mutually independent.

Note that the state space of the equivalent CTMC is the reachability set $R[M_0]$ of the ETPN. The transition rate from one marking to another can be computed as follows. Let $M_i, M_j \in R[M_0]$. For $M_j \neq M_i$, the transition rate is given by

$$q_{ij} = \sum_{t_k \in T_{ij}} F(M_i, t_k)$$

where T_{ij}, as usual, is the subset of enabled transitions in M_i such that the firing of any transition in T_{ij} leaves the marking process in M_j. For $M_j = M_i$, the transition rate is given by

$$q_{ii} = -\sum_{j \neq i} q_{ij}$$

Example 5.11

The transition rate matrix (infinitesimal generator) of the equivalent CTMC of the ETPNs of Figure 5.4 can be respectively seen to be

$$\begin{bmatrix} -s & s & 0 \\ p & -(p+f) & f \\ 0 & r & -r \end{bmatrix} ; \quad \begin{bmatrix} -s & s & 0 \\ p & -(p+f) & f \\ r & 0 & -r \end{bmatrix}$$

Note that the above matrices are identical to the ones in Example 3.28. The performance analysis of these CTMC models has already been discussed in that example.

Example 5.12

Instead of a single machine, we now consider the activities of two identical machines working on an inexhaustible source of raw workpieces. We assume that the setup times, processing times, failure rates, and repair rates for the two machines are the same. To capture the interactions in

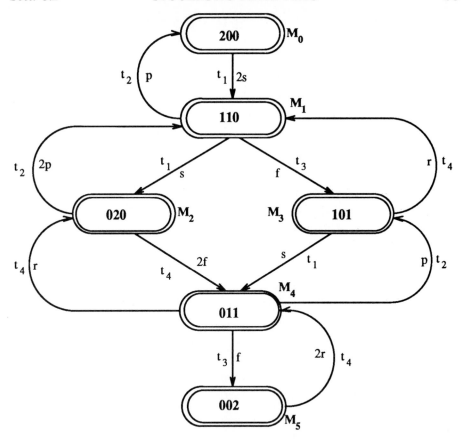

Figure 5.6 Reachability graph with initial marking (200)

this system, we can use the same ETPN models (Figure 5.4) with two changes: (i) The initial marking is changed to state (200), meaning that both machines are being set up for their next operations. (ii) The firing rates are marking dependent, and are given for each $M \in R[M_0]$ by

$$F(M, t_1) = sM(p_1)$$
$$F(M, t_2) = pM(p_2)$$
$$F(M, t_3) = fM(p_2)$$
$$F(M, t_4) = rM(p_3)$$

In the case of t_4, we have assumed that two separate facilities are available to repair both the machines concurrently, if both are in failed condition.

There are six markings in the reachability set now. The transition rate diagram of the equivalent CTMC is shown in Figure 5.6.

PROBLEMS

1. Investigate the complications that will arise in the analysis of SPNs in the following cases:

   (a) Firing times are non-exponential, and

   (b) deterministic and exponential firing times coexist.

2. In discrete time stochastic Petri nets proposed by Molloy [1985], each transition has a firing time that is a geometric random variable. Outline a proof for showing the equivalence between discrete time SPNs and discrete time Markov chains.

3. Investigate whether or not the class of all ETPNs is the same as the class of continuous time Markov chains.

4. Consider a manufacturing system comprising three failure-prone machines and exactly two repair facilities, each of which can attend to one failed machine at a time. Assuming the rest of the details as in Example 5.8, complete the definition of an ETPN for this system. Obtain the reachability graph of the ETPN and the transition probabilities. Also compute the transition rate matrix of the equivalent Markov chain.

5. (Dining Philosophers' Problem). Figure 5.P.2 shows an ETPN model for the classical dining philosophers' problem with three philosophers and three forks. Taking the philosophers as assembly stations and the forks as assem-

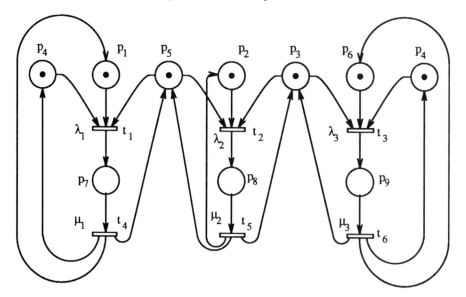

Figure 5.P.2

bling robots, the above problem represents a familiar situation in automated manufacturing. Obtain the reachability graph, transition probabilities, and the infinitesimal generator of the equivalent CTMC.

6. Write a computer program that

(a) generates the reachability graph of a bounded ETPN, and

(b) computes the transition rate matrix of the underlying Markov chain.

5.3 GENERALIZED STOCHASTIC PETRI NETS

Generalized stochastic Petri nets (GSPNs), proposed by Ajmone Marsan, Balbo, and Conte [1984], constitute the most extensively used class of SPNs. GSPNs are obtained by allowing transitions to belong to two different classes: *immediate* transitions and *exponential* transitions. Immediate transitions fire in zero time once they are enabled. Exponential transitions have the same significance as in ETPNs. The basic motivation for proposing GSPNs was to avoid having to associate a time with each transition when it is sufficient to associate times only with the activities that are believed to have the largest impact on system performance. A typical example is that of a physical system in which the durations of activities differ by orders of magnitude. In such a case, it is advantageous to model the short activities only from the logical point of view. A strong feature of AMSs that supports the above is the orders of magnitude difference exhibited by the mean times between machine failures, mean processing times, and material handling times. GSPNs are particularly useful because the firing rules are so defined as to reduce the number of states of the associated Markov chain model, thus reducing the solution complexity. Moreover, the availability of a logical structure that can be used in conjunction with the timed one allows the construction of compact performance models of complex systems.

5.3.1 Definition and Firing Rules

In this section we define a GSPN and discuss the transition firing rules to generate the reachability graph.

Definition: A *generalized stochastic Petri net* is an eight-tuple $(P, T, IN, OUT, INH, M_0, F, S)$ where

1. $(P, T, IN, OUT, INH, M_0)$ is an inhibitor-marked Petri net,

2. T is partitioned into two sets: T_I of *immediate* transitions and T_E of *exponential* transitions,

3. $F : (R[M_0] \times T_E) \rightarrow \mathbb{R}$ is a firing function that associates to each $t \in T_E$ in each $M \in R[M_o]$, an exponential random variable with rate $F(M, t)$,

4. each $t \in T_I$ has zero firing time in all reachable markings, and

5. S is a set, possibly empty, of elements called *random switches*, which associate probability distributions to subsets of conflicting immediate transitions.

In the graphical representation of GSPNs, a horizontal or vertical line represents an immediate transition and a rectangular bar represents an exponential transition. Other conventions regarding graphical representation remain the same.

In a GSPN marking, several transitions may be enabled simultaneously. Let M_i be a reachable marking and let T_i be the set of enabled transitions in M_i. If T_i comprises only exponential transitions, then transition $t_j \in T_i$ fires with probability

$$\frac{F(M_i, t_j)}{\sum_{t_k \in T_i} F(M_i, t_k)}$$

The above situation is identical to the one in any ETPN. If T_i comprises exactly one immediate transition t_j, then t_j is the one that fires. If T_i comprises two or more immediate transitions, then a probability mass function is specified on the set of enabled immediate transitions by an element of S. The firing transition is selected according to this probability distribution. In this case, the set of all enabled immediate transitions, together with the associated probability distribution (switching distribution), is called a *random switch*. The set S is a collection of all random switches of the GSPN model. The probabilities in a switching distribution may be either independent of the current marking, in which case we have a *static* random switch, or dependent on the current marking, in which case we have a *dynamic* random switch.

GSPN markings in which only exponential transitions are enabled are designated as *tangible* markings while the rest of the markings are called *vanishing* markings. Tangible markings represent states in which the system stays for nonzero time whereas vanishing markings are those in which logical changes occur in negligible time.

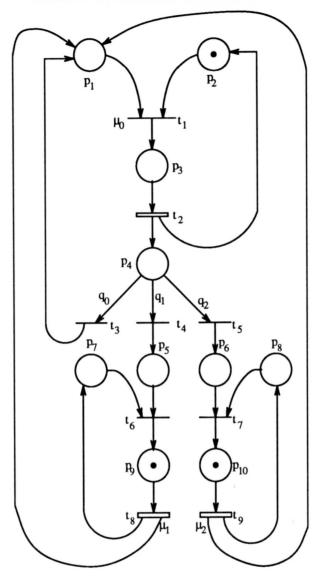

Figure 5.7 GSPN model of a central server FMS

Example 5.13

Consider the closed central server model of a simple FMS that comprises an AGV and two machines M_1 and M_2 (Example 3.25, Figure 3.13). Figure 5.7 depicts a GSPN model of this system assuming that there are two fixtures in the system and that in the initial state, AGV is idle, M_1 is processing one of the parts, and M_2 is processing the other part. Table

Table 5.4 Description of the GSPN model of Figure 5.7

Places

  1 : Queue of parts waiting for the AGV
  2 : AGV available
  3 : AGV transporting a part
  4 : A part that has just been transported by the AGV
  5 : Queue of parts waiting for M_1
  6 : Queue of parts waiting for M_2
  7 : M_1 available
  8 : M_2 available
  9 : M_1 processing a part
10 : M_2 processing a part

Immediate Transitions

  1 : AGV starts transporting a part
  3 : Finished part gets unloaded from the system
  4 : Part joins the queue for M_1
  5 : Part joins the queue for M_2
  6 : M_1 starts processing a part
  7 : M_2 starts processing a part

Random Switch

(t_3, t_4, t_5) with associated probabilities (q_0, q_1, q_2).

Exponential Transitions

  2 : Part transfer by the AGV; firing rate = μ_0
  8 : Processing by M_1; firing rate = μ_1
  9 : Processing by M_2; firing rate = μ_2

Initial Marking

$p_2 : 1$; $p_9 : 1$; $p_{10} : 1$

5.4 gives the interpretation of the elements of this GSPN model. The GSPN model has 10 places, 6 immediate transitions $\{t_1, t_3, t_4, t_5, t_6, t_7\}$, 3 exponential transitions $\{t_2, t_8, t_9\}$ with firing rates μ_0, μ_1, μ_2, respectively, and no inhibitor arcs. The initial marking is $M_1 = (0100000011)$, which we shall denote as $p_2 p_9 p_{10}$ specifying only those places having a token. There is exactly one random switch (static, in this case) comprising the

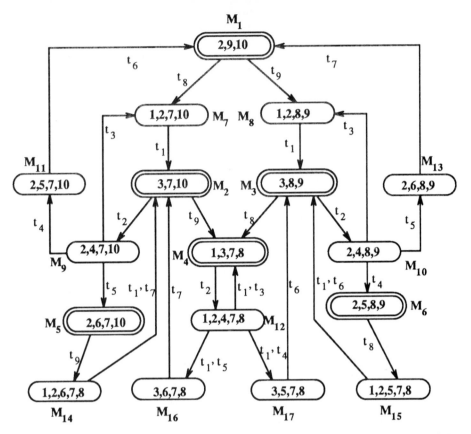

Figure 5.8 Embedded Markov chain for the GSPN model of Figure 5.7

transitions t_3, t_4, and t_5 with corresponding probabilities q_0, q_1, and q_2.

In the initial marking $p_2 p_9 p_{10}$, the exponential transitions t_8 and t_9 are enabled and hence this is a tangible marking. Here t_8 fires with probability $\frac{\mu_1}{\mu_1 + \mu_2}$ and t_9 fires with probability $\frac{\mu_2}{\mu_1 + \mu_2}$. When t_8 fires, the new marking is $p_1 p_2 p_7 p_{10}$, which is a vanishing marking, as an immediate transition t_1 is enabled in it. Note that t_9 is also enabled here. Only t_1 fires since t_9 is exponential, resulting in the marking $p_3 p_7 p_{10}$, which is a tangible marking. Now t_2 and t_9 are enabled and they can fire with probabilities $\frac{\mu_0}{\mu_0 + \mu_2}$ and $\frac{\mu_2}{\mu_0 + \mu_2}$, respectively. If t_2 fires, the new marking is $p_2 p_4 p_7 p_{10}$, a vanishing marking enabling t_3, t_4, and t_5. At this stage, the random switch can be invoked to choose the next transition to fire. The evolution of the marking process proceeds as described above and one can construct the reachability graph of the GSPN model in this way. Figure 5.8 shows the reachability graph, with the associated probabilities for transition firings. Vanishing

Table 5.5 Interpretation of the tangible markings in Figure 5.8

M_1 : $p_2p_9p_{10}$: Machines M_1 and M_2 busy; AGV idle

M_2 : $p_3p_7p_{10}$: AGV and M_2 busy; M_1 idle

M_3 : $p_3p_8p_9$: AGV and M_1 busy; M_2 idle

M_4 : $p_1p_3p_7p_8$: AGV busy and the other part waiting for the AGV

M_5 : $p_2p_6p_7p_{10}$: M_2 busy and the other part waiting for M_2

M_6 : $p_2p_5p_8p_9$: M_1 busy and the other part waiting for M_1

markings are shown as single ovals and tangible markings as double ovals. There are 6 tangible markings $\{M_1, ..., M_6\}$ and 11 vanishing markings $\{M_7, ..., M_{17}\}$. The interpretation of the tangible markings is given in Table 5.5. Note that these are identical to the six states given in Example 3.25.

In Figure 5.8, it is also to be noted that in vanishing markings such as M_{12} and M_{14}, two immediate transitions have been simultaneously fired. For example, consider $M_{12} = p_1p_2p_4p_7p_8$. In this marking, t_1, t_3, t_4, and t_5 are the enabled transitions. Among t_3, t_4, and t_5, only one can fire, as determined by the random switch. Transition t_1 is concurrent with each of t_3, t_4, and t_5 and its firing does not in any way affect the latter transitions. Thus we fire the transitions $\{t_1, t_3\}$ with probability q_0, transitions $\{t_1, t_4\}$ with probability q_1, and the transitions $\{t_1, t_5\}$ with probability q_2. Concurrent firing of immediate transitions as detailed above is not always possible and must be decided with care.

5.3.2 Analysis of GSPNs

The marking process of a GSPN $(P, T, IN, OUT, INH, M_0, F, S)$ can be shown to be a semi-Markov process with a discrete state space, given by the reachability set $R[M_0]$. The embedded Markov chain (EMC) of this marking process comprises tangible markings as well as vanishing markings. The transition probability matrix (TPM) of this EMC can be computed using the firing rates and the random switches.

Example 5.14

The reachability graph in Figure 5.8 is essentially the state transition diagram of the EMC of the marking process of the GSPN model being discussed. The transition probabilities for each marking can be computed by examining the set of transitions enabled in the marking. For example, in marking M_1, exponential transitions t_8 and t_9 are enabled and the probability of transiting from M_1 to M_7 is $\frac{\mu_1}{\mu_1+\mu_2}$ and the probability of transiting from M_1 to M_8 is $\frac{\mu_2}{\mu_1+\mu_2}$. In marking M_{11}, only one transition t_6 is enabled and therefore the transition probability from M_{11} to M_1 is 1. As another example, in marking M_9, three (conflicting) immediate transitions t_3, t_4, and t_5 are enabled and by invoking the random switch, the corresponding transition probabilities are fixed as q_0, q_1, and q_2, respectively. It will be instructive to compute and verify all other transition probabilities.

The marking process of a GSPN leaves each vanishing marking as soon as it enters the marking, because an immediate transition fires. Thus sojourn time in each vanishing marking is zero, and consequently from the performance evaluation point of view, it suffices to study the evolution of tangible markings alone. In order to remove vanishing markings from the EMC, a reduced embedded Markov chain (REMC) is defined, including only tangible markings and the transition probabilities in the REMC are deduced from those in EMC as follows:

Let the tangible markings be $M_1, M_2, ..., M_s$ and the vanishing markings be $M_{s+1}, M_{s+2}, ..., M_{s+v}$, where s is the number of tangible markings and v is the number of vanishing markings in the reachability set. The TPM of the EMC can be partitioned as

$$\begin{bmatrix} TT & TV \\ VT & VV \end{bmatrix}$$

where TT gives the one-step transition probabilities from tangible markings to tangible markings, TV gives the one-step transition probabilities from tangible markings to vanishing markings, and so on. If A is the TPM of the REMC, then it can be shown that

$$A = TT + \sum_{k=0}^{\infty} TV * VV^k * VT \qquad (2)$$

where + and * above denote matrix addition and matrix multiplication, respectively. A computationally efficient method for obtaining A has been outlined by Ajmone Marsan, Balbo, and Conte [1984].

Example 5.15

For the GSPN model of Figure 5.7, the REMC is shown in Figure 5.9. The transition probability matrix of the REMC can be computed using

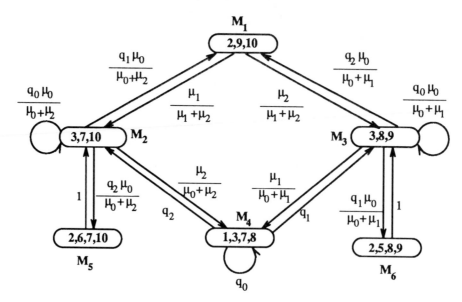

Figure 5.9 Reduced embedded Markov
chain for the GSPN model of Figure 5.7

(2). The individual transition probabilities are labeled on the directed arcs
connecting the tangible markings.

In order to ensure the existence of a unique steady-state probability
distribution for the marking process of GSPNs, the following simplifying
assumptions are made:

1. The GSPN is bounded. That is, the reachability set is finite.
2. Firing rates do not depend on time parameters. This ensures that the
   equivalent Markov chain is homogeneous.
3. The GSPN model is proper and deadlock-free. That is, the initial
   marking is reachable with a nonzero probability from any marking in
   the reachability set and also there is no "absorbing" marking.

Most of the GSPN models discussed in this book satisfy the above
conditions. However, in Section 5.5 we discuss GSPN models having
deadlocks. The above assumptions make the marking process of a GSPN,
a finite state space, homogeneous, irreducible, and positive recurrent
Markov process. The steady-state probability distribution can therefore
be computed as follows:

Let $Y = (y_1, y_2, ..., y_s)$ be a vector of real numbers. Then the solution of the following equations

$$YA = Y$$

$$\text{and } \sum_{i=1}^{s} y_i = 1 \tag{3}$$

gives the stationary probabilities of the REMC. y_i gives the relative number of visits to M_i by the marking process. To obtain the steady-state probabilities of the marking process, we then use the expression

$$\pi_i = \frac{y_i m_i}{\sum\limits_{j=1}^{s} y_j m_j} ; \qquad i = 1, 2, ..., s \tag{4}$$

where π_i is the steady-state probability of marking M_i in the marking process (proportion of time the marking process spends in M_i) and m_i is the mean sojourn time of the marking M_i. It has been shown in Section 5.2 that

$$m_i = \frac{1}{\sum\limits_{t_k \in T_i} F(M_i, t_k)} \tag{5}$$

where T_i is the set of enabled transitions in M_i.

Example 5.16

It is easy to verify that the GSPN model of Figure 5.7 satisfies assumptions 1, 2, and 3 above. Hence, unique steady-state probabilities exist. The mean sojourn times are given, using (5), by

$$m_1 = \frac{1}{\mu_1 + \mu_2}; \quad m_2 = \frac{1}{\mu_0 + \mu_2}; \quad m_3 = \frac{1}{\mu_0 + \mu_1};$$

$$m_4 = \frac{1}{\mu_0}; \quad m_5 = \frac{1}{\mu_2}; \quad m_6 = \frac{1}{\mu_1}$$

We can now get the steady-state probabilities by first solving for $y_1, y_2, ..., y_6$ using (3) and then substituting in (4). These probabilities are next used in computing various performance measures. It may be noted that the steady-state probability of each vanishing marking is identically equal to zero.

5.3.3 Computation of Performance Measures

Let $(P, T, IN, OUT, INH, M_0, F, S)$ be a GSPN with the set of reachable tangible markings given by $\{M_1, M_2, ..., M_s\}$, with steady-state probabilities $(\pi_1, \pi_2, ..., \pi_s)$. Certain generic mean performance measures can be defined as shown below. The discussion holds for an ETPN model also and in general for any SPN model.

1. Probability that a particular condition C holds:

$$PROB(C) = \sum_{j \in S_1} \pi_j \tag{6}$$

where $S_1 = \{j \in \{1, 2, ..., s\} : C \text{ is satisfied in marking } M_j\}$

2. Probability that a place p_i has exactly k tokens ($k = 0, 1, 2, ...$):

$$PROB(p_i, k) = \sum_{j \in S_2} \pi_j \tag{7}$$

where $S_2 = \{j \in \{1, 2, ..., s\} : M_j(p_i) = k\}$

3. Expected number of tokens in a place p_i:

$$ET(p_i) = \sum_{k=1}^{K} k PROB(p_i, k) \tag{8}$$

where K is the maximum number of tokens p_i may contain in any reachable marking.

4. Throughput rate of an exponential transition t_j :

$$TR(t_j) = \sum_{i \in S_3} \pi_i F(M_i, t_j) q_{ij} \tag{9}$$

where $S_3 = \{i \in \{1, 2, ..., s\} : t_j \text{ is enabled in } M_i\}$, and q_{ij} is computed as follows. $q_{ij} = 1$ if t_j is not in conflict with any of the enabled transitions in M_i. Otherwise, q_{ij} is the probability that t_j fires among the conflicting enabled transitions in M_i.

5. Throughput rate of immediate transitions:
The throughput rates of immediate transitions can be computed from those of the exponential transitions and the structure of the GSPN model. This will be illustrated in Example 5.17.

6. Mean waiting time in a place p_i:
This can be computed by invoking Little's result as

$$WAIT(p_i) = \frac{ET(p_i)}{\displaystyle\sum_{t_j \in IT(p_i)} TR(t_j)} = \frac{ET(p_i)}{\displaystyle\sum_{t_j \in OT(p_i)} TR(t_j)} \qquad (10)$$

Recall in the above that $IT(p_i)$ is the set of input transitions of p_i and $OT(p_i)$, the set of output transitions of p_i.

Example 5.17

We illustrate the computation of some typical performance measures for the GSPN model of Figure 5.7.

1. Probability that AGV queue is empty

$$= PROB(p_1,0) = \pi_1 + \pi_2 + \pi_3 + \pi_5 + \pi_6$$

2. Mean length of AGV queue $= PROB(p_1,1) = \pi_4$

3. Mean number of customers in the AGV queue and the AGV (or the AGV subsystem) $= (\pi_2 + \pi_3) + 2\pi_4$

4. Utilization of AGV $= PROB(p_3,1) = PROB(p_2,0) = \pi_2 + \pi_3 + \pi_4$

5. Throughput rates of exponential transitions

$$TR(t_2) = \pi_2\mu_0 + \pi_3\mu_0 + \pi_4\mu_0 = (\pi_2 + \pi_3 + \pi_4)\mu_0$$
$$TR(t_8) = \pi_1\mu_1 + \pi_3\mu_1 + \pi_6\mu_1 = (\pi_1 + \pi_3 + \pi_6)\mu_1$$
$$TR(t_9) = (\pi_1 + \pi_2 + \pi_5)\mu_2$$

6. The throughput rates of the immediate transitions can be computed as:

$$TR(t_1) = TR(t_2); \quad TR(t_3) = q_0\, TR(t_2)$$
$$TR(t_4) = q_1\, TR(t_2); \quad TR(t_5) = q_2\, TR(t_2)$$
$$TR(t_6) = TR(t_8); \quad TR(t_7) = TR(t_9)$$

7. Mean waiting time in AGV queue:

$$WAIT(p_1) = \frac{ET(p_1)}{TR(t_3) + TR(t_8) + TR(t_9)}$$

8. Production rate of parts is given by $TR(t_3)$, the throughput rate of t_3.

9. Mean MLT is given by $\frac{2}{TR(t_3)}$, since the population of the network is 2.

5.3.4 Representational Power of GSPN Models

In this section we show the flexibility and power of GSPN models by presenting three examples. The models presented show how priorities, dynamic routing schemes, and changes in the architecture of the physical system can be captured by GSPNs. The discussion is again centered on the central server FMS with one AGV and two machines.

Example 5.18

In the FMS being discussed, let us make the following change in decision rules: If M_1 and M_2 are both available, the waiting part is assigned to M_2 (probably because M_2 is faster). If M_1 alone is available or M_2 alone is available, the part is assigned to the available machine. Finally, if both M_1 and M_2 are currently busy, the part is assigned to one of the queues probabilistically, as in the previous case. The existence of priorities and conditional decisions make the CQN model non-product form and it may be required to use approximate techniques to find the solution. GSPNs can, however, be used to model the new decision rule exactly. Figure 5.10 shows the new GSPN model. Note that this model has two additional places p_{11} and p_{12} and five additional transitions $t_{10}, ..., t_{14}$, compared to the original model (Figure 5.7). The interpretation of these is included in Table 5.6. The transition t_5 of the previous model, however, is missing in the new model in order to facilitate the modeling of the new decision rules. The priorities manifest in these decision rules are captured by the three inhibitor arcs from p_7 to t_{11}, p_8 to t_{11}, and p_8 to t_{10}. For example, t_{10} fires only if the waiting part finds a token in p_7 (that is, M_1 is available) and there is no token in p_8 (that is, M_2 is not available). Further, the lone random switch in the previous model is now replaced by two random switches in the new model, since the probabilistic routing to M_1 or M_2 arises only in the event that both the machines are busy. Table 5.6 also shows the probability assignments to these random switches.

Figure 5.11 shows the reachability graph of the new GSPN model with the same initial marking $M_1 = (0100000011)$ as before. It is interesting to note that the number of tangible markings is now 4 (compared to 6 in the previous model) and the number of vanishing markings is 9 (compared to 11 previously). The reduction in the number of markings is obviously due to the new decision rules. The analysis of this GSPN model and performance evaluation can be carried out in the same way as detailed before. It would be instructive to compute the TPM of the EMC, the TPM of the REMC, the

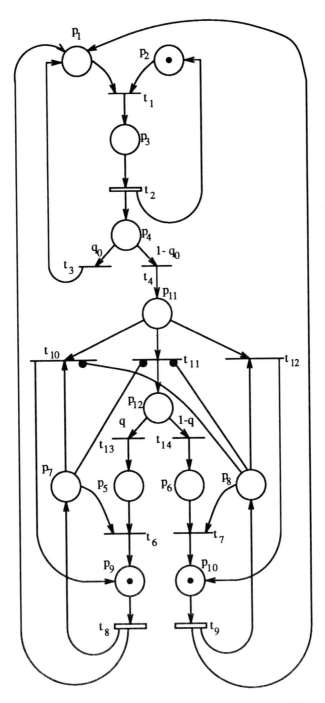

Figure 5.10 A GSPN that models priorities

Table 5.6 Legend for Figure 5.10

Places

11 : A part that will be scheduled onto M_1 or M_2

12 : A part that finds both the machines M_1 and M_2 busy

Transitions

10 : M_1 available while M_2 is busy

11 : M_1 and M_2 both busy

12 : M_2 available

13 : A part is assigned to the M_1 queue

14 : A part is assigned to the M_2 queue.

Inhibitor Arcs

p_7 to t_{11}; p_8 to t_{11}; p_8 to t_{10}

Random Switches

$[t_3 : q_0; \quad t_4 : 1 - q_0]$

$[t_{13} : q; \quad t_{14} : 1 - q]$ $\qquad$ where $q = \dfrac{q_1}{q_1 + q_2}$ and $q_0 + q_1 + q_2 = 1$

---

steady-state probabilities, and different performance measures to compare the performance of the two systems discussed so far.

Example 5.19

Here we modify further the decision rule of Example 5.18. If a part finds both machines busy, it will be assigned to the queue that has fewer waiting parts. Further, if the two queues comprise the same number of waiting parts, the routing will be based on the probabilities q_1 and q_2. The above decision rule can be captured by the GSPN model of Figure 5.10, by making the random switch $[t_{13}, t_{14}]$ dynamic. Consider the following definitions for the switching probabilities:

$$
\begin{aligned}
Prob\,(t_{13}) &= 0 && \text{if } M\,(p_5) > M\,(p_6) \\
&= \frac{q_1}{q_1 + q_2} && \text{if } M\,(p_5) = M\,(p_6) \\
&= 1 && \text{if } M\,(p_5) < M\,(p_6)
\end{aligned}
$$

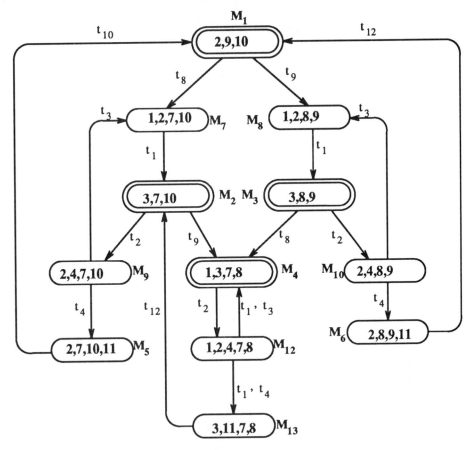

Figure 5.11 Embedded Markov chain of the modified GSPN model

$$Prob\,(t_{14}) = 0 \qquad\qquad \text{if } M\,(p_6) > M\,(p_5)$$
$$= \frac{q_2}{q_1 + q_2} \qquad \text{if } M\,(p_6) = M\,(p_5)$$
$$= 1 \qquad\qquad \text{if } M\,(p_6) < M\,(p_5)$$

In the above definitions, M is the *current* marking of the GSPN. The probabilities are now being assigned to t_{13} and t_{14} in accordance with the latest decision rule. The above example shows the use and power of dynamic random switches as a modeling paradigm in GSPNs.

Example 5.20

Let us say the number of fixtures in the system is increased to seven. With respect to the GSPN models of Figures 5.7 and 5.10, consider the following initial marking:

$$p_1 : 2; \quad p_3 : 1; \quad p_5 : 1; \quad p_6 : 1; \quad p_9 : 1; \quad p_{10} : 1$$

The above refers to the situation where the AGV, M_1, and M_2 are all busy; two parts are waiting in the AGV queue, and one part each is waiting in the M_1 and M_2 queues. This is one manifestation of the FMS system with seven fixtures. Because of the irreducibility of the underlying Markov chain, there are several other initial markings that can represent the given system.

In addition, let us say we have two identical M_1 machines and two identical M_2 machines instead of one of each type in the previous case. Then the initial marking

$$p_1 : 1; \quad p_3 : 1; \quad p_5 : 1; \quad p_9 : 2; \quad p_{10} : 2$$

will yield the desired GSPN model. Of course, here again there are several other initial markings that can generate the same reachability graph, because of the reversibility of this GSPN model. There is another important change that needs to be done in this case, namely in the firing rates of t_8 and t_9. To account for the simultaneous activity of the two machines of each type, we define the following *dynamic* (or *marking-dependent*) firing rates:

$$t_8 : \quad M(p_9)\mu_1 \quad \text{and} \quad t_9 : \quad M(p_{10})\mu_2$$

Note that the changes effected as shown in this example significantly vary the reachability set, EMC, REMC, and the steady-state probabilities, but the new values can be computed in an automated way.

PROBLEMS

1. Figure 5.P.3 shows a part of a GSPN model comprising immediate transitions t_1, t_2, t_3. Can t_1, t_2 be fired simultaneously? Obtain sufficient conditions under which two or more immediate transitions can be concurrently fired in a GSPN.

2. Show that the steady-state probability distribution of the tangible markings of the GSPN is the same as that of a CTMC embedded within the marking process. From the EMC and the REMC, how can one obtain the transition rate matrix of the CTMC?

3. Derive the expression

$$A = TT + \sum_{k=0}^{\infty} TV * VV^k * VT$$

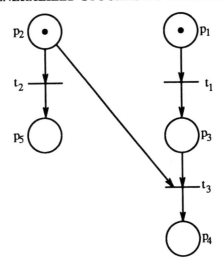

Figure 5.P.3

How can the above be simplified if it is known that

(a) there are no loops among vanishing states?

(b) there are loops among the vanishing states?

(c) What are the time and space complexities of the above computations?

4. Construct a GSPN model for the closed central server model with one AGV and three machines, M_1, M_2, M_3. Assuming that there is only one fixture, obtain the reachability graph, EMC, REMC, steady-state probabilities, throughput rate, and lead time. Next, assume that machine M_1 is faster than M_2 and M_2 is faster than M_3. If a part finds two or more machines available, it is assigned to the fastest machine. Construct a GSPN model for the above, complete in all respects.

5. In the GSPN model of Figure 5.7, assume the initial marking as

$$p_2 : 1; \quad p_7 : 1; \quad p_9 : 1; \quad p_{10} : 1$$

That is, there are two identical machines of type M_1, one of which is free in the initial marking. The firing rate of t_8 now becomes $M(p_9)\mu_1$. Obtain the reachability graph, EMC, REMC, and steady-state probabilities.

6. In Example 5.19 we considered if the processing rates of the machines M_1 and M_2 are different, then an even better routing policy to use is the *shortest expected delay routing* (SEDR), where the part is routed to the queue which results in the least expected waiting time for the part. Modify the dynamic random switch of the GSPN models so as to model SEDR. Assuming

$\mu_1 = 2\mu_2$ and four fixtures, draw the reachability graphs of the GSPN models for SQR and SEDR.

7. Develop a software package for automated analysis of GSPNs. The input is a GSPN model (with random switches) and the output should be the generic steady-state performance measures of the model. Assume that the input GSPN model is bounded, proper, and live.

5.4 GSPN MODELING OF KANBAN SYSTEMS

In this section we show how GSPNs can be used in the modeling and analysis of a novel discipline for cell coordination in cellular manufacturing systems. This scheme is called the *Kanban* scheme. The Kanban philosophy originated in the Japanese industry and is used in *pull* production systems. This is one of the Japanese techniques that has been the focus of much attention in recent years. Conventional production operations employ *push* systems wherein a forecast of demand or a firm order, which includes allowances for lead times, is determined for each stage of the production process. The push process is controlled through inventory levels at each stage in the system. To protect against an incorrect forecast, in-process inventory levels are often inflated to include safety stocks that can result in high carrying costs. The *pull* systems, on the other hand, are designed to minimize in-process inventory and fluctuations of in-process inventory. In the ideal pull system, in-process inventory at each stage is one unit. When demand for a preceding stage's output is generated by the succeeding stage, the former's unit of inventory is transferred to the latter where it is processed. As a result, each stage produces *just-in-time* (JIT) to meet the demand needed by succeeding stages, which is ultimately controlled by the final product demand. The Japanese method of stage-to-stage control in pull production systems employs Kanbans, or cards, that communicate the demands to a preceding stage from the succeeding stage. The JIT technique implemented with Kanbans has been particularly successful in several Japanese firms such as the Toyota Motor Company.

Mitra and Mitrani [1988a, 1988b] have studied the performance of Kanban coordination in a class of flow-line type of cellular manufacturing systems. They have established the superiority of the Kanban scheme over classical production systems, using a stochastic coupling argument, and have obtained performance estimates by solving fixed-point equations. Our aim in this section is to show how GSPNs can be used to approach this problem. A similar GSPN-based modeling effort for Kanban production systems has been presented by Mascolo *et al.* [1989].

5.4.1 Description of the System

The system described by Mitra and Mitrani [1988a, 1988b] comprises a linear network of production stages or cells in which operations are performed prior to the emergence of the finished product at the end of the line. There is a queue of consumers who arrive randomly according to a Poisson process, each consumer requiring one product and waiting until a finished product is available from the last cell. The queuing space for waiting consumers is limited to M and arriving consumers leave the system without service when the queue is full. The stream of arriving consumers modulates the entire production process; when the queue of consumers is not empty, the effect is to pull products from the line, and when it is empty, the effect is to cut back on the production. Figure 5.12 gives a schematic of this manufacturing facility. Note that there are N cells indexed $1, 2, ..., N$. Each cell, called from now on a Kanban cell, consists of:

(i) a *manufacturing center* comprising one or more identical machines, and an input buffer large enough to avoid blocking and starving;

(ii) an *output hopper*, where completed parts await removal; and

(iii) a *bulletin board*, where requests for new parts are posted.

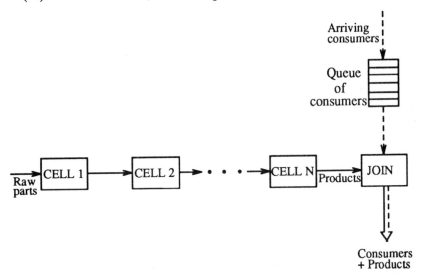

Figure 5.12 A linear cellular manufacturing system

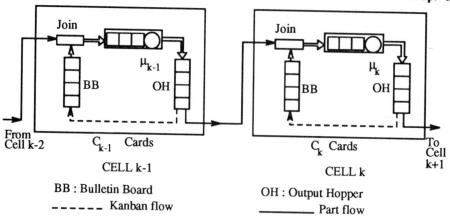

Figure 5.13 Flow of Kanbans and parts in contiguous cells

In cell k $(k = 1, 2, ..., N)$, there are exactly C_k cards, or Kanbans, $C_k \geq 1$. Every part must acquire one of these Kanbans in order to enter a given cell and must continue to hold the Kanban throughout its stay in that cell. Consequently, the total number of unprocessed and processed parts in cell K cannot exceed C_k. Any unattached cards that are present in the cell are to be found on the bulletin board and are considered as requests for raw parts from the previous stage. The bulletin board and the output hopper are only introduced to implement the coordination policy here. The flow of parts and Kanbans is illustrated in Figure 5.13.

Let P be a part that has just completed service at cell $k - 1$ and K be the Kanban attached to it. P and K move to the output hopper of cell $k - 1$. If the bulletin board in cell k is empty, then P and K wait at the output hopper of cell $k - 1$. Otherwise, the following actions occur: P is transferred from cell $k - 1$ to cell k where it is attached to the leading Kanban there and moves to the manufacturing node; K goes to the bulletin board of cell $k - 1$. In the case of cell 1, we assume that the pool of raw parts preceding it is never empty and hence the bulletin board is always empty; as soon as a Kanban appears there requesting input, that request is satisfied and a new part enters the cell. Also in cell N, a Kanban in the output hopper is not released until a consumer arrives and takes away the finished part to which this Kanban was attached.

Note that there is a fixed number of Kanbans circulating within the geographical confines of each cell. The presence of the Kanbans at some designated places signals to the neighboring cells on the status of the inventory. Thus Kanbans provide a way of collecting and communicating information. Moreover, the presence of Kanbans decouples the manufacturing activity from material handling, and these two become loosely coupled concurrent processes in each cell.

Since the Kanban scheme is much different from conventional production systems, it would be of interest to study the performance of this system. Performance measures of interest would be throughput rate, WIP inventory, and manufacturing lead time. A related problem of interest would concern optimal allocation of Kanbans to cells, i.e., optimally allocating a certain total amount of storage space among Kanban cells.

5.4.2 GSPN Model

We discuss two cases here: finite demand for products and infinite demand for products. In the latter case, there is at least one consumer waiting at any time for finished products (Poisson process with rate infinity). In the former case, demands for finished products arrive according to a Poisson process with finite rate, say λ.

We consider a three-cell system for illustrating GSPN modeling. Let N_i and n_i be the number of Kanbans and number of machines, respectively, in cell i $(i = 1, 2, 3)$; μ_i the service rate of each machine in cell i, and M the maximum number of requests that can queue up for finished parts. Figure 5.14 gives a schematic of the GSPN model for this three-cell system. The model has 18 places and 11 transitions whose description is given in Table 5.7.

A possible initial state of the above system is: $p_1 : 1$; $p_2 : N_1$; $p_3 : n_1$; $p_7 : N_2$; $p_8 : n_2$; $p_{12} : N_3$; $p_{13} : n_3$; $p_{17} : M$. There are four exponential transitions, of which t_3, t_6, and t_9 describe the processing inside the three cells and t_{10} captures the arrivals of demands. Note that t_3, t_6, and t_9 have marking-dependent firing rates. The elegance of this model lies in the simple way it captures
(i) the release of Kanbans and their movement inside the designated cell,
(ii) the joining of parts and Kanbans, and
(iii) the pulling effect of the waiting demands.

The model is also flexible since by altering the initial marking, we can take care of changes in (i) numbers of Kanbans in the cells, (ii) numbers of machines in the cells, and (iii) the maximum number of consumers that can queue up for consumption of finished products. Also, by making a simple change, namely by making t_{10} an immediate transition, the GSPN becomes a model for the infinite demand case.

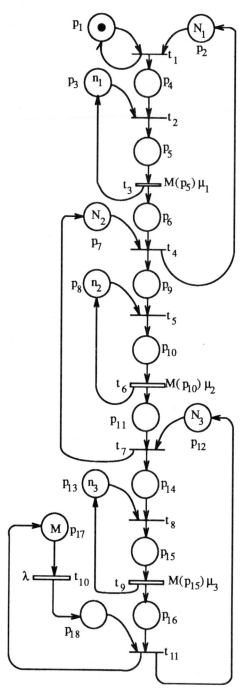

Figure 5.14 GSPN model of a 3–stage Kanban system

Table 5.7 Legend for Figure 5.14

Places

1 : Raw part ready for processing
2 : Kanbans available in bulletin board 1
3 : Machines available in cell 1
4 : Part and Kanban pairs in input buffer of cell 1
5 : Parts getting processed in cell 1
6 : Part and Kanban pairs in output hopper 1
7 : Kanbans in bulletin board 2
8 : Machines available in cell 2
9 : Part and Kanban pairs in input buffer of cell 2
10 : Parts getting processed in cell 2
11 : Part and Kanban pairs in output hopper 2
12 : Kanbans in bulletin board 3
13 : Machines available in cell 3
14 : Part and Kanban pairs in input buffer 3
15 : Parts getting processed in cell 3
16 : Part and Kanban pairs in output hopper 3
17 : Consumers who will arrive into the system in the future
18 : Waiting consumers in queue

Immediate Transitions

1 : A part and a Kanban enter input buffer 1
2 : A machine in cell 1 starts processing a part
4 : A part and a Kanban enter input buffer 2
5 : A machine in cell 2 starts processing a part
7 : A part and a Kanban enter input buffer 3
8 : A machine in cell 3 starts processing a part
11 : A consumer takes away a finished part and leaves the system

Exponential Transitions

3 : Processing of parts by machines in cell 1; Rate $= M(p_5)\mu_1$
6 : Processing of parts by machines in cell 2; Rate $= M(p_{10})\mu_2$
9 : Processing of parts by machines in cell 3; Rate $= M(p_{15})\mu_3$
10 : Arrival of consumers into the system; Rate $= \lambda$

Relevant performance measures for the system can be computed as follows:

1. Throughput rate $= TR(t_9)$
2. Machine utilizations:

$$\text{Cell 1}: M(p_5)/n_1$$
$$\text{Cell 2}: M(p_{10})/n_2$$
$$\text{Cell 3}: M(p_{15})/n_3$$

3. In-process inventory:

$$\text{Cell 1}: ET(p_4) + ET(p_5)$$
$$\text{Cell 2}: ET(p_9) + ET(p_{10})$$
$$\text{Cell 3}: ET(p_{14}) + ET(p_{15})$$

4. Manufacturing lead time:

$$= \frac{ET(p_4) + ET(p_5)}{TR(t_1)} + \frac{ET(p_9) + ET(p_{10})}{TR(t_4)} + \frac{ET(p_{14}) + ET(p_{15})}{TR(t_7)}$$

5.4.3 Numerical Results

Infinite Demand Case

Table 5.8 gives the throughput and lead time for the three-cell system with $n_1 = n_2 = n_3 = 1$; $N_1 + N_2 + N_3 = 6$; $\mu_1 = \mu_2 = \mu_3 = 3$ per hour and infinite demand for finished parts (Case 1). Since $N_1 + N_2 + N_3 = 6$, there are 10 different ways in which the Kanbans can be distributed across the three cells. Table 5.8 lists the throughput and lead time for these 10 allocations. Let (N_1, N_2, N_3) denote the vector of numbers of Kanbans allocated to the three cells.

From the Table 5.8, note that the maximum throughput corresponds to the allocation (1,4,1) whereas minimum MLT corresponds to (1,1,4). The actual allocation will be based on which is the more important index: throughput or MLT. Another point to note is that the allocation for maximum throughput (MLT) does not necessarily correspond to minimum MLT (throughput).

Tables 5.9 and 5.10 give the throughput and MLT values for the cases $\mu_1 = 3$; $\mu_2 = 1$; $\mu_3 = 3$ (Case 2) and $\mu_1 = 3$; $\mu_2 = 2$; $\mu_3 = 1$ (Case 3), respectively. In the former case, the allocation (1,1,4) again leads to minimum MLT but also corresponds to minimum throughput. The maximum throughput is again given by the allocation (1,4,1). In the latter case, (1,1,4) once again gives minimum MLT and (1,4,1), maximum throughput. However, (1,1,4) has a fairly high throughput, only slightly less than that for (1,4,1).

Table 5.8 Results for the infinite demand case (Case 1)

N1	N2	N3	Throughput (parts/ h)	MLT (h)
1	2	3	2.130988	1.800578
3	2	1	2.130988	2.58896
1	3	2	2.207422	1.97299
3	1	2	2.100950	2.39742
2	1	3	2.100950	2.00787
2	3	1	2.207422	2.35245
2	2	2	2.177932	2.22076
1	1	4	1.950311	1.552017
1	4	1	2.236514	2.080417
4	1	1	1.950311	2.88004

Table 5.9 Results for the infinite demand case (Case 2)

N1	N2	N3	Throughput (parts/ h)	MLT (h)
1	2	3	0.973531	3.426503
3	2	1	0.973531	5.461998
1	3	2	0.989266	4.34785
3	1	2	0.970481	4.55118
2	1	3	0.970481	3.53284
2	3	1	0.989266	5.351865
2	2	2	0.985219	4.46685
1	1	4	0.922522	2.536934
1	4	1	0.993817	5.231874
4	1	1	0.922522	5.75251

Finite Demand Case

It is reasonable to expect that throughput values will be less and MLT values higher in the case of finite demand. For a mean demand of 2 per hour and $\mu_1 = \mu_2 = \mu_3 = 3$ per hour, Table 5.11 lists these values for different Kanban allocations. As in the case of infinite demand, (1,1,4) leads to minimum MLT, with a striking difference seen with the next

Table 5.10 Results for the infinite demand case (Case 3)

N1	N2	N3	Throughput (parts/ h)	MLT (h)
1	2	3	0.979592	5.78942
3	2	1	0.932748	6.35525
1	3	2	0.980448	5.790955
3	1	2	0.932480	6.142057
2	1	3	0.964611	5.80709
2	3	1	0.966150	6.139430
2	2	2	0.965943	5.838661
1	1	4	0.974601	5.49957
1	4	1	0.980591	5.95288
4	1	1	0.857012	6.833867

Table 5.11 Results for the finite demand case

N1	N2	N3	Throughput (parts/ h)	MLT (h)
1	2	3	1.727679	3.945123
3	2	1	1.513570	3.9015328
1	3	2	1.687442	3.208910
3	1	2	1.613553	3.479980
2	1	3	1.696112	3.082805
2	3	1	1.543845	3.788271
2	2	2	1.667576	3.385493
1	1	4	1.692009	2.624236
1	4	1	1.554014	3.628167
4	1	1	1.430529	4.088930

smallest MLT. Interestingly, (1,1,4) gives the second highest throughput, behind the allocation (1,2,3). Fluctuations in demand can change these allocations in an unpredictable way. In such situations, GSPN models will be of much use.

PROBLEMS

1. Consider the following *modified Kanban* scheme presented by Mitra and Mitrani [1988a]: There is no input buffer in any cell; as a result, in any cell there can be at most as many parts as the number of machines in that cell. Each cell now has only a single location for storing parts and Kanbans, namely the output hopper. The bulletin board in each cell, as usual, holds Kanbans that are released when a finished part moves out of the cell. For a three-cell production line with this modified scheme, develop a GSPN model and compare the performance with that of the original Kanban scheme.

2. Consider a conventional flow line with three stages, one machine in each stage and a finite buffer of capacity N_i in stage i $(i = 1, 2, 3)$. Assume an infinite source and an infinite sink. Two policies are possible for operating this flow line: (i) A machine starts processing a next part only when the buffer in the next stage is not full, and (ii) a machine starts processing whenever a part is available but gets blocked after processing if the buffer in the next stage is full. Develop GSPN models for these two situations. How are these policies related to the Kanban and the modified Kanban schemes?

3. Figure 5.P.4 shows a simple assembly network comprising three machine centers M_1, M_2, and M_3, with service rates μ_1, μ_2, and μ_3, respectively. B_i $(i = 1, 2, 3, 4, 5)$ are buffers of adequate capacities for storing parts and Kanbans. There are N_i Kanbans $(i = 1, 2)$ circulating in machine center M_i. The schematic shows the flow of parts and Kanbans. M_3 is an assembly station that assembles the leading parts in B_3 and B_4 into a single finished product. After each assembly operation at M_3, two Kanbans are released, of which one each goes to M_1 and M_2. Develop a GSPN model of the above system and study the performance, assuming that raw parts are available. How can one determine optimal values for N_1 and N_2?

4. In Problem 3, it has been implicitly assumed that there is always a waiting demand for finished products. If there is only a finite demand, then, after the assembly operation, the two Kanbans will be released only if there is a demand waiting. Construct a GSPN model for this situation and compare the performance with that of the previous model.

5. A central server FMS with a Kanban scheme to regulate the number of parts inside the FMS is shown in Figure 5.P.5. Here, as usual, there is a limited number N of fixtures. Let $n\,(\leq N)$ be the number of Kanbans. A Kanban always accompanies every part inside the system. There is an exogenous arrival process of customer demands that will decide whether or not a fresh raw part would be allowed entry into the system when a finished part comes

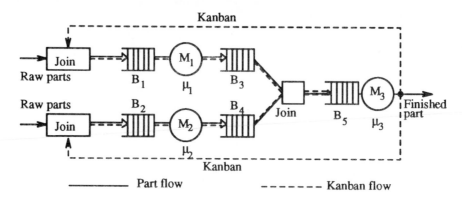

Figure 5.P.4

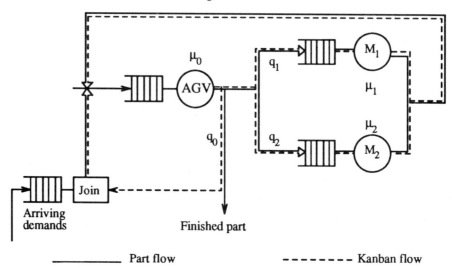

Figure 5.P.5

out of the system. As a result, the number of parts undergoing processing varies from 0 to N. Assuming a finite queue for waiting demands, develop a GSPN model for the above system. What can you say about the throughput, MLT, and in-process inventory of this system, compared to the classical central server FMS?

5.5 DEADLOCK ANALYSIS USING PETRI NETS

In this section we focus on the problem of deadlocks in automated manufacturing systems. We consider a simple and illustrative example and discuss the role of GSPN models in (i) modeling deadlocks, (ii) prevention and avoidance of deadlocks, and (iii) performance evaluation in the presence of deadlocks. We have already introduced and studied the problem of deadlocks in Sections 2.7 and 3.8.

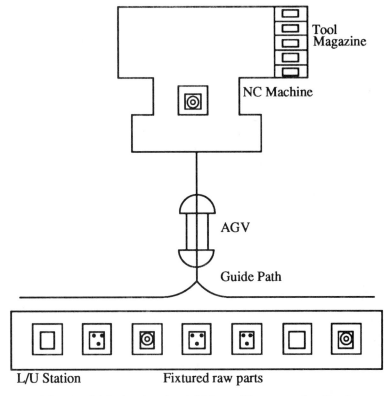

Figure 5.15 A simple AMS to illustrate deadlock

The simple AMS we discuss is depicted in Figure 5.15. There is a load/unload (L/U) station at which raw parts are always available. An AGV carries a raw part from the L/U station to an NC machine which carries out some operations on the raw part. The finished part is carried by the AGV to the L/U station where it is unloaded. It is assumed that the AGV can only carry one part at a time and the NC machine can only process one part at a time. Also the AGV takes a certain amount of time to carry a part from L/U to machine or from machine to L/U. However, if it is not carrying a part, its transit time between the L/U and NC machine is very small. Imagine the following sequence of events, starting with an initial state in which the AGV and the machine are free and raw parts are available: (i) The AGV carries a raw part, say part 1, and loads it onto the NC machine, which starts processing part 1. (ii) The AGV returns to the L/U station and carries another raw part, say part 2, to the machine, but waits for the machine, which is still processing part 1. Thus AGV gets blocked, waiting for the machine. (iii) The machine finishes the operations on part 1 and starts waiting for the AGV to carry the finished part 1 to the L/U station. At this juncture, the machine gets blocked waiting for the AGV. If the machine and the AGV can only accommodate one part at a time and there is no additional buffer space, then the two resources here are involved in a deadlock since each keeps waiting for the other indefinitely. Even if some buffer space is provided for raw parts and finished parts in the above system, a deadlock can still occur because the AGV can fill the entire buffer with raw parts during the processing of part 1 by the machine.

Recall from Section 2.7 that there are four necessary conditions for the occurrence of deadlocks: mutual exclusion, no preemption, hold and wait, and circular wait.

5.5.1 Deadlock Prevention

Deadlock prevention consists in falsifying one or more of the necessary conditions using *static* resource allocation policies. We show how the reachability graph of a GSPN model can be used to arrive at resource allocation policies that enforce deadlock prevention. Figure 5.16 shows a GSPN model of this system, with the description of the places and transitions given in Table 5.12.

In the above GSPN model, there are two sets of conflicting immediate transitions, $\{t_1, t_2\}$ and $\{t_5, t_6\}$. The set $\{t_1, t_2\}$ models the assignment of AGV to a raw part or a finished part. The set $\{t_5, t_6\}$ models whether or not the AGV is released after carrying a part from L/U station to the machine and finding the machine free. Transition t_5 represents the release of the AGV whereas t_6 models the holding of AGV until the machine finishes processing and the AGV unloads the finished part.

Figure 5.17 depicts the reachability graph of the above GSPN model. There are 16 markings, $M_0, M_1, ..., M_{15}$. The description of these markings is given in Table 5.13. We distinguish the markings into three classes: vanishing markings, tangible markings, and deadlocks in which none of the transitions is enabled. Vanishing markings model the states in which the system stays for zero time and they only indicate logical changes of state. Tangible markings are those in which the system will sojourn for non-zero time due to the progress of one or more timed activities in the system. Deadlocks are absorbing states in which the system will have to stay forever. In Figure 5.17, vanishing markings are shown as single circles with light border, tangible markings as single circles with heavy border, and deadlocks as double circles. The labels on the arcs indicate the transitions to be fired. From the graph, it can be inferred that:

1. The deadlock M_2 can be prevented by firing t_1 in preference to t_2 in the marking M_0. That is, the deadlock M_2 can be prevented by assigning the AGV to only a raw part, when no finished part is waiting.

2. The deadlock M_{15} can be prevented by firing t_6 in preference to t_5 in the marking M_4. This means that we don't release the AGV after the AGV transports a raw part to the machine and the machine takes up the raw part for processing. In this case, we hold the AGV until the machine finishes processing and the AGV unloads the finished part.

3. The deadlock M_{15} can also be prevented by firing t_2 in preference to t_1 in marking M_7, that is, by assigning the AGV to a finished part when a finished part is waiting.

As shown above, an exhaustive path anaysis of the reachability graph can lead to a set of resource allocation policies that prevent the occurrence of deadlocks. It is enough to do such an analysis just once in order to devise deadlock prevention policies.

5.5.2 Deadlock Avoidance

Deadlock prevention is accomplished by static policies and is known to result in poor resource utilization. Also, the reachability analysis technique to arrive at deadlock prevention policies can become infeasible if the state space is very large as in the case of a real-life AMS. Deadlock avoidance is the preferred alternative in such cases. In deadlock avoidance, we attempt to falsify one or more of the necessary conditions in a dynamic way by keeping track of the current state and the possible future conditions. The idea is to let the necessary conditions prevail as long as they do not cause a deadlock but falsify them as soon as a deadlock becomes a possibility in the immediate future. As a result, deadlock avoidance leads to better resource utilization.

In this section we present an on-line monitoring and control system based on GSPNs, for implementing deadlock avoidance. This system will avoid most of the deadlocks, and for deadlocks that are not predicted by

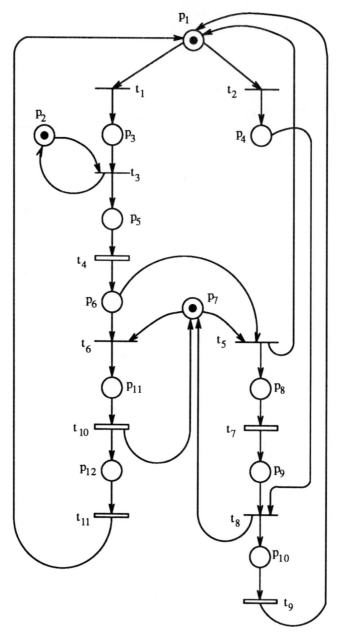

Figure 5.16 GSPN model for the example FMS

this scheme, recovery mechanisms have to be used. We first present some definitions.

Table 5.12 Description of the GSPN model of Figure 5.16

Places

  1 : AGV available

  2 : Raw parts available

  3 : AGV available to carry a raw part

  4 : AGV available to carry a finished part

  5 : AGV carrying a raw part to the NC machine

  6 : AGV, with raw part, waiting for the NC machine

  7 : NC machine available

  8 : NC machine processing a part; AGV released

  9 : NC machine waiting for AGV, after finishing processing

10 : AGV unloading the finished part

11 : NC machine processing a part; AGV not released

12 : AGV, not released during processing by machine, unloading a finished part

Immediate Transitions

  1 : AGV assigned to raw part

  2 : AGV assigned to finished part

  3 : AGV starts transporting a raw part

  5 : AGV released after finding machine free

  6 : AGV not released after finding machine free

  8 : AGV starts unloading a finished part

Timed Transitions

  4 : AGV carrying a raw part to the NC machine

  7 : Machine processing a part; AGV released

  9 : AGV carrying a finished part to L/U station

10 : Machine processing a part; AGV not released

11 : AGV, not released during processing by machine, carrying a finished part.

Definition: The *look ahead* of a deadlock avoidance policy is the number of steps of future evolution of the system computed, before making a resource allocation decision.

Definition: Given a PN model (P, T, IN, OUT, M_0), a marking $M \in R[M_0]$ is said to be *blocked* if there exists a $t \in T$ such that

(a) t has two or more input places,

(b) there exists a $p \in IP(t)$ such that $M(p) \geq IN(p, t)$, and

(c) t is disabled in M.

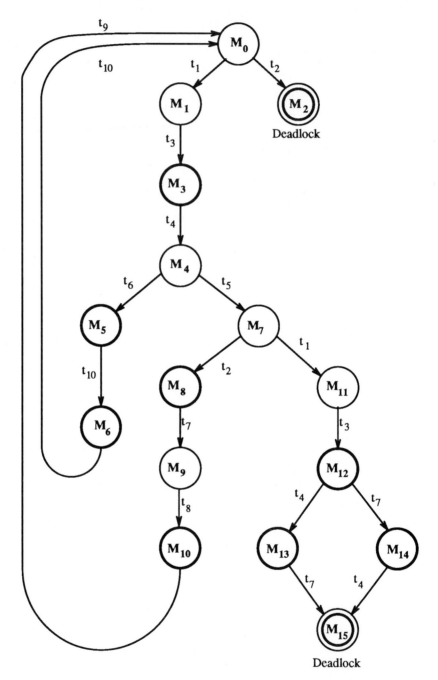

Figure 5.17 Reachability graph of the model of Figure 5.16

Table 5.13 Reachable markings of the GSPN model of Figure 5.17

Marking	p1	p2	p3	p4	p5	p6	p7	p8	p9	p10	p11	p12
M0	1	1	0	0	0	0	1	0	0	0	0	0
M1	0	1	1	0	0	0	1	0	0	0	0	0
M2	0	1	0	1	0	0	1	0	0	0	0	0
M3	0	1	0	0	1	0	1	0	0	0	0	0
M4	0	1	0	0	0	1	1	0	0	0	0	0
M5	0	1	0	0	0	0	0	0	0	0	1	0
M6	0	1	0	0	0	0	1	0	0	0	0	1
M7	1	1	0	0	0	0	0	1	0	0	0	0
M8	0	1	0	0	0	0	0	1	0	0	0	0
M9	0	1	0	1	0	0	0	0	1	0	0	0
M10	0	1	0	0	0	0	1	0	0	1	0	0
M11	0	1	1	0	0	0	0	1	0	0	0	0
M12	0	1	0	0	1	0	0	1	0	0	0	0
M13	0	1	0	0	0	1	0	1	0	0	0	0
M14	0	1	0	0	1	0	0	0	1	0	0	0
M15	0	1	0	0	0	1	0	0	1	0	0	0

Note: The motivation for the above definition is to capture markings in which processes are blocked waiting for resources. Blocking can be represented by a partially enabled transition having two or more input places. A blocked marking is to be distinguished from a deadlocked marking in which all transitions are disabled. Blocking is a necessary but not a sufficient condition for the occurrence of a deadlock. A blocked marking is often a good portent of a deadlock.

Definition: A marking M of a PN is designated *safe* if it is neither blocked nor deadlocked.

Note: The term *safe* here is not to be confused with the *safeness* property of Petri nets in the classical Petri net literature.

Notation: A marking M can only be of three types: safe, blocked, and deadlocked. We use the labels S, B, and D, respectively, to designate a marking.

Definition: Given a PN model (P, T, IN, OUT, M_0) and a marking $M \in R[M_0]$, the future set of markings reachable from M in i steps, $i \geq 0$, is denoted and defined by

$L_i(M) = \{(\sigma, M', c) : M'$ is reachable from M in i steps, by firing the transition sequence σ and is of type c where c may be S, B, or $D\}$.

Note: Given a marking M of type c, we have

$$L_0(M) = \{(\epsilon, M, c)\}$$

where ϵ is the null transition sequence. Also for $i \geq 0, j \geq 0$, if $M' \in L_i(M)$, then the elements of $L_j(M')$ will be contained in $L_{i+j}(M)$. Hence if $L_{i+j}(M)$ is known, $L_j(M')$ can be obtained. We first motivate GSPN-based deadlock avoidance using an example and then discuss the on-line controller.

Example 5.21

Consider the GSPN model of Figure 5.16 and the reachability graph of Figure 5.17. We discuss this example for a look ahead of 1. Thus, we look at the $L_1(.)$ function only. Let us say we start in the initial marking M_0. This is a vanishing marking in which two conflicting immediate transitions t_1 and t_2 are enabled. When we fire t_1, we obtain marking M_1, which is a safe state. When we fire t_2, we obtain marking M_2, which is a deadlock. Thus, we have

$$L_1(M_0) = \{(t_1, M_1, S), (t_2, M_2, D)\}$$

To avoid the deadlock, we have to fire t_1 in preference to t_2. That is, we should assign the resource AGV to a raw part. In this case, we have predicted a deadlock with a look ahead of 1. After firing t_1, the system reaches the state M_1. M_1 is a vanishing marking in which only one immediate transition is enabled. We have

$$L_1(M_1) = \{(t_3, M_3, S)\}$$

So, we can fire t_3, which means that the AGV starts transporting the raw part. M_3 is a tangible marking that represents the transport of a raw part by the AGV from the L/U station to the machine. As soon as the AGV finishes, the Petri net marking can be updated to M_4. State M_4 is a vanishing marking in which two conflicting immediate transitions t_5 and t_6 are enabled. We see that

$$L_1(M_4) = \{(t_6, M_5, S), (t_5, M_7, S)\}$$

Since both the next states are safe, we can choose any transition to fire. Let us choose t_5. That is, we release the AGV after the AGV reaches the machine and finds the machine available. Thus the current marking is M_7, which is again a vanishing marking with two conflicting transitions t_1 and t_2. We find

$$L_1(M_7) = \{(t_2, M_8, S), (t_1, M_{11}, S)\}$$

The choice here is between assigning the released AGV to a raw part or a finished part. Let us say we fire t_1, that is, we assign the AGV to the next raw part (which is already available). We reach the marking M_{11}, which is a vanishing marking with t_3 as the only enabled transition. We have

$$L_1(M_{11}) = \{(t_3, M_{12}, S)\}$$

The firing of t_3 means that the AGV starts transporting a fresh raw part. The marking M_{12} is a tangible marking in which the machine and the AGV are both busy. Depending on whichever finishes faster, we will reach M_{13} or M_{14}. If we assume that the AGV transport time and the machine processing time are independent continuous random variables, then the AGV and the machine cannot finish simultaneously. We have

$$L_1(M_{12}) = \{(t_4, M_{13}, B), (t_7, M_{14}, B)\}$$

Since t_4 and t_7 are activities in the physical system, we do not have any control over their progress. However, whether t_4 or t_7 fires first, we end up in a blocked state. In M_{13}, the AGV is blocked, waiting for the machine (t_5 and t_6 are disabled) whereas in M_{14}, the machine is blocked, waiting for the AGV (t_8 is disabled). Let us say AGV finishes first, so we reach the marking M_{13}. Now,

$$L_1(M_{13}) = \{(t_7, M_{15}, D)\}$$

M_{13} is a tangible marking and eventually t_7 fires, resulting in the dead-locked state M_{15}, in which both the AGV and the machine are blocked.

Thus using a look ahead of 1, we are able to avoid only one deadlock (M_2). This will be the case with look aheads of 2 and 3 also. It can be shown that a look ahead of 4 will avoid both the deadlocks. We can make the following observations:

1. Greater look ahead implies greater probability of avoiding deadlocks. However, there can be systems where only infinite look ahead will guarantee total deadlock avoidance. For this reason, deadlock avoidance may have to be supplemented by deadlock recovery.

2. In the case of look ahead equal to 1, the deadlock M_{15} is predicted in M_{13} or M_{14}. In the case of look ahead of 2, the deadlock is predicted in M_{12} (two steps earlier), and if look ahead equals 3, the deadlock is predicted in M_{11} itself. So the cost of deadlock recovery becomes less with increasing look ahead.

3. The Petri net framework is suitable for implementing deadlock avoidance. Vanishing markings with conflicting transitions naturally model resource allocation decisions; tangible markings model the progress of timed activities, which are not controllable once started. The evolution of the system can be easily determined by computing the future markings using the L function.

On-line Controller for Deadlock Avoidance

We now present an on-line controller for deadlock avoidance in any AMS, using GSPNs. The controller is basically an on-line monitoring system. Figure 5.18 shows the components of the proposed controller. These components are described below.

Physical System: This block corresponds to the actual AMS in operation.

Data Acquisition System: This unit is responsible for gathering and for status information of all resources in the AMS, using various sensors. The output of this unit can be used to determine the current marking of the GSPN model of the AMS.

GSPN Model: This corresponds to a data structure that efficiently stores the GSPN model of the AMS. This data structure also includes a field for the current marking, which is updated constantly by the real-time controller.

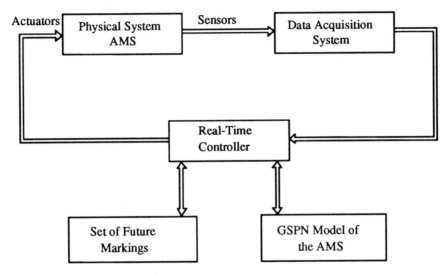

Figure 5.18 On-line control system for deadlock avoidance

Set of Future Markings: This is another data structure that efficiently stores the sets $L_1(M), L_2(M), ..., L_n(M)$, where n is the look ahead employed and M is a current marking. These sets are crucially used by the real-time controller to select the immediate transitions to fire. When the marking of the PN model changes, the L sets for the new marking can be computed easily from those of the current marking.

Real-Time Controller (RTC): The inputs to this unit are the look ahead to be employed and the sensor output data for the current state of the AMS. The controller has access to the two data structures, namely the GSPN model and the set of future markings. This unit mainly performs three functions in each iteration.

1. Determine the current marking of the GSPN model.

2. Classify the current marking into deadlock, tangible marking, or vanishing marking.

3. Look ahead into the system evolution and initiate appropriate actions.

The RTC first checks if the previous marking, say M_p, was tangible or vanishing. If M_p was tangible, then it obtains the current marking M by reading off appropriate sensor data output values. This is because in a tangible marking several activities are in progress and the next marking is decided by which activity finishes first. The finishing of an activity is indicated by a sensor, which is read off by the data acquisition system.

If the previous marking M_p was vanishing, then the RTC computes the current marking M as the marking obtained by firing in M_p the transition that was selected to fire in the previous iteration. Having determined M, the RTC updates the GSPN model so as to reflect the change in marking.

In the second step, the RTC classifies the current marking M into a deadlock or a tangible marking or a vanishing marking. To this end, the RTC first computes the set E of enabled transitions in M. If E is empty, then M is a deadlock. If E contains only timed transitions, then M is a tangible marking; otherwise M is a vanishing marking. The actions of the RTC now depend on this classification.

(a) If M is a deadlock, the RTC initiates appropriate deadlock recovery actions or informs the operator if necessary.

(b) If M is a tangible marking, then one or more activities are in progress. Thus, we have to monitor these activities so as to determine the next state of the AMS. The RTC in this case generates signals to activate appropriate sensors to monitor these activities. Note that typical activities include processing by a machine, part transfer by a robot, loading of raw parts, unloading of finished parts, transport of semi-finished parts, etc.

(c) If M is a vanishing marking, then at least one immediate transition is enabled and a decision may be required to be made about assigning or releasing some resource. Here we use the look ahead into the system evolution up to n steps where n is the look ahead. We select an immediate transition to fire, so as to avoid a deadlock as far as possible. First, the RTC computes $L_1(M)$ by selecting appropriate elements of $L_2(M_p)$ where M_p is the previous marking (note that $L_1(M)$ is a subset of $L_2(M_p)$). If $L_1(M)$ contains only deadlocks, then the RTC initiates advance deadlock recovery. Otherwise it computes $L_2(M)$, using $L_3(M_p)$. Again it repeats the steps as in the case of $L_1(M)$. If each $L_i(M)$ contains no deadlocks for $i = 1, 2, ..., n - 1$, it computes $L_n(M)$. If $L_n(M)$ contains only deadlocks, the RTC initiates advance deadlock recovery. If $L_n(M)$ contains at least one safe state, it will select, for firing, an immediate transition enabled in M that would lead to a safe state at the end of n steps. If $L_n(M)$ contains no safe states, the RTC selects for firing an immediate transition that would lead to a blocked state after n steps. The immediate transition that is finally chosen to fire will depend on the actual system. Depending on the immediate transition selected to fire, appropriate actuators are set.

We have thus seen that deadlock avoidance can be implemented effectively by an on-line monitoring and control system that employs the PN model to look ahead into the future evolution in order to make a resource allocation decision.

5.5.3 Performance Evaluation in the Presence of Deadlocks

The marking process of a GSPN having reachable deadlocked markings is essentially a Markov chain with absorbing states. Hence the theory of Markov chains with absorbing states (Section 3.8) can be used to evaluate measures of performance such as mean time before deadlock, mean number of finished parts before deadlock, and probability of a particular deadlock. We start with a GSPN model and obtain the reduced embedded Markov chain (REMC), which will not comprise any of the vanishing markings. For the sake of convenience, let us order the non-vanishing markings in such a way that deadlocked markings appear only after all the tangible markings. Then the transition probability matrix of the REMC would be of the form

$$\begin{bmatrix} T & C \\ 0 & I \end{bmatrix}$$

where T is the matrix of transition probabilities among tangible markings (not to be confused with the notation for the set of transitions) and matrix C gives the transition probabilities from tangible markings to deadlocked markings. The fundamental matrix can then be defined as

$$F = (I - T)^{-1}$$

Recall that f_{ij}, the $(i, j)^{\text{th}}$ element of F, gives the mean number of times tangible marking M_j is visited, starting from tangible marking M_i before reaching a deadlock. Knowing the mean sojourn times of the tangible markings, one can easily compute the mean time before deadlock. Also, the $(i, j)^{\text{th}}$ element of the matrix G, where $G = FC$, gives the long-term probability that the marking process reaches the jth deadlock, starting from tangible marking M_i.

Example 5.22

As an example, we consider the single AGV, single NC machine system depicted in Figure 5.15. Assume that there is a buffer in front of the machine. In the GSPN model of Figure 5.16, the buffer was not modeled and so we construct another GSPN model, as in Figure 5.19. Table 5.14

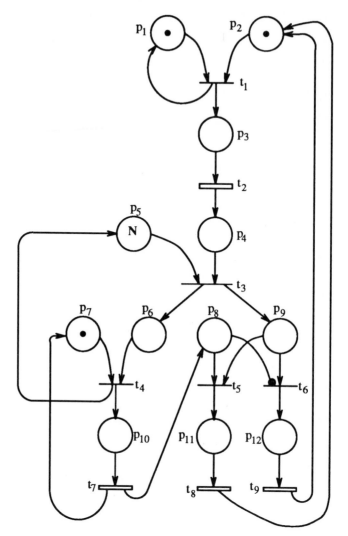

Figure 5.19 GSPN model for Example 5.22

gives a description of the places and transitions of this model. In the present system, the AGV travels with a raw part to the buffer and deposits the part in the buffer if a buffer position is available. If a finished part is ready to be unloaded, the AGV carries the finished part and travels back to the L/U. Otherwise, the AGV returns to L/U, empty-handed. The machine checks for raw parts in the buffer and starts processing one if available. After finishing processing, it will wait for a buffer position and deposits the finished part in the buffer as soon as a position becomes available. A

Table 5.14 Legend for Figure 5.19

Places

  1 : Raw parts available
  2 : AGV available at the L/U station
  3 : AGV transporting a raw part from L/U to machine
  4 : AGV with raw part waiting for a position in the buffer
  5 : Buffer positions available
  6 : Raw parts in buffer waiting for machine
  7 : NC machine available
  8 : Finished parts in buffer waiting for AGV
  9 : AGV available at the buffer
 10 : Machine processing a part
 11 : AGV traveling to L/U with a finished part
 12 : AGV traveling to L/U without a finished part

Immediate Transitions

  1 : AGV starts transporting a raw part
  3 : A raw part on the AGV moves to the buffer
  4 : Machine starts processing a part
  5 : AGV starts returning with a finished part
  6 : AGV starts returning to L/U without a finished part

Exponential Transitions

  2 : AGV journey from L/U to machine with a raw part
  7 : Part processing by the machine
  8 : AGV journey from machine to L/U with a finished part
  9 : AGV journey from machine to L/U without a finished part.

---

deadlock will result when the buffer is filled with raw parts or finished parts or both, the AGV is waiting with a raw part for a buffer position, and the machine is waiting with a finished part for a buffer position. Clearly, there are many such deadlocks possible in the system.

Note that a deadlock can result whatever the buffer capacity. However, intuitively, the mean time before deadlock will increase with increase in buffer capacity. If our interest is in avoiding a deadlock in a given observation period, say a shift period, then the risk of deadlock is reduced with larger number of buffer positions. The GSPN model of Figure 5.19 can

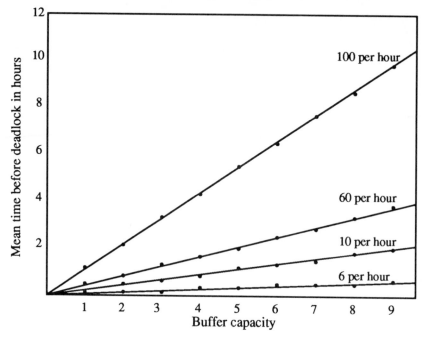

Figure 5.20 Mean time to deadlock

be used to study the effect of buffer capacity on the mean time to deadlock. For example, Figure 5.20 gives a plot of mean time before deadlock versus buffer capacity for different service rates of the machine (6/ h, 10/ h, 60/ h, and 100/ h). The AGV travel time is assumed to have a mean of 1 min.

PROBLEMS

1. For the GSPN model of Figure 5.19, discuss how the mean number of parts produced before deadlock can be computed. Also, what would be the effect in the following cases?

   (a) AGV is much faster compared to the machine.

   (b) NC machine is much faster compared to the AGV.
   How can the effect be investigated using the same GSPN model?

2. Modify the GSPN model of Figure 5.19 in order to implement the following priority rule: The AGV picks up a raw part for transport only if no finished part is waiting. Will this increase or decrease the time before deadlock?

3. Solve Problems 4, 5, and 6 of Section 3.8 using GSPN models.

4. An important application of GSPNs would be to evaluate and compare the effectiveness of different deadlock prevention algorithms. When a deadlock prevention algorithm is implemented in a system, the system will not have deadlocks and hence the GSPN model can be evaluated in the usual way. For the familiar system of Figure 5.15, the following are some possible deadlock prevention algorithms.

  (a) A raw part is loaded onto the AGV only if a buffer position is available; this position is reserved for this raw part.

  (b) There are two AGVs instead of one; one AGV is meant exclusively for raw parts and the other for finished parts.

  (c) The AGV is used in a cyclical way, i.e., the AGV transports a raw part, waits till a finished part is available, unloads the finished part, and repeats the cycle again.

  (d) If the AGV carrying a raw part finds the buffer full, it returns to L/U, unloads the raw part, and travels to the buffer to unload a finished part.

Write down GSPN models for the above and discuss the relative effectiveness in terms of throughput, resource utilization, etc.

5. For the dining philosophers' problem presented in Figure 5.P.2 of Section 5.2, the following gives some deadlock prevention algorithms. Construct a GSPN model in each case and evaluate the throughput and resource utilization.

  (a) The even philosopher picks up his left fork first and then waits for the right fork. The odd philosopher picks up his right fork first and then waits for the left fork.

  (b) Each philosopher picks up his left fork first and picks up the right fork if available; otherwise each releases the left fork and goes back to thinking mode.

  (c) Let P_0, P_1, P_2 be the philosophers, and F_0, F_1, F_2 the forks, with F_i ($i = 0,1,2$) as the left fork of P_i. Each fork is used in a cyclical sequence. For example, after P_0 uses F_0, P_2 alone can use it, then followed by P_0, P_2, ...

  (d) P_0 gets priority over P_1 and P_2 for using F_1 and F_0, respectively. P_1 gets priority over P_2 for using F_2.

6. Develop a software package that can compute the performance measures of a GSPN model with deadlocks. The initial part of this package, until the generation of the reduced embedded Markov chain, will be common with the package for GSPN Analysis (Problem 7 of Section 5.3). The second part of this package will be similar to the package for analysis of Markov chains with absorbing states (Problem 3 of Section 3.8)

5.6 EXTENDED CLASSES OF TIMED PETRI NETS

So far we have discussed exponential timed Petri nets and generalized stochastic Petri nets. In the literature, a number of extensions have been proposed to the basic timed Petri net model. In this section we briefly review some of the important classes of extended timed Petri net models.

5.6.1 Colored Stochastic Petri Nets

Colored stochastic Petri nets are based on the formalism of colored Petri Nets (CPNs). CPNs proposed by Jensen [1981] are a high-level Petri net model that leads to compact net models by using the concept of colors. In fact, CPNs have the same modeling description power of classical Petri nets, but are more concise from a graphical viewpoint. This conciseness is achieved by merging analogous places (transitions) in a model into a single place (transition) and associating colors to tokens, places, and transitions to distinguish among various elements. A transition can fire with respect to each of its colors. By firing a transition, tokens are removed and added at the input and output places in the normal way, except that a functional dependency is specified between the color of the transition firing and the colors of the involved tokens.

For example, we can associate a set (MACHS) of machines processing jobs of various part types with a single place. Such a set has tokens of different colors, each identifying a particular type of machine. It may sometimes be necessary to characterize a token with two or more attributes. For example, the color (part type i, machine j) can characterize the state of part i in relation to machine j. In general, a color set can be any subset of the Cartesian product of a set of basic color sets, which proves convenient in modeling the physical object under consideration.

Definition: A CPN is a quintuple (P, T, C, IN, OUT) where

1. $P = \{p_1, p_2, ..., p_n\}$, $n > 0$, is a set of places,
   $T = \{t_1, t_2, ..., t_m\}$, $m > 0$, is a set of transitions such that $P \cup T \neq \phi$ and $P \cap T = \phi$.

2. $C(p_i)$ and $C(t_j)$ are sets of colors associated, respectively, with place $p_i \in P$ and transition $t_j \in T$, given by

$$C(p_i) = \{a_{i1}, a_{i2}, ..., a_{iu_i}\}; \quad u_i = \mid C(p_i)\mid; \quad i = 1, 2, ..., n$$
$$C(t_j) = \{b_{j1}, b_{j2}, ..., b_{jv_j}\}; \quad v_j = \mid C(t_j)\mid; \quad j = 1, 2, ..., m$$

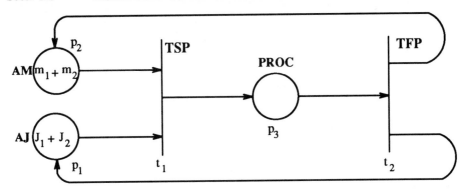

Figure 5.21 Colored Petri net model of a simple AMS

3. $IN\,(p,t):\ C\,(p)\ X\ C\,(t) \to$ **N** is an *input function*, and
   $OUT\,(p,t):\ C\,(p)\ X\ C\,(t) \to$ **N** is an *output function*.

In this book, we assume that in a CPN, the color sets are finite.

Pictorially, places in CPNs are represented by circles and transitions by horizontal or vertical bars. If $IN\,(p_i,t_j)\,(a_{ih},b_{jk}) \neq 0$ for some h and k, then we draw a directed arc from place p_i to transition t_j. This directed arc is labeled with linear function $IN\,(p_i,t_j)$. Similarly, if $OUT\,(p_i,t_j)\,(a_{ih},b_{jk}) \neq 0$ for some h and k, we draw a directed arc from t_j to p_i and label it with $OUT\,(p_i,t_j)$.

Example 5.23

We consider the manufacturing system of Section 5.1. Figure 5.21 depicts a CPN model of this system. The places and transitions have the following interpretation.

$p_1 = AJ$: Available fresh jobs

$p_2 = AM$: Available machines

$p_3 = PROC$: Processing in progress

$t_1 = TSP$: Transition indicating start of processing

$t_2 = TFP$: Transition indicating finishing of processing

In the CPN model, we have three color sets, $MACHS$, $PARTS$, and $PARTS\ X\ MACHS$, where $MACHS = \{m_1, m_2\}$ and $PARTS = \{J_1, J_2\}$. Also, it can be seen that

$$C\,(AJ) = \{J_1, J_2\}$$
$$C\,(AM) = \{m_1, m_2\}$$

$$C(PROC) = MACHS \; X \; PARTS$$
$$C(TFP) = C(TSP) = MACHS \; X \; PARTS$$

We can now define the input and output functions. First, we consider the input function of transition TSP with reference to its various colors and color J_1 of place AJ.

$$IN\,(AJ,TSP)\,(J_1,(m_1,J_1)) = 1$$
$$IN\,(AJ,TSP)\,(J_1,(m_1,J_2)) = 0$$
$$IN\,(AJ,TSP)\,(J_1,(m_2,J_1)) = 1$$
$$IN\,(AJ,TSP)\,(J_1,(m_2,J_2)) = 0$$

Further, with respect to color J_2 of place AJ, we have

$$IN\,(AJ,TSP)\,(J_2,(m_1,J_1)) = 0$$
$$IN\,(AJ,TSP)\,(J_2,(m_1,J_2)) = 1$$
$$IN\,(AJ,TSP)\,(J_2,(m_2,J_1)) = 0$$
$$IN\,(AJ,TSP)\,(J_2,(m_2,J_2)) = 1$$

More concisely, we can represent the $IN\,(p_1,t_1)$ by the $\mid C\,(p_1) \mid X \mid C\,(t_1) \mid$ matrix:

$$IN\,(p_1,t_1) = \begin{bmatrix} 1 & 0 & 1 & 0 \\ 0 & 1 & 0 & 1 \end{bmatrix}$$

Similarly, $IN\,(p_2,t_1)$ is a $\mid C\,(p_2) \mid X \mid C\,(t_1) \mid$ matrix given by

$$IN\,(p_2,t_1) = \begin{bmatrix} 1 & 1 & 0 & 0 \\ 0 & 0 & 1 & 1 \end{bmatrix}$$

Now, it is easy to see that

$$OUT\,(p_3,t_1) = IN\,(p_3,t_2) = I_4$$

Similarly, $OUT\,(p_1,t_2)$ and $OUT\,(p_2,t_2)$ are $\mid C\,(p_1) \mid X \mid C\,(t_2) \mid$ and $\mid C\,(p_2) \mid X \mid C\,(t_2) \mid$ matrices given by

$$OUT\,(p_1,t_2) = \begin{bmatrix} 1 & 0 & 1 & 0 \\ 0 & 1 & 0 & 1 \end{bmatrix} = IN\,(p_1,t_1)$$

$$OUT\,(p_2,t_2) = \begin{bmatrix} 1 & 1 & 0 & 0 \\ 0 & 0 & 1 & 1 \end{bmatrix} = IN\,(p_2,t_1)$$

Definition: A marking of a CPN is a function M defined on P such that for $p \in P$, $M(p) : C(p) \to \mathbf{N}$. A marked CPN is a CPN with a marking defined on it.

Let M denote the current marking of a CPN. The marking M is an $(n \times 1)$ vector with components $M(p_i)$, where $M(p_i)$ represents the marking of place p_i. $M(p_i)$ is represented by the formal sum of colors:

$$M(p_i) = \sum_{h=1}^{u_i} n_{ih} a_{ih}$$

where n_{ih} is the number of tokens of color a_{ih} in place p_i. Thus

$$M(p_i)(a_{ih}) = n_{ih}$$

denotes the number of tokens of color a_{ih} (in place p_i) in the current marking.

Definition: A transition t_j of a CPN is said to be *enabled* with respect to a color b_{jk} in a marking M if and only if

$$M(p_i)(a_{ih}) \geq IN(p_i, t_j)(a_{ih}, b_{jk}) \quad \forall\, p_i \in P,\, a_{ih} \in C(p_i).$$

When a transition is enabled it can *fire*. When a transition t_j, enabled in a marking M, fires with respect to a color b_{jk}, a new marking M' is reached according to the following equation

$$M'(p_i)(a_{ih}) = M(p_i)(a_{ih}) + OUT(p_i, t_j)(a_{ih}, b_{jk}) - IN(p_i, t_j)(a_{ih}, b_{jk})$$
$$\forall\, a_{ih} \in C(p_i);\; p_i \in P$$

Example 5.24

Consider the CPN model shown in Figure 5.21. Suppose we start the process with one job of each part type and one machine of each type; then the initial marking is

$$M_0 = \begin{bmatrix} J_1 + J_2 \\ m_1 + m_2 \\ 0 \end{bmatrix}$$

In this marking the transition t_1 is enabled with respect to all its four colors. It can fire individually with respect to any one of the colors. Also, it can fire concurrently with respect to colors (m_1, J_1) and (m_2, J_2) or (m_1, J_2) and (m_2, J_1). The markings reached in all these cases are given by

$$
M_1 = \begin{bmatrix} J_2 \\ m_2 \\ (m_1, J_1) \end{bmatrix} ; \quad
M_2 = \begin{bmatrix} J_1 \\ m_1 \\ (m_2, J_2) \end{bmatrix} ; \quad
M_3 = \begin{bmatrix} J_1 \\ m_2 \\ (m_1, J_2) \end{bmatrix} ;
$$

$$
M_4 = \begin{bmatrix} J_2 \\ m_1 \\ (m_2, J_1) \end{bmatrix} ; \quad
M_5 = \begin{bmatrix} 0 \\ 0 \\ (m_1, J_1) + (m_2 + J_2) \end{bmatrix} ; \quad \text{and}
$$

$$
M_6 = \begin{bmatrix} 0 \\ 0 \\ (m_1, J_2) + (m_2, J_1) \end{bmatrix}
$$

Note that the above markings are the same as the ones in Figure 5.2.

The concepts of reachability set, reachability graph, boundedness, properness, deadlocks, and liveness can now be easily extended to CPNs.

Definition: A *colored generalized stochastic Petri net* is an eight-tuple $(P, T, C, IN, OUT, M_0, F, S)$ where

1. (P, T, C, IN, OUT, M_0) is a marked CPN;

2. T is partitioned into two sets: T_I of immediate transitions and T_E of exponential transitions;

3. F is a firing function that associates to each color $C(t)$ of a transition $t \in T_E$ in each reachable marking an exponential random variable;

4. each color $C(t)$ of every transition $t \in T_I$ has zero firing time in all reachable markings; and

5. S is a set, possibly empty, of random switches that associate probability distributions to subsets of colors of conflicting immediate transitions.

The graphical representation of a colored GSPN will follow the conventions used in CPNs and GSPNs.

A colored GSPN when unfolded gives an ordinary GSPN and hence the analysis of colored GSPNs is identical to that of ordinary GSPNs.

Example 5.25

In the CPN model of Figure 5.21, let us designate t_1 as an immediate transition and t_2 as an exponential transition. Also, if for transition t_1, we specify random switches for the colors (m_1, J_1) and (m_1, J_2) and for colors (m_2, J_1) and (m_2, J_2), then the resulting model is a colored GSPN model. It is easy to see that when unfolded, this colored GSPN would give a GSPN model with eight places, four immediate transitions, and four exponential transitions. In fact, this GSPN model will be the same as the classical PN model of Figure 5.1 with transitions t_1, t_2, t_3, and t_4 designated as immediate transitions and t_5, t_6, t_7, and t_8 designated as exponential transitions. The reachability set of the colored GSPN model has seven markings as in Example 5.24. Of these, M_0, M_1, M_2, M_3, and M_4 are vanishing markings and M_5 and M_6 are tangible markings.

An important feature of the colored GSPN model of Example 5.25 is that it can model a system with an arbitrary number of machine types and an arbitrary number of part types by redefining the color sets $MACHS$ and $PARTS$. However, the reachability set will be the same as that of the unfolded GSPN model and thus the solution of the model is no less complex. Nevertheless, the colored GSPN model has the following advantages:

1. Under certain conditions, the reachability set of a colored GSPN model can be pruned significantly on the lines suggested by Lin and Marinescu [1988]. In such situations, colored GSPNs would be more efficient.

2. Colored GSPN models are very compact and such a modeling framework would be congenial for purposes of specification and discrete event simulation of AMSs.

5.6.2 Extended Stochastic Petri Nets

Proposed by Dugan, Trivedi, Geist, and Nicola [1984], extended stochastic Petri nets (ESPNs) represent a significant effort in including nonexponential random variables in the analysis of SPN-based models. They are an extension of GSPNs. In addition to *general* firing time distributions, the definition of an ESPN includes *inhibitor arcs*, and special arcs called *counter arcs*, *counter-alternate arcs,* and *probabilistic arcs*.

If there are probabilistic arcs from a transition to a subset of its output places, then, on firing the transition a token is deposited in exactly one place in the subset.

Example 5.26

Figure 5.22(a) depicts an ESPN transition t_1 with probabilistic arc to places p_1, p_2, and p_3. When t_1 fires, a token is deposited in p_4 with probability 1, and a token is deposited in one of the places p_1, p_2, and p_3 with probabilities

q_1, q_2, and $1 - q_1 - q_2$, respectively. Figure 5.22(b) shows a GSPN fragment semantically equivalent to the above ESPN construct. Note that we need one additional place, p_5, and three additional transitions, t_2, t_3, and t_4.

A counter arc from a place to a transition is labeled with a positive integer value k and the transition is enabled only if there are at least k tokens in that place and k tokens are removed on transition firing. Associated with a particular counter arc can be a counter-alternate arc, which enables an alternative transition when the count is between 1 and $(k - 1)$, inclusive. The alternative transition can fire once each time a token is deposited in the counting input place until there are k tokens present. The count remains unchanged by the firing of the alternative transition, as it removes no token from the counter input place.

Example 5.27

Figure 5.22(c) shows two transitions t_1 and t_2 with a place p_1 connected to t_1 with a counter arc labeled 3 and a counter-alternate arc labeled $\bar{3}$. Let M be a current marking. If $M(p_1) = 0$, then neither t_1 nor t_2 is enabled. If $M(p_1) = 1$ or 2, then t_2 will fire, without removing any tokens from p_1. If $M(p_1) \geq 3$, t_2 is disabled and only t_1 fires, removing 3 tokens from p_1.

In ESPNs, a transition can belong to one of three classes – *exclusive, competitive,* and *concurrent.* A transition is exclusive if in all markings

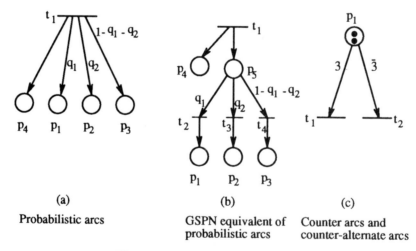

(a)

Probabilistic arcs

(b)

GSPN equivalent of probabilistic arcs

(c)

Counter arcs and counter-alternate arcs

Figure 5.22 Special arcs in ESPNs

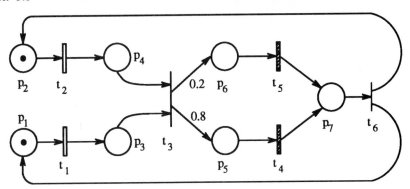

Figure 5.23 An ESPN model

enabling it, it is the lone enabled transition. A transition is competitive if in all markings enabling it, it is in conflict with all other enabled transitions. Finally, a transition is concurrent if there exists a reachable marking in which there is at least one other enabled transition not in conflict with this transition. The marking process of an ESPN has been shown to be a semi-Markov process provided that (i) all concurrent transitions are associated with exponential firing times and (ii) all competitive transitions follow a firing policy whereby once disabled, the elapsed firing time is set to zero. The exclusive and competitive transitions can be associated with non-exponential firing times. The analysis of such ESPNs can be carried out using the theory of semi-Markov processes.

Example 5.28

Figure 5.23 depicts an ESPN model for the following situation. There is an assembly system that produces two types of assembled products, say type 1 and type 2. Each type of assembled product is made of two components, which are machined by two machines M_1 and M_2. The two components are produced concurrently by M_1 and M_2. After the assembly operation is completed, the assembled part is unloaded immediately and M_1 and M_2 will start processing components. The requirement for type 1 and type 2 parts is in the ratio 4:1. Table 5.15 gives a description of this ESPN model.

Note that t_3 has probabilistic arcs with probabilities 0.8 and 0.2 to model the relative frequency of production of the two types of products. Transitions t_1 and t_2 are concurrent transitions and are therefore constrained to have exponential firing times for tractability. Transitions t_4 and t_5, which are represented in Figure 5.23 by shaded rectangular boxes, are exclusive transitions and can therefore be associated with any arbitrary firing time

Table 5.15 Legend for Figure 5.23

Places

1 : M_1 processing a part
2 : M_2 processing a part
3 : A part processed by M_1
4 : A part processed by M_2
5 : Type 1 assembly in progress
6 : Type 2 assembly in progress
7 : Assembled part ready for unloading

Immediate Transitions

3 : Assembly starts
6 : Assembled part unloaded

Timed Transitions

1 : Processing by M_1
2 : Processing by M_2
4 : Assembly operation of Type 1
5 : Assembly operation of Type 2

---

distribution. For example, they may have firing times that have constant duration or are normally distributed or are uniformly distributed. In any case, the marking process is a semi-Markov process that can be analyzed using standard techniques.

5.6.3 Petri Nets with Deterministic and Exponential Firing Times

Petri nets with deterministic and stochastic transition firing times were proposed by Ajmone Marsan and Chiola [1986]. These are abbreviated as DSPNs. DSPNs are extensions of GSPNs where the transitions are of three types: *immediate, exponential,* and *deterministic.* The deterministic transitions have a constant firing time. The graphical representation of DSPNs is the same as GSPNs except that deterministic transitions are represented by dark rectangular boxes. We discuss below some important notions required for understanding the analysis of DSPNs.

Definition: A DSPN is a 8-tuple $(P, T, IN, OUT, INH, M_0, F, S)$

where the components P, T, IN, OUT, INH, M_0, and S have the same significance as in a GSPN and

1. T is partitioned into three sets: T_I of *immediate* transitions, T_E of *exponential* transitions, and T_D of *deterministic* transitions.
2. $F : R[M_0] X (T_E \cup T_D) \rightarrow \mathbf{R}$ is a *firing function* that associates

    (a) to each $t \in T_E$ in each $M \in R[M_0]$, an exponential random variable with rate $F(M, t)$, and
    (b) to each $t \in T_D$ in each $M \in R[M_0]$, a real number $F(M, t)$ which is the constant firing time of t in M.

3. Each $t \in T_I$ in each $M \in R[M_0]$ has zero firing time in all reachable markings.

Preselection and Race Policies

Starting from the initial marking M_0 of a DSPN, the evolution of markings proceeds in much the same way as in GSPNs. In each reachable marking M of the DSPN, there is a set $ET(M)$ of enabled transitions and the next marking is decided by which subset of these enabled transitions is chosen to fire next. *Preselection* and *race* are two policies suggested in the literature for assigning a probability to each subset of transitions of $ET(M)$ which can fire next. In preselection, these probabilities are predefined as in the case of the random switches of a GSPN. In the race policy, these probabilities depend on the firing times of the enabled transitions, as in the case of the exponential transitions of a GSPN.

Resampling, Enabling Memory, and Age Memory Policies

Much of the difficulty in analyzing a DSPN is caused by the co-existence of deterministic transitions and exponential transitions. Exponential distribution, being memoryless, leads to simplifications in the analysis, but we have to explicitly keep track of memory in the case of deterministic transitions. In the literature, three different policies have been suggested for handling the memory of deterministic transitions: *resampling, enabling memory*, and *age memory*.

Definition: Let M be a reachable marking of a DSPN. A *history* of M is a sequence of transition firings that results in M starting from M_0, together with the firing times of these transitions.

That is, if we choose the sequence

$$M_0 \overset{t_{n_1}}{\underset{e_1}{\to}} M_1 \overset{t_{n_2}}{\underset{e_2}{\to}} M_2 \overset{t_{n_3}}{\underset{e_3}{\to}} \ldots \overset{t_{n_k}}{\underset{e_k}{\to}} M_k (= M) \qquad (11)$$

where $M_1, M_2, \ldots, M_{k-1}$ are intermediate markings, $t_{n_1}, t_{n_2}, \ldots, t_{n_k}$ are the transitions that are involved in the firing sequence, and e'_is $(i = 1, 2, \ldots, k)$ are the time instants (epochs) at which t_{n_i} finish firing, then the history of M corresponding to the above sequence is the set of transitions t_{n_i} and the set of epochs e'_is. The epoch corresponding to M_0 is assumed to be zero.

Definition: Let t_j be a transition, M a marking, and Z a history of M represented by the sequence (11). The *age epoch* $e_A(t_j, M, Z)$ is the time instant e_i $(i = 1, 2, \ldots, k)$ from which t_j has been firing intermittently or continuously without completing firing by the instant e_k. The *enabling epoch* $e_E(t_j, M, Z)$ is the time instant e_i $(i = 1, 2, \ldots, k)$ at which t_j got enabled and has been continuously firing up to e_k, without finishing firing.

Definition: The *residual firing time* $RFT(t_j, M, Z)$ of a transition t_j in a marking M under a history Z is the time duration for which the transition should fire in M in order to finish firing.

Let M be any reachable marking and Z any history of M in a DSPN. Then $RFT(t_j, M, Z) = 0$ if $t_j \in T_I$; $RFT(t_j, M, Z)$ for $t_j \in T_E$, is an exponential random variable with rate $F(M, t_j)$; and $RFT(t_j, M, Z)$ for $t_j \in T_D$, is either a deterministic duration less than or equal to $F(M, t_j)$ or a random variable which takes values less than or equal to $F(M, t_j)$.

The policies resampling, enabling memory, and age memory are three different ways of looking at the RFT of a deterministic transition. Let t_j be a deterministic transition enabled in a marking M and let M have a history Z as represented in (11). Then we define $AM(t_j, M, Z)$ as the total duration of time for which t_j has fired between the epochs $e_A(t_j, M, Z)$ and e_k.

Also, we define $EM(t_j, M, Z)$ as the total duration of time for which t_j has fired between the epochs $e_E(t_j, M, Z)$ and e_k.

If τ_j is the deterministic duration associated with t_j, then the three policies have the following interpretation:

$$\text{Resampling} : RFT(t_j, M, Z) = \tau_j$$
$$\text{Age memory} : RFT(t_j, M, Z) = \tau_j - AM(t_j, M, Z)$$
$$\text{Enabling memory} : RFT(t_j, M, Z) = \tau_j - EM(t_j, M, Z)$$

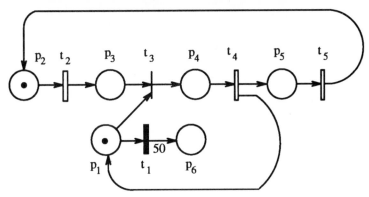

Figure 5.24 DSPN model for Example 5.29

To see the difference among these three policies, we present the following example.

Example 5.29

Consider the DSPN of Figure 5.24. t_1 is deterministic with duration 50, t_3 is immediate, and the other transitions are exponential with some rates. The initial marking M_0 is $(1, 1, 0, 0, 0, 0)$. Let us be interested in reaching marking $M = M_0$ itself. One possible sequence of transition firings and epochs which will take us from M_0 to M is

$$M_0 \xrightarrow[15]{t_2} M_1 \xrightarrow[15]{t_3} M_2 \xrightarrow[40]{t_4} M_3 \xrightarrow[60]{t_5} M_4 \, (= M), \quad \text{where}$$

$M_1 = (1, 0, 1, 0, 0, 0)$, $M_2 = (0, 0, 0, 1, 0, 0)$, and $M_3 = (1, 0, 0, 0, 1, 0)$. As usual, the time instants 15, 15, 40, and 60 indicate, respectively, the epochs at which t_2, t_3, t_4, and t_5 finished firing. For the above history Z of marking M, it is easy to see that

$$e_A (t_1, M, Z) = 0$$
$$e_E (t_1, M, Z) = 40$$
$$AM (t_1, M, Z) = 15 + 20 = 35$$
$$EM (t_1, M, Z) = 20$$

Thus we have,

$$RFT (t_1, M, Z) = 50 \text{ for the resampling policy}$$
$$= 15 \text{ for the age memory policy, and}$$
$$= 30 \text{ for the enabling memory policy.}$$

The analysis of a DSPN depends on the firing policy assumed. The firing policy is made of two components where the first component refers to either preselection or race and the second component is one of resampling, enabling memory, and age memory.

It has been seen that the policies – preselection with enabling memory and preselection with age memory – are irrelevant since they may lead to negative residual firing times. The practical significance of other policies is discussed below.

Race with Resampling: This can represent parallel conflicting activities which are such that the first one to finish decides a change in state (race); also, the only useful work is done by the activity that terminates first and the work done by the other activities is lost (resampling).

Preselection with Resampling: This policy can model a set of conflicting activities that cannot be performed in parallel. When the system enters a new state, it must first choose which of the conflicting activities to perform next. The chosen activity is then performed up to completion and the state of the system changes. As an example, we can consider a robot that must sequentially execute a series of transfer operations.

Race with Age Memory: Using this policy, we can describe a set of concurrent activities where the work performed by those activities that do not complete is not lost. That is, if an activity is interrupted by a change of state, it will resume, from where it had left off, in the first marking that enables it again. An example is provided by a manufacturing system where, on breakdown of a machine, the job on the machine is not discarded but reworked after repair of machine.

Race with Enabling Memory: This describes a set of concurrent activities where the work performed by an activity that does not complete is lost unless it remains enabled in the new state. An example is a manufacturing system where, on breakdown of a machine, the part being processed is discarded.

Combination of Policies: It is often useful to have two or more policies coexisting in the same net. An immediate example is the GSPN model, which uses preselection for immediate transitions and race for exponential transitions.

It is easy to see that the marking process of an arbitrary DSPN need not be even a semi-Markov process. However, when in any reachable marking of the DSPN, at most one concurrent deterministic transition is enabled, the DSPN can be analyzed through the embedded Markov chain approach. A solution procedure for such DSPNs has been outlined by Ajmone Marsan and Chiola [1986]. Without going into the details of this solution procedure, we shall only provide a manufacturing situation that leads to such a model.

Example 5.30

A single machine system produces parts of two types. The raw parts arrive into two separate buffers, according to Poisson processes of rates λ_1 and λ_2, respectively. Each buffer can hold at most two parts, and a freshly arriving raw part that finds its buffer will leave the system without service. The machine when free will idle if no part is waiting for service. It will start processing a waiting type 1 (type 2) part if no type 2 (type 1) part is waiting. If parts of both types are waiting, it will choose one of the part types probabilistically (with probabilities) q_1 and $1 - q_1$, say. The processing times are deterministic durations τ_1 and τ_2.

Figure 5.25 gives a DSPN that models the above system. A description of this DSPN is given in Table 5.16. This DSPN can be analyzed through the embedded Markov chain approach, since at most one concurrent deterministic transition (t_7 or t_8) will be enabled in any reachable marking.

5.6.4 Space of Timed Petri Nets

In this section we have so far discussed three variations of timed Petri nets. The space of timed Petri nets includes a rich variety of extensions and variations of the basic model and we enlist the significant proposals. The list is not exhaustive and it is possible several important proposals are omitted.

Deterministic Timed Petri Nets

These are timed Petri nets in which places or transitions are associated with deterministic time durations. These were originally proposed by Ramchandani [1973] and later investigated by Sifakis [1977]. Ramamoor-

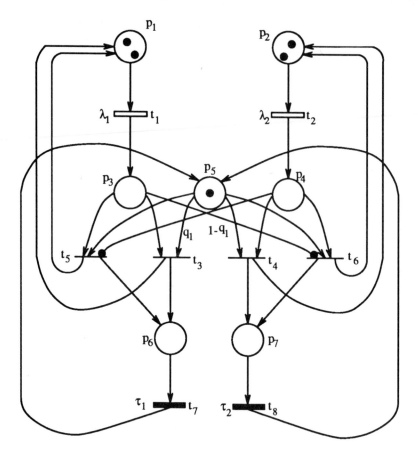

Figure 5.25 DSPN model for Example 5.30

thy and Ho [1980] and Zuberek [1980] obtained some results for such Petri nets. Dubois and Stecke [1983] were the first to employ this class of nets to manufacturing situations. The theory of a subclass of these nets, called timed event graphs or timed decision-free nets, has been well understood owing to the studies of Ramamoorthy and Ho [1980] and Philippe [1985]. However, the analysis of general Petri nets with deterministic times is a difficult problem.

Exponential Timed Petri Nets

ETPNs have been discussed in Section 5.2. They were independently proposed by Natkin [1980] and Molloy [1981]. Numerical Petri nets proposed by Symons [1980] also belong to this category.

Table 5.16 Legend for Figure 5.25

Places

1 : Empty positions in the buffer for type 1 parts
2 : Empty positions in the buffer for type 2 parts
3 : Type 1 parts waiting in buffer
4 : Type 2 parts waiting in buffer
5 : Machine available
6 : Machine processing type 1 parts
7 : Machine processing type 2 parts

Immediate Transitions

3 : A type 1 part is selected for processing
4 : A type 2 part is selected for processing
5 : Machine starts processing a type 1 part
6 : Machine starts processing a type 2 part

Exponential Transitions

1 : Arrival of type 1 parts
2 : Arrival of type 2 parts

Deterministic Transitions

7 : Processing of a type 1 part
8 : Processing of a type 2 part

Random Switch

$t_3 : q_1 ; \quad t_4 : 1 - q_1$

Discrete Time Stochastic Petri Nets

These are nets in which the times are discrete random variables. Assuming geometric random variables, Molloy [1985] has shown the equivalence of these to discrete time Markov chains. Wiley [1985] has studied such nets with non-geometric random variables and has shown that the anaysis of free choice nets, especially decision-free nets, can be carried out efficiently.

Generalized Stochastic Petri Nets

The proposal of GSPNs by Ajmone Marsan, Balbo, and Conte [1984] is a significant landmark in the evolution of timed Petri nets.

Extended Stochastic Petri Nets

ESPNs, which were proposed at Duke University in 1984, have been discussed in Section 5.6.2. ESPNs represent the first major effort in the direction of handling non-exponential distributions. Recently, Ciardo [1989] has defined semi-Markov SPNs in order to describe precisely the class of nets whose marking process is a semi-Markov process.

Generalized Timed Petri Nets

GTPNs were proposed by Holliday and Vernon [1985] and have been extensively used in computer system applications. The times in GTPNs are deterministic durations, and these have all the features of GSPNs such as random switches (static and dynamic), immediate transitions, and state-dependent firing durations. The marking process of a GTPN will be a general stochastic process with an embedded Markov chain. Typically, the reachability set of a GTPN is larger than that of a comparable GSPN; however, efficient analysis algorithms are available for GTPNs.

Colored Stochastic Petri Nets

We discussed these in Section 5.6.1. As already stated, they can lead to compact models, but their solution complexity is the same as that of the unfolded net model, except in very special situations.

Petri Nets with Deterministic and Stochastic Times

DSPNs, discussed in Section 5.6.3, are a special class of ESPNs, but the class of ESPNs for which analysis techniques have been proposed does not include the class of DSPNs for which an analysis technique has been devised by Ajmone Marsan and Chiola [1986]. The analysis of DSPNs having two or more concurrently enabled transitions with deterministic firing times is, however, an intrinsically difficult problem.

Regenerative Stochastic Petri Nets (RSPNs)

RSPNs have regenerative processes as their marking processes. Haas and Shedler [1986] have shown that RSPNs can be analyzed in the setting of generalized semi-Markov processes. Recently, they have extended their work to SPNs with simultaneous transition firings (Haas and Shedler [1987]). Symmetric stochastic Petri nets, proposed by Prisgrove and Shedler [1986], constitute a special class of RSPNs.

Stochastic Activity Networks

Sanders and Meyer [1987] have developed a very general framework using stochastic activity networks to address not only performance but also performability-related issues. These networks constitute a nontrivial extension of the basic SPN model.

Product Form SPNs

Recently, Lazar and Robertazzi [1987] have identified a class of SPNs having product form solution for steady-state probabilities. In a similar vein, Florin and Natkin [1989] have provided necessary and sufficient ergodicity condition for a class of unbounded SPNs that may include synchronization features also.

General Theory for SPNs

Ajmone Marsan *et al* [1989] have developed a comprehensive theoretical framework that includes most classes of SPNs in the literature. Their framework is comprised by two specifications – one, the way in which the next transition to fire is chosen, and second, the way in which the model keeps track of past history. The latter has been detailed in Section 5.6.3.

PROBLEMS

1. Construct a colored SPN model of the dining philosophers' problem, whose SPN model was depicted in Figure 5.P.2.
2. Develop a colored GSPN model for the dining philosophers' problem, assuming that each philosopher picks up his left fork first and then waits for the right fork.
3. Design a package that accepts a colored GSPN model as input and produces the reachability graph together with transition probabilities.

5.7 INTEGRATED PFQN-GSPN MODELS

The concept of flow-equivalence in queuing networks, which we saw in Section 4.13, can be used in building realistic and efficiently solvable performance models that include two parts: one a queuing network part and the other a Petri net part. In particular, we shall consider models that include a PFQN (product form queuing network) part and a GSPN part. Such models were first considered by Balbo, Bruell, and Ghanta

[1986] to evaluate computer systems with non-product form features such as priorities, blocking, forking and joining, dynamic routing, and multiple resource holding. In this section we bring out the use of such models, which we shall refer to as integrated PFQN-GSPN models (IQP models for short) in the AMS context.

An IQP model can be of two types: (i) IQP model with GSPN as the high-level model and (ii) IQP model with PFQN as the high-level model. If the high-level model is a GSPN, then some of its transitions represent flow-equivalents of subsystems computed using PFQN models of the subsystems. If the high-level model is a PFQN, some of its individual nodes correspond to flow-equivalents of subsystems computed using GSPN models of these subsystems. IQP models have the following advantages over GSPNs and PFQNs.

1. IQP models have a solution efficiency comparable to that of PFQNs and a representational power equaling that of GSPNs.
2. The flow-equivalents computed in the integrated technique are exact since they are computed by solving PFQNs or GSPNs.
3. The accuracy of solution given by IQP models is very good, especially when the subsystems in the given system are loosely coupled.
4. In the area of queuing networks, different kinds of approximations have been developed for different non-product form features. The integrated models provide a unified technique for all non-product form features.
5. There are few techniques available in queuing theory to handle situations where two or more non-product form features are present in a subsystem. The IQP technique can handle any combination and any number of non-product form features in a subsystem, in a unified way.

A limitation of the integrated technique is that it could be used only to compute average performance measures. However, this is true of any approximation technique based on flow-equivalence. Another limitation arises when the non-product form features are distributed across all subsystems. In such a case, the efficiency of IQP models suffers. The efficiency of these models will be very good if the non-product form features are localized in a single subsystem.

It is not necessary that the high-level model and the models for computing flow-equivalents be of different types (i.e., one is a PFQN and the other is a GSPN). If the high-level model and the model for flow-equivalents are both PFQNs, then we have the classical flow-equivalence

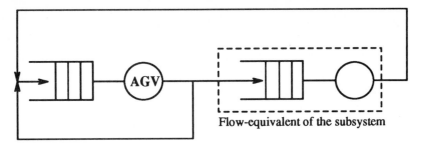

Figure 5.26 High-level PFQN model

of queuing networks discussed in Section 4.13. If one is a PFQN and the other a GSPN, we have IQP models discussed in the present section.

We now present two examples to illustrate the efficacy of IQP models.

Example 5.31

In this example we construct an IQP model of a central server FMS with parts routed dynamically. The dynamic routing policy considered is the shortest queue routing (SQR), which has a good deal of intuitive appeal. We have already presented in Section 5.3 a GSPN model for a central server FMS with one AGV, two machines M_1 and M_2, and dynamic routing (Example 5.19; Figure 5.10). To construct an IQP model, we first observe that the non-product form feature, SQR in this case, is localized in the subsystem comprising the machines M_1 and M_2. Therefore a GSPN model of this subsystem can be used to compute the flow-equivalent. The AGV node together with this flow-equivalent will make up a high-level PFQN model as shown in Figure 5.26. The GSPN model for the subsystem is shown in Figure 5.27, with description of the model in Table 5.17.

In the GSPN model for computing the flow-equivalent, observe that the AGV part is short-circuited. The transitions t_1 and t_2 will constitute a dynamic random switch as follows:

$$
\begin{aligned}
Prob\,(t_1) &= 0 && \text{if } M\,(p_2) > M\,(p_3) \\
&= 1 && \text{if } M\,(p_2) < M\,(p_3) \\
&= 0.5 && \text{if } M\,(p_2) = M\,(p_3) \\
Prob\,(t_2) &= 1 && \text{if } M\,(p_2) > M\,(p_3) \\
&= 0 && \text{if } M\,(p_2) < M\,(p_3) \\
&= 0.5 && \text{if } M\,(p_2) = M\,(p_3)
\end{aligned}
$$

Note in the above that ties are resolved with equal probabilities.

To compute the flow-equivalent, we observe that the number of jobs in the subsystem at any time can only vary from 0 to N where N is the total number of jobs in the closed network model of our FMS. The GSPN model is to be run for each of the populations $0, 1, 2, ..., N$, and to compute the service rate of the flow-equivalent server, we have to sum the throughput rates of the transitions t_5 and t_6. The PFQN high-level model of Figure 5.26 can now be solved using standard computational algorithms. It would now be very efficient to study the effect of variations of parameters connected with the AGV node on the performance of the overall system because the experimentation is required on a two-node PFQN.

To see the computational advantage obtained, notice that the exact GSPN model of Figure 5.10 will have $O(N)$ states where N is the total number of jobs. Solving the exact GSPN model will therefore entail solving a Markov chain with $O(N)$ states. On the other hand, the GSPN submodel of Figure 5.27 has at most two states for any value of N, because of SQR. In particular, when the population n is even, the submodel has only one tangible state, and for odd n there are exactly two tangible states. This would mean that the flow-equivalent can be obtained by solving $(N + 1)$

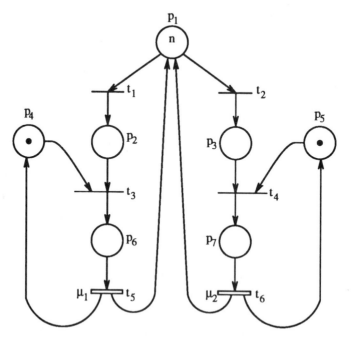

Figure 5.27 GSPN model for computing the flow-equivalent

Table 5.17 Legend for Figure 5.27

Places

1 : Parts ready to be routed to M_1 or M_2

2 : Queue of parts waiting for M_1

3 : Queue of parts waiting for M_2

4 : M_1 available

5 : M_2 available

6 : M_1 processing a part

7 : M_2 processing a part

Immediate Transitions

1 : Part routed to queue for M_1

2 : Part routed to queue for M_2

3 : M_1 starts processing a part

4 : M_2 starts processing a part

Exponential Transitions

5 : Processing of part by M_1

6 : Processing of part by M_2

Dynamic Random Switch

The transitions t_1 and t_2 constitute a dynamic random switch to model shortest queue routing.

Markov chains of at most two states each. Finally, the solution of the PFQN high-level model is also a very trivial affair. We can therefore conclude that the exact GSPN model leads to a time complexity of $O\left(N^3\right)$ whereas the IQP model leads to $O\left(N\right)$ complexity.

Example 5.32

Here we employ a GSPN high-level model and compute the flow-equivalent using a PFQN submodel. The system considered is a central server FMS with a non-product form feature in the AGV subsystem rather than in the machine subsystem.

The FMS in question, depicted in Figure 5.28, has a total of N fixtures, thus limiting the maximum number of in-process jobs to N. Raw parts are always available; however, a fixture released on the unloading of a finished part is not utilized for a waiting raw part until a specific demand for a

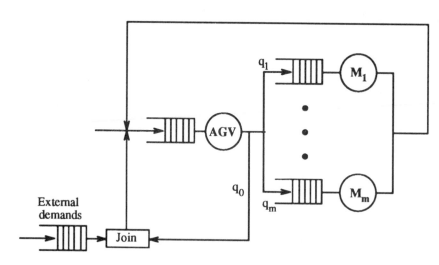

Figure 5.28 A central server FMS with external demands

finished part is posted in the demand queue. These demands are random and are assumed to constitute a Poisson arrival stream. When K ($K > 0$) demands are waiting unfulfilled, no further demands are entertained and the demands that arrive when the demand buffer is full are assumed to be lost. There are two potential non-product form features in the AGV subsystem here, namely *finiteness* of the demands buffer and the *joining* operation for demands and fixtures. Assuming product form characteristics for the machine subsystem, we then have a model that is congenial for IQP modeling. Note that the overall model here is not a closed queuing network, but a network in which a maximum of N jobs can circulate.

A high-level GSPN model of the above system is shown in Figure 5.29 (description of the model is in Table 5.18). In this model, t_7 is an exponential transition that aggregately represents the machine subsystem. Needless to say, t_7 has a marking-dependent firing rate that can be computed by solving the PFQN model shown in Figure 5.30.

Thus the solution of the IQP model in this case proceeds in the following way. In stage 1, the flow-equivalent of the PFQN model of Figure 5.30 is computed by solving this simple model for different populations n ranging from 0 to N. This will determine the marking-dependent firing rates of the transition t_7. In stage 2, the GSPN model of Figure 5.29 is analyzed using the standard techniques. This GSPN model has only three exponential transitions whereas the exact GSPN model for the entire system

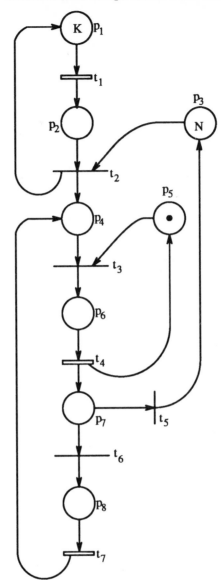

Figure 5.29 High-level GSPN model for Example 5.32

will have $m + 2$ exponential transitions where m is the number of machines.

The accuracy of performance estimates obtained using the IQP technique depends on the structure of the network. This is investigated in the following discussion.

Table 5.18 Legend for Figure 5.29

Places

1 : Future demands for products
2 : Queue of waiting demands for products
3 : Fixtures available
4 : Queue of parts waiting for AGV
5 : AGV available
6 : AGV transporting a part
7 : A part just transported by AGV
8 : Service in progress in the machine subsystem

Immediate Transitions

2 : A fixtured part is released into the system
3 : AGV starts transporting a part
5 : Part carried by AGV is for unloading
6 : Part carried by AGV is for some additional machining

Exponential Transitions

1 : Arrival of demands for finished products
4 : Transport operation by AGV
7 : Service in the machine subsystem

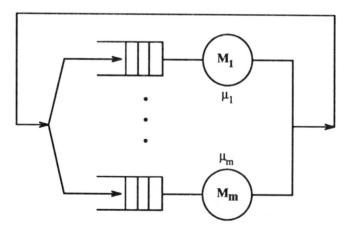

Figure 5.30 PFQN submodel for computing the flow-equivalent

Error Analysis

The integrated PFQN-GSPN modeling technique is essentially an approximate technique for obtaining mean values of performance measures. It has the advantages of computational efficiency of PFQNs and representational power of GSPNs. The accuracy of performance estimates using the integrated technique will depend on the degree of coupling between the subnetworks. The method leads to highly accurate estimates if this degree of coupling is very small. We shall see this first with a simple abstract example.

Example 5.33

Consider a CQN model with two subnetworks A and B, as shown in Figure 5.31. Let the network B contain some non-product form features whereas the network A is product form. If we employ the IQP modeling, we typically compute the flow-equivalent of network B using a GSPN model, which is run for different populations in the network. The computation of the flow-equivalent assumes that the duration for which a population in network B remains constant is long enough to offset any interference from network A. That is, between two successive interactions between the subnetworks A and B, network B reaches an equilibrium. If this condition is not met, then the flow-equivalent is bound to be inaccurate. In the specific case of the CQN of Figure 5.31, this condition is met when either the value of p is close to 1 or the relative throughput of network B is much higher than that of A.

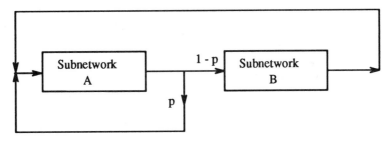

Figure 5.31 A CQN model with two subnetworks

We shall now present some numerical experiments to see the accuracy of the IQP modeling technique These numerical experiments are on the central server model with various non-product form features. The results show that the accuracy is very good for central server type of models.

Example 5.34

Table 5.19 shows the mean throughput and mean lead time values for Example 5.31, with the following parameters.

$$\mu_0 = \text{AGV Service Rate} = 50 \text{ parts/ h}$$
$$\mu_1 = M_1 \text{ Service Rate} = 10 \text{ parts/ h}$$
$$\mu_2 = M_2 \text{ Service Rate} = 5 \text{ parts/ h}$$
$$q_1 = q_2 = \frac{1 - q_0}{2}$$

Note that the throughput is the number of finished parts/ h and the lead time is the typical time spent by a job inside the system. The numerical results in Table 5.19 show the estimates using the IQP modeling and exact GSPN modeling. The estimates obtained through IQP models are found to be remarkably accurate, especially for small values of q_0 (exit probability). This corroborates the effectiveness of IQP modeling, especially when the

Table 5.19 Performance values for Example 5.31

	Mean Throughput (parts/ h)		Mean Lead Time (h)	
Exit prob	Exact GSPN Model	IQP Model	Exact GSPN Model	IQP Model
0.99	49.50	49.50	0.16161	0.16161
0.95	47.49992	47.49993	0.16842	0.16842
0.90	44.98879	44.98999	0.17782	0.17781
0.80	39.14079	39.21808	0.20439	0.20398
0.70	30.37088	30.60465	0.26341	0.26139
0.60	21.44702	21.63114	0.37301	0.36983
0.50	14.71864	14.81111	0.54352	0.54013
0.40	9.91265	9.95348	0.80705	0.80374
0.30	6.39908	6.41611	1.25017	1.24686
0.20	3.74009	3.74664	2.13898	2.13524
0.10	1.66394	1.66592	4.80784	4.80215
0.05	0.78844	0.78921	10.14656	10.13663
0.01	0.15134	0.15147	52.85555	52.85521

Table 5.20 Performance values for Example 5.32

Exit prob	Mean Throughput (parts/h)		Mean Lead Time (h)	
	Exact GSPN Model	IQP Model	Exact GSPN Model	IQP Model
0.99	19.86499	19.86499	0.03396	0.03396
0.90	19.62480	19.62429	0.05668	0.05671
0.80	18.50368	18.49833	0.09763	0.09784
0.70	15.84976	15.83368	0.16315	0.16376
0.60	12.29868	12.27539	0.26070	0.26186
0.50	8.92581	8.90384	0.40232	0.40405
0.40	6.17814	6.16185	0.61550	0.61781
0.30	4.04035	4.03002	0.96859	0.97164
0.20	2.37657	2.37095	1.67004	1.67440
0.10	1.06081	1.05850	3.76461	3.77304
0.05	0.50316	0.50211	7.94671	7.96081
0.01	0.09664	0.9645	41.38727	41.47170

parameter values make the interacting networks loosely coupled.

Example 5.35

Table 5.20 shows the mean throughput and mean lead time values for Example 5.32, with the same parameters as above. The results again show the remarkable accuracy of IQP modeling.

PROBLEMS

1. Consider the following variant of Example 5.31. Instead of SQR policy, the shortest expected delay routing (SEDR) is used, where the routing is done to the machine that leads to the minimum queuing time. Work out how IQP modeling may be used in this case.

2. In the classical central server model, let the processing time on each machine be a sum of two independent exponential random variables (for example, tool loading time + processing time, or processing time + inspection time). Investigate how IQP modeling can be employed in this case.

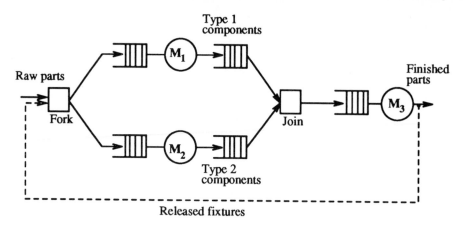

Figure 5.P.6

3. Figure 5.P.6 depicts a simple assembly network that consists of three machines M_1, M_2, and M_3, of which M_3 is an assembly workstation. M_3 assembles a type 1 component and a type 2 component, to produce a finished part. Type 1 components are produced by M_1 and type 2 components by M_2 and they wait in separate logical (or physical) queues as shown. There are n fixtures each available for type 1 and type 2 components. As soon as a finished part is produced, the following sequence of events is assumed to occur instantaneously: (i) A fixture of type 1 and a fixture of type 2 are released. (ii) The released fixtures are used to fixture available raw parts (assumed to be always available). (iii) A fixtured, type 1 raw part enters the queue for M_1 and a fixtured, type 2 raw part enters the queue for M_2. Note the significance of the fork-and-join operations shown in the Figure 5.P.6. How can you solve the above system by IQP modeling? Assume independence and exponentiality for all processing times.

4. Let the non-product form features of Example 5.31 (SQR) and Example 5.32 (finite demands) coexist in the central server FMS model. Now, both parts of the model have non-product form features. IQP modeling cannot be applied to this new example because PFQNs can be employed neither as a high-level model nor for computing a flow-equivalent. However, the system can be evaluated in the following three ways:

(a) A GSPN model for the entire system is evaluated. This method gives the exact performance values since no flow-equivalence is involved.

(b) A flow-equivalent of the machine subsystem is computed using GSPNs, and a high-level GSPN model that includes this flow-equivalent and the

AGV subsystem can be evaluated.

(c) A flow-equivalent of the AGV subsystem is computed using GSPNs, and a high-level GSPN model that includes this flow-equivalent and the machine subsystem can be evaluated.

Develop the models in each of the above cases and compare the performance estimates for typical parameter values.

5.8 BIBLIOGRAPHIC NOTES AND BIBLIOGRAPHY

The seminal thesis work of Carl Adam Petri [1962, 1966] was the genesis for Petri net modeling. Classical Petri nets have been well surveyed by Peterson [1977], Agerwala [1979], and more recently by Murata [1989]. Textbooks by Peterson [1981], Reisig [1985], and Silva [1985] are devoted to classical Petri nets. The two Springer-Verlag volumes edited by Brauer, Reisig, and Rozenberg [1987a, 1987b] comprise state-of-the-art survey papers on classical and stochastic Petri nets by leading researchers in this field. The notation and terminology related to Petri nets have been comprehensively presented by Best and Fernandez [1986].

Timed Petri nets were originally proposed by Ramchandani [1973]. Petri nets with stochastic times were independently proposed by Molloy [1981], Natkin [1980], and Symons [1980]. GSPNs were introduced by Ajmone Marsan, Balbo, and Conte [1984]. Stochastic nets have been the topic of several Ph.D. theses, such as by Dugan [1984], Molloy [1981], Natkin [1980], and more recently Ciardo [1989]. Application of Petri nets to manufacturing has been the focus of the Ph.D. theses of Al-Jaar [1989], Narahari [1987], Wiley [1985], and Zhou [1990]. The papers by Dubois and Stecke [1983] and Narahari and Viswanadham [1985] were among the first in the area of Petri net modeling of manufacturing systems. GSPNs have been well surveyed in the paper by Ajmone Marsan, Chiola, and Conte [1987] and in the book by Ajmone Marsan, Balbo, and Conte [1986]. Pagnoni [1987] has also made a survey of SPNs. A comprehensive survey of Petri nets in manufacturing has been presented by Al-Jaar and Desrochers [1990] and earlier by Martinez, Alla, and Silva [1986]. Vernon, Zahorjan, and Lazowska [1987] have made a detailed comparison of the power and efficiency of SPN models and queuing network models.

As discussed in Section 5.6, several extensions and variations have been proposed to the basic timed Petri net model. Among the first to be investigated were Petri nets with deterministic times (DTPNs). Important contributions in this context are by Sifakis [1977], Zuberek [1980], Ramamoorthy and Ho [1980], and Philippe [1985]. Application of DTPNs to manufacturing have been considered by Bobbio and Aira [1987], Hillion and Proth [1989], and Dubois and Stecke [1983]. Extended stochastic Petri nets were proposed by Dugan [1984] and discussed by Dugan *et al* [1984]. Colored stochastic Petri nets have been considered by Bruno and Biglia [1985], Chiola, Bruno, and Demaria [1988], Lin and Marinescu [1987], and Zenie [1985]. The basic colored Petri net formalism was developed by Jensen [1981] and an independent development of a high-level Petri net called Predicate-Transition Nets was due to Genrich and Lautenbach [1981]. Narahari and Viswanadham [1986], Kamath and Viswanadham [1986], and Viswanadham and Narahari [1987] have looked at some manufacturing models based on colored Petri nets. DSPNs were originated by Ajmone Marsan and Chiola [1986]. The class of regenerative stochastic Petri nets has been investigated by Haas and Shedler [1986, 1987, 1989] and symmetric SPNs by Prisgrove and Shedler [1986]. Holliday and Vernon [1985] developed the generalized timed Petri nets. Stochastic Activity Networks are due to Sanders and Meyer [1987]. Discrete time SPNs were introduced and studied by Molloy [1985] and Wiley [1985]. A theory of *product form* SPNs has been studied by Lazar and Robertazzi [1987]. Florin and Natkin [1989] have derived necessary and sufficient conditions for the ergodicity of unbounded SPNs. A comprehensive theoretical framework for all SPN models has been developed by Marsan *et al* [1989].

Performance modeling of AMSs using SPNs is a relatively recent topic. Dubois and Stecke [1983] were the first to use timed Petri nets. The theses of Al-Jaar [1989] and Narahari [1987] have considered SPN modeling of AMSs. Al-Jaar and Desrochers [1990] have made a detailed survey of this topic. Important publications in this context are by Abraham and Sciomachen [1986], Archetti *et al* [1987], Ajmone Marsan *et al* [1987], Balbo *et al* [1987a, 1987b], Laftit and Proth [1989], Merabet [1986], and Viswanadham and Narahari [1988]. Deadlock analysis in manufacturing systems, discussed in Section 5.5, has been put together from the papers by Narahari and Viswanadham [1985], Narahari *et al* [1990], and Viswanadham *et al* [1990]. The GSPN models developed in Section 5.4 are based on the earlier stochastic models developed by Mitra and Mitrani [1988a, 1988b, 1989]. In an independent effort, Mascolo *et al* [1989, 1990] have presented GSPN models for several Kanban-based manufacturing situations in the literature. Integrated analytical models, which form the subject of Section 5.7, were proposed by Ghanta [1984] and described by Balbo, Bruell, and Ghanta [1986, 1988]. These models use the classical flow-equivalence paradigm in queuing networks earlier discussed by Chandy, Herzog, and Woo [1975] and by Chandy and Sauer [1978].

Several powerful software packages are now available for the analysis of stochastic Petri net models. Some of these are described by Ajmone Marsan *et al* [1985], Chiola [1987], Ciardo, Muppala, and Trivedi [1989], Cumani [1985], Dugan *et al* [1985], Holliday and Vernon [1986].

A topic of computational and practical importance is the analysis of large and complex stochastic Petri net models. This is the subject of the thesis of Ciardo [1989]. Some important references in this context, which lay the basis for the decomposition and aggregation of SPN models, are: Ajmone Marsan *et al* [1989], Ammar and Liu [1985], Ciardo and Trivedi [1990], and Curtois [1977].

BIBLIOGRAPHY

1. **Abraham, C.T., and A. Sciomachen** [1986]. Planning for Automated Guided Vehicle Systems by Petri Nets, *IBM Research Report* RC-12288, Yorktown Heights, New York, November 1986.

2. **Agerwala, T.** [1979]. Putting Petri Nets to Work, *IEEE Computer,* Vol. 12, No. 12, December 1979, pp. 85–94.

3. **Ajmone Marsan, M., G. Balbo, G. Ciardo, and G. Conte** [1985]. A Software Tool for the Automatic Analysis of Generalized Stochastic Petri Net Models, in *Modelling Techniques and Tools for Performance Analysis,* INRIA, Elsevier Science Publishers B.V (North-Holland), Amsterdam.

4. **Ajmone Marsan, M., G. Balbo, and G. Conte** [1984]. A Class of Generalized Stochastic Petri Nets for the Performance Analysis of Multiprocessor Systems, *ACM Transactions on Computer Systems*, Vol. 2, No. 2, May 1984, pp. 93–122.

5. **Ajmone Marsan, M., G. Balbo, and G. Conte** [1986]. *Performance Models of Multiprocessor Systems,* The MIT Press, Cambridge, Massachusetts.

6. **Ajmone Marsan, M., G. Balbo, G. Chiola, and G. Conte** [1987]. Generalized Stochastic Petri Nets Revisited: Random Switches and Priorities, *Proceedings of International Workshop on Petri Nets and Performance Models*, Madison, Wisconsin, August 1987, pp. 44–53.

7. **Ajmone Marsan, M., G. Balbo, A. Bobbio, G. Chiola, G. Conte, and A. Cumani** [1989]. The Effect of Execution Policies on the Semantics and Analysis of Stochastic Petri Nets, *IEEE Transactions on Software Engineering*, Vol. 15, No. 7, July 1989, pp. 832–846.

8. **Ajmone Marsan, M., and G. Chiola** [1986]. On Petri Nets with Deterministic and Exponential Transition Firing Times, *Proceedings of Seventh European Workshop on Applications and Theory of Petri Nets*, Oxford, UK, July 1986, pp. 167–182. Also in *Advances in Petri Nets 1987*, (Ed.) Rozenberg, G., *Lecture Notes in Computer Science*, Vol. 266, pp. 132–145, 1987.

9. **Ajmone Marsan, M., G. Chiola, and G. Conte** [1987]. Stochastic Petri Nets as a Tool for the Analysis of High Performance Distributed Architectures, in *Supercomputing Systems*, (Eds.) Kartashev, L., and S. Kartashev, Van Nostrand, New York.

10. **Al-Jaar, R.Y.** [1989]. *Performance Evaluation of Automated Manufacturing Systems using Generalized Stochastic Petri Nets*, Ph.D. Dissertation, Rensselaer Polytechnic Institute, Computer Integrated Manufacturing Report DOC #CIM CC89THI93, Troy, New York, March 1989.

11. **Al-Jaar, R.Y., and A.A. Desrochers** [1990]. Petri Nets in Automation and Manufacturing, in: *Advances in Automation and Robotics*, Volume 2, (Ed.) Saridis, G.N., JAI Press, New Haven, Connecticut.

12. **Ammar, H.H., and R.W. Liu** [1985]. Analysis of Generalized Stochastic Petri Nets by State Aggregation, *Proceedings of International Workshop on Timed Petri Nets*, Torino, Italy, 1985, IEEE Computer Society Press, pp. 88–95.

13. **Archetti, F., E. Faginoli, and A. Sciomachen** [1987]. Computation of the Makespan in a Transfer Line with Station Breakdowns using Stochastic Petri Nets, *Computers and Operations Research*, Vol. 14, No. 5, pp. 409–414.

14. **Balbo, G., S.C. Bruell, and S. Ghanta** [1986]. Combining Queuing Network and Generalized Stochastic Petri Net Models for the Analysis of Software Blocking Phenomena, *IEEE Transactions on Software Engineering*, Vol. SE-12, No. 4, April 1986, pp. 561–576.

15. **Balbo, G., S.C. Bruell, and S. Ghanta** [1988]. Combining Queuing Networks and Generalized Stochastic Petri Nets for the Solution of Complex Models of System Behaviour, *IEEE Transactions on Computers*, Vol. C-17, No. 10, October 1988, pp. 1251–1268.

16. **Balbo, G., G. Chiola, G. Franceschinis, and G.M. Roet** [1987a]. Generalized Stochastic Petri Nets for the Performance Evaluation of FMS, *Proceedings of 1987 IEEE International Conference on Robotics and Automation,*

March 1987, pp. 1013–1018.

17. **Balbo, G., G. Chiola, G. Franceschinis, and G.M. Roet** [1987b]. On the Efficient Construction of the Tangible Reachability Graph of Generalized Stochastic Petri Nets, *Proceedings of International Workshop on Petri Nets and Performance Models*, Madison, Wisconsin, August 1987, pp. 136–145.

18. **Best, E., and C. Fernandez** [1986]. Notations and Terminology on Petri Net Theory: Revised Version, *Petri Nets Newsletter,* No. 23, April 1986, pp. 21–46.

19. **Bobbio, A., and G.S. Aira** [1987]. Modelling Automated Production Systems by Deterministic Petri Nets, *Proceedings of Third International Conference on Simulation in Manufacturing*, Turin, Italy, November 1987, pp. 127–136.

20. **Brauer, W., W. Reisig., and G. Rozenberg** (Ed.) [1987a]. *Advances in Petri Nets 1986, Part I. Petri Nets: Central Models and Their Properties*, Proceedings of Advanced Course, Bad Honnef, Germany, September 1986, Lecture Notes in Computer Science, Vol. 254, Springer-Verlag, New York.

21. **Brauer, W., W. Reisig., and G. Rozenberg** (Ed.) [1987b]. *Advances in Petri Nets 1986, Part II. Petri Nets: Applications and Relationships to Other Models of Concurrency*, Proceedings of Advanced Course, Bad Honnef, Germany, September 1986, Lecture Notes in Computer Science, Vol. 255, Springer-Verlag, New York.

22. **Bruno, G., and P. Biglia** [1985]. Performance Evaluation and Validation of Tool Handling in Flexible Manufacturing Systems, *Proceedings of International Workshop on Timed Petri Nets*, Torino, Italy, July 1985, pp. 64–71.

23. **Chandy, K.M., U. Herzog, and L. Woo** [1975]. Parametric Analysis of Queuing Network Models, *IBM Journal of Research and Development*, Vol. 19, No. 1, January 1975, pp. 36–42.

24. **Chandy, K.M., and C.H. Sauer** [1978]. Approximate Methods for Analyzing Queuing Network Models of Computer Systems, *ACM Computing Surveys*, Vol. 10, No. 3, September 1978, pp. 281–318.

25. **Chiola, G.** [1987]. A Graphical Petri Net Tool for Performance Analysis, *Proceedings of Third International Workshop on Modeling Techniques and Tools for Performance Evaluation*, AFCET, Paris, March 1987.

26. **Chiola, G., G. Bruno, and T. Demaria** [1988]. Introducing a Color Formalism into Generalized Stochastic Petri Nets, *Proceedings of Ninth European Workshop on Applications and Theory of Petri Nets*, pp. 202–215.

27. **Ciardo, G.** [1989]. *Analysis of Large Stochastic Petri Net Models*, Ph.D. Dissertation, Duke University, Durham, North Carolina.

28. **Ciardo, G., J. Muppala, and K.S. Trivedi** [1989]. SPNP: Stochastic Petri Net Package, in *Proceedings of Third International Workshop on Petri Nets and Performance Models*, PNPM 89, Kyoto, Japan, December 1989.

29. **Ciardo, G., and K.S. Trivedi** [1990]. Solution of Large GSPN Models, *Proceedings of First International Workshop on Numerical Solution of Markov Chains*, Raleigh, North Carolina, January 1990.

30. **Cumani, A.** [1985]. ESP – A Package for the Evaluation of Stochastic Petri Nets with Phase-Type Distributed Transition Times, *Proceedings of International Workshop on Timed Petri Nets*, Torino, Italy, July 1985.

31. **Curtois, P.J.** [1977]. *Decomposability: Queuing and Computer Systems Applications*, Academic Press, New York.

32. **Dubois, D., and K.E. Stecke** [1983]. Using Petri Nets to Represent Production Processes, *Proceedings of 22nd IEEE Conference on Decision and Control*, December 1983, pp. 1062–1067.

33. **Dugan, J.B.** [1984]. *Extended Stochastic Petri Nets: Applications and Analysis*, Ph.D. Dissertation, Dept. of Electrical Engineering, Duke University, Durham, North Carolina.

34. **Dugan, J.B., A. Bobbio, G. Ciardo, and K.S. Trivedi** [1985]. The Design of a Unified Package for the Solution of Stochastic Petri Net Models, *Proceedings of International Workshop on Timed Petri Nets*, Torino, Italy, July 1985, pp. 6–13.

35. **Dugan, J.B., K.S. Trivedi, R.M. Geist, and V.F. Nicola** [1984]. Extended Stochastic Petri Nets: Applications and Analysis, *Proceedings of Performance '84*, Paris, December 1984, pp. 507–519.

36. **Florin, G., and S. Natkin** [1989]. Necessary and Sufficient Ergodicity Condition for Open Synchronized Queuing Networks, *IEEE Transactions on Software Engineering*, Vol. 15, No. 4, April 1989, pp. 367–380.

37. **Genrich, H.J., and K. Lautenbach** [1981]. System Modelling with High-Level Petri Nets, *Theoretical Computer Science*, Vol. 13, pp. 109–136.

38. **Ghanta, S.** [1984]. *On the Integration of Queuing Networks and Generalized Stochastic Petri Nets for the Performance Evaluation of Computer Systems*, Ph.D. Dissertation, University of Minnesota, Minneapolis, Minnesota.

39. **Haas, P.J., and G.S. Shedler** [1986]. Regenerative Stochastic Petri Nets, *Performance Evaluation*, Vol. 6, pp. 189–204.

40. **Haas, P.J., and G. S. Shedler** [1987]. Stochastic Petri Nets with Simultaneous Transition Firings, *Proceedings of International Workshop on Petri Nets and Performance Models*, Madison, Wisconsin, August 1987, pp. 136–145.

41. **Haas, P.J., and G.S. Shedler** [1989]. Stochastic Petri Net Representation of Discrete Event Simulations, *IEEE Transactions on Software Engineering*, Vol. 15, No. 4, April 1989, pp. 381–393.

42. **Hillion, H.P., and J.M. Proth** [1989]. Performance Evaluation of Job-Shop Systems using Timed Event Graphs, *IEEE Transactions on Automatic Control*, Vol. AC-34, No. 1, January 1989, pp. 3–9.

43. **Holliday, M.A., and M.K. Vernon** [1985]. A Generalized Timed Petri Net Model for Performance Analysis, *Proceedings of International Workshop on Timed Petri Nets*, Torino, Italy, July 1985, pp. 181–190.

44. **Holliday, M.A., and M.K. Vernon** [1986]. The GTPN Analyzer: Numerical Methods and User Interface, *Computer Sciences Technical Report*, No. 639, University of Wisconsin, Madison.

45. **Jensen, K.** [1981]. Colored Petri Nets and the Invariant Method, *Theoretical Computer Science*, Vol. 14, pp. 317–336.

46. **Kamath, M., and N. Viswanadham** [1986]. Applications of Petri Net-Based Models in the Modeling and Analysis of Flexible Manufacturing Systems, Proceedings of *IEEE International Conference on Robotics and Automation*, San Francisco, California, March 1986, pp. 312–317.

47. **Laftit, S., and J.M. Proth** [1989]. Evaluation of Job-Shops with Random Manufacturing Times: A Petri Net Approach, *INRIA Research Report*, No. 1112, INRIA-LORRAINE, Rocqluencourt, France, October 1989.

48. **Lazar, A.A., and T.G. Robertazzi** [1987]. Markovian Petri Net Protocol Models with Product Form Solution, *Proceedings of the INFOCOM '87*, San Francisco, California, March 30 – April 2, 1987.

49. **Lin, C., and D.C. Marinescu** [1987]. On Stochastic High-Level Petri Nets, *Proceedings of International Workshop on Petri Nets and Performance Models*, Madison, Wisconsin, August 1987, pp. 34–43.

50. **Martinez, J., H. Alla, and M. Silva** [1986]. Petri Nets for Specification of FMSs, in *Modelling and Design of Flexible Manufacturing Systems* (Ed.) Kusiak, A., Elsevier Science Publishers, Amsterdam, pp. 389–406.

51. **Mascolo, M.D., Y. Frein, Y. Dallery, and R. David** [1989]. Modeling of Kanban Systems using Petrti Nets, *Proceedings of Third ORSA/TIMS Special Interest Conference on FMS: Operations Research Models and Applications*, Massachusetts Institute of Technology, Cambridge, Massachusetts, August 1989.

52. **Mascolo, M.D., Y. Frein, Y. Dallery, and R. David** [1990]. A Unified Modeling of Kanban Systems using Petri Nets, *International Journal of Flexible Manufacturing Systems* (in press).

53. **Merabet, A.A.** [1986]. Synchronization of Operations in a Flexible Manufacturing Cell: The Petri Net Approach, *Journal of Manufacturing Systems*, Vol. 5, No. 3, pp. 161–169.

54. **Mitra, D., and I. Mitrani** [1988a]. Analysis of a Novel Discipline for Cell Coordination in Production Lines – Part I: *AT&T Bell Laboratories Memorandum*, June 1988.

55. **Mitra, D., and I. Mitrani** [1988b]. Analysis of a Novel Discipline for Cell Coordination in Production Lines – Part II: Stochastic Demands, *AT&T Bell Laboratories Memorandum*, October 1988.

56. **Mitra, D., and I. Mitrani** [1989]. Control and Coordination Policies for Systems with Buffers, *ACM Performance Evaluation Review*, Vol. 17, No. 1, May 1989, pp. 156–164.

57. **Molloy, M.K.** [1981]. *On the Integration of Delay and Throughput Measures in Distributed Processing Systems*, Ph.D. Dissertation, University of California, Los Angeles.

58. **Molloy, M.K.** [1985]. Discrete Time Stochastic Petri Nets, *IEEE Transactions on Software Engineering*, Vol. SE-11, No. 4, April 1985, pp. 417–423.

59. **Murata, T.** [1989]. Petri Nets: Properties, Analysis, and Applications, *Proceedings of the IEEE*, Vol. 77, No. 4, April 1989, pp. 541–580.

60. **Narahari, Y.** [1987]. *Petri Net-Based Techniques for Modelling, Analysis, and Performance Evaluation*, Ph.D. Dissertation, Department of Computer Science and Automation, Indian Institute of Science, Bangalore, India, July 1987.

61. **Narahari, Y., and N. Viswanadham** [1985]. A Petri Net Approach to Modelling and Analysis of Flexible Manufacturing Systems, *Annals of Operations Research*, Vol. 3, pp. 449–472.

62. **Narahari, Y., and N. Viswanadham** [1986]. On the Invariants of Colored Petri Nets, *Advances in Petri Nets – 1985, Lecture Notes in Computer Science*, Vol. 222, Springer-Verlag, New York, pp. 330–345.

63. **Narahari, Y., N. Viswanadham, and K.R. Krishna Prasad** [1990]. Markovian Models for Deadlock Analysis in Automated Manufacturing Systems, *Sadhana*, Indian Academy Proceedings in Engineering Sciences, Vol. 15, December 1990, pp. 343–353.

64. **Natkin, S.** [1980]. *Les reseaux de Petri stochastiques et leur application a l'evaluation des systems informatiques*, Ph.D. Dissertation (in French), CNAM — Paris, June 1980.

65. **Pagnoni, A.** [1987]. Stochastic Nets and Performance Evaluation, *Advances*

in Petri Nets – 1986, Part I. Petri Nets: Central Models and Their Properties, Lecture Notes in Computer Science, Vol. 254, Springer-Verlag, New York, pp. 460–478.

66. **Peterson, J.L.** [1977]. Petri Nets, *ACM Computing Surveys*, Vol. 9, No. 3, September 1977.

67. **Peterson, J.L.** [1981]. *Petri Net Theory and the Modeling of Systems*, Prentice-Hall, Englewood Cliffs, New Jersey..

68. **Petri, C.A.** [1962]. *Kommunikation mit Automaten*, Ph.D. Dissertation (in German), Shriften des Institutes fur Instrumentelle Mathematik, Bonn, Germany.

69. **Petri, C.A.** [1966]. *Communication with Automata*, Technical Report RADC-TR-65–377, Rome Air Development Center, New York.

70. **Philippe,** C. [1985]. Timed Event Graphs: A Complete Study of Their Controlled Execution, *Proceedings of International Workshop on Timed Petri Nets*, Torino, Italy, July 1985, pp. 47–54.

71. **Prisgrove, L.A., and G. S. Shedler** [1986]. Symmetric Stochastic Petri Nets, *IBM Journal of Research and Development*, Vol. 30, No. 3, May 1986, pp. 278–293.

72. **Ramamoorthy, C.V., and G.S. Ho** [1980]. Performance Evaluation of Asynchronous Concurrent Systems using Petri Nets, *IEEE Transactions on Software Engineering*, Vol. SE-6, No. 5, September 1980, pp. 440–449.

73. **Ramchandani,** C. [1973]. *Analysis of Asynchronous Concurrent Systems by Timed Petri Nets*, Ph.D. Dissertation, Massachusetts Institute of Technology, Cambridge, Massachusetts.

74. **Reisig,** W. [1985]. *Petri Nets: An Introduction*, EATCS Monographs on Theoretical Computer Science, Springer-Verlag, New York.

75. **Sanders, W.H., and J.F. Meyer** [1987]. Performability Evaluation of Distributed Systems using Stochastic Activity Networks, *Proceedings of International Workshop on Petri Nets and Performance Models*, Madison, Wisconsin, pp. 111–120.

76. **Sifakis,** J. [1977]. Use of Petri Nets for Performance Evaluation, in *Measuring, Modeling and Evaluating Computer Systems*, (Ed.) Beilner, H., and E. Gelenbe, North-Holland, Amsterdam, pp. 75–93.

77. **Silva,** M. [1985]. *Petri Nets in Automation and Computer Engineering*, Madrid, Spain, Editorial AC (in Spanish) 1985. (English translation to be published by Kluwer Academic Press, Hingham, Massachusetts, 1990).

78. **Symons, F.J.W.** [1980]. Introduction to Numerical Petri Nets, a General

Graphical Model of Concurrent Processing Systems, *Australian Telecommunication Review*, Vol. 14, No. 1, January 1980, pp. 28–33.

79. **Vernon, M.K., J. Zahorjan, and E.D. Lazowska** [1987]. A Comparison of Performance Petri Nets and Queuing Network Models, *Proceedings of International Workshop on Modeling Techniques and Tools for Performance Evaluation*, AFCET, Paris, March 1987, pp. 181–192.

80. **Viswanadham, N., and Y. Narahari** [1987]. Colored Petri Net Models for Automated Manufacturing Systems, Proceedings of *1987 IEEE International Conference on Robotics and Automation*, Raleigh, North Carolina, March-April 1987, pp. 1985–1989.

81. **Viswanadham, N., and Y. Narahari** [1988]. Stochastic Petri Net Models for Performance Evaluation of Automated Manufacturing Systems, *Information and Decision Technologies*, Vol. 14, pp. 125–142.

82. **Viswanadham, N., Y. Narahari, and T.L. Johnson** [1990]. Deadlock Prevention and Deadlock Avoidance in Flexible Manufacturing Systems Using Petri Net Models, *IEEE Transactions on Robotics and Automation*, Vol. 6, No. 6, December 1990, pp. 713–723.

83. **Wiley, R.P.** [1985]. *Performance Analysis of Stochastic Timed Petri Nets*, Ph.D. Dissertation, Report LIDS-TH-1525, Laboratory for Information and Decision Systems, Massachusetts Institute of Technology, Cambridge, Massachusetts.

84. **Zenie, A.** [1985]. Colored Stochastic Petri Nets, *Proceedings of International Workshop on Timed Petri Nets*, Torino, Italy, July 1985, pp. 262–271.

85. **Zhou, M.C.** [1990]. *A Theory for the Synthesis and Augmentation of Petri Nets in Automation*, Ph.D. Dissertation, Department of Electrical, Computer, and Systems Engineering, Rensselaer Polytechnic Institute, Troy, New York.

86. **Zuberek, W.M.** [1980]. Timed Petri Nets and Preliminary Performance Evaluation, *Proceedings of Seventh Annual Symposium on Computer Architecture*, pp. 88–96.

Chapter 6
EPILOGUE

We would like to conclude this book with some comments on what has not been covered in this text.

Starting with a logical overview of the architecture and operation of automated manufacturing systems in Chapter 2, we went on to dwell on three principal analytical modeling paradigms – Markov chains, queuing models, and Petri nets. Using a fairly large collection of pedagogical examples, we have attempted to illustrate the theory, analysis, and applications of these modeling paradigms. Wherever possible, we have introduced and dealt with topics having research flavor. We expect the reader after concluding this text, to be confident about tackling design and operation issues of AMSs that come within the purview of analytical modeling. Further, we hope this book helps provide a firm foundation for prospective graduate students in this area.

The subject of AMS modeling comprises a wide gamut of conceptual issues, theory, techniques, and tools. To sweep this spectrum in a single text is an impossible task. We have therefore consciously focused on analytical modeling tools without straying into issues with possibly strong relevance. We would like to dwell briefly on some relevant topics and issues for which we could not find a place in this already bulky tome.

Prescriptive Models

Development of optimal or suboptimal scheduling and operating rules for AMSs calls for the use of techniques from mathematical programming, control theory, Markov decision processes, and stochastic programming. We have not touched upon these topics since the focus is on descriptive or evaluative models rather than on prescriptive models. A strong reason for this is the availability of excellent textbooks on these topics.

Logical Models

Models such as finite automata, classical Petri nets, and finitely recursive processes are useful in representing and investigating logical properties of AMSs, such as controllability, error-free operation, absence of instabilities such as deadlocks, boundedness, etc. We have touched upon logical analysis in Sections 5.1 and 5.5 (deadlocks), but the overall emphasis in the book is on quantitative models.

We would like to mention that a great deal of attention is currently being given to the design of feedback controllers for event-driven systems such as AMSs. In the near future, one could expect algorithmic methods for the design of such controllers, which we have described in the form of the flowcharts of Figures 2.12 and 2.22.

Discrete Event Simulation

Simulation has been an important modeling tool in studying AMSs. In fact, simulation would very well complement the analytical approaches to modeling. The reason we have omitted a discussion of simulation is the availability of excellent books and manuals on this topic and also the fantastic amount of software that is available in the form of simulation languages, special-purpose simulation tools, and graphical animation packages.

While simulation is the recommended tool during the operation of systems, analytical models have definite value during the planning and design stages in terms of providing rapid feedback on decision alternatives.

Perturbation Analysis

Infinitesimal perturbation analysis has emerged as a major tool for analyzing the sensitivity of system performance to relevant system parameters in an efficient way. The theory of perturbation analysis has been developed in the wider context of analysis of discrete event dynamical systems. The Chapter 4 bibliography contains several classical references to work in this area. Also, we have not covered the more general problem of sensitivity analysis.

Case Studies

One of the important aims of performance modeling is to study system design issues and to address synthesis aspects of system design. This text provides all the background required for tackling design issues, without quite going into any major case studies of system design. A major percentage of our examples serve a pedagogical purpose and cannot quite be called case studies or real-life studies. Most of the examples are abstractions of real-world situations. Analytical modeling tools can and have been employed in real-world system design. At this stage, we feel that models of real-life flexible manufacturing cells and FMSs in electronic and metal-cutting industries could be formulated using the techniques and tools of this book.

Numerical Methods

Real-world AMSs are bound to lead to large, complex performance models. Powerful computational techniques will have to be employed to analyze such models. In Section 3.11 we have attempted, albeit in a limited way, to give an idea of the computational difficulties. In fact, the techniques of aggregation and uniformization discussed therein are time-honored algorithms for solving large models. Surveying the large amount of literature in this area is beyond the scope of this book.

The techniques and tools discussed in this text, supplemented with packages for numerical solution of large and complex models and simulation and graphical animation facilities, would comprise a useful engineer's workbench for planning, configuring, and designing AMSs.

Workload Modeling

In computer system performance analysis, a topic that has received much attention is workload modeling. This topic has utmost relevance to AMS modeling too. In most models that we have presented in this book, the workload is implicitly specified. Recall that in most of the situations modeled in the book, we have assumed a Poisson stream of raw parts or a perennial supply of raw parts or a closed style of operation (constant population) where the exit of a finished part signals the entry of a raw part. A discussion of explicit modeling of workload for AMSs is now a topic of research rather than a topic for a text like this one.

Research Perspective

Several sections in this book have a research flavor and discuss issues that are currently active research topics. Because ours is mainly a textbook, we have only given a cursory treatment to some recent topics, such as transient analysis, performability modeling, numerical methods, and approximate analysis techniques. Moreover, we could not include several significant research results in this area, especially those of the last 5 years. We have tried to include as many references as we can in the chapter bibliographies. We should, however, state that our bibliographies are neither exhaustive nor completely up-to-date.

It is our firm conviction that there is a strong need for a well-formulated "science" of manufacturing, i.e., a set of scientific principles and theories based on which new generation manufacturing systems can be designed and operated. In our view, this book offers a discussion of several issues that are relevant for the development of such a generic science.

INDEX